Encyclopedia of Physical Education, Fitness, and Sports

Training, Environment, Nutrition, and Fitness

G. Alan Stull

Volume Editor

Thomas K. Cureton, Jr.

Series Editor

Sponsored by

The American Alliance for Health,
Physical Education, Recreation, and Dance

BRIGHTON PUBLISHING COMPANY

P.O. Box 6235
Salt Lake City, Utah 84106

ISBN 0-89832-016-X

Library of Congress Cataloging in Publication Data (Revised)
Main entry under title:

Encyclopedia of physical education, fitness, and
   sports.

   Vols. 2-   published by Brighton Pub. Co., Salt
Lake City, Utah.
   Includes bibliographies and indexes.
   CONTENTS: [1] Frost, R. B. Sports, dance, and
related activities.--[2] Stull, G. A. Training, environment, nutrition, and fitness.
   1. Sports--Dictionaries. 2. Physical education
and training--Dictionaries. I. Cureton, Thomas Kirk,
1901-
GV567.E49   796.03   76-46608

About the Alliance

Since 1885 when the original organization was founded by a group of people interested in "physical training," the American Alliance for Health, Physical Education, Recreation, and Dance has been the professional home of educators concerned with physical activity, health, and fitness.

Alliance sponsorship of the publication of this four-volume *Encylopedia* crowns more than 95 years of program efforts devoted to professional development, research, and scholarship.

In that time the Alliance has provided numerous vehicles for the growth and dissemination of the knowledge base of the profession. These include an Alliance network of periodicals reaching all members and many segments of the public; professional meetings and conventions; professional books and reports; and collaboration with the professions, government, business, and media.

The Alliance has been attentive to the responsibility of providing reference materials representative of the profession. These materials have helped members initiate, develop, and conduct programs in health, leisure, and movement-related activities for the enrichment of human life.

The AAHPERD *Journal of Physical Education and Recreation* has been the major journal of the profession for nearly 50 years. The *Research Quarterly* has been published since 1929. *Completed Research in Health, Physical Education, and Recreation* was started in 1958 and is published annually. *Health Education* has been published since 1969. The annual convention of the Alliance provides continuous reporting of current research, with abstracts available in an annual volume since 1971.

The educational world is just awakening to the importance of motor behavior. For eons the cognitive aspects of scholarship were explored with great emphasis upon the history and heritage of knowledge. As the world recognizes greater responsibility for motor behaviors as well, the area of physical activity assumes its rightful place in the education of human beings.

For many years the Alliance has recognized the growing need for a compendium of knowledge related to physical education, sport, and fitness. Students, teachers, leaders from other disciplines, the Alliance Research Consortium, the American Academy of Physical Education—all have encouraged the development and publication of such a reference.

Yet, perhaps like most achievements realized through group effort, one individual can be pointed out as primarily responsible for bringing this *Encyclopedia* into being. Dr. Thomas K. Cureton, professor emeritus of physical education, University of Illinois at Champaign, has been the conscience of the profession in promoting, preparing, and urging its publication. Under his determined and persevering leadership, the idea of the *Encyclopedia of Physical Education, Fitness, and Sports* was initiated and the volumes organized and published.

As meaning and ideas are gleaned from this work, future scholars will be in debt to Dr. Cureton and to the hundreds of other professional women and men who have contributed to these volumes. It is with a sense of great achievement that the American Alliance for Health, Physical Education, Recreation, and Dance joins with the publisher in the presentation of a reference unique in the annals of physical education.

With the publication of these volumes, at long last an inclusive analysis of the areas represented by the art and science of movement-oriented activities will be available for use. It should be a valuable asset to the professional libraries of Alliance members and will undoubtedly become part of the professional collections of most university, school, and city libraries.

The American Alliance for Health, Physical Education, Recreation, and Dance is a voluntary, professional organization presently made up of the following seven associations: Association for the Advancement of Health Education (AAHE), American Association for Leisure and Recreation (AALR), the American School and Community Safety Association (ASCSA), Association for Research, Administration, Professional Councils and Societies (ARAPCS), National Association for Girls and Women in Sport (NAGWS), National Association for Sport and Physical Education (NASPE), and National Dance Association (NDA).

The purpose of the Alliance is to support, encourage, and assist member groups as they initiate, develop, and conduct programs in health, leisure, and movement-related activities for the enrichment of human life. Headquarters are in the AAHPERD Center, 1900 Association Drive, Reston, Virginia 22091.

Series Editor

Thomas K. Cureton, Jr., series editor of the four-volume *Encyclopedia of Physical Education, Fitness, and Sports*, is professor emeritus of physical education at the University of Illinois. He retired in 1969. He has, however, continued to speak, write, study, work, and spread the gospel of physical fitness.

Educated at Yale University, Springfield College, and Columbia University, Dr. Cureton's contributions to his profession and his influence on the lives of those with whom he has come in contact are immeasurable. His inspirational teaching, his passion for research, and his untiring pursuit of knowledge have brought him fame and appreciation. During his long professional career, thousands of graduate students have come under his guidance. Through their accomplishments as well as his own, his influence in the field of physical education and fitness is felt worldwide.

Dr. Cureton has contributed more than 50 books and monographs and at least 600 articles to the professional literature of his field.

He has been honored by many organizations in the areas of health, fitness, and youth leadership. He has served as consultant on fitness to the President's Council on Physical Fitness and Sports under three United States presidents. He is a Founding Fellow of the American College of Sports Medicine. His contributions to the YMCA program have been recognized by the Roberts-Gulick Award for Distinguished Leadership. The American Alliance for Health, Physical Education, Recreation, and Dance has accorded him its highest honor—the Gulick Award.

Dr. Cureton is still a vigorous participant in physical activities. In 1973 he broke four national meet records for his age class in the National AAU Masters' Swimming Championships. He continues his active professional life as Director of the Physical Fitness Institute at the University of Illinois.

Volume Editor

Dr. G. Alan Stull is Professor and Director of the School of Physical Education, Recreation, and School Health Education at the University of Minnesota. A native of Easton, Pennsylvania, he received his B.S. degree from East Stroudsburg State College in 1955 and his M.S. and Ed.D. degrees from the Pennsylvania State University in 1957 and 1961, respectively. He has been a faculty member at Pennsylvania State, the University of Maryland, and the University of Kentucky. At the latter institution he also served as Chairman of the Department of Health, Physical Education, and Recreation, and later as Associate Dean for Graduate Studies in the College of Education.

Dr. Stull has held many offices in professional organizations at the state, district, and national levels. He served as President of the Association for Research, Administration, Professional Councils and Societies in 1976-77, and was the ARAPCS Representative on the Board of Governors of the American Alliance for Health, Physical Education, and Recreation, 1976-79. He was Chairman of the Research Section in AAHPER in 1972-73 and Chairman of the Research Committee of the National College Physical Education Association for Men in 1976-77. At present he is Chairman of the *Research Quarterly* Advisory Committee and also chairs the Position Stands Committee of the American College of Sports Medicine. He has served as an associate editor of the *Research Quarterly, Journal of Motor Behavior*, and *American Corrective Therapy Journal*.

Dr. Stull is a life member of AAHPERD, a Fellow in the American College of Sports Medicine, and a Fellow in the American Academy of Physical Education. In addition, he is a member of the Minnesota Association for Health, Physical Education, and Recreation, the National Association for Physical Education in Higher Education, and Phi Epsilon Kappa. He has authored some 35 research articles and several chapters in edited texts. Dr. Stull has also co-authored with Dr. Chauncey A. Morehouse a textbook in statistical principles with application for physical education and has presented more than 20 research papers at various professional conferences. In 1974 he received the Alumni Distinguished Service Award from East Stroudsburg State College.

Preface

Volume II of the Encyclopedia of Physical Education, Fitness, and Sports has been organized into five sections dealing with principles and procedures of training and conditioning for physical fitness and sport, the effects of various environmental factors on physical performance, the nutritional aspects of physical activity, youth fitness, and adult fitness. The volume, a collection of 55 chapters authored by 48 individuals, was developed with the distinct purpose of transmitting useful information that can be applied in a practical setting, while simultaneously providing the necessary scientific documentation to support a sound, theoretical base for the concepts covered.

Section 1, edited by Sharon A. Plowman, consists of twelve chapters dealing with the theory and practice of training and conditioning. The first three chapters provide a general overview of the human body's response to regular exercise, whereas the final eight chapters explicate exercise programs and training methods one might elect to employ to enhance one's current level of physical fitness.

Section 2 concentrates on those environmental factors known to affect physical performance. Section editor Christine L. Wells has assembled nine chapters detailing the alterations in performance one should anticipate when exercising in either extreme heat or cold, at high altitude, or in excessive levels of air pollution. Suggested alterations in activity level, possible deleterious consequences, and precautions one should take while exercising under such extreme environmental conditions are also included in the section.

The nutritional aspects of physical performance are addressed in Section 3. This section was edited by Melvin H. Williams and is the largest in the volume. Included in the 19 chapters are discussions relating to general nutritional requirements for both male and female athletes, nutritional faddism in athletics, the energy foods, vitamins, iron supplementation, electrolyte solutions, body composition and weight control, and the use of alcohol and caffeine as ergogenic aids.

Section 4, on youth fitness, covers the knowledge and practices relative to the development of physical fitness prior to adulthood. The seven chapters, edited by Gary S. Krahenbuhl and Robert P. Pangrazi, cover such topics as fitness testing for youth, the effects of growth and maturation on fitness components, individual differences in fitness aptitude, physical working capacity of youth, coronary heart disease risk in children, and fitness programs for the overweight child.

The final section, edited by Jay T. Kearney, concerns physical fitness in adulthood. The eight chapters examine motivation for participation in conditioning programs, the economics of exercise for fitness and health, general guidelines to employ in adult fitness programs, an overview of specific adult fitness programs, the association between physical activity level and incidence of coronary heart disease, and the effects of exercise on the elderly.

Although the number of people who contributed significantly to this volume is too extensive to identify each individually, the editor would be remiss if he failed to mention some of the more prominent. Sincere gratitude is extended to Dr. Thomas K. Cureton, Jr., Series Editor, for his encouragement, counsel, support, and dedication to the project. Appreciation is extended to the section editors and authors* who gave so unselfishly of their time and knowledge and also worked so diligently to meet established deadlines. To Raymond A. Ciszek, Staff Liaison of AAHPERD, Gerald C. Spencer, President of Brighton Publishing Company, and Linda Bedell of Addison-Wesley Publishing Company, the editor expresses his indebtedness for their willingness to take on this project and their assistance during the preparation of the manuscript. Appreciation is extended to the leadership of the Research Consortium of the Alliance, especially David H. Clarke, Harold B. Falls, and Don R. Kirkendall, for their invaluable assistance and advice. To the secretaries in the School of Physical Education, Recreation, and School Health Education, University of Minnesota—Mary Cossette, Mary Berger, Sue Holmen, Kay Kerchner, Linda Kerchner, Linda Johnson and Karen Pringle, who typed the preliminary and final drafts of this volume, and to Clarice Yernberg who contributed significantly to the art work—the editor is most grateful. Appreciation and genuine affection are extended to the Stull family—Bobbi, J.D., George, Minnie, Frank, Darlene, Ron, Jim, and Wendy—who were so understanding and supportive during the three years the volume was in preparation. Lastly, to all the unidentified individuals whose efforts and talents have made this volume possible, the editor conveys a very sincere thank you to each.

Minneapolis,   G.A.S.
June 1980

---

*Background information on the accomplishments and affiliations of the contributing authors will be found in the Biographical Appendix alphabetized by authors' surnames.

Contents

Section 2

ENVIRONMENTAL ASPECTS OF PHYSICAL PERFORMANCE

Section 3

NUTRITIONAL ASPECTS OF PHYSICAL PERFORMANCE

Section 4

YOUTH FITNESS

Section 5

ADULT FITNESS

TRAINING AND CONDITIONING FOR PHYSICAL FITNESS AND SPORT

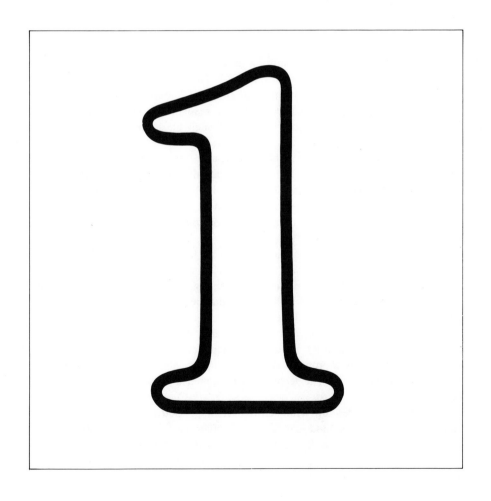

Introduction

The individual who wishes to condition himself or herself for athletic, aesthetic, health, employment, or recreational reasons is faced with a number of important questions, such as how to begin, the duration and intensity of the workout, the type of activity, and the changes that can realistically be expected through training. This section is intended to answer such questions based on research findings.

The first two chapters by Ribisl and Clarke establish basic guidelines and principles that underlie methods for cardiovascular and neuromuscular training and conditioning. These chapters emphasize that the basic principles are similar for the development of both these components of physical fitness, but the specific objectives and characteristics of the participant will require individualization and modification.

The results of consistent participation in an individually prescribed, scientifically designed exercise program are presented in the next chapter by Gettman, entitled "The Physiological Effects of Training." Attention is given to the cardiorespiratory, metabolic, biochemical, and neuromuscular effects with emphasis on the specificity of these changes.

The remaining chapters report on selected examples of chronic exercise programs. Following a brief introduction and definition of the technique, the authors deal with how a program should be implemented and what strengths and weaknesses it possesses. The techniques presented are basically calisthenic and running programs.

In his chapter dealing with aerobic training, Gettman discusses the point based running program and indicates that other large muscle, continuous activities may be used as well. Souter presents information relative to traditional calisthenics with special attention to the importance of the slow, static stretch technique for the development of flexibility. Plowman's chapter on circuit training describes how calisthenics and running can be combined for a variable and comprehensive program.

The individual interested in running programs will find descriptions of different training alternatives. For example, Powell describes the Fartlek system of training that is based on running long distances with free, untimed changes of pace. Next, Fox discusses an interval training program in which repeated bouts are interrupted by lighter work or rest periods. Bowerman then describes the conditioning aspects of jogging and offers recommendations for conducting a sound jogging program. McSwegin's chapter discusses slow distance training designed to tax the aerobic system only.

In his chapter dealing with low, medium, and high gear continuous activity, Cureton provides specific guidelines for gradually increasing the intensity and duration of training sessions. In the final paper, Orban outlines the 5BX and XBX exercise programs created for the Royal Canadian Air Force but subsequently adopted by thousands of civilians.

SAP

Section Editor

Dr. Sharon Ann Plowman, a native of Pennsylvania, is currently an associate professor of physical education at Northern Illinois University. She received her B.A. degree from Gettysburg College and M.S. and Ph.D. degrees from the University of Illinois, Urbana. During the 1977-78 academic year, Dr. Plowman spent her sabbatical leave studying at the Institute of Environmental Stress at the University of California, Santa Barbara. She was formerly a faculty member at Bryn Mawr College.

Dr. Plowman is a Fellow in the American College of Sports Medicine and a member of AAHPERD and the Illinois AHPER. She has held many important positions of leadership in professional associations and has also had six articles published in scholarly journals. In addition, Dr. Plowman has presented about ten papers at professional conferences. In 1975 she was the recipient of the Excellence in Teaching Award at Northern Illinois University and in 1976 received the AAHPER's Mabel Lee Award.

1

Guidelines and Principles of Cardiovascular Conditioning and Exercise Prescription

Paul M. Ribisl

The science of training and conditioning has become refined considerably over the past 20 years with the increased interest in and support of research dealing with the physiology of training. An expansion of research facilities where exercise science is studied has led to an increased quantity and improved quality of research dealing with the biomechanics, biochemistry, and physiology of training in animals and humans. This has provided a better insight into the mechanisms involved in the adaptive process and has assisted in the development of sound guidelines and principles.

INITIAL CONSIDERATIONS

Establishment of Objectives

Prior to the development of a training or conditioning program an obvious prerequisite is the establishment of specific objectives to give proper direction to the program. Physical fitness may mean something different to different individuals. For instance, different athletes may require varying emphases for various sports depending upon the specific requirements of each sport; that is, a gymnast requires high levels of muscular strength and flexibility with lesser emphasis on cardiorespiratory endurance in contrast to the marathon runner with quite the opposite needs. Even the nonathlete who is interested in improving physical fitness may want to emphasize one area over another; for example, the sedentary overweight individual may need to emphasize body composition (weight loss) and cardiorespiratory endurance while a lean, underdeveloped individual may desire to stress improved muscular strength with concomitant weight gain.

It is beyond the purpose of this chapter to cover all components of physical fitness. Therefore, major emphasis is placed upon cardiorespiratory endurance, although the same principles could be modified for use with muscular strength, endurance (see Chapter 2), flexibility (see Chapter 5), and body composition.

Cardiorespiratory endurance is best developed through vigorous aerobic activity involving large muscle groups. Included in the category of vigorous aerobic activity are the following:

walking	jogging	cross-country skiing
hiking	canoeing	racquetball
bicycling	tennis	swimming
basketball	running	

Once the proper type of activity has been selected then the principles that follow can be applied in designing both the daily training sessions and long-range programs.

Individualization

Programs designed for a group rather than for the individual are known to be effective because of the motivation and support that comes from being in a group. However, it is most desirable to prepare a separate prescription for each person. The prescription should be based upon an assessment of the initial status of the individual and should be tailored to unique deficiencies or needs. These needs and/or deficiencies can be efficiently identified with the utilization of either *norms* (based on estimates of the population) or *standards* (based upon empirical standards of desirable performance) and an appropriate program can then be designed to meet these needs.

Medical Evaluation

A medical evaluation is usually suggested prior to participation in sport or initiation of a vigorous training program. In view of the liability aspects of organized exercise programs, it would seem prudent to follow existing guidelines for individuals of various ages and with certain health problems. A more comprehensive treatment of this topic is presented elsewhere (ACSM, 1975); however, some general comments may be warranted.

Although a medical examination is rarely required for participation in physical education programs in the schools, most schools do require a routine physical exam in connection with competitive athletic programs. The need for this exam becomes more obvious with increasing age as individuals develop a variety of medical contraindications to exercise. A report from the American Heart Association (Erb, Fletcher, and Sheffield 1979) outlines the standards developed by an AHA committee on cardiovascular exercise training programs.

It is suggested that these be reviewed for guidance in the development of exercise programs for the adult population of normal, at-risk, and diseased individuals.

PRINCIPLES OF PROGRAM DESIGN AND IMPLEMENTATION

In the design of an effective physical fitness program, certain principles of training and conditioning should be understood. These principles have been developed and refined over the past 20 years or more of research into the physiology of the training mechanism, and they should serve as the basis for sound decision making in *program design*. In addition, certain guidelines have also been formulated to give proper direction in the *implementation* of the program design.

In designing a complete training or conditioning program, attention should be given to the specific principles that apply both to the *daily training sessions* and the *long-range plan for training*. The daily training sessions can be considered as the acute or immediate phase of training, while the long-range training program deals with the longitudinal aspects of the program that are modified by continued application of the daily stimulus.

Daily Training Sessions

Warm-up. All physical activity should be preceded by some period of warmup. As a rule, the more strenuous the activity the longer should be the warmup. Conversely, light activity requires little or no warm-up. The topic of warm-up has been thoroughly reviewed by Franks (1972); however, the primary concern of this chapter deals with safety during training rather than competitive performance.

In theory the possible incidence of muscle injury in strenuous physical activity is greater when warm-up has *not* preceded the activity. This is due to the higher resistance to stretch (relaxation) in the antagonist muscles, making one more susceptible to muscle pulls. The warm muscle will both contract and relax more easily due to reduced viscosity of muscle and increased elasticity of connective tissue. In addition, the effect of warm-up on the heart is extremely beneficial. Strenuous activity without warm-up has been shown to elicit an abnormal electrocardiographic response in young, presumably healthy males (Barnard, et al. 1973). In contrast, this effect is not observed if a brief warm-up period precedes the work. This becomes an even more important point in older individuals with suspected or confirmed coronary heart disease.

The nature of the warm-up depends upon the needs that have been identified, but in general the various stretching exercises for improving flexibility would be included in the early part of the warm-up. This could be followed by some of the muscular strength and muscular endurance activities (i.e., calis-

7

thenics) and finally a brisk walk to elevate total body temperature. This warm-up might involve 10 to 15 minutes of activity prior to the application of the training stimulus.

Training stimulus. The training stimulus is without question the most important component of a training program. Although it is preceded by a warm-up and followed by a cool-down, the primary purpose of the former is to prepare the body for the safe application of the training stimulus while the latter merely allows the body to recover safely from it. The training stimulus has also been studied more extensively than any other aspect of training.

The proper training stimulus is obtained by the manipulation of three independent factors—intensity, duration, and frequency. However, even though each is a clearly separate quality, all must be considered in the formulation and adjustment of the training stimulus. There is an interdependence of these factors that becomes more and more apparent with the study of the manipulation of these factors and the resulting physiological response to training.

Intensity. The intensity of exertion refers to the percentage of maximum exertion or maximum capacity that is achieved during the training stimulus. It is an extremely important component since exercise at too low an intensity will fail to produce a significant training effect regardless of the duration and frequency. Conversely, too high an intensity can be either ineffective or hazardous. It can be ineffective because work at too high an intensity will fatigue the individual very quickly, causing the participant to discontinue exercising. It can also be hazardous due to the extra stress placed upon the muscles and cardiovascular system. High heart rates and high blood pressures cause an increase in myocardial oxygen demand due to the added load on the heart. In the healthy heart this is not dangerous. However, in the individual with diagnosed or undiagnosed coronary heart disease, this could precipitate an ischemic condition that could lead to arrhythmia, fibrillation, or even infarction. The proper intensity needs to be determined if the training is going to be both safe and effective.

Early studies by Karvonen, Kentala, and Mustala (1975), and Hollman and Venrath (1962) revealed that training heart rates below 130 beats per minute did not produce significant gains in cardiovascular fitness, while sustained exercise at heart rates above 150 beats per minute produced significant training effects. The use of these *absolute* heart rate values has been criticized due to the fact that there are large discrepancies in maximal heart rate values among individuals (Fox, Naughton, and Haskell 1971). In addition, since the maximum heart rate declines about ten beats per decade, then a heart rate of 160 may be submaximal for a 20 year old and maximal for a 60 year old.

The more widely accepted approach today is to work at a given percentage of one's maximum functional capacity. This level can be determined in several ways. The more accurate method would be to measure the functional capacity (i.e., maximal oxygen uptake) and work at a given percentage of this value. This is a valid method for research studies but, unfortunately, too expensive for most individuals in that it requires trained personnel, expensive equipment, and considerable time for testing and computation. It is, therefore, not practical for most situations. Another method is based upon the linear relationship that exists between heart rate and oxygen uptake. Instead of working at a percentage of the functional capacity, the individual works at a percentage of the heart rate range; that is, the difference between the HR max and HR rest. Recent research (Davis and Convertino 1975) has revealed a good relationship between the percentage of this HR range and the corresponding percentage of the maximal oxygen uptake (max VO2). The use of heart rate simplifies the process and makes it more practical to apply this information to training large or small groups of individuals without the need for sophisticated tools or techniques. An illustration of this method is presented in Table 1.1.

Table 1.1
Determination of Training Heart Rate

Absolute Heart Rate		Percent of HR Range	Training Guide
180	–	100 ———	HR max, 100%
168	–	90	
156	–	80	Training Zone, 70-90%
144	–	70	
132	–	60 ———	Minimum Threshold, 60%
120	–	50	
108	–	40	
96	–	30	
84	–	20	
72	–	10	
60	–	0 ———	HR rest, 0%

Steps:

1. *Determine HR max* (HR = 180). This can be obtained from a graded exercise test in which the subject is taken progressively through his range from rest to maximum or it can be estimated from the formula found in Table 1.2.

2. *Determine HR rest* (HR = 60). This is the resting HR obtained prior to the graded exercise test.

3. *Compute HR range* (HR = 120). Subtract HR rest from HR max, i.e., $180 - 60 = 120$.

4. *Develop HR scale*. Determine HR for each % HR range using the formula:

$$\frac{\text{HR for}}{\text{desired \%}} = \left(\frac{\% \text{ desired} \times \text{HR range}}{100}\right) + \text{HR rest}$$

$$\frac{\text{HR for}}{80\%} = \left(\frac{80 \times 120}{100}\right) + 60$$

$$= 156$$

After the various percentages have been calculated, the proper percentage must be selected for training. This depends upon the training objective and desired results as well as upon status of fitness, age, and health. In general, the lower the initial fitness level, the lower should be the initial percentage. For sedentary, untrained individuals several weeks at 40 to 60 percent would be preferable, in contrast to active, trained individauls who can train easily at 70 to 90 percent of their capacity. If the training objective is to maintain a high level of fitness for competition, then training at higher percentages such as 85 and 90 percent is preferred. For those who are merely interested in maintaining a reasonable level of fitness, the training level should be between 70 and 85 percent. Age and health status also have a bearing on the intensity that is selected. With increasing age the likelihood of undetected cardiovascular disease also increases, and for this reason the intensity should be lowered accordingly to reduce the hazards associated with overexertion. The data in Table 1.2 present a *theoretical* approach that would adjust the training heart rate downward with advancing age. Two factors are responsible for the lower values: (1) HR max declines approximately 10 beats per decade, and (2) the training intensity has been reduced 5 percent per decade after 20 years of age so that older individuals would not be expected to train at as high a percentage of their capacity as their younger counterparts who might tolerate the work more easily. Thus, a 20 year old may work at 85 percent while a 70 year old might only work at 60 percent of capacity.

Table 1.2
Age-adjusted Training Heart Rates

Age	Hr Max*	−	Hr Rest	Hr (Range × Intensity)	+	Hr Rest	=	Training Hr
10	210	−	70	(140 × .85)	+	70	=	189
20	200	−	70	(130 × .85)	+	70	=	180
30	190	−	70	(120 × .80)	+	70	=	166
40	180	−	70	(110 × .75)	+	70	=	152
50	170	−	70	(110 × .70)	+	70	=	140
60	160	−	70	(90 × .65)	+	70	=	128
70	150	−	70	(80 × .60)	+	70	=	118

* HR max can be roughly estimated by the formula:
(220 minus age); i.e., the estimated HR max for a 20 year old is 220 − 20 or a HR max of 200 beats/min.

The precise intensity for optimal training results has not been established with any degree of certainty. Guidelines have been established for adult populations by the American Heart Association (AHA 1972) and the American College of Sports Medicine (ACSM 1975). Both organizations recommend a training intensity that approximates 60 to 80 percent of the functional capacity or maximal oxygen uptake. These percentages are not adjusted for age although the

ACSM does recommend lower training levels for individuals with lower functional capacities. Using a baseline intensity of 60 percent, the ACSM recommends adding this percentage to the functional capacity in METS* to arrive at the average conditioning intensity. Thus, a person with a low functional capacity of 5 METS would only train at 60 + 5 or 65 percent of his/her functional capacity, while a person with a high functional capacity of 20 METS would train at 60 + 20 or 80 percent of his/her functional capacity.

The research literature dealing with the effectiveness of various intensities has been carefully reviewed elsewhere (Pollock 1973). The consensus of the currently available studies is that the improvement in functional capacity is directly related to the level of intensity in the training, with significantly greater improvements being realized at higher levels of intensity than at lower intensities. In general, the minimum training threshold for significant improvement is 60 percent of the functional capacity, although some improvement is realized at intensities as low as 40 or 50 percent in older individuals or those with low functional capacities. Few studies have examined the upper limit of training intensity that is considered optimal for improving the functional capacity. Since the most significant gains have occurred with training at the 80 to 85 percent intensity level, it appears reasonable to accept this as the upper safe limit for most individuals. With regards to the optimal range, most of the research is supportive of the 60 to 80 percent rage of optimal intensity, adjusted for level of functional capacity, as recommended by the ACSM (1975) in its guidelines.

Duration. This second factor in the exercise prescription refers to the length of time the individual trains at the prescribed intensity. The duration of effort is closely related to the intensity of effort, and this interrelationship requires that both must be considered simultaneously rather than separately. This relationship can be seen in Fig. 1.1 and can be described as an inverse, nonlinear relationship. Maintenance of a high level of intensity is possible for only a short duration of effort due to the limited availability of immediate energy stores. The high energy phosphates can sustain maximal effort for less than 30 seconds, while the short-term glycolytic process can extend this to about two minutes of high level work. If the duration of effort is to be further extended, then the long-term oxidative process must provide the energy and the intensity must be reduced accordingly. For this reason, the duration cannot be prescribed without first considering the intensity.

The duration of effort is an important variable in the exercise prescription since exercise for too short a duration will fail to provide the proper stimulus for

---

* METS are a convenient means of expressing the energy requirement of work. One MET is the equivalent of resting oxygen consumption, which is approximately 3.5 ml · kg^{-1} · min^{-1}. METS during exercise are determined simply by dividing the work metabolic rate by the resting metabolic rate to yield METS.

11

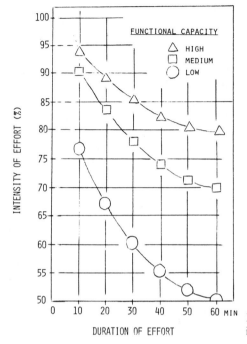

Fig. 1.1 Theoretical relationship between intensity and duration of effort.

adaptation. Although some improvement in cardiorespiratory fitness can be measured after only a few exercise sessions as short at five to ten minutes per day, these changes are not considered to be physiologically significant. In general, it can be stated that the magnitude of the gains in physical fitness are roughly proportional to the duration of effort if all other factors remain constant. This is based upon the bulk of the published evidence where the durations of effort have been as short as five minutes and as long as 60 minutes.

A consensus has not been established for the optimal duration of effort required to produce an optimal cardiorespiratory training effect, but it appears that it is between 30 and 45 minutes per day. Training at durations of 10, 15 or 20 minutes per day has consistently produced less significant gains than training at 30 to 45 minutes per day, while 60 minutes per day appears to offer little advantage over 30 to 45 minutes per day. For this reason the recommended optimal duration is between 30 and 45 minutes per day.

Although the trend is to find greater physiological improvement associated with greater duration, an earlier point must be re-emphasized. There is a strong interdependence of intensity and duration of effort in the production of a training effect. Research has revealed that as long as the training threshold is exceeded, the intensity of effort does not significantly affect the magnitude of the training change if the *total workload* is held constant. This brings out an important point: one should think more in terms of *total workload* when prescribing exercise than of either intensity or duration. The key is to determine the correct blend of intensity and duration that will produce the desired workload.

The desired workload, as well as the percentage of intensity and duration of effort, will depend upon the functional capacity of the individual and the stated objectives of the training program. Figure 1.1, depicting a *theoretical* relationship between intensity and duration of effort, shows that an individual with a low functional capacity should work closer to 60 percent intensity for 30 minutes, while individuals with medium or high functional capacities should work at 80 and 85 percent intensity respectively, if time were held constant. Obviously, those working at 80 to 85 percent would be performing more *total work* than the individual at 60 percent. Therefore, the latter individual would have to work for a much *longer* duration in order to realize the same workload as the others.

As previously stated, the actual workload that will produce a desirable training stimulus is somewhat dependent upon the stated training objectives, but previous research has revealed that significant cardiorespiratory gains are realized if the intensity and duration are sufficient to utilize about 300 to 500 kilocalories (kcal) per workout. For a 70-kg individual this would require running three to five miles since the energy cost of running is about 100 kcal per mile.

Frequency. The third factor in the exercise prescription deals with the number of exercise sessions per week. Frequency is also an important factor since the correct exercise stimulus must be applied on a frequent and regular basis in order to produce significant training changes.

How often one needs to exercise for optimal fitness has not been clearly established, but it is dependent to a large degree on the objectives of the training program as well as the intensity and duration of the workouts. It is usually recommended that untrained beginners exercise on alternate days at lower intensities and durations to reduce muscle soreness and injuries, while well-trained competitive distance runners may exercise as often as twice per day, five days per week at fairly high intensities and durations with no complications. A recent study (Gettman et al. 1976) compared the effects of training one, three, and five days per week at 85 percent intensity for 30 minutes per session over 20 weeks. The results revealed significant cardiorespiratory improvements that were in direct proportion to the frequency of training. Although greater changes were observed in the five day per week program than the one day per week program, significant improvements in cardiorespiratory fitness were nevertheless observed with training only one day per week. The results of this study also support the general trend of similar studies indicating that when the other training factors are held constant (i.e., intensity and duration) improvements in fitness are directly proportional to the frequency of training. However, total workload should also be considered in examining the importance of frequency.

A review of the existing research reveals that the total workload during training is a more important consideration than mere frequency of training. For instance, even if an individual were to exercise every day (but at a workload in which the intensity and duration are well below the threshold levels), little if any improvement would be realized in spite of the frequent workouts. In contrast, if exercise were performed only once per week, but at an optimal intensity and duration, significant fitness gains could be produced.

It is important to realize that many research studies fail to control the total workload when comparing different frequencies of training, and this leads to conflicting results. It should not be surprising when a group that exercises four days a week (30 minutes per session at 75 percent intensity) achieves significantly greater gains in fitness than a group that only exercises two days a week (also for 30 minutes per session at 75 percent intensity). Very simply, the four day per week group is doing twice as much work each week as the two day per week group and is, thereby, exposed to a significantly stronger training stimulus. For this reason, the total workload should be kept in mind when designing or evaluating training programs.

Regularity. In conjunction with frequency of training, regularity is often mentioned as being important to the effectiveness of a training program. The patterns or spacing of training sessions have traditionally been symmetrically spaced on alternate days of the week either to avoid a detraining effect of too long a layoff between workouts or to provide a day of rest to avoid injury or fatigue. A recent study (Moffatt, Stamford, and Neill 1977) challenged this tradition and examined the effectiveness of two patterns of training frequency, each three days per week. One group trained on consecutive days (Mon-Tues-Wed) while the other trained on alternate days (Mon-Wed-Fri) with both utilizing interval training for ten weeks. The results revealed that both groups improved significantly, and there were no differences between groups on any physiological variable. Even though most guidelines imply that regularity is important, there is little scientific evidence to support such a position. Although it may appear reasonable from a common-sense standpoint, further study is required before the importance of regularity is confirmed.

Cool-down. Just as every workout should be preceded by a brief warm-up period, each workout should also be followed by a cool-down period. The need for a cool-down varies with the intensity of the exercise as well as the heat load generated by the work.

The more intense the exercise, the greater is the need for a gradual cool-down or tapering of the workout. When the body is working at near maximal intensity, cardiac output is near maximum and the peripheral vessels are dilated near capacity to provide adequate blood flow and perfusion of the muscles. In order to maintain this high rate of blood flow, the venous return must be maintained. The venous return, however, is largely dependent upon the pumping action of the working muscles; hence, the term venous pump. The contraction of the muscles compresses the veins and sends the blood in the direction of the heart due to the unidirectional flow provided by the valves. However, if at this point the individual were to stop abruptly, there would be considerable pooling of blood in the extremities due to both hydrostatic pressure and the fact that the peripheral vessels are dilated and are capable of holding large quantities of blood. This would be aggravated by the loss of the pumping action of the muscle, and the sharp reduction in venous return could cause dizziness and even fainting. Even more serious complications could arise in the individual with previously compromised circulation due to ischemic heart disease. These deleterious effects are readily eliminated by a gradual tapering of the activity at the end of a workout and the maintenance of rhythmical muscular activity.

The above condition can be even further complicated by exercise in the heat since additional vasodilation occurs in the cutaneous layers of the skin to facilitate loss of body heat. This emphasizes the physiological need for a brief tapering period that allows the body to cool more effectively while still maintaining the venous pump. The duration of the cool-down is not fixed at a certain length of time, but should probably be geared more to the subjective symptoms of the individual.

Long-Range Training Sessions

The previous section dealt with guidelines for the daily training sessions while this section addresses the long-range aspects of training. There are three separate phases to be considered in a long-range program—a starter program, an overload program, and a maintenance program.

Starter program. A starter program refers to the initial phase of training designed for the sedentary, unconditioned individual who is just starting a conditioning program. The major reason for a starter program is that most individuals who have been sedentary prior to training are more prone to muscle soreness because the muscles have been in relative disuse. They are quite unaccustomed to the stress and strain of vigorous exercise. The aches and pain associated with the first few days or weeks of training can be either eliminated or significantly reduced by a properly designed starter program.

The starter program should begin well below the capacity of the individual since the emphasis is on gradually "seasoning" the muscles, tendons, ligaments, and joints rather than immediately providing a significant overload. The overload can come later. It is extremely important that musculoskeletal injuries and soreness be kept at a minimum during the early stages of training because these injuries are usually slow to heal and can retard the training schedule by weeks or even months. This is discouraging to the participant and may be a deterrent to resuming a training program.

Although scientific evidence is lacking, it appears that the older and more unconditioned the individual, the lower should be the starting level. The rate of progression should also be slower. This allows for a safe and gradual adaptation

15

that is well within the limits of the participant. Younger individuals who are less sedentary can adapt more easily and do not need as long a period for the starter program.

The factors of intensity, duration, and frequency should be considered in designing a starter program. Although standards are not presently available, it would seem prudent to use an intensity in the 40 to 60 percent range, a duration of 20 to 30 minutes per session and a frequency of three to four days per week. While the frequency is similar to the level that will be recommended for an overload or maintenance program, the intensity and duration are kept below optimal training levels to reduce the likelihood of muscle soreness, injury, and overexertion. As the individual adapts to the training, the intensity and duration can be gradually increased according to the capability of the individual.

The length of the starter program is variable and depends upon the ability of the individual to adapt. Cooper (1975) has recommended a ten-week starter program for sedentary adults, but this can be shortened for younger and more active individuals. The most important objective is for the individual to adapt to the training without musculoskeletal problems.

Overload program. The principle of training that has achieved the most attention is the overload principle. Very simply, this states that in order for an adaptive response to occur, the body must be subjected to a load that is significantly greater than that to which it is accustomed. This concept is illustrated in Fig. 1.2, which describes a theoretical pattern of change in physical fitness during the starter, overload, and maintenance phases of a typical program. The overload phase is characterized by periodic increments in loan and subsequent adaptation to the load. It follows then that setting the proper overload is dependent upon both progression and adaptation.

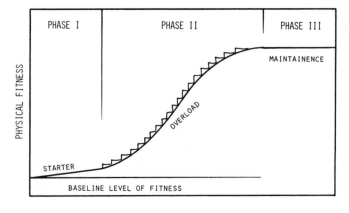

Fig. 1.2 Theoretical concept of the three phases of training.

Progression. The overload must be applied very gradually if the organism is to adapt to the work. Application of too great a load to the body will result in premature fatigue and, if continued, could result in musculoskeletal injury. Application of a load that is too light will either retard the adaptation or provide an inadequate stimulus.

Overload is applied by the manipulation of the three factors of intensity, duration, and frequency. In the starter program the intensity and duration should be kept *below* optimal levels to allow a gradual adaptation for the unconditioned individual. After the starter program is completed, then the overload can be safely applied and the intensity, duration, and/or frequency can be increased. Research indicates that during the overload phase the intensity should exceed the threshold (i.e., 60 percent of capacity) with the individual operating in the 70 to 85 percent intensity range for a duration of 30 to 45 minutes per session and a frequency of three to five days per week. As indicated earlier, total workload is important and total expenditure should be between 300 and 500 kcal per session. It should also be mentioned that there is a self-correcting mechanism in operation when the work intensity is based upon the percentage of HR range. As the individual adapts to the training and the level of fitness is enhanced, it will take more and more work to elevate the HR into the optimal range thereby providing a continuous and progressive overload. Therefore, this method does not require repeated adjustment. This will also allow the individual to increase the total workload, moving from the minimum level of 300 kcal per session toward a more optimal level of 600 kcal per session. The rate of progression is dependent upon how well the individual adapts to the applied overload, and adaptation is the key to the success of any program.

Adaptation. Unless progressive adaptation were occurring in the body systems, greater workloads could not be tolerated and further increments in the workload should not be applied until adaptation to the previous level has been achieved. The stepwise increments in fitness illustrated in Fig. 1.2 imply that continuous adaptation to progressive increments is occurring, and the increases in workload are well tolerated. The illustration is obviously oversimplified but, nevertheless, serves to demonstrate how the three phases of a program are interrelated. Other physiological effects of training are covered in detail in other sections of this publication (see Chapter 3).

Specificity. Closely allied to the process of adaptation is the concept of specificity of training. This concept states that the adaptive changes that occur with training are specific to the *type* of training (aerobic or anaerobic) as well as the specific *muscles* involved with the training. An excellent review of this topic has been completed by McCafferty and Horvath (1977), which elucidates the mechanisms involved in the training response.

17

The concept of specificity provides more support for the importance of *peripheral adaptation* (muscles and subcellular system) than it does for *central adaptation* (heart, blood, and vascular system) in explaining training changes. Several studies have demonstrated that there is little transfer of adaptation from either one *part* of the body to another (i.e., arm training versus leg training) or from one *type* of training to another (aerobic versus anaerobic).

Studies utilizing swimming as the mode of training have revealed that little or no change is observed in the capacity of the legs for work (treadmill). In contrast, the capacity for work with the arms is significantly improved (swim ergometer). The obvious conclusion is that the cellular adaptation to the swim training is localized in the arm muscles that are used in swimming. Since the legs are used to a minimal degree during swimming, no cellular adaptation takes place and the capacity for work is unchanged.

Similar results are found in comparing the specificity of the type of training. Aerobic-type training produces a specific adaptation in the oxidative mechanisms of long-term energy production (i.e., increased myoglobin, mitochondrial density, fatty acid oxidation, substrate storage, and capillarization), while anaerobic training produces a specific adaptation in the high energy phosphates and glycolytic mechanism of short-term energy production (i.e., increased phosphate pool of ATP-CP, glycogen, and glycolytic enzymes). For this reason, there is little transfer from one type of training to another.

In light of the specificity of the training response as it relates to both the type of training and the muscles used, it is recommended that individuals perform their training in the mode of activity in which they desire a training effect (i.e., running, swimming, or bicycling) using the type of activity that develops the capacity they are striving to improve (aerobic or anaerobic).

Maintenance program. The final phase of the long-range training program is the maintenance program. It is unlikely that overload and adaptation can continue forever and at some point the individual will need to determine the desired level of fitness. The training objective of a competitive athlete differs from that of the individual who is interested in maintaining a reasonable level of cardiorespiratory fitness. Although the competitor may continue to strive for further improvement, the noncompetitive individual must be satisfied with attaining a given level and then maintaining that level for a definite or indefinite period of time. This trend is presented in Fig. 1.2 where a slow increase in the starter program is followed by stepwise increases in the overload phase towards an asymptote in the maintenance program. This trend is a theoretical model and the rate of adaptation will vary among both individuals and programs, but the basic trend will remain essentially the same. Two factors modifying the trend are the plateau effect and detraining.

Plateau effect. This refers to a brief or prolonged period of stabilization in the level of fitness or performance. This is a fairly common occurrence in training programs and, realistically, one should not always expect a consistent incremental improvement with training. Brief plateaus should be anticipated as a natural part of the training cycle since the human organism is quite variable. However, a prolonged plateau might be reason to reassess the individual or the program to discern whether the plateau is due to fatigue and overtraining or whether it represents a natural upper limit of one's capacity or potential. In the case of overtraining or staleness, the fatigue does not disappear with cessation of the workout and the individual may experience general weakness during other parts of the day. Susceptibility to illness may increase, and certain blood changes may arise. The solution is to reduce the total workload by modifying the intensity, duration, and frequency of training to a level that is compatible with adequate recovery. If these symptoms do *not* accompany a prolonged plateau, then it is possible the individual has reached his/her potential and should perhaps accept this as the maintenance level.

REFERENCES

American College of Sports Medicine. 1975. *Guidelines for Graded Exercise Testing and Exercise Prescription.* Philadelphia: Lea and Febiger.

American Heart Association. 1972. *Exercise Testing and Training of Apparently Healthy Individuals: A Handbook for Physicians.* Dallas: American Heart Association.

Barnard, R.J., G.W. Gardner, N.V. Diaco, R.N. MacAlpin, and A.A. Kattus. 1973. Cardiovascular responses to sudden strenuous exercise-heart rate, blood pressures, and ECG. *J Appl Physiol,* 34, 833-837.

Cooper, K.H. 1975. *The New Aerobics.* New York: M. Evans.

Davis, J.A. and V.A. Convertino. 1975. A comparison of heart rate methods for predicting endurance training intensity. *Med Sci Spts,* 7, 295-298.

Erb, B., G. Fletcher, and T. Sheffield. 1979. Standards for cardiovascular exercise treatment programs: AHA committee report. Dallas: American Heart Association.

Fox, S.M., J.P. Naughton, and W.H. Haskell. 1971. Physical activity and the prevention of coronary heart disease. *Ann Clin Res,* 3, 404-432.

Franks, B.D. 1972. Physical warm-up. In *Ergogenic Aids and Muscular Performance,* W.P. Morgan (ed.). N.Y.: Academic Press.

Gettman, L.R., M.L. Pollock, J.L. Durstine, A. Ward, J. Ayres, and A.C. Linnerud. 1976. Physiological responses of men to 1, 3 and 5 day per week training programs. *Res Quart,* 47, 638-646.

Hollman, W. and H. Venrath. 1963. Die Beeinflussung von Herzgrösse, maximaler O2-Aufnahme and Ausdauergrenz durch eine Ausdauertraining mittlere und hoher Intensität. *Der Sportartzt, Heft,* 9, 189.

Johnson, B.L. and J.K. Nelson, 1974. *Practical Measurements for Evaluation in Physical Education.* Minneapolis: Burgess.

Karvonen, M.J., E. Kentala, and O. Mustala. 1957. The effects of training on heart rate. A longitudinal study. *Ann Med Exper Fenn,* 35, 307-315.

McCafferty, W.B. and S.M. Horvath. 1977. Specificity of exercise and specificity of training. *Res Quart,* 48, 358-371.

Moffatt, R.J., B.A. Stamford, and R.D. Neill. 1977. Placement of tri-weekly training sessions: Importance regarding enhancement of aerobic capacity. *Res Quart,* 48, 583-591.

Myers, C.R., L.A. Golding, and W.E. Sinning. 1973. *The Y's Way to Physical Fitness.* Emmaus, Pa: Rodale Press.

Pollock, M.L. 1973. The quantification of endurance training programs. In *Exercise and Sport Science Reviews,* J.H. Wilmore (ed.). Vol 1. New York: Academic Press.

Siegel, G.H. 1973. Legal aspects of informed consent, stress testing and exercise programs. In *Exercise Testing and Exercise Training in Coronary Heart Disease,* J.P. Naughton and H.K. Hellerstein (eds.). New York: Academic Press.

2

Muscular Strength and Endurance: Methods for Development

David H. Clarke

Present day popular concepts give the impression that jogging and distance running are not only the most important exercises for cardiovascular conditioning, but they seem to imply that they are the only ones necessary to improve fitness. There is no question that such aerobic conditioning is essential, although the purpose of such activity may vary between young and old from athletic preparation to health considerations. Surely, this has considerable merit for most of the population and should begin at the earliest moment. However, what is frequently neglected is that component of physical fitness that embraces muscular strength and endurance. For a balanced approach, both types of exercise are important.

A misconception also exists that distance running, because it is a muscular activity, will provide all of the necessary activity required to develop muscular strength and endurance. This may be true in part for some of the muscles of the lower extremity, such as those of the legs and hips, because they are repeatedly stressed throughout the exercise. In such an instance they respond to training by developing considerable endurance, and because they involve some of the largest muscles in the body, there is an extensive requirement for additional blood supply to meet the demands of the muscle cells for oxygen and removal of metabolic byproducts. This in turn stimulates the heart for greater action, increasing the overall cardiac output. Thus running becomes not only a cardiovascular activity but causes a number of very specific changes to take place in certain local muscles. However, only those muscles directly stressed will respond to this stimulus; other unused muscles will not benefit from such training. In order to bring all the muscles under the umbrella of conditioning, specific emphasis must be placed on local strength and endurance work.

Separating that portion of activity described as strength from that called endurance is not easy, although both are components of physical fitness. Muscular strength is the maximum amount of tension that muscles can apply in a single contraction, and muscular endurance is the ability of the muscles to sustain work through repetitions of time or effort. Theoretically, the weight lifter who performs a maximum lift is exhibiting muscular strength, whereas the performer doing a maximum number of sit-ups is engaging in muscular endurance exercise. Actually, it may not be necessary to compartmentalize the two, since there is evidence that strength will be developed when both strength and endurance training are undertaken, and conversely, muscular endurance will be enhanced with programs emphasizing both strength and endurance (Clarke and Stull 1970; Stull and Clarke 1970).

The opportunities for performing muscular strength exercises during training are quite limited if one adopts the classical definition that strength is equivalent to one repetition maximum (1 RM). As an indicator of progress made in a fitness program it has validity and signifies clear gains made in a standardized manner. Those familiar with weight training programs will note the difficulties encountered in obtaining such a measure, and so pure strength identified in theory becomes somewhat elusive in actual practice.

TYPES OF EXERCISE

The emphasis, therefore, will be placed on endurance, with the expressed belief that both strength and endurance outcomes will be obtained. This leaves open the question of what form the exercise should take once the decision has been made to engage in exercise that is other than a single maximum effort. A brief review of the major types of exercise follows:

1. Isometric. The isometric muscular contraction requires the performer to adopt a given tension and maintain it for a period of time, usually a few seconds (Hettinger and Muller 1953). No joint range of motion occurs, but the tension usually remains constant.

21

2. Isotonic. The typical weight training exercise employs an isotonic movement, one in which force is exerted through a range of motion, such that muscle length changes during contraction. The amount of resistance is usually equivalent to the weight that can be lifted several times. The isotonic movement can generally be subdivided into two phases.

> a. *Concentric.* The first phase of isotonic movement is the concentric contraction characterized by a shortening of the overall muscle length. It usually occurs when the weight is lifted against gravity and the force of contraction is greater than the resistance against which it is working.
>
> b. *Eccentric.* The second phase of an isotonic activity is called eccentric and is defined as a muscular contraction performed during a lengthening movement. Thus, lowering the weight with gravity would be an example of an eccentric contraction. In this case the force of contraction is less than the resistance.

3. Isokinetic. A rather new procedure designed to place the muscle under more systematic tension is the isokinetic contraction. Called accommodating resistance exercise (Hislop and Perrine 1967), and employing specialized apparatus, the limb motion is kept at a constant, preset velocity so that any muscular exertion encounters an equal counteracting force. Increased muscular effort produces increased resistance, rather than increased speed of movement, as would be true with the usual isotonic contraction.

PRINCIPLES TO BE OBSERVED IN EXERCISE

The following specific principles apply to a fitness exercise program and are generally applicable to all exercise forms (Clarke and Clarke 1978).

1. Exercise should be adapted to an individual's exercise tolerance. The individual's exercise tolerance refers to the initial capacity to perform an activity. When a strength and muscular endurance training program is instituted, the subject's tolerance must be determined for each movement or exercise performed. Sometimes it must be determined from subjective observation of the individual, but in the main it can be determined by careful objective assessment of initial performances. For example, some individuals will find it impossible to do even one chin-up, or a dip from the parallel bars, necessitating a modification of pull-ups and push-ups in the exercise program. On the other hand, the amount of weight required for the bench press can be determined rather precisely after two or three trials.

2. Overloading is necessary to induce improvement in performance. Overloading implies that at each exercise session the performer attempts to exceed the previous level of work by some amount. The usual technique is to try to perform additional repetitions of an exercise, bearing in mind that at first the attempt may fail, but as the training program continues, eventually more work will be possible. If the performer neglects to enhance previous performance, then the fitness program may be ineffective.

3. The exercise plan should provide for progression. Closely allied to the previous principle is that of progression. Current weight training regimens usually suggest that as soon as some increment in repetitions has occurred, the amount of weight lifted should be increased. This makes it necessary, therefore, that principle 2 be followed—that the performer attempt additional repetitions in order that such progression can occur. Failure to do so would retard the objectives of the exercise program, although occasionally a case can be made for simply increasing duration (repetitions), especially when additional muscular endurance is sought, rather than concentrating on strength development.

4. The psychological limits of effort should be advanced. A great proportion of early training gains in muscular strength and endurance are thought to be explained not simply by muscle hypertrophy, but by an enhancement of the neurological pathways involved in the new movement. If this sort of motor learning does indeed occur, it would signal an increase in the ability to lift a load without necessarily causing hypertrophy. Moreover, an individual first beginning an exercise program may adopt a somewhat cautious approach to the exercise and involuntarily hold back and not exert a maximum effort. The early training may be devoted to advancing these psychological limits of effort so that the true maximum is achieved.

5. Proper preparation is needed for full maximum work. Beginning an exercise session with an exhaustive maximum work bout, whether running or muscular training, is unacceptable practice. Warm-up should precede both as a routine part of the exercise period. Most performers feel there may be a greater chance for muscle or connective tissue injury if some warm-up is not permitted. This is, however, a difficult area to research and the literature fails to support such a notion. There is evidence that going all-out without first warming up can produce symptoms of cardiac abnormality (Barnard, et al. 1973), particularly with running, but probably in other forms of vigorous exercise as well. For those engaging in progressive resistance exercise, the first set of any exercise should be a submaximal one. For example, if the 10 RM is 100 lb., the first and second sets of 10 repetitions would be 50 and 75 lb. respectively, or one-half and three-fourths of the 10 RM. For exercises such as sit-ups, the individual may be able to reduce the number of repetitions before going all-out.

6. Muscular soreness will result. One of the most serious drawbacks at the beginning stages of any exercise program is the predictable residual muscular soreness following the first exercise session. This is most noticeable in people who have not engaged in training and it can be very incapacitating. Unfortunately, the performer may have no idea that the exercise will lead to this, because there are virtually no warning signs during exercise. The very absence of such symptoms frequently stimulates the individual to overextend, which in turn leads to greater debility later. It is at this point that the individual may decide to return to a sendentary existence. The first symptoms of soreness are evident anywhere from eight to 24 hours after exercise and will continue for several days, depending upon the degree and type of prior exercise (Clarke 1975). Greater soreness accompanies those exercises that rely heavily upon eccentric contractions, with the peak of soreness occurring some 48 hours after exercise (Talag 1973). Very little treatment seems to be effective in speeding recovery, so the individual may be unable to continue the activity program at the usual intensity until the pain has subsided. Fortunately, once this interval has passed, no further soreness of this sort is likely to occur.

7. Progress must be tested and recorded at set times. Most individuals share a desire to know how they are progressing throughout the exercise sessions, so it is desirable to keep extensive notes and records of performance on a daily basis. This forms the basis for self-testing. However, an additional technique is to keep a separate chart of progress on a weekly or perhaps monthly basis. A daily record sometimes obscures the progress that is being made, whereas the other plan amplifies the gains more visually. A chart can serve as an excellent motivating device by providing constant checks on progress. Body weight and other items of interest may also be included. Measurement of progress in fitness can also be obtained by the use of standardized tests, such as certain motor performance or fitness tests, or even tests of maximal oxygen uptake or physical work capacity. If available, they should be given at the beginning of the program and readministered at intervals of five or six weeks.

THE DEVELOPMENT OF MUSCULAR STRENGTH AND ENDURANCE

Important consideration should be given to the methods required for development of muscular strength and endurance. Once the exercises have been selected, the performer still must understand the nature of the activities and the specific protocols available (Clarke 1973). The following type of training may be employed:

Isotonic Training

The usual practice in most weight training regimens is to raise and lower a given amount of weight through a range of motion. While these procedures combine elements of both concentric and eccentric contractions, they cannot be separated very easily in most weight training movements. Most research investigations have employed some form of progressive resistance exercise. One of the earlier initial recommendations suggested that 10 RM would be the most effective means for strength development (DeLorme and Watkins 1948), although subsequent analysis has modified this somewhat. For example, Hansen (1967) found that 100 contractions of the elbow flexor muscles increased strength to only a moderate degree, some 13 percent, but caused a large increase in muscular endurance. Capen (1950) used both weight training and general conditioning to monitor changes in strength, endurance, and power, and found weight training superior for strength development. Both groups improved in athletic power as measured by the broad jump, vertical jump, and shot put.

Berger has employed various combinations of repetitions, sets of the exercise per session, and number of training sessions per week in an effort to make a definitive statement about an optimum conditioning regimen. Employing the criterion of 1 RM as a measure of strength (single maximum bench press), groups performing 2, 10 and 12 RM made significantly smaller gains than groups training with 4, 6, and 8 RM, indicating that between 3 and 9 repetitions for 1 set per training session would represent the optimal range (Berger 1962b). In a comprehensive study, combinations were examined of 1, 2, and 3 sets at the same time employing 2, 6, and 10 repetitions (Berger 1962a). All combinations of training caused significant increases in strength, but training with 3 sets per training session was more effective for strength improvement than either 1 or 2 sets. In this context, 1 set was about as effective as 2 sets. Also, 6 repetitions per set were more effective for improving strength than 2 repetitions per set. An overall recommendation for an optimum training regimen would be to employ 6 RM for 3 sets and exercise 3 times a week.

Concentric versus Eccentric Training.

The difficulty in isolating the eccentric (lengthening) phase of any movement must be underscored once again, because most exercises encompass both shortening and lengthening in a single repetition. However, it is a valid concern to study such movement in order to gain insight into which part leads to the major training effect for isotonic contractions. Johnson, et al. (1976) worked with arms and legs on one side of the body by concentric (shortening) contractions, and the opposite side by eccentric means. Employing arm curls, arm presses, and knee flexion and extension exercises, the concentric movements were performed against a resistance of 80 percent of 1 RM for 10 repetitions, and the eccentric contractions employed 6 repetitions at 120 percent of the 1 RM training 3 times a week for 6 weeks. Both types of exercise resulted in significant strength gains, but neither was significantly more effective than the other. Since these results are in basic agreement with others (Laycoe and Marteniuk 1971; Seliger, et al. 1968), it signifies that both forms of the isotonic movement contribute an important part to strength development.

Isometric Training

A mid-1950s report startled the training community by indicating that isometric exercise would lead to sizable gains in strength (Hettinger and Muller 1953). The main findings suggested that an optimum training regimen would be to exert a given isometric tension at two-thirds maximum for 6 seconds 5 times a week. With such a program there would be an average increase in strength of 5 percent per week. Such a regimen would certainly be helpful because of the relative ease with which it could be done.

However, subsequent research has not always confirmed the extent of these earlier results. Rose, Radzyminski, and Beatty (1975) had subjects hold maximum quadriceps contractions for 5 seconds and achieved final strength gains after several months of from 80 percent to nearly 400 percent. Hansen (1961) on the other hand found only a 3.7 percent increase in elbow flexion strength after 5 weeks of training, which later increased to 11 percent in subsequent research (Hansen 1963). Rarick and Larsen (1958) employed the Hettinger-Muller protocol of two-thirds maximum held for 6 seconds each day. Wrist flexion contractions at 80 percent maximum for 5 periods of 6 seconds each were given to a second group of postpubescent boys. Both conditions resulted in a significant increase in strength after 4 weeks of training, but there was no difference between them. The gains amounted to 14 and 16 percent, respectively, for the two groups.

Conversely, Mayberry (1959) found contradictory results when one group of men and women trained with one maximal contraction and another employed a load of 50 percent maximum. No significant gains in strength occurred for either group participating in over 20 training sessions taking place over a relatively short period of time. Training at an intensity of 25 percent of maximum has been found to be ineffectual as a training stimulus (Cotten 1967), so the best prescription for training seems to be a tension ranging from 50 percent to maximum, given once a day and held for as little as 5 seconds.

Isokinetic Training

The isokinetic procedure requires the use of specialized equipment in order to place the muscle under systematic tension and to keep the velocity of movement the same regardless of the effort. This permits the tension to remain the same throughout the range of motion. A typical weight lifting movement fails to do this, so that at certain points in the arc of movement the exercise is fairly readily accomplished, which at other places (called "sticking points") the contraction is more difficult. Theoretically the muscle will benefit at the point of greatest weakness and therefore may not be uniformly stressed. Isokinetic exercise is designed to correct for this, and when Thistle, et al. (1967) compared these procedures to the usual isotonic exercises (10 RM) administered to the quadriceps muscles over an 8-week period, the isokinetic group scored better. In fact, total work ability improved by 35 percent, as compared to 28 percent for the isotonic group, findings that were very similar to those obtained for maximum strength. Moffroid, et al. (1969) utilized knee extensor and knee flexor muscles and compared isokinetic training with the isotonic and isometric procedures over a 4-week period. None of the groups improved significantly when tested for isokinetic work of the quadriceps muscles, but isokinetic training imrpoved isokinetic work of the hamstring muscles.

Changes in muscular strength were investigated by Pipes and Wilmore (1975) as a result of an 8-week training program. The major finding was that the isokinetic training procedures were generally superior to the isotonic exercise; further, the isokinetic training that emphasized high speed, as contrasted with low speed, caused the greater increases. Thus, the isokinetic procedure seems to be very effective as a means for achieving gains in muscular strength and endurance when given at high speed and when 10 to 15 repetitions are given per set.

CROSS-TRANSFER OF STRENGTH DEVELOPMENT

The usual expectation of an individual engaging in an exercise program is that the muscles will hypertrophy and become stronger. It is ordinarily the impression that only those muscles actually exercised will respond in this way, so it means that a variety of specific exercises are needed to ensure an overall conditioning effect. These ideas are basically correct, although there is need for some slight modification to account for the phenomenon known as cross-transfer of training.

The basic definition of cross-transfer applied to strength development is that corresponding muscles in the unexercised part of the body will increase in strength at the same time as those in the exercised portion. First identified at the turn of the century, Scripture, Smith, and Brown (1894) attributed it to some sort of indirect practice, although it was soon suggested that some central mechanism must be operating in addition to various peripheral factors (Davis 1898), even suggesting a diffusion of motor impulses to the opposite extremity (Wissler and Richardson 1900). A number of studies have confirmed the existence of cross-transfer. Hellebrandt, Parrish, and Houtz (1947) found in female subjects that exercise of the knee extensors and elbow flexor muscles caused a concurrent training effect in the contralateral musculature. This was later confirmed for wrist extension (Hellebrandt, Houtz, and Krikorian 1950) and for knee extension (Rose, Radzyminski, and Beatty 1957; Logan and Lockhart 1962).

Isometric training may also produce a cross-transfer effect. Meyers (1967) had one group of subjects perform three 6-second maximum isometric contractions of the elbow flexor muscles three times a week for 6 weeks, while a second group gave twenty 6-second maximal contractions. The subjects in the first group gained significantly in strength of the contralateral limb, but the second group failed to do so. Gardner (1963) employed the classic prescription of two-thirds maximal knee extensor contractions held for 6 seconds and had subjects assigned to hold knee joint angles of 115, 135, and 145 degrees. After six weeks of training no significant improvement of the nonexercised limb was found in any of the gruops. This was corroborated for exercise involving the wrist flexors as well (Mayberry 1959). The general conclusion is that cross-transfer of training is likely to occur when the exercise is isotonic rather than isometric, but it is also true that the training effect is not as substantial as that found in direct exercise; its usefulness is enhanced when the contralateral limb is immobilized due to some trauma (Hellebrandt, Houtz, and Partridge 1957). In order for it to be effective, motor innervation to the contralateral musculature must be intact (deVries, 1974).

RETENTION OF STRENGTH

A rather important question frequently raised concerns how long newly acquired muscular strength and endurance can be expected to last. All observers realize the transient nature of the training effect and know that if hypertrophy is to be maintained there must be continuing attention and work. The literature on retention is not complete, and only recently have systematic efforts been applied to understanding this problem. In fact, the usual procedure has been to examine strength at some post-training time only as a matter of incidental interest, which may account for some of the variance found. For example, McMorris and Elkins (1954) claimed that subjects had retained 45 percent of their elbow flexion strength gain one year after a 12-week training period, and Berger (1965) found that strength was not reduced after 6 weeks of post-training after only 3 weeks of initial exercise, substantiating a finding previously noted for a 4-week elbow flexion training program (Clarke, Shay, and Mathews 1954).

A few studies have focused on the question of retention as a main objective. Waldman and Stull (1969) employed an elbow flexion ergometer as a device used for an 8-week training session. Subjects were then placed in groups that engaged in no further training for 8, 10, or 12 weeks, after which they were retested for muscular endurance. A significant reduction in newly formed endurance was found by all groups, so Sysler and Stull (1970) employed periods as short as 1, 3, and 5 weeks after training. In this instance, more endurance was last after 3 and 5 weeks than after only 1 week. Retraining after the subsequent loss was accomplished in only one-fourth the time it took for the initial training to occur (Waldman and Stull 1969).

REFERENCES

Barnard, R. J., G. W. Gardner, N. V. Diaco, R. N. MacAlpin, and A. A. Kattus. 1973. Cardiovascular responses to sudden strenuous exercise—Heart rate, blood pressure, and ECG. *J Appl Physiol,* 34, 833-837.

Berger, R. A. 1965. Comparison of the effect of various weight training loads on strength. *Res Quart,* 36, 141-146.

Berger, R. A. 1962a. Effect of varied weight training programs on strength. *Res Quart,* 33, 168-181.

Berger, R. A. 1962b. Optimum repetitions for the development of strength. *Res Quart,* 33, 334-338.

Capen, E. K. 1950. The effect of systematic weight training on power, strength and endurance. *Res Quart,* 21, 83-93.

Clarke, D. H. 1973. Adaptations in strength and muscular endurance resulting from exercise. In *Exercise and Sports Sciences Reviews,* J. H. Wilmore (ed.). Vol. 1. New York: Academic Press.

Clarke, D. H. 1975. *Exercise Physiology.* Englewood Cliffs, N.J.: Prentice-Hall.

Clarke, D. H. and H. H. Clarke. 1978. *Developmental and Adapted Physical Education.* 2nd ed. Englewood Cliffs, N.J.: Prentice-Hall.

Clarke, D. H. and G. A. Stull. 1970. Endurance training as a determinant of strength and fatigability. *Res Quart,* 41, 19-26.

Clarke, H. H., C. T. Shay, and D. K. Mathews. 1954. Strength and endurance (conditioning) effects of exhaustive exercise of the elbow flexor muscles. *J Assoc Phys Mental Rehab,* 8, 184-188.

Cotten, D. 1967. Relationship of the duration of sustained voluntary isometric contraction to changes in endurance and strength. *Res Quart,* 38, 366-374.

Davis, W. W. 1898. Research in cross-education. *Studies Yale Psych Lab,* 6, 6-50.

DeLorme, T. L. and A. L. Watkins. 1948. Techniques of progressive resistance exercise. *Arch Phys Med,* 29, 263-273.

deVries, H. A. 1974. *Physiology of Exercise for Physical Education and Athletics.* 2nd ed. Dubuque: Wm. C. Brown.

Gardner, G. W. 1963. Specificity of strength changes of the exercised and non-exercised limb following isometric training. *Res Quart,* 34, 98-101.

Hansen, J. W. 1967. Effect of dynamic training on the isometric endurance of the elbow flexors. *Int Z Angew Physiol,* 23, 367-370.

Hansen, J. W. 1963. The effect of sustained isometric muscle contraction on various muscle functions. *Int Z Angew Physiol,* 19, 430-434.

Hansen, J. W. 1961. The training effect of repeated isometric muscle contractions. *Int Z Angew Physiol,* 18, 474-477.

Hellebrandt, F. A., S. J. Houtz, and A. M. Krikorian. 1950. Influence of bimanual exercise on unilateral work capacity. *J Appl Physiol,* 2, 446-452.

Hellebrandt, F. A., S. J. Houtz, and M. J. Partridge. 1957. Cross education in the prosthetic training of the below-elbow amputee. *Am J Phys Med,* 36, 196-211.

Hellebrandt, F. A., A. M. Parrish, and S. J. Houtz. 1947. Cross Education. The influence of unilateral exercise on the contralateral limb. *Arch Phys Med,* 28, 76-85.

Hettinger, T. and E. A. Muller. 1953. Muskelleistung und muskeltraining. *Arbeitsphysiol,* 15, 11-126.

Hislop, H. J. and J. J. Perrine. 1967. The isokinetic concept of exercise, *Phys Ther,* 47, 114-117.

Johnson, B. L., J. W. Adamczyk, K. O. Tennoe, and S. B. Stromme. 1976. A comparison of concentric and eccentric muscle training. *Med Sci Spts,* 8, 35-38.

Laycoe, R. R. and R. G. Marteniuk. 1971. Learning and tension as factors in static strength gains produced by static and eccentric training. *Res Quart,* 42, 299-306.

Logan, G. A. and A. Lockhart. 1962. Contralateral transfer of specificity of strength training. *J. Am Phys Ther Assoc,* 42, 658-660.

Mayberry, R. P. 1959. Isometric exercise and the cross-transfer of training effect as it relates to strength. *Proc College Phys Ed Assoc,* 62, 155-158.

McMorris, R. O. and E. C. Elkins. 1954. A study of production and evaluation of muscular hypertrophy. *Arch Phys Med Rehab,* 35, 420-426.

Meyers, C. R. 1967. Effects of two isometric routines on strength, size, and endurance in exercised and nonexercised arms. *Res Quart,* 38, 430-440.

Moffroid, M., R. Whipple, J. Hofkosh, E. Lowman, and H. Thistle. 1969. A study of isokinetic exercise. *Phys Ther,* 49, 735-746.

Pipes, T. V. and J. H. Wilmore. 1975. Isokinetic vs. isotonic strength training in adult men. *Med Sci Spts,* 7, 262-274.

Rarick, G. L. and G. L. Larsen. 1958 Observations on frequency and intensity of isometric muscular effort in developing static muscular strength in post-pubescent males. *Res Quart,* 29, 333-341.

Rose, D. L., S. F. Radzyminski, and R. R. Beatty. 1957. Effect of brief maximal exercise on the strength of the quadriceps femoris. *Arch Phys Med Rehab,* 38, 157-164.

Scripture, E. W., T. L. Smith, and E. M. Brown. 1894. On the education of muscle control and power. *Studies Yale Psych Lab,* 2, 114-119.

Selinger, V., L. Dolejs, V. Karas, and I. Pachlopnikova. 1968. Adaptation of trained athletes' energy expenditure to repeated muscle contractions. *Int Z Angew Physiol,* 26, 227-234.

Stull, G. A. and D. H. Clarke. 1970. High-resistance, low-repetition training as a determiner of strength and fatigability. *Res Quart,* 41, 189-193.

Sysler, B. L. and G. A. Stull. 1970. Muscular endurance retention as a function of length of detraining. *Res Quart*, 41, 105-109.

Talag, T. S. 1973. Residual muscular soreness as influenced by concentric, eccentric, and static contractions. *Res Quart,* 44, 458-469.

Thistle, H. G., H. J. Hislop, M. Moffroid, and E. W. Lowman. 1967. Isokinetic contraction: A new concept of resistive exercise. *Arch Phys Med Rehab,* 48, 279-282.

Waldman, R. and G. A. Stull. 1969. Effects of various periods of inactivity on retention of newly acquired levels of muscular endurance. *Res Quart,* 40, 396-401.

Wissler, C. and W. W. Richardson. 1900. Diffusion of the motor impulse. *Psych Rev,* 7, 29-38.

3

Physiological Effects of Training

Edward L. Fox

INTRODUCTION

Over the past few years, a great deal of new information concerning the effects of chronic exercise programs (physical training) has become available. A general review of these effects has recently been written by Fox (1977) and Mathews and Fox (1976). Several excellent detailed review articles covering specific biochemical (Gollnick and Hermansen 1973; Hooloszy 1973, 1975; and Holloszy and Booth 1976; Hooloszy et al. 1971, 1975; Howald 1975), cardiovascular (Scheuer and Tipton 1977), and neuromuscular (Burke and Edgerton 1975; Edgerton 1976) adaptations to training have also been recently written. The purpose of this report is to discuss in particular the new findings concerning the physiological effects of physical training.

In this report, the effects of training refer to those adaptive responses in humans and animals following chronic exposure to regularly scheduled exercise programs. For the most part, these programs consist of exercise activities involving large muscle groups such as would be involved in running, swimming, or cycling. However, whenever appropriate, the adaptive responses following weight resistance training are included. The physiological effects of training are limited to two major categories: (1) cardiorespiratory effects; and (2) metabolic, biochemical, and neuromuscular effects. Before discussing these effects, a few words relative to some of the more important factors influencing these changes seem appropriate.

Specificity of Training Effects

Not all of the known effects of training can be elicited from any single training regimen. The training effects produced are specific to the type of exercise performed during the training program. For example, in one study the increase in endurance capacity (maximal oxygen consumption) following eight weeks of training on a bicycle ergometer was much less when measured during running compared to cycling (Pechar et al. 1974). Similar metabolic specificity has been demonstrated with swim versus run training (Magel et al. 1974).

Additionally, in comparing high power (short, intensive runs) and low power (longer, lower intensity runs) interval training programs, it was found that blood lactic acid levels during submaximal exercise performance were lower following the low power program whereas gains in maximal oxygen consumption were the same (Fox 1975; Fox et al. 1977b). This demonstrates yet another type of metabolic specificity.

Training effects have also been shown to be specific to the muscle groups used during the training program. In subjects whose arm muscles were trained, little if any training effect was found for the legs (Clausen et al. 1973; Fox, McKenzie, and Cohen 1975a). The opposite was also found to be true; that is, subjects whose legs were trained showed minimal training effects when working with the arms.

Not only are training effects specific according to muscle groups, but also according to specific movement patterns performed by the same muscle groups (Burke and Edgerton 1973; Edgerton 1976). In other words, neuromuscular training effects appear to be motor skill specific. This means that training programs designed to improve a given sports skill should contain, whenever possible, exercise activities closely related to those actually performed during the execution of the sports skill in question. This applies to weight resistance programs as well as to running, swimming, cycling, or other cardiorespiratory programs.

Training Frequency, Length, and Intensity

Generally, the more intensive, the more frequent, and the longer the training program, the greater will be the magnitude of some, but not all, of the training effects produced. For example, with interval training programs for men (Fox et al. 1975) and women (Lesmes et al. 1978), gains in maximal oxygen consumption did not seem to be affected by either frequency (two versus four days per week) or length of training (seven versus thirteen weeks). The most important factor affecting gains in maximal oxygen consumption, at least with interval training, was found to be the intensity of the program (Fox et al. 1973, 1975b). This also appears to be a general conclusion for continuous types of training programs (Faria 1970; Karvonen, Kentala, and Mustala 1957; Sharkey and Holleman 1967; Shepard 1968) although the interplay with duration (amount of time per workout) cannot be ignored (Kearney et al. 1976). (See also Chapter 1.)

In men, but not women, interval training frequency and length of training were found to influence the magnitude of the submaximal exercise heart rate response (Fox et al. 1973, 1975b; Lesmes et al. 1978; Pollock, Cureton, and Greninger 1969). The longer and more frequent the training, the lower were the submaximal heart rate levels at any given workload.

Sex and Age Influences

Not nearly enough studies have been conducted using female subjects to make valid comparisons of their adaptive responses to training with those of males.

32

However, based on the studies available (Cohen 1975; Kilbom 1971; Lesmes et al. 1978), it is clear that there are no major differences between the training responses of females and males when exposed to the same relative training stress. Nevertheless, Scheuer and Tipton (1977) have pointed out that female rats develop greater degrees of absolute cardiac hypertrophy than males. Also, the body weight of male rats does not usually follow the normal growth curve during training whereas the females does. Until further comparative studies are conducted on humans, the extent and magnitude of the differences, if any, in training responses between the sexes will remain uncertain.

The physical working capacity of both sexes declines with age. Whether this is related to the aging process per se or to the fact that physical activity levels decrease with age is not exactly known. However, it is known that people of all ages can and do respond to physical training programs. In addition, the relative magnitude of the responses appears to be just as great with older compared to younger people (Adams and deVries 1973; deVries 1970).

Types of Training Programs

The above information emphasizes that not all the effects of training can be expected from a single training program. Whenever possible, the type of program that brings about a specific adaptation will be identified. Two types of regimens most commonly identified are sprint (anaerobic) and endurance (aerobic) programs. Endurance training generally refers to chronic exercise programs consisting of prolonged, usually continuous work bouts of relatively low intensity. Sprint or anaerobic training most often refers to programs of short, repeated work bouts of relatively high intensity

RESTING CARDIORESPIRATORY EFFECTS OF TRAINING

The major resting cardiovascular and respiratory effects of training (mainly endurance training) include: (1) cardiac hypertrophy (increased size of the heart); (2) bradycardia (decreased heart rate) and increased stroke volume; (3) increased myoglobin, hemoglobin and blood volume; (4) blood pressure changes; and (5) increases in static lung volumes and pulmonary diffusion capacity.

Cardiac Hypertrophy

Although it has been suspected for a long time that exposure to chronic exercise results in cardiac hypertrophy, only recently has the nature of this hypertrophy in humans been elucidated. For example, it has now been shown with echocardiography that the cardiac hypertrophy of endurance athletes such as distance runners and swimmers (Morganroth et al. 1975) and basketball players (Roeske et al. 1975) consists of an increased left ventricular end-diastolic dimension (increased size of the ventricular cavity) without an increased thickness of the myocardial wall. Morganroth et al. (1975) further showed that with nonendurance athletes (e.g., wrestlers and shot putters), the cardiac hypertrophy was caused by just the opposite effect, that is, an increased thickness of the myocardial wall with a normal left ventricular end-diastolic dimension.

While it cannot definitely be concluded from the above cross-sectional studies that cardiac hypertrophy is an obligatory adaptive response to physical training, it seems reasonable that it not only is, but that it is specific to the type of sports activity in which the athlete participates. As an example, it is known that endurance training and performance requires prolonged efforts during which time the cardiac output is sustained at very high levels (Fox and Costill 1972). A large ventricular volume (cavity) would in this case seem to be a mandatory adaptation. By the same token, athletes who train for and participate in brief, powerful activities are subjected to intermittently elevated arterial blood pressure, much like that generated during straining. Here too, it is reasonable that a thickened ventricular wall would be required to easily and repeatedly overcome such a stress.

Cardiac hypertrophy is probably attributable to one or more of the following adaptations (Scheuer and Tipton 1977):

1. Increased myocardial fiber diameter (Hakkila 1955) and other structural changes (Sohal et al. 1968).
2. Hyperplasia (increased number) of myocardial cells and increased sarcoplasmic volume per fiber (Leon and Bloor 1968, 1976).
3. Increased mitochondrial size and number (Arcos et al. 1968).
4. Increased vascularity (Eckstein 1957; Leon and Bloor 1968; Tepperman and Pearlman 1961).

Bradycardia and Increased Stroke Volume

Athletes, particularly endurance athletes, usually have a resting bradycardia (Frick, Elovainio, and Somer 1967; Morganroth et al. 1975) and an increased resting stroke volume (Bevegard, Holmgren, and Jonsson 1963; Frick, Konttmen, and Sarajas 1963; Morganroth et al. 1975; Roeske et al. 1975). Thus, the pumping efficiency of the heart is increased following physical training, since for a given cardiac output, a slower beating heart with a larger stroke volume represents a reduction in the energy utilization by the myocardium.

The physiological mechanisms underlying both the resting bradycardia and increased stroke volume have not definitely been determined. The evidence thus far suggests that the bradycardia involves primarily an increased parasympathetic activity (Frick, Elovainio, and Somer 1967; Tipton 1965; Tipton, Barnard, and Tcheng 1969). However, based on the evidence recently reviewed by Scheuer and Tipton (1977), a simultaneous reduction in sympathetic tone cannot be completely ruled out. As for the increased stroke volume, several factors are probably involved; for example, an increased ventricular volume, as discussed before, and an increased myocardial contractility (Penpargkul and Scheuer 1970). The latter is probably controlled largely by nervous and humoral influences.

Increased Myoglobin, Hemoglobin, and Blood Volume

Myoglobin or muscle hemoglobin has been shown to increase following training (Pattengale and Holloszy 1967). Myoglobin chemically binds oxygen and thus acts as a muscular store for oxygen. However, its main function is aiding the diffusion of oxygen from the cell membrane to the mitochondria.

Although research in this area is not always consistent, physical training generally results in increased blood volume (Kjellberg, Rudhe, and Sjöstrand 1949a, 1949b; Oscai, Williams, and Hertig 1968) and total body hemoglobin (Kjellberg, Rudhe, and Sjöstrand 1949a, 1949b). Since the majority of the increase in blood volume results from increased plasma volume (Oscai, Williams, and Hertig 1968), blood hemoglobin concentration is usually either unchanged or slightly decreased following training.

Both total blood volume and hemoglobin are important with respect to the oxygen transport system particularly during exercise at altitude. Also, since deep body heat is carried by circulatory convection to the periphery for dissipation, blood volume is an important factor during exercise in the heat.

Blood Pressure Changes

Following some training programs, it has been found that resting diastolic and systolic blood pressures are significantly reduced in both men and women (Boyer and Kasch 1970; Kilbom 1971; Mann et al. 1969; Pollock, Cureton, and Greninger 1969). In most of these studies, the subjects were middle-aged or older, had higher than normal blood pressures including hypertension, and/or were poorly fit prior to the start of the training program. In younger people, those less than 30 years, with average blood pressures and fitness levels, resting blood pressures do not usually change with training (Ekblom et al. 1968; Frick, Konttmen, and Sarajas 1963).

The mechanism responsible for decreased resting blood pressures has not been firmly established. However, there is a possibility that a decrease in sympathetic tone may in part be involved (Scheuer and Tipton 1977).

Respiratory Effects

Most of the static lung volumes (e.g., inspiratory and expiratory reserve volumes, residual volume, total lung volume, and vital capacity) are generally larger in athletes than in nonathletes of the same sex and body size (Holmgren 1967; Bachman and Horvath 1968). These changes may be a result of an increase in the strength of the skeletal muscles responsible for ventilation. At any rate, it should be pointed out that there is little, if any, correlation between athletic performance and static lung volumes (Cumming 1969).

With respect to pulmonary diffusion capacity, a number of studies have shown that athletes have greater capacities than do nonathletes (Kaufman et al. 1974; Magel and Andersen 1969; Maksud et al. 1971; Newman, Smalley, and Thompson 1961; Reuschlein et al. 1968). However, this should not be interpreted to mean that diffusion capacity per se is directly affected by training. On the contrary, several longitudinal studies have failed to show an increase in pulmonary diffusion capacity following several weeks of training (Reddan et al. 1963; Reuschlein et al. 1968; Saltin et al. 1968).

In the case of athletes, the larger diffusion capacities may be related to the larger lung volumes just mentioned. The latter would provide for a greater alveolar capillary surface area and, in turn, a greater diffusion capacity.

CARDIORESPIRATORY EFFECTS DURING EXERCISE

During exercise, major training changes have been observed in the oxygen transport system, muscle glycogen utilization, and muscle and blood lactic acid accumulation.

Changes in the Oxygen Transport System

Submaximal exercise. During submaximal exercise at a given power output, the amount of oxygen consumed per minute (VO_2) has been shown to decrease (Ekblom et al. 1968; Fox et al. 1975b) or remain the same (Fox, McKenzie, and Cohen 1975a; Saltin and Karlsson 1971). Pulmonary ventilation is also decreased, but to a greater extent than the VO_2. Therefore, the ventilatory efficiency or ventilation equivalent, that is, the amount of oxygen consumed per liter of air ventilated, is increased. A decrease in VO_2 is thought to be a result of an increased mechanical efficiency (skill). Although in this regard, a decreased VO_2 is most pronounced between highly skilled athletes and nonathletes, such a difference has also been observed between good and average competitive runners (Fox and Costill 1972).

The amount of oxygen consumed or transported to the working muscles is a function of the cardiac output which, in turn, is made up of the heart rate (HR) and stroke volume (SV), and the arterial-mixed venous oxygen difference (a - v O_2 diff). The latter reflects the extraction of oxygen by the active tissues (muscles) and the distribution of blood to active and inactive organs. The relationship of these factors is: $VO_2 = (HR) \cdot (SV) \cdot (a - v\ O_2\ diff)$. Like VO_2, the cardiac output following training at a given submaximal workload has been shown to be either slightly decreased (Ekblom et al. 1968; Hanson et al. 1968; Tabakin, Hanson, and Levy 1965) or unchanged (Saltin et al. 1968). However, in any case, it is a common finding that the stroke volume in increased (Bevegard, Holmgren, and Jonsson 1963; Fox et al. 1975b, Frick, Konttmen, and Sarajas 1963; Saltin et al. 1968) and the heart rate decreased

(Ekblom et al. 1968; Fox et al. 1973, 1975a, 1975b; Frick, Elovainio, and Somer 1967; Frick, Konttmen, and Sarajas 1963; Karvonen, Kentala, and Mustala 1957). As previously mentioned, such a combination represents an efficient system with respect to oxygen utilization by the myocardium.

In humans, the training bradycardia during submaximal exercise is thought to be caused primarily by a reduced sympathetic drive without an increased parasympathetic tone (Frick, Elovainio, and Somer 1967). A decreased sympathetic drive could, in turn, be related to an effect directly on the myocardium itself (intracardiac mechanism). For example, with an increased stroke volume at the same or slightly decreased cardiac output, the need for a higher heart rate through sympathetic stimulation would be greatly reduced (Frick, Elovainio, and Somer 1967).

Conversely, there is considerable evidence that an indirect effect (extracardiac mechanism) resulting from alterations in the trained skeletal muscles may also be involved. It has been shown, for example, that a training bradycardia results from modification of nervous impulses arising from the muscles and joints and by descending impulses from the motor cortex (Claussen, Trap-Jensen, and Lassen 1970; Clausen et al. 1973; Fox et al. 1975b; Saltin et al. 1976).

For a given submaximal work load, blood flow to the working muscles has been shown in the majority of studies to be decreased following training in man (Grimby, Häggendal, and Saltin 1967; Klassen, Andrew, and Becklake 1970); however, recently Saltin et al. (1976) found it to be unchanged. Even with a slightly reduced VO_2 the working muscles apparently compensate for the lowered blood flow in the trained state by extraction of more oxygen as evidenced by the fact that increases in the a - v O_2 diff have also been documented (Ekblom et al. 1968; Rowell 1974). An increased oxygen extraction by skeletal muscle is said to be related to biochemical and other cellular training changes occurring within the muscle itself (Holloszy and Booth 1976). These changes will be discussed in more detail later.

Maximal exercise. Under maximal exercise conditions, maximal oxygen consumption (max VO_2) increases anywhere from 5 to 20 percent on the average (Ekblom et al. 1968; Fox 1975; Fox et al. 1973, 1975b, 1977a, 1977b; Kilbom 1971; Pechar et al. 1974; Saltin et al. 1968). The max VO_2 is considered to be the single most accurate measure of endurance fitness since it is highest in athletes who compete and train for endurance activities (Saltin and Astrand 1967).

The increase in max VO_2 following training is a result of two factors: (1) an increased maximal cardiac output (Ekblom et al. 1968; Kilbom 1971); and (2) an increased oxygen extraction from the blood by the skeletal muscles (Rowell 1974). However, an increased oxygen extraction as judged from changes in the a - v 0_2 diff has not been found to occur in females following training (Kilbom 1971). The reason for this is not known.

Since the maximal heart rate is usually decreased following training (Ekblom et al. 1968; Fox et al. 1973, 1975b; Pechar et al. 1974; Pollock, Cureton, and Greninger 1969; Saltin et al. 1968), the increase in maximal cardiac output is due entirely to an increased stroke volume. This latter increase may be at least in part related to the increased heart (ventricular) volume referred to earlier. At any rate, one of the major differences in the oxygen transport systems of athletes and nonathletes under maximal exercise stress is the magnitude of the stroke volume (Ekblom and Hermansen 1968).

During maximal exercise, blood flow to the working skeletal muscles does not change following training when expressed on a per kilogram muscle mass basis (Grimby, Häggendal, and Saltin 1967). However, blood flow to the total working musculature has been shown to increase (Saltin et al. 1968). This can be interpreted to mean that the increased blood flow is distributed over a larger muscle mass, thus keeping the flow per kilogram of muscle constant.

Muscle Glycogen Utilization and Lactic Acid Accumulation

During submaximal exercise at a given work load and VO₂, muscle glycogen depletion and muscle and blood lactic acid accumulation are less following training (Fox 1975; Fox et al. 1975b, 1977a, 1977b; Karlsson et al. 1972; Klassen, Andrew, and Beklake 1970; Saltin and Karlsson 1971). It has been suggested that these effects are related to the increased ability of trained muscle to use (oxidize) free fatty acids as a fuel and/or to the increase in the number and size of the muscle mitochondria that also occurs following training (Holloszy 1973; Holloszy and Booth 1976; Holloszy et al. 1971; Saltin 1975). Depletion of muscle glycogen stores and accumulation of lactic acid have both been implicated in muscular fatigue (Saltin 1975). Thus, the glycogen sparing effect and the decreased lactate accumulation during submaximal exercise following training appear to be important factors in delaying fatigue and increasing endurance capacity.

With maximal exercise to exhaustion, the lactic acid levels in both blood and muscle are generally greater following training (Karlsson et al. 1972). Some researchers have interpreted this to mean that tolerance to lactate is also increased with training. However, because the maximal work load is higher, the increased lactate production represents a greater functional capacity to generate energy through anaerobic glycolysis.

A summary of the cardiorespiratory effects of training is given in Table 3.1. More detailed reviews of these effects can be found in the reports written by Scheuer and Tipton (1977) and Rowell (1974).

METABOLIC, BIOCHEMICAL, AND NEUROMUSCULAR EFFECTS OF TRAINING

In discussing biochemical adaptations, it should be emphasized that skeletal muscle contains several types of fibers or motor units that differ in their

Table 3.1
A Summary of the Major Cardiorespiratory Effects of Training

Variable	Rest	TRAINING EFFECT	
		Submaximal Exercise*	Maximal Exercise
Cardiac Volume and Mass	increased	--------	--------
Cardiac Output	unchanged or decreased (?)	unchanged or decreased	increased
Heart Rate	decreased	decreased	decreased or unchanged
Stroke Volume	increased	increased	increased
Muscle Myoglobin Concentration	increased	--------	--------
Total Hemoglobin & Blood Volume	increased	--------	--------
Blood Pressures hypertensives / normals	decreased / unchanged	decreased / unchanged	decreased / unchanged
Static Lung Volumes	increased	--------	--------
Pulmonary Diffusion Capacity	increased (?)	increased	increased
Pulmonary Ventilation	unchanged	decreased	increased
Oxygen Consumption (VO_2)	unchanged	decreased or unchanged	increased
Oxygen Extraction by Muscle (a $-$ $\bar{v}O_2$ diff)	unchanged	increased	increased
Muscle Glycogen Depletion	--------	decreased	increased
Muscle and Blood Lactic Acid Levels	unchanged	decreased	increased
Blood Flow to Working Muscles (per kg muscle tissue)	--------	decreased or unchanged (?)	unchanged

* Same absolute work load before and after training.

metabolic potentials. For example, in rats there are three fiber types: (1) fast twitch red (FOG), which is high in both anaerobic (glycolytic) and aerobic (oxidative) potentials; (2) fast twitch white (FG), which is high in glycolytic but low in aerobic potential; and (3) slow twitch red (SO), which is low in glycolytic and high in oxidative potential. In humans, only two fiber types have been studied, FG and SO.

Research on humans by Edgerton et al. (1975), Gollnick et al. (1973a, 1973b), and Saltin and Karlsson (1971) has shown that FG fibers are preferentially recruited during the performance of short duration, high power output work such as sprinting. However, during prolonged, lower intensity exercise such as distance running, SO fibers are preferentially used to perform the work. This again emphasizes that some of the biochemical alterations produced within the different types of fibers will be specific to whether the training program consists of sprint-like or endurance-like exercises.

Biochemical Effects of Endurance Training

The major skeletal muscle biochemical alterations resulting from endurance training are:

Increased oxidative capacity. The capacity of skeletal muscle to break down (oxidize) glycogen and free fatty acids is greatly increased with training (Baldwin et al. 1972; Molé, Oscai, and Holloszy 1971; Morgan et al. 1971). This increase occurs in all fiber types (Holloszy et al. 1975). Along with this increase is a parallel increase in aerobic (oxidative) adenosine triphosphate (ATP) production. Functionally, this is reflected by the increased max VO_2 mentioned earlier. The increase in oxidative capacity of skeletal muscle may account for at least 50 percent of the increased max VO_2 resulting from endurance training (Holloszy 1973). If this is true, then the other 50 percent increase would be due mainly to an increased stroke volume.

The increase in oxidative capacity is brought about through three major subcellular changes:

1. Increases in the number, size, and membrane surface area of skeletal muscle mitochondria (Holloszy 1967; Hoppeler et al. 1973; Kiessling et al. 1971);

2. Increases in the activities or concentrations of enzymes involved in the Krebs cycle and electron transport system (Benzi et al. 1975; Gollnick et al. 1972, 1973c; Holloszy 1967; Morgan et al. 1971); and

3. Increases in the activities of enzymes responsible for the release of free fatty acids from adipose tissue (Borensztajn et al. 1975), their activation, transport and breakdown (Molé, Oscai, and Holloszy 1971).

With respect to the first change, it should be mentioned that the mitochondrial volume per unit volume of myofibrils is less in females than males (Howald

1975). The significance of this difference is not immediately apparent. However, it would appear to represent a definite biochemical limitation with respect to the overall aerobic capacity of the female.

An excellent review of the mitochondrial and related changes has been written by Howald (1975), whereas detailed discussions of specific enzyme changes have been presented by Holloszy (1973, 1975), Holloszy and Booth (1976), and Holloszy and his coworkers (1971, 1975).

Increased muscle glycogen and triglyceride stores. Glycogen and triglyceride stores in human muscle increase substantially following endurance training (Gollnick et al. 1973c; Morgan et al. 1971; Taylor 1975). The increased stores of glycogen are accompanied by increased activities of the enzymes responsible for glycogen synthesis and breakdown (glycogen cycle enzymes) (Taylor 1975). Since muscle glycogen is an important fuel during exercise, it is easy to understand the positive relationship that has been found between initial muscle glycogen levels and subsequent endurance performance (Bergstrom et al. 1967). In addition, Hickson and his associates (1977) have shown a similar relationship between endurance performance and blood free fatty acid levels (triglyceride is the muscular storage form of free fatty acids). (See Chapter 22.)

Anaerobic changes. As might be expected, changes in the anaerobic potential of muscle following endurance training are neither appreciable nor consistent. They are as follows:

1. Glycolytic enzymes. In the vastus lateralis muscle of man (which contains both FG and SO fibers), activity levels of several key glycolytic enzymes were found to decrease by 25 percent on the average after training (Morgan et al. 1971), whereas others were significantly increased (Gollnick et al. 1973c) or not changed (Morgan et al. 1971).

2. Phosphagen stores. Muscular stores of adenosine triphosphate and phosphocreatine (collectively referred to as phosphagens) have been found to increase in man with training (Eriksson, Gollnick, and Saltin 1973; Karlsson et al. 1972). However, their significance with respect to maximal or prolonged exercise efforts appears to be minimal (Gollnick and Hermansen 1973; Karlsson et al. 1972).

Skeletal muscle hypertrophy. Hermansen and Wachtlova (1971) found that the leg muscles of highly trained distance runners were 30 percent larger compared to untrained subjects. They also found that the capillary density of the muscles of the athletes (the number of capillaries per muscle fiber) was increased by 50 percent over the nonathletes. In a later study by Gollnick and his coworkers (1973c), it was shown that training caused a significant increase in the percentage area of SO fibers. Since the area of the FG fibers was unchanged, this would suggest a selective hypertrophy of SO fibers following endurance training in man.

Ratio of FG and SO fibers. A common question concerning fiber types and training is, "Can fiber types within a mixed muscle be interconverted through endurance training?" While the answer is not by any means simple, it appears, at least in the case of man, that interconversion of FG and SO fibers does not occur with training. Data of Gollnick et al. (1973c) and Saltin et al. (1976) support this conclusion. The proportion of FG and SO fibers in a mixed muscle is probably more a function of genetics than anything else.

Biochemical Effects of Sprint Training

It might be expected from the rather large and impressive aerobic changes produced through endurance training that sprint training would result in an increased anaerobic capacity. While there is some validity to this notion, neither the number nor magnitude of the changes is impressive. Whether this is the true picture or whether it is due to a relative lack of research can only be answered with more research.

Animal studies. Saubert et al. (1973) subjected rats to an 11-week training program of repeated 30-second sprints. Their results showed that the activities of two of several key glycolytic enzymes (phosphorylase and pyruvate kinase) were only slightly increased following training, and only in the SO fibers. Similar findings on rats were obtained by Saudte, Exner, and Pelte (1973). However, the latter researchers also found a small but significant increase in activity of creatine kinase, one of the ATP turnover enzymes. Saubert et al. (1973) concluded that most skeletal muscles possess sufficient anaerobic capacity to meet the demands of sprint work without further adaptation.

Human studies. Thorstensson, Sjodin, and Karlsson (1975) studied several ATP turnover enzymes before and after eight weeks of sprint training in young males. As in the rat experiments, small but significant increases in the activities of some of the ATP turnover enzymes were found after training (e.g., magnesium stimulated ATPase, myokinase, and creatine kinase). Total phosphagen stores were increased but only as a result of muscular hypertrophy. The muscular hypertrophy was found in both FG and SO fibers. Anaerobic performance as measured by a stair-climbing test was also shown to be improved following the sprint program. The max VO_2 was unchanged.

Sprint versus endurance training. In a comparative study of sprint versus endurance training on rats, significant aerobic and anaerobic changes were noted with both types of training, but no differences were found between the two programs (Hickson, Heusner, and Van Huss 1976). Similar findings on man have been reported by Fox (1975) and Fox and his associates (1977b). However, in these studies there was a lower blood lactic acid accumulation during submaximal exercise following the endurance program.

Saltin and his fellow researchers (1976) conducted a comparative study in humans where one leg was sprint trained and the other endurance trained. They found that aerobic capacity as measured by max VO_2 and aerobic enzyme activity increased significantly following both types of training with greater increases found in the endurance trained leg. In addition, a selective hypertrophy of SO fibers was found in the endurance-trained leg, whereas in the sprint-trained leg, hypertrophy was evident in both SO and FG fibers but was more pronounced in the latter. Detailed reviews of the anaerobic and aerobic changes following training have been written by Gollnick and Hermansen (1973), Holloszy (1973, 1975), Holloszy and Booth (1976), and Holloszy et al. (1971, 1975).

Biochemical Effects of Weight Resistance Training

The most obvious physiological effects of weight training are increases in muscular strength and endurance. However, as with sprint training, the biochemical effects of weight resistance programs have not been extensively studied.

Hypertrophy and fiber types. Muscular hypertrophy (increase in fiber size) following weight resistance programs was scientifically documented for over 80 years (Morpurgo 1897). Morpurgo's classic study also showed that the increased size was due entirely to increases in the diameters of existing fibers and not to an increased number of new fibers. This hypothesis has recently been challenged. For example, longitudinal fiber splitting occurs in rats following weight training (Ho et al. 1977), and in man is a common finding in competitive power lifters (Prince, Hikida, and Hagerman 1976). Since the split fibers demonstrate normal enzyme function and adequate capillary blood supply and motor end-plate material, muscle fiber splitting may represent a physiological adaptation to weight training (Ho et al. 1977).

Major contributors to increases in skeletal muscle size following weight training programs appear to be:

1. an increased diameter of existing fibers, due in turn to increases in the number of myofibrils per fiber (Goldspink 1964), total protein (Gordon 1967; Penman 1969), and connective tendinous and ligamentous tissues; and

2. an increased number of fibers resulting from longitudinal fiber splitting (Ho et al. 1977; Prince, Hikida, and Hagerman 1976).

There is some evidence of a selective hypertrophy of FG fibers with weight training. Thorstensson and his coworker (1976) found an increased FG/SO percent area ratio following eight weeks of weight training in men, whereas Gollnick and his associates (1972) found that the percent area of FG fibers was generally larger in the muscles of weight lifters than in untrained subjects and particularly endurance athletes. No evidence of interconversion of FG and SO fibers in man has been found following weight training programs (Thorstensson et al. 1976).

Enzyme changes. No changes in the ATP turnover enzymes have been found subsequent to weight training programs (Thorstensson et al. 1976). Furthermore, Gollnick and his colleagues (1972) found that succinate dehydrogenase activity, an oxidative enzyme, was 30 percent lower, whereas phosphofructokinase activity, a glycolytic enzyme, was the same in weight lifters muscle compared to untrained subjects.

The above findings support the idea that the large improvements in muscular strength and endurance resulting from weight training exercises are not due to metabolic or fiber type alterations within the muscle. Apparently, as pointed out by Thorstensson et al. (1976), neuromuscular factors such as an improved coordination of different muscles and even of different motor units within the same muscle seem to be implicated. A summary of the major biochemical effects of training on skeletal muscle is given in Table 3.2.

Training and Other Neuromuscular Changes

Most neuromuscular research involving exercise has centered around changes in the skeletal muscles. However, exercise training also causes adaptations in the

Table 3.2
A Summary of Major Biochemical Effects of Training on Skeletal Muscle

| Variable | TRAINING EFFECT | | |
	Sprint Training	Endurance Training	Weight Resistance Training
Oxidative Capacity (fats and carbohydrates)	increased	increased	unchanged or decreased (?)
Glycogen Stores	increased (?)	increased	increased (?)
Triglyceride Stores	?	increased	?
Glycolytic Enzyme Activity	increased (SO fibers only)	increased decreased unchanged	unchanged
ATP Turnover Enzyme Activities	increased	increased (?)	unchanged
Phosphagen Stores concentration total stores	unchanged increased	increased increased	unchanged (?) increased (?)
Hypertrophy	SO & FG fibers (greater in FG)	SO fibers only	FG fibers only
Fiber Type Interconversion Fiber Splitting	no no	no no	no yes

neuromuscular junction and motoneuron. These effects include cellular and subcellular adaptations in morphology, modifications of transmission properties, pharmacological responses, reflex alterations, and biochemical responses within the motoneuron itself. Excellent reviews of these changes have been written by Burke and Edgerton (1975) and Edgerton (1976).

Unfortunately, the neuromuscular changes have thus far provided little information concerning their functional significance as related to training programs. However, as just mentioned, the relatively small metabolic and biochemical changes following sprint and weight resistance programs in the face of large performance changes provide strong evidence that neuromuscular alterations are extremely important. Continued research in this area is obviously needed.

REFERENCES

Adams, G. M. and H. A. deVries. 1973. Physiological effects of an exercise training regimen upon women aged 52-79. *J Gerontol*, 28, 50-55.

Arcos, J. C., R. S. Sohal, S. C. Sun, M. F, Argus, and G. E. Burch, 1968. Changes in ultrastructure and respiratory control of mitochondria of rat heart hypertrophied by exercise. *Exp Mol Pathol*, 8, 49-65.

Bachman, J. and S. Horvath. 1968. Pulmonary function changes which accompany athletic conditioning programs. *Res Quart*, 39, 235-239.

Baldwin, K., G. Klinkerfuss, R. Terjung, P. Mole, and J. Holloszy. 1972. Respiratory capacity of white, red, and intermediate muscle: Adaptive response to exercise. *Amer J Physiol*, 222, 373-378.

Benzi, G., P. Panceri, M. DeBernardi, R. Villa, E. Arcelli, L. d'Angelo, E. Arrigoni, and F. Berte. 1975. Mitochondrial enzymatic adaptation of skeletal muscle to endurance training. *J Appl Physiol*, 38, 565-569.

Bergstrom, J., L. Hermansen, E. Hultman, and B. Saltin. 1967. Diet, muscle glycogen and physical performance *Acta Physiol Scand*, 71, 140-150.

Bevegard, S., A. Holmgren, and B. Jonsson. 1963. Circulatory studies in well-trained athletes at rest and during heavy exercise, with special reference to stroke volume and the influence of body position. *Acta Physiol Scand*, 57, 26-50.

Bioleau, R., E. Buskirk, D. Hortman, J. Mendes, and W. Nicholas. 1971. Body composition changes in obese and lean men during physical conditioning. *Med Sci Spts*, 3, 183-189.

Borensztajn, J., M. Rone, S. Babirak, J. McGarr, and L. Oscai. 1975. Effect of exercise on lipoprotein lipase activity in rat heart and skeletal muscle. *Amer J Physiol*, 229, 394-397.

Boyer, J. L. and F. W. Kasch. 1970. Exercise therapy in hypertensive men. *JAMA*, 211, 1668-1671.

Burke, R. and V. R. Edgerton. 1975. Motor unit properties and selective involvement in movement. In *Exercise and Sports Sciences Review*, J. H. Wilmore (ed.). Vol. 3. New York: Academic Press.

Clausen, J., J. Trap-Jensen, and N. Lassen. 1970. The effects of training on the heart rate during arm and leg exercise. *Scand J Clin Lab Invest,* 26, 295-301.

Clausen, J., K. Klausen, B. Rasmussen, and J. Trap-Jensen. 1973. Central and peripheral circulatory changes after training of the arms or legs. *Amer J Physiol,* 225, 675-682.

Cohen, K. 1975. Metabolic Alterations with Sprint Versus Endurance Interval Training in Females. Doctoral dissertation, The Ohio State University.

Costill, D., R. Bowers, and W. Kramer. 1970. Skinfold estimates of body fat among marathon runners. *Med Sci Spts,* 2, 93-95.

Cumming, G. 1969. Correlation of athletic performance with pulmonary function in 13 to 17 year old boys and girls. *Med Sci Spts,* 1, 140-143.

deVries, H. A. 1970. Physiological effects of an exercise training regimen upon men aged 52-88. *J Genrontol,* 25, 325-336.

Eckstein, R. 1957. Effect of exercise and coronary artery narrowing on coronary collateral circulation. *Circ Res,* 5, 230-238.

Edgerton, V. R. 1976. Neuromuscular adaptation to power and endurance work. *Can J Appl Spt Sci,* 1, 49-58.

Edgerton, V., B. Essen, B. Saltin, and D. Simpson. 1975. Glycogen depletion in specific types of human skeletal muscle fibers in intermittent and continuous exercise. In *Metabolic Adaptation to Prolonged Physical Exercise,* H. Howald and J. Poortmans (eds.). Basel: Birkhäusen Verlag.

Ekblom, B., P. Åstrand, B. Saltin, J. Stenberg, and B. Wallström. 1968. Effect of trianing on circulatory response to exercise. *J Appl Physiol,* 24, 518-528.

Ekblom, B. and L. Hermansen. 1968. Cardiac output of athletes. *J Appl Physiol,* 25, 619-625.

Eriksson, B., P. Gollnick, and B. Saltin. 1973. Muscle metabolism and enzyme activities after training in boys 11-13 years old. *Acta Physiol Scand,* 87, 485-497.

Faria, I. E. 1970. Cardiovascular response to exercise as influenced by training of various intensities. *Res Quart,* 41, 44-50.

Fox, E. L. 1975. Differences in metabolic alterations with sprint versus endurance interval training. In *Metabolic Adaptation to Prolonged Physical Exercise,* H. Howald and J. Poortmans (eds.). Basel: Birkhäusen Verlag.

Fox, E. L. 1977. Physical training: Methods and effects. *Orthop Clin N Amer,* 8, 533-548.

Fox, E. L. and D. L. Costill. 1972. Estimated cardiorespiratory responses during marathon running. *Arch Environ Health,* 24, 315-324.

Fox, E. L., R. L. Bartels, C. E. Billings, D. K. Mathews, R. Bason, and W. M. Webb. 1973. Intensity and distance of interval training programs and changes in aerobic power. *Med Sci Spts,* 5, 18-22.

Fox, E. L., D. C. McKenzie, and K. Cohen. 1975a. Specificity of training: Metabolic and circulatory responses. *Med Sci Spts,* 7, 83.

Fox, E. L., R. L. Bartels, C. E. Billings R. O'Brien, R. Bason, and D. K. Mathews. 1975b. Frequency and duration of interval training programs and changes in aerobic power. *J Appl Physiol,* 38, 481-485.

Fox, E. L., J Klinzing, and R. L. Bartels. 1977a. Interval training: Metabolic changes as affected by relief interval heart rates of 120 and 140 beats per minute. *Fed Proc,* 36, 449.

Fox, E. L., R. L. Bartels, J. Klinzing, and K. Ragg. 1977b. Metabolic responses to interval training programs of high and low power output. *Med Sci Spts,* 9, 191-196.

Frick, M. H., R. O. Elovainio, and T. Somer. 1967. The mechanism of bradycardia evoked by physical training. *Cardiologia,* 51, 46-54.

Frick, M. H., A. Konttmen, and S. Sarajas. 1963. Effects of physical training on circulation at rest and during exercise. *Amer J. Cardiol,* 12, 142-147.

Goldspink, G. 1964. The combined effects of exercise and reduced food intake on skeletal muscle fibers. *J Cell Comp Physiol,* 63, 209-216.

Gollnick, P., R. Armstrong, C. Saubert, K. Piehl, and B. Saltin. 1972. Enzyme activity and fiber composition in skeletal muscle of untrained and trained men. *J Appl Physiol,* 33, 312-319.

Gollnick, P. D. and L. Hermansen. 1973. Biochemical adaptations to exercise: Anaerobic metabolism. In *Exercise and Sports Sciences Reviews,* J. H. Wilmore (ed.). Vol 1. New York: Academic Press.

Gollnick, P., R. Armstrong, C. Saubert, W. Sembrowich, R. Shepherd, and B. Saltin. 1973a. Glycogen depletion pattern in human skeletal muscle fibers during prolonged work. *Pflüegers Arch,* 34, 1-12.

Gollnick, P., R. Armstron, W. Sembrowich, R. Shepherd, and B. Saltin. 1973b. Glycogen depletion pattern in human skeletal muscle after heavy exercise. *J Appl Physiol,* 34, 615-618.

Gollnick, P., R. Armstrong, B. Saltin, C. Saubert, W. Sembrowich, and R. Shepherd. 1973c. Effect of training on enzyme activity and fiber composition of human skeletal muscle. *J Appl Physiol,* 34, 107-111.

Gordon, E. 1967. Anatomical and biochemical adaptations of muscle to different exercises. *JAMA,* 201, 755-758.

Grimby, E., E. Häggendal, and B. Saltin. 1967. Local Xenon 133 clearance from the quadriceps muscle during exercise in man. *J Appl Physiol,* 22, 305-310.

Hakkila, J. 1955. Studies on the myocardial capillary concentration in cardiac hypertrophy due to training. *Ann Med Exper Biol Fenn,* 33, 7-82.

Hanson, J., B. Tabakin, A. Levy, and W. Nedde. 1968. Long-term physical training and cardiovascular dynamics in middle-aged men. *Circulation,* 38, 783-799.

Hermansen, L. and M. Wachtlova. 1971. Capillary density of skeletal muscle in well-trained and untrained men. *J Appl Physiol,* 30, 860-863.

Hickson, R., W. Heusner, and W. Van Huss. 1976. Skeletal muscle enzyme alterations after sprint and endurance training. *J Appl Physiol,* 40, 868-872.

Hickson, R., M. Rennie, R. Conlie, W. Winder, and J. Holloszy. 1977. Effect of increasing plasma free fatty acids on endurance. *Fed Proc,* 36, 450.

Hirsch, J. 1971. Adipose cellularity in relation to human obesity. *Advances Internal Med,* 17, 289-300.

Ho, K., R. Roy, J. Taylor, W. Heusner, W. Van Huss, and R. Carrow. 1977. Muscle fiber splitting with weight-lifting exercise. *Med Sci Spts,* 9, 65.

Holloszy, J. 1967. Biochemical adaptations in muscle. *J Biol Chem*, 242, 2278-2282.

Holloszy, J. O. 1973. Biochemical adaptations to exercise: Aerobic metabolism. In *Exercise and Sports Sciences Reviews*, J. H. Wilmore (ed.). Vol 1. New York: Academic Press.

Holloszy, J. O. 1975. Adaptation of skeletal muscle to endurance exercise. *Med Sci Spts*, 7, 155-164.

Holloszy, J. O. and F. W. Booth. 1976. Biochemical adaptations to endurance exercise in muscle. *Ann Rev Physiol*, 38, 273-291.

Holloszy, J. O., F. W. Booth, W. Winder, and R. Fitts. 1975. Biochemical adaptation of skeletal muscle to prolonged physical exercise. In *Metabolic Adaptation to Prolonged Physical Exercise*, H. Howald and J. Poortmans (eds.). Basel: Birkhäuser Verlag.

Holloszy, J. O., L. Oscai, P. Molé, and I. Don. 1971. Biochemical adaptations to endurance exercise in skeletal muscle. In *Muscle Metabolism During Exercise*, B. Pernow and B. Saltin (eds.). New York: Plenum Press.

Holmgren, A. 1967. Cardiorespiratory determinants of cardiovascular fitness. *Canad Med Assoc J*, 96, 697-702.

Hoppeler, H., P. Lüthi, H. Claussen, E. Weibel, and H. Howald. 1973. The ultrastructure of the normal human skeletal muscle. A morphometric analysis on untrained men and women and well-trained orienteers. *Pflüegers Arch*, 344, 217-232.

Howald, H., 1975. Ultrastructural adaptation of skeletal muscle to prolonged physical exercise. In *Metabolic Adaptation to Prolonged Physical Exercise*, H. Howald and J. Poortmans (eds.). Basel: Birkhäuser Verlag.

Karlsson, J., L. Nordesjo, L. Jorfeldt, and B. Saltin. 1972. Muscle lactate, ATP and CP levels during exercise after physical training in man. *J Appl Physiol*, 33, 199-203.

Karvonen, M. J., E. Kentala, and O. Mustala. 1957. The effects of training on heart rate. *Ann Med Exper Biol Fenn*, 35, 307-315.

Kaufmann, D., E. Swenson, J. Fenel, and A. Lucas. 1974. Pulmonary function of marathon runners. *Med Sci Spts*, 6, 114-117.

Kearney, J. T., G. A. Stull, J. L. Ewing, Jr., and J. W. Strein. 1976. Cardiorespiratory responses of sedentary college women as a function of training intensity. *J Appl Physiol*, 41, 822-825.

Kiessling, Kl., K. Piehl, and C. Lundquist. 1971. Effect of physical training on ultrastructural features in human skeletal muscle. In *Muscle Metabolism During Exercise*, B. Pernow and B. Saltin (eds.). New York: Plenum Press.

Kilbom, Å. 1971. Physical training in women. *Scand J Clin Lab Invest*, 28, Suppl 119.

Kjellberg, S., U. Rudhe, and T. Sjöstrand. 1949a. Increase of the amount of hemoglobin and blood volume in connection with physical training. *Acta Physiol Scand*, 19, 146-151.

Kjellberg, S., U. Rudhe, and T. Sjöstrand. 1949b. The amount of hemoglobin and the blood volume in relation to the pulse rate and cardiac volume during rest. *Acta Physiol Scand*, 19, 136-145.

Klassen, G., G. Andrew, and M. Becklake. 1970. Effect of training on total and regional blood flow and metabolism in paddlers. *J Appl Physiol*, 28, 397-406.

Leon, A. S. and C. M. Bloor. 1968. Effects of exercise and its cessation on the heart and its blood supply. *J Appl Physiol,* 23, 485-490.

Leon, A. S. and C. M. Bloor. 1976. The Effect of complete and partial deconditioning on exercise-induced cardiovascular changes in the rat. *Adv Cardiol,* 18, 81-92.

Lesmes, G., E. L. Fox, C. Stevens, and R. Otto. 1978. Metabolic adaptations of young females to high intensity interval training of different frequencies. *Med Sci Spts,* 10, 229-232.

Magel, J. and K. Andersen. 1969. Pulmonary diffusing capacity and cardiac output in young trained Norwegian swimmers and untrained subjects. *Med Sci Spts,* 1, 131-139.

Magel, J. R., F. Foglia, W. D. McArdle, B. Gutin, G. S. Pechar, and F. I. Katch. 1974. Specificity of swim training on maximum oxygen uptake. *J Appl Physiol,* 38, 151-155.

Maksud, M. G., L. H. Hamilton, K. D. Coutts, and R. L. Wiley. 1971. Pulmonary function measurements of Olympic speed skaters from the U.S. *Med Sci Spts,* 3, 66-71.

Mann, G., H. Garrett, A. Farhi, H. Murray, and F. Billings. 1969. Exercise to prevent coronary heart disease. *Amer J Med,* 46, 12-27.

Mathews, D. K. and E. L. Fox. 1976. *The Physiological Basis of Physical Education and Athletics.* 2nd ed. Philadelphia. W. B. Saunders.

Mole, P., L. Oscai, and J. Holloszy. 1971. Adaptation of muscle to exercise: Increase in levels of palmityl CoA synthetase, carnitine palmityl transferase, and palmityl CoA dehydrogenase, and in the capacity to oxidize fats. *J Clin Invest,* 50, 2323-2330.

Moody, D., J. Kollias, and E. Buskirk. 1969. The effect of a moderate exercise program on body weight and skinfold thickness in overweight college women. *Med Sci Spts,* 1, 75-80.

Moody, D., J. Wilmore, R. Girandola, and J. Royce. 1972. The effects of a jogging program on the body composition of normal and obese high school girls. *Med Sci Spts,* 4, 210-213.

Morgan, T., L. Cobb, F. Short, R. Ross, and D. Gunn. 1971. Effects of long-term exercise on human muscle mitochondria. In *Muscle Metabolism During Exercise,* B. Pernow and B. Saltin (eds.). New York: Plenum Press.

Morganroth, J., B. Maron, W. Henry, and S. Epstein. 1975. Comparative left ventricular dimensions in trained athletes. *Ann Intern Med,* 82, 521-524.

Morpurgo, B. 1897. Über Aktivatäts-Hypertrophie der willkurlichen Muskeln. *Virchows Arch Pathol Anat Physiol,* 150, 522-544.

Newman, F., B. Smalley, and M. Thompson. 1961. A comparison between body size and lung function of swimmers and normal school children. *J Physiol,* 156, 9P.

Oscai, L., S. Babirak, F. Dubach, J. McGarr, and C. Spirakis. 1974. Exercise or food restriction: Effect on adipose tissue cellularity. *Amer J Physiol,* 227, 901-904.

Oscai, L., C. Spirakis, C. Wolff, and R. Beck. 1972. Effects of exercise and of food restriction on adipose tissue cellularity. *J Lipid Res,* 13, 588-592.

Oscai, L., B. Williams, and B Hertig. 1968. Effect of exercise on blood volume. *J Appl Physiol,* 24, 622-624.

Pattengale, P. and J. O. Holloszy. 1967. Augmentation of skeletal muscle myoglobin by a program of treadmill running. *Amer J Physiol,* 213, 783-785.

Pechar, G. S., W. O. McArdle, F. I. Katch, J. R. Magel, and J. Deluca. 1974. Specificity of cardiorespiratory adaptation to bicycle and treadmill training. *J Appl Physiol,* 36, 753-756.

Penman, K. 1969. Ultrastructural changes in human striated muscle using three methods of training. *Res Quart,* 40, 764-772.

Penpargkul, S. and J. Scheuer. 1970. The effect of physical training upon the mechanical and metabolic performance of the rat heart. *J Clin Invest,* 49, 1859-1868.

Pollock, M. L., T. K. Cureton, and L. Greninger. 1969. Effects of frequency of training on working capacity, cardiovascular function, and body composition of adult man. *Med Sci Spts,* 1, 70-74.

Pollock, M., J. Dimmick, H. Miller, Z. Kendrick, and A. Linnerud. 1975. Effects of mode of training on cardiovascular function and body composition of adult men. *Med Sci Spts,* 7, 139-145.

Prince, F., R. Hikida, and F. Hagerman. 1976. Human muscle fiber types in power lifters, distance runners and untrained subjects. *Pflüegers Arch,* 363, 19-26.

Reddan, W., F. Bongiorno, J. Burpee, P. Reuschlein, J. Gee, and J. Rankin. 1963. Pulmonary function in endurance athletes. *Fed Proc,* 22, 396.

Reuschlein, P., W. Reddan, J. Burpee, J. Gee, and J. Rankin. 1968. Effect of physical training on the pulmonary diffusing capacity during submaximal work. *J Appl Physiol,* 24, 152-158.

Roeske, W. R., R. A. O'Rourke, A. Klein, G. Leopold, and J. S. Karliner, 1975. Noninvasive evaluation of ventricular hypertrophy in professional athletes. *Circulation,* 53, 286-292.

Rowell, L. B. 1974. Human cardiovascular adjustments to exercise and thermal stress. *Physiol Rev,* 54, 75-159.

Saltin, B. 1975. Adaptive changes in carbohydrate metabolism with exercise. In *Metabolic Adaptation to Prolonged Physical Exercise,* H. Howald and J. Poortmas (eds.). Basel: Birkhäuser Verlag.

Saltin, B. and P. O. Åstrand. 1967. Maximal oxygen uptake in athletes. *J Appl Physiol,* 23, 353-358.

Saltin, B., G. Blomquist, J. H. Mitchell, R. L. Johnson, K. Wildenthal, and C. B. Chapman. 1968. Response to exercise after bed rest and after training. *Circulation,* 38 (Suppl 7), 1-78.

Saltin, B. and J. Karlsson. 1971. Muscle glycogen utilization during work of different intensities. In *Muscle Metabolism During Exercise,* B. Pernow and B. Saltin (eds.). New York: Plenum Press.

Saltin, B., K. Nazar, D. L. Costill, E. Stein, E. Jansson, B. Essén, and P. D. Gollnick. 1976. The nature of the training response; Peripheral and central adaptations to one-legged exercise. *Acta Physiol Scand,* 96, 289-305.

Saubert, C., R. Armstrong, R. Shephard, and P. Gollnick. 1973. Anaerobic enzyme adaptations to sprint training in rats. *Pflüegers Arch,* 341, 305-312.

Scheuer, J. and C. M. Tipton. 1977. Cardiovascular adaptations to physical training. *Ann Rev Physiol,* 39, 221-251.

Sharkey, B. J. and J. P. Hollman. 1967. Cardiorespiratory adaptations to training at specified intensities. *Res Quart,* 38, 698-704.

Shephard, R. J. 1968. Intensity, duration and frequency of exercise as determinants of the response to a training regime. *Int Z Angew Physiol,* 26, 272-278.

Sohal, R. S., S. C. Sun, L. H. Colcolough, and G. E. Burch. 1968. Ultrastructural changes of the intercalated disc in exercised rat hearts. *Lab Invest,* 18, 49-53.

Staudte, H., G. Exner, and D. Pelte. 1973. Effects of short-term, high intensity (sprint) training on some contractile and metabolic characteristics of fast and slow muscles of the rat. *Pflüegers Arch,* 344, 159-168.

Tabakin, B., J. Hanson, and A. Levy. 1965. Effects of physical training on the cardiovascular and respiratory response to graded upright exercise in distance runners. *Brit Heart J,* 27, 205-210.

Taylor, A. 1975. The effects of exercise and training on the activities of human skeletal muscle glycogen cycle enzymes. In *Metabolic Adaptations to Prolonged Physical Exercise,* H. Howald and J. Poortmans (eds.). Basel: Birkhäuser Verlag.

Teppermen, J. and D. Pearlman. 1961. Effects of exercise and anemia on coronary arteries of small animals as revealed by the corrosion-cast technique. *Circ Res,* 9, 576-584.

Thorstensson, A., B. Hulten, W. von Döbeln, and J. Karlsson. 1976. Effect of strength training on enzyme activities and fiber characteristics in human skeletal muscle. *Acta Physiol Scand,* 96, 392-398.

Thorstensson, A., B. Sjodin, and J. Karlsson. 1975. Enzyme activities and muscle strength after "spring training" in man. *Acta Physiol Scand,* 94, 313-318.

Tipton, C. M. 1965. Training and bradycardia in rats. *Amer J. Physiol,* 209, 1089-1094.

Tipton, C. J., R. J. Barnard, and T. K. Tcheng. 1969. Resting heart rate investigations with trained and nontrained hypophysectomized rats. *J Appl Physiol,* 26, 585-588.

Wilmore, J. and C. Brown. 1974. Physiological profiles of women distance runners. *Med Sci Spts,* 6, 178-181.

Wilmore, J., J. Royce, R. Girandola, F. Katch, and V. Katch. 1970. Body composition changes with a 10-week program of jogging. *Med Sci Spts,* 2, 113-117.

4

Aerobics

Larry R. Gettman

The word "aerobic" literally means "with air" or "with oxygen" and refers to the oxidative metabolic process whereby energy is provided to drive various cellular reactions such as muscular contraction. When ample oxygen is available, the aerobic process allows for a prolonged production of work by the muscles leading to an endurance effort.

In 1968, Dr. Kenneth H. Cooper, then a Major in the USAF Medical Corps, coined the term "aerobics," which refers to a variety of large muscle exercises that demand a high amount of oxygen so that they can be continued for long periods. This, in effect, stimulates heart and lung activity sufficiently long enough to produce beneficial changes in the body—the so-called endurance training effect. Walking, jogging, running, swimming, and cycling are the most popular forms of aerobic exercise, although there are many others. Any activity that demands a high amount of oxygen for a rather prolonged period of time and promotes good circulation and supply of energy may be considered aerobic.

The main objective of an aerobic exercise program is to increase the maximum amount of oxygen that the body can process within a given time (Cooper 1970). This is called the aerobic capacity or maximum oxygen uptake (max VO_2) and is usually determined by measuring the maximum amount of oxygen an individual can take up during a specified period of time—usually on a per minute basis. Aerobic capacity depends on one's ability to breathe large amounts of air, to circulate large volumes of blood, which carries oxygen to the active site, and to take up that oxygen from the blood by the muscle.

THE AEROBIC POINT SYSTEM

Cooper (1968) proposed a point system for quantifying endurance exercises based on the average amount of net oxygen required for those exercises. The net oxygen requirement refers to that amount used above an average resting value of 3.5 ml O_2 per kg of body weight per minute (ml $\cdot$ kg^{-1} $\cdot$ min^{-1}). For example, running a mile in eight minutes earns five aerobic points and requires a net oxygen value of 35 ml $\cdot$ kg$^{-1} \cdot$ min^{-1}. A total of 30 aerobic points would result if two miles were run three days per week. This would produce a desirable training effect for a person in a low fitness category and is the goal for a beginning exerciser for a 12- to 20-week exercise program. The 30-point-per-week goal is too low for those individuals in higher fitness categories where 50 points per week or more are required to improve and maintain fitness.

IMPLEMENTATION OF AN AEROBICS PROGRAM

Before starting an aerobics activity program, one must identify his or her current status of health and fitness, age, sex, and general objectives for initiating the program. The special considerations for admitting individuals into exercise programs outlined by the American College of Sports Medicine (1975) are recommended. They include a comprehensive medical history questionnaire review, a physical examination, a 12-lead resting electrocardiogram (ECG), resting blood pressure, blood analyses, and a graded exercise test monitored for heart rate, blood pressure, and ECG. If the resting and exercise ECG tests are not available, Cooper (1970) has suggested that initial fitness levels be assessed by ascertaining the distance one can run in 12 minutes, or measuring the time required to run a distance of 1.5 miles. The following precautions are outlined:

1. Do not take the 12-minute or 1.5-mile test prior to beginning an exercise program if you are over 30 years of age.
2. Be sure to have a medical examination before you take the 12-minute or 1.5-mile test.
3. It is safer to postpone the field test until a six-week "starter" program has been completed. A starter program generally consists of a low intensity level of exercise so that the stress on the body is mild.
4. If a person complies with the above, yet experiences extreme fatigue, shortness of breath, light-headedness or nausea, he or she should stop immediately, walk at a slow comfortable pace for about five minutes, and consult a physician.

The medical examination often is not required for young children and adolescents participating in school physical education programs. In this case, the six-week starter program of walking and jogging is mandatory before submitting the students to high intensity physical stress. The 12-minute test has been used successfully in several school-aged fitness programs (Cooper et al. 1975; Goode et al. 1976; Gutin, Fogle, and Stewart 1976; Maksud and Coutts 1971). Studies by Krahenbuhl et al. (1977) and Gutin, Fogle, and Stewart (1976) have shown that running tests in the longer distances such as 1,609 meters and 1,200 yards correlate highest with max VO_2.

The type of workout in an endurance activity program depends upon the participant's age, sex, initial level of fitness, and duration, frequency, and intensity of exercise. These principles have been summarized elsewhere by Pollock (1973) and by Ribisl in Chapter 1 of this volume. Obviously, older individuals and those with low levels of fitness start an exercise program at a low intensity level and progress slowly. For the average individual, the initial experience with aerobic training should be moderate, allowing for gradual adaptation. This principle is especially important for children; the approach to an exercise program for children should provide enjoyable, fun experiences. Highly structured, competitive activities are not recommended until ages 10 or 11 when goal-directed behaviors begin to appear. Table 4.1 is presented as a guideline for initiating a program and progressing from low to middle to high fitness levels.

Table 4.1
Guidelines for Aerobic Exercise Prescription

Factor	Low Fitness Level	Ave. Fitness Level	High Fitness Level
Frequency (Days/Week)	3	3 or 4	5
Duration (Mins/Workout)	10-20	15-45	30-60
Intensity			
(% Max HR Range)	60-70	70-80	80-90
(% max VO₂)	50-60	60-70	70-80
Mode* (type of exercise)	walk, jog swim, cycle	walk, jog run, swim cycle	jog, run swim, cycle

* Other activities may be used provided they are continuous and rhythmical in nature.

The aerobic exercise sessions referred to previously should be preceded by a five- to ten-minute warm-up. A gradual warm-up consisting of stretching exercises for the arms, legs, and back, a few calisthenics (e.g., sit-ups and push-ups), and brisk walking will increase internal body temperature. Active warm-up increases blood flow to the muscles and prepares the body for vigorous exercise. It would also appear to decrease the chance of injury in that muscles and tendons are more resilient after warm-up.

The 30-minute aerobic program follows the warm-up and generally consists of walking, jogging, running, cycling, or swimming. These activities are high in energy cost and have been shown to increase aerobic capacity significantly (Pollock 1973). As indicated by Ribisl in Chapter 1, other activities that produce significant aerobic effects if practiced vigorously would include handball, racquetball, basketball, tennis, soccer, rope skipping, cross-country skiing, badminton, football, rugby, hockey, rowing, skating, and volleyball.

Just as the warm-up gradually prepares the body for vigorous exercise, a five- to ten-minute cool-down of walking and stretching exercises allows the gradual recovery of the body systems after the vigorous aerobic session is complete. (See Chapter 1.) The walking cool-down maintains the "muscle pump" in the legs, which promotes blood flow return to the heart. If the cool-down procedure is not followed and an individual stops immediately after vigorous exercise, the blood may pool in the legs. The person may faint, in this case, due to the reduced blood flow to the brain.

The aerobic exercise point charts outlined by Cooper (1970) are age-adjusted. School-aged children and adolescents may follow the recommendations listed for the age category "under 30." The same principles of training apply to children as for adults, and vigorous programs of aerobic exercise have been successfully implemented in several schools (Cooper et al. 1975; Goode et al. 1976; Stewart and Gutin 1976). When embarking on a program, each individual is categorized into a level of fitness according to the results from the exercise stress test or 12-minute field test, and age by decade group.

After identifying one's fitness and age category, a six-week starter program is employed. During this time the stress introduced to the body is minimal. Weeks seven to 20 are considered the conditioning phase of the program, where a substantially increased amount of stress is gradually introduced. Although any one or a combination of the wide variety of activities can be used, it is suggested that a beginner stick with one type of activity. Some form of walking and jogging is probably the most popular because of its convenience and low expense. An example of a 20-week walk/jog program for a person of average fitness is outlined in Table 4.2. The pace of walking and jogging varies depending upon each individual's ability. By completing workouts of 2.0, 2.5, and 3.0 miles in approximately 30 minutes, 5, 9, and 14 aerobic points are earned, respectively. Practiced three days per week this would result in 15, 27, and 42 points, which approximates the recommended progression in training.

Table 4.2
Guidelines for Progressive Program*

Weeks 1 & 2	Walk 1/10 mile, jog 1/10 mile for 2 miles
3 & 4	Walk 1/10 mile, jog 2/10 mile for 2 miles
5 & 6	Walk 1/10 mile, jog 3/10 mile for 2 miles
7 & 8	Walk 1/10 mile, jog 4/10 mile for 2 miles
9 & 10	Walk 1/10 mile, jog 4/10 mile for 2½ miles
11 & 12	Walk 1/10 mile, jog 5/10 mile for 2½ miles
13 & 14	Walk 1/10 mile, jog 6/10 mile for 2½ miles
15 & 16	Walk 1/10 mile, jog 7/10 mile for 3 miles
17 & 18	Walk 1/10 mile, jog 8/10 mile for 3 miles
19	Walk 1/10 mile, jog 9/10 mile for 3 miles
20	Jog for 3 miles

* Warm-up with stretching and calisthenics, walk and then jog, then cool down by walking one-quarter mile immediately following last jog segment.

In order to maintain the fitness gained through the 20-week program, the three-mile workouts recommended during week 20 could be continued on a regular basis thereafter. On the other hand, the individual could increase the distance jogged, speed of jogging, and/or days per week of exercise if continued improvement in fitness is desired.

Since most children and adolescents are likely to be involved in some type of physical education program, the total amounts of walking and jogging outlined in Table 4.2 may not be necessary. Cooper and his coworkers (1975) have reported a 17.5 percent improvement in the 12-minute run-walk test for 778 students (mean age 15.4 years) who added progressively five to 14 minutes of jogging to their daily physical education classes. Goode et al. (1976) found that the addition of six minutes daily of large muscle activity (skipping, running, hopping, etc.) was sufficient to produce a significant improvement in aerobic power in 12- to 14-year-old boys and girls. Stewart and Gutin (1976) used alternating interval running programs of 250 and 600 yards four times per week for eight weeks and showed significant improvements in submaximal working capacity in boys 10 to 12 years old.

LIMITATIONS

Certain criticisms have been directed against the aerobics point system, and many center around discrepancies in assessing points to a wide variety of activities. The point system is based on the average energy (oxygen) cost of the activity, and a number of activities are exceedingly difficult to assess. The oxygen cost of certain sport activities can only be measured by portable equipment, and current literature contains mainly studies utilizing relatively few subjects. More research is needed for quantifying the exact aerobic component of various activities using a large number of subjects.

REFERENCES

American College of Sports Medicine, 1975. *Guidelines for Graded Exercise Testing and Exercise Prescription*. Philadelphia: Lea and Febiger.

Cooper, K. H. 1968. *Aerobics*. New York: Bantam Books.

Cooper, K. H. 1970. *The New Aerobics*. New York: Bantam Books.

Cooper, K. H., J. G. Purdy, A. Friedman, R. L. Bohannon, R. A. Harris, and J. A. Arends. 1975. An aerobics conditioning program for the Fort Worth, Texas School District. *Res Quart,* 46, 345-350.

Gettman, L. R. and M. L. Pollock. 1977. Evaluation of physical fitness programs for police officers. *The Police Yearbook*. Gaithersburg, Md: International Association of Chiefs of Police, Inc.

Goode, R. C., A. Virgin, T. T. Romet, P. Crawford, J. Duffin, T. Pallandi, and Z. Woch. 1976. Effects of a short period of physical activity in adolescent boys and girls. *Canad J Appl Sport Sci,* 1, 242-250.

Gutin, B., R. K. Fogle, and K. Stewart. 1976. Relationship among submaximal heart rate, aerobic power, and running performance in children. *Res Quart,* 47, 536-539.

Krahenbuhl, G. S., R. P. Pangrazi, L. N. Burkett, M. J. Schneider, and G. Petersen.

1977. Field estimation of VO_2 max in children eight years of age. *Med Sci Sports,* 9, 37-40.

Maksud, M. G. and Coutts, K. D. 1971. Application of the Cooper 12-minute run-walk test to young males. *Res Quart,* 42, 54-59.

Pollock, M. L. 1973. Quantification of endurance training programs. In *Exercise and Sport Sciences Reviews,* J. Wilmore (ed.). Vol 1. New York: Academic Press.

Stewart, K. J. and B. Gutin. 1976. Effects of physical training on cardiorespiratory fitness in children. *Res Quart,* 47, 110-120.

5

Calisthenics and Stretching Exercises

Edward B. Souter

The term "calisthenics" has a Greek derivation meaning "beautiful strength." Calisthenic exercises are systematic methods of moving the body, generally executed without apparatus, in a rhythmical sequence. The stretching exercises are either of the light, bobbing calisthenic type or of the holding, static posture type.

Calisthenics and stretching exercise movements were practiced in prehistoric cultures and used to elevate the soul, improve health, and defend oneself against attack (Bucher 1952; Crampton 1975; Minnick 1975; Oyama 1974). In previous American generations, gymnastic and calisthenic forms of exercise were the main ingredient of the physical education program. This emphasis reached its peak between 1900 and 1910 (Irwin 1951; Staley 1935) but has declined in popularity since that time.

Calisthenics, although being replaced to some degree in schools by play activities, have remained popular with those promoting health through physical culture (MacFadden 1936). Today the Y.M.C.A. continues to use a variety of calisthenic exercises in its promotion of health and fitness (Myers 1975). (See Chapter 53.)

In contemporary American society, national youth and adult physical fitness campaigns are still being conducted, and calisthenic activities remain a major part of those programs. The military has also retained calisthenics as a basis of physical training (P.T.) (Camp 1918; Neilson 1942; U.S. Department of War 1941), although since World War II the philosophy behind calisthenics has been broadened. A discussion of the need for physical conditioning in the United States Navy (1950) condemned the use of calisthenics as a form of discipline. It stated, "Today we look upon physical education as a means of attaining some of our most cherished educational goals and calisthenics are being used in the program with a far more modern intrepretation. Under such names as free exercises, conditioning exercises, corrective exercises, and warm-up exercises, they are still a part of the program."

ADVANTAGES OF CALISTHENICS

Calisthenic and stretching exercises are considered an integral part of most conditioning programs and are routinely used for rehabilitative purposes and to help prevent injuries. They can be used by people of all ages, are easy to learn, and are relatively simple to perform. They require no equipment, can be performed in a limited space either indoors or outdoors with or without others. All major muscle groups and joints can be developed and stretched, exercises can be mild or vigorous, and a complete body development program can be completed in a short period of time. Both aerobic and anaerobic exercises are possible. All basic components of motor fitness can be developed: strength, endurance (muscular and circulorespiratory), power, agility, balance, and flexibility. They can be done harshly with force, gracefully, rhythmically to music, to vocal count, and at a fast or slow pace. They can be conducted for discipline or military objectives, or casually, socially, and recreationally. They have been recognized for generations as being beneficial to health.

Why, then, do we do any other exercises when we have such an all-inclusive exercise system? As Boring (1975) has written, "Perhaps the only disadvantage of significance to calisthenics is that many persons have difficulty in motivating themselves to work diligently enough to realize the potential benefits from them."

DISADVANTAGES OF CALISTHENICS

The common impression is that calisthenics are not fun, and it is difficult to motivate people to participate in them. With the development of new exercise machines, more efficient systems to strengthen the body have become available. In addition, a more objective, visible method of assessing improvement is possible, thereby providing an important source of motivation.

With the development of weight training and other forms of machine resistance equipment, the overload resistance is more easily set, can be increased gradually and systematically, and the angle of resistance can be readily controlled. With load resistance gauges and a visual observation of the weight lifted, along with other motivational aspects of machine and weight training, calisthenic forms of exercises have become less favorable, particularly in regard to the development of muscular strength and endurance.

Furthermore, Åstrand and Rodahl (1970) warn that "intensive activities involving small muscle groups (chinning the bar, push-ups, weight lifting) may be harmful for untrained individuals and cardiac patients since these activities produce a high heart rate and high blood pressure at a given cardiac output and oxygen uptake."

Most general calisthenic programs fail to make the same contributions to cardiovascular fitness as specific large muscle activities, such as endurance running, vigorous cycling, or continuous swimming. The volume of blood pumped through the cardiovascular system is greatest when a large muscle mass, such as the legs, is rhythmically and continuously activated for a sustained period of time. The manner in which calisthenics are often done with 10 or 15 repetitions of light arm and leg movements becomes nothing more than preparation for the more vigorous sports activity to follow. They may fail to warm the body to a point of perspiration, to stretch connective tissues, to hypertrophy or strengthen muscles, or to make any significant contribution to cardiorespiratory fitness. However, if the calisthenic program is designed to overload the large muscles and to be continuous for a significant length of time, improvements in all these areas are possible.

CALISTHENIC PROGRAMS AND CONCEPTS

Boring (1975) recommended a 15-minute continuous calisthenic program, designed for wrestlers but applicable for general use, which raises the heart and breathing rates, stresses and stretches the muscles of the legs, trunk, and neck, and helps prepare the body for more strenuous work. The program consists of:

1. 100 jumping jacks
2. 100 scissor jumps (legs spread forward and backward)
3. 100 vertical jumps
4. 100 runs in place (knees lifted until straight out from hips, counting each time the left foot hits the ground)
5. 100 hops on the right foot
6. 100 hops on the left foot followed by walking and a gastrocnemius stretch
7. 100 accordion sit-ups
8. 2 minutes of neck bridges
9. hamstring-back stretch
10. trunk stretch

11. trunk stretch to the opposite side

12. 50 push-ups from the knees with the back held straight.

He also outlined a more strenuous calisthenic program, and for greater muscular overload has recommended two-man calisthenics.

If a person were limited in time and wanted only to begin the warm-up process before a sport activity, at least three areas of the body should be exercised. The trunk should be moved sideward, forward, and backward without excessive hyperextension. Side bends and forward bends could work these areas. The push-ups from the knees or regular push-ups would exercise the shoulders, chest, and triceps muscles. A continuous rhythmical leg exercise, such as running in place or scissor jumps, would activate the circulatory respiratory functions and generally stress the body. With three or four exercises of this nature carried on for a period of time, the body could generally be warmed up, toned, and conditioned.

DiGennaro (1974) has described a systematic, progressive, calisthenic circuit program that, if done in its entirety, would exercise all the major muscle groups and joints and place significant demands upon heart and lung functions. As in other activities, the results depend upon the effort exerted by the participant, the amount of time devoted to the continuous activity, and the type of exercises chosen in the circuit.

Åstrand and Rodahl (1970) have stated that "calisthenics may be performed in such a manner that they entail an excellent training effect of the aerobic power (straddle jump, sequences of movements engaging large muscle groups)." With Åstrand acting as a technical adviser, Brattnäs and Gullers (1973) have attempted to introduce to America the Swedish form of calisthenics that they consider one of their most popular sports. One out of every 20 persons is considered to be actively involved in some gymnastic group. This form of calisthenics is termed rhythmical gymnastics and emphasizes grace and rhythm along with exercises for as many muscle groups of the body as possible. It is assumed that exercise should be fun and a part of the daily routines for everyone. Music is used along with exercise to help with rhythm and motivation. Major industrial firms in Sweden encourage their employees to take calisthenic exercise breaks that emphasize stretching and light exercise.

Many people do have an interest in exercise and are willing to take time, such as during lunch hours, to get that needed stretch and movement in an effort to reduce the tensions created in work. The stretching routines need not require changing into gym clothes. Gym clothes are more appropriate when time permits so that one can participate in more vigorous activities. In order to encourage participation, the activities should be fun, relaxing, and socially and emotionally rewarding. Activities need not be formal, but leadership is important.

Cureton (Mitchell 1966) has developed a form of rhythmical calisthenics that have been performed by hundreds of thousands of people, particularly in

Y.M.C.A. and Y.W.C.A. gyms throughout the country. The concept stated simply is that the law of life is movement, rhythmical continuous movement, and one hour a day of exercise at least three days a week for a lifetime is the plan. Cureton's (1975, 1969) home exercise program requires no equipment and consists of three levels of activity: low gear, middle gear, and high gear, each progressive in nature, including an extended warm-up, more vigorous exercises, and a taper-down period. These programs are described in detail in Chapter 11 of this volume.

The popularity of stretching exercises in professional athletics has extended to the point where a number of teams have added a new coach to their staff, the flexibility coach. One example is the Pittsburgh Steelers football team, which claims its stretching program helped cut injuries significantly, a decisive factor propelling the team to the National Football League Championship. Coach Uram explains that gone forever are the days when just big, strong men are needed. Today the big men need to be flexible (Jackson 1976-77). Several of the new stretching coaches have written and published their own books on the subject (Anderson 1975; Uram, n.d.).

Despite the increased emphasis on sports and games in recent years, calisthenics and stretching exercises have remained a part of the overall physical education and athletic program. In 1972 Pycior found that calisthenics remained a standard routine in the secondary schools he studied in Orange, California. Ninety-six percent of the junior and senior high schools surveyed used warm-up and conditioning exercises daily, and the remaining four percent used them almost daily. He found little variety in the exercises offered and a lack of maximum student effort in performing them. The researcher concluded that a more systematic approach with greater variety and an enthusiastic attitude shown by the teachers would improve the benefit of the exercises and increase student interest. He illustrated numerous forms of calisthenics that might be used. Based on Pycior's study one could conclude that the calisthenic exercises have become a tradition in many secondary schools and too often as part of the routine without appropriate explanation to the students as to their designed purposes and values.

Conditioning, prevention of injuries, and the potential for increasing athletic performance have been the main reasons typically cited for the continued use of calisthenics and stretching exercises in athletics. Each sport has its unique conditioning needs as does each athlete. Both must be considered in choosing the most appropriate combination of exercises.

Athletic training and conditioning texts and specific books on various sports generally include a section on conditioning specific to the sport. Many include calisthenics, and as time passes more are including the static stretch exercises (Boring 1975; Klafs and Arnheim 1977; Spackman 1970). Even when weight training is used for conditioning, calisthenics and stretching exercises are still recommended (Hooks 1962).

Stretching Exercises

Over the past four decades researchers have devoted considerable attention to the application of exercises to general fitness and athletic endeavors. For example, Cureton (1941) investigated the effects of flexibility exercises as an aspect of physical fitness. The flexibility exercises he used, calisthenic in form, were related to the development of "suppleness," a measure of the full range of joint mobility. This range of mobility was considered to reflect the structural make-up, the relative muscular strength compared to the ability to relax opposing muscles (reciprocal inhibition), and the state of condition of the muscles.

Flexibility exercises given for conditioning the full range of contraction and extension of the muscles are considered excellent massage and a means to produce both physical elongation and strengthening of the musculature. Such exercises, if increased to appropriate amounts, are considered potentially capable of enabling one to condition the muscles, tendons, ligaments, and bones to greater tensile strength and elasticity, a factor basic to preventing injuries in certain sports.

In regard to overcoming resistance to joint mobility, Cureton contends that every movement of the body involves stretching the muscles and connective tissue that oppose the motion. The muscles and ligaments are considered analogous to stretching rubber bands, and overcoming this resistance is one of the principal sources of wasteful work and physiological fatigue. In the endurance-type flexibility calisthenics, it is considered possible to reduce the resistance by improving the neuromuscular control (including reciprocal innervation), reducing the internal viscosity of the tissue, and eliminating adhesions and needless fat around the joints.

DeVries (1961a, 1961b) added a new dimension to stretching exercises with his studies on the static form of stretching as a means of lessening or helping to prevent residual muscle soreness induced by physical overexertion. Using electromyographic (EMG) equipment in order to record resting muscle action potentials, deVries observed that by employing a technique similar to the one used by swimmers to stretch the calf muscle of the leg to relieve a cramp, localized symptomatic and EMG observed distress could be significantly lessened or possibly prevented. These results supported the hypothesis that the cause of such distress, as seen in certain conditions as chronic shin splints, could at least in part be due to tonic muscle spasm. In summarizing his earlier study, deVries (1961a) stated, "Even though stretching reduced muscle soreness, no clear cut causal relationship between tonic muscle spasm and muscle distress had been demonstrated. It was concluded that only permissive support was provided for the hypothesis."

In one of the seven subjects studied, deVries (1961a) found that after two one-minute periods of using the toe pointer exercise (Fig. 5.1), increased EMG activity along with symptomatic pain resulted. In this individual case the pain in the tibialis anterior, or so called leg shin splint, was increased by stretching the area involved. DeVries (1961a) stated, "Certainly nothing in this report is meant to be construed as precluding the possibility of tearing or rupturing of muscle fibers in a violent movement followed by severe symptoms." He concludes that "static stretching seems to provide a useful technique for the relief of chronic muscular distress such as shin splints in some athletes."

In a more recent study of factors involved in delayed muscle soreness, Abraham (1977), using surface electromyograms, found no relationship between the development of muscle pain and the EMG activity of sore muscles. Static stretching did not alter the electrical activity of exercise,caused sore muscles, although it reduced the pain for one to two minutes. Similar pain relief was demonstrated when subjects slowly flexed and extended the involved ares. The combined results found from the EMG methods and other chemical analysis resulted in Abraham concluding that delayed muscle soreness after stressful exercise was most likely related to disruption of the connective tissue elements in the muscle and/or their attachments.

The different conclusions reported by deVries and Abraham should stimulate further research into the cause or possible causes of residual muscle soreness and the appropriateness of using static stretching exercises to relieve or help prevent such soreness. In regard to using static stretching exercises to increase joint flexibility the problem is not so complex. It is a common observation that this method is less likely to cause injury to tissues that the calisthenic bouncing form of exercises and that it is effective in increasing joint flexibility.

In a study to evaluate static stretching, deVries (1962) compared it with the conventional calisthenic or ballistic stretching exercises, many of which came from Kiphuth's exercises for stretching swimmers. Flexibility tests designed by Cureton (1941) were used to evaluate trunk flexion and extension and shoulder elevation in the two groups of subjects. The static stretching exercises involved the locking of a desired joint area in a position that resulted in the muscles and connective tissues being pulled to their greatest length. This position was then held without movement for a least one minute which invoked the inverse myotatic reflex resulting in the inhibition or relaxation of the groups of muscles involved (deVries 1974). A number of the exercises used were described by Rathbone (1959) and were of the Hatha Yoga type. The results showed that both methods significantly improved static flexibility in all three measures, but that there was no significant difference between the two methods. This led deVries (1962) to conclude that the static stretching methods were preferable because they required less expenditure of energy, were less likely to cause muscle soreness, and provided some degree of prevention and/or relief from soreness.

DeVries (1962) diagrammed the exercises used in his studies. The toe pointer exercise (1961a) was found to relieve shin splints except in one subject where pain and elevated levels of EMG activity occurred. This finding should caution persons with such injuries against forcing a stretch that increases the pain, due to the possibility of creating further injury. In the toe pointer exercise, the toes are pointed backward as the person sits back on his heels. The exerciser then leans back on his hands, which are extended behind his body and his knees are raised slightly off the ground.

A compound exercise using two of the positions described by deVries can be done together. The toe pointer and the shoulder stretch, illustrated in Fig. 5.1, is an example. If a person has difficulty in clasping the hands behind the back, one arm can assist the other in increasing the range of stretch.

The toe pointer stretches the flexors of the foot including the tibialis anterior, extensors hallucis, and digitorum longus in addition to the vasti (vastus lateralis, vastus medialis, and vastus intermedius). The shoulder stretch involves the anterior deltoid, pectoralis major, latissimus dorsi, and the long head of the triceps brachii.

In these exercises, as in all exercises, a degree of restraint is needed. Persons who dislocate their shoulders easily should not do this routine for their shoulders. Persons with previous knee or ankle injuries should not force the movements, and if pain is experienced it may be better to abstain from the exercise rather than incur further injury with forced movements. The muscles and connective tissues can be stretched more as one becomes adjusted to body tolerances, as long as the tissues are warm and injuries do not interfere. If in doing the toe pointer, pain is increased or not relieved, a trainer or physician should be consulted.

The following general stretching exercise routines are only a few of the possible hundreds that could be used. Many can be devised to stretch any major muscle group of the body. All that is needed is time to explore the various locked joint positions and to feel which positions stretch the muscle groups desired. The ones illustrated can be used in athletics, general conditioning or rehabilitation. They can be employed by older people who are beginning to become less flexible and are of particular value in activities that involve jogging or running. By themselves they do not constitute a fitness program. Exercises that train the heart and lungs, increase the pulse rate, and stress the muscles are the basic ingredients of a good fitness program. The appropriate concept is that none of the basic fitness areas should be neglected.

The gastrocnemius stretch, Fig. 5.2, involves the foot extensors including the gastrocnemius, soleus tibialis posterior, flexor hallicus and digitorum longus, peroneus brevis and longus, and plantaris. It is done leaning against an object with the feet kept parallel, the heels flat and the back straight. The approximate distance from the object can be adjusted in order to feel the stretch on the back of the calf of the leg.

The hamstring-back stretch, Fig. 5.3, is a basic stretch involving the hamstrings, extensors of the spine, and foot extensors. It is performed while sitting. One attempts to reach as far forward as possible while keeping the knees and legs flat on the ground.

In the trunk twist, Fig. 5.4, the gluteus maximus, abductors of the hip, and rotators of the spine and head are stretched. It is advisable to have another person ascertain that the trunk and the head are twisted in the same direction and that the arm in front of the body is over the leg on the opposite side of the body. A more advanced position is where one arm is placed between the legs to grasp the arm around the back. Both sides should be stretched.

The upper back stretch, Fig. 5.5, is one in which the legs are raised over the head and the feet are extended to the floor, if possible. As demonstrated, the primary muscles involved are the spine and head extensors, with limited involvement of the hamstrings and extensors of the foot. In one position the knees are brought around the ears, and in the more difficult positions the legs are held straight. Each position should be assumed very slowly, and if it is painful, the stretch should be relaxed to the point that pain is no longer experienced. For those who have neck injuries or are overweight, this position may be uncomfortable and a modified exercise might be more favorable.

In the back stretch, Fig. 5.6, there need not be a stress on the neck. It is an excellent exercise for the extensors of the spine and neck as well as the vasti muscles. The head can remain on the ground or supported by one hand. Alternate knees can be brought up to the chest or both knees may be flexed together as another form of exercise.

The groin stretch, Fig. 5.7, involves the adductors of the thigh and can be performed by pressing the elbows onto the knees or by raising the feet. The position should be held for at least one minute. Warming the body with light calisthenics or jogging before stretching will be helpful.

SUMMARY

In a short chapter it is not possible to review even a portion of the excellent calisthenic forms of exercise that have been used or are being used today. The approach in this paper has been to feature static stretching since people are less familiar with this form of exercise and it is presently receiving a great deal of attention. Static stretching, a sound method for increasing flexibility, is limited mainly for that one purpose. Calisthenics, on the other hand, can be used to warm the body prior to static stretching and can also be used to develop all the other components of motor fitness. The objectives sought help to determine the forms of exercises to be used.

In using any form of stretching exercise in the athletic warm-up, it is advisable to utilize activities that increase the body temperature prior to stretching. Exercises that elevate the cardiorespiratory function and the body temperature tend to increase the pliability of connective tissue.

In deVries' (1974) review of literature, he stated that dynamic flexibility is improved 20 percent by local warming of a joint and is decreased by cooling the joint. From his experiences he indicates that static flexibility seems to be similarly affected. A general method of estimating the appropriate warm-up needed in normal weather conditions would be the onset of perspiration. The intensity and duration of the warm-up must be adjusted to the event for which the individual is preparing and to the individual characteristic and needs of the athlete.

Fig. 5.1 Toe pointer and shoulder stretch.

Fig. 5.2 Gastrocnemius stretch.

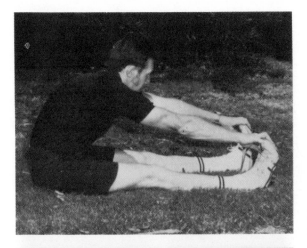

Fig. 5.3 Hamstring-neck stretch.

Fig. 5.4 Trunk twist.

Fig. 5.5 Upper back stretch.

Fig. 5.6 Knee tuck back stretch.

Fig. 5.7 Groin stretch.

Fig. 5.8 Lunch hour exercising group California State University, Long Beach.

REFERENCES

Abraham, W. M. 1977. Factors in delayed muscle soreness. *Med Sci Spts,* 9, 11-20.

Anderson, B. 1975. *Stretching.* P. O. Box 1002, Englewood, Colorado, 80110.

Åstrand, P. O. and K. Rodahl. 1970. *Textbook of Work Physiology.* New York: McGraw-Hill.

Boring, W. J. 1975. *Science and Skills of Wrestling.* St. Louis: C. V. Mosby.

Brattnäs, B. and K. W. Gullers. 1973. *Fit for Fun a Swedish Message.* Stockholm: Gullersproduktion AB.

Bucher, C. A. 1952. *Foundations of Physical Education.* St. Louis: C. V. Mosby.

Camp, W. 1918. Uncle Sam's athletic system. *Outlook.* 118 (March 27). 482-484.

Crampton, P. 1975. *Kung Fu Theory and Practice.* New York: Arco.

Cureton, T. K., Jr. 1941. Flexibility as an aspect of physical fitness. *Res Quart,* 12, 831-390.

Cureton, T. K., Jr. 1965. *Physical Fitness and Dynamic Health.* New York: Dial.

Cureton, T. K., Jr. 1969. *The Physiological Effects of Exercise Programs on Adults.* Springfield, Ill.: Charles C. Thomas.

deVries, H. A. 1961a. Electromyographic observations of the effects of static stretching upon muscular distress. *Res Quart,* 32, 468-479.

deVries, H. A. 1961b. Prevention of muscular distress after exercise. *Res Quart,* 32, 177-185.

deVries, H. A. 1962. Evaluation of static stretching procedures for improvement of flexibility. *Res Quart,* 33, 222-229.

deVries, H. A. 1974. *Physiology of Exercise.* 2nd ed. Dubuque: Wm. C. Brown.

Di Gennaro, J. 1974. *Individualized Exercise and Optimal Physical Fitness.* Philadelphia: Lea and Febiger.

Hooks, G. 1962. *Application of Weight Training to Athletics.* Englewood Cliffs, N.J.: Prentice Hall.

Irwin, L. W. 1951. *The Curriculum in Health and Physical Education.* St. Louis: C. V. Mosby.

Jackson, L. 1976-77. Pro-footballers stress flexibility. *Strength and Health,* 44, 68.

Klafs, E. C. and D. D. Arnheim. 1977. *Modern Principles of Athletic Training.* St. Louis: C. V. Mosby.

MacFadden, B. (ed.) 1931. *The Encyclopedia of Health and Physical Culture.* Vol. III. New York: MacFadden.

Minnick, M. 1975. *The Kung Fu Exercise Book.* New York: Bantam Books.

Mitchell, C. 1966. Run for your life. *The Healthy Life-Time Life Special Report.*

Myers, C. 1975. *The Official Y.M.C.A. Physical Fitness Handbook.* New York: Popular Library.

Neilson, N. P. 1942. Building strong bodies for wartime service. *NEAJ,* 31, 275-276.

Oyama, M. 1974. *What is Karate?* Tokyo: Japan Publications Trading Co.

Pycior, D. L. 1972. *Selected Exercises for Physical Education Instructors*. Unpublished thesis, California State College, Long Beach.

Rathbone, J. L. 1959. *Corrective Physical Education*. Philadelphia: W. B. Saunders.

Spackman, R. R. 1970. *Conditioning for Gymnastics*. Springfield, Ill.: Charles C. Thomas.

Staley, S. C. 1935. *The Curriculum in Sports (Physical Education)*. Philadelphia: W. B. Saunders.

United States Department of War. 1941. *Basic Field Manual—Physical Training* (FM 21-20). Washington, D.C.: U.S. Printing Office.

United States Navy. 1950. *Conditioning Exercises, Games, Tests*. Annapolis: United States Naval Institute.

Uram, Paul. n.d. *Refining Human Movement*. Personal distribution. Pittsburgh Steelers, Three Rivers Stadium, Pittsburgh, Pa.

6

Circuit Training

Sharon A. Plowman

Circuit training is a method of conditioning in which participants follow a prescribed route around an activity area stopping at set stations along the way to perform selected calisthenics or weight training exercises at a pre-established dosage.

Circuit training was formalized in the early 1950s at the University of Leeds, England by R. E. Morgan and G. T. Adamson (Sorani 1966) in an attempt to find a workable type of fitness program that would appeal to students and effectively improve their fitness levels. With its physiological principles and inherent goals and motivation, circuit training seems to do just that.

As a conditioning program, circuit training is extremely flexible with an almost limitless number of variations possible. Although originally intended solely for physical education classes for the development of cardiovascular-respiratory fitness, muscular strength, and muscular endurance, a circuit can be very easily and successfully used for the development of some other of the basic motor fitness elements, such as agility and power, and/or as part of an athlete's training. Circuits are generally not used for skill development. Once learned, however, certain basic skills can be incorporated into a circuit.

DEVELOPMENT OF A CIRCUIT

In order to devise a circuit, several factors need to be taken into consideration. Decisions made concerning these factors will almost automatically structure the circuit. They are ranked in order of decreasing importance here.

Aims and Objectives

The most obvious concern is the purpose for which the program is being designed. Is it general overall fitness? Is it for conditioning individuals for a particular physical education activity? Is it preseason, in-season or off-season conditioning or training for a particular sport?

If general fitness is the primary interest, then a decision must be made as to how much emphasis is to be placed on cardiovascular aspects and on each of the selected motor fitness areas such as agility, balance, flexibility, strength, power, and endurance. Since flexibility can best be developed through the use of static stretch or proprioceptive neuromuscular facilitation techniques where slow movement and sustained holds are emphasized (see Chapter 5) and circuits inherently emphasize speed, it is recommended that flexibility exercises *not* be included. Of course, flexibility is and should be one of the main components of general fitness and athletic conditioning and as such must be considered. Five to 15 minutes of flexibility exercises preceding the running of the circuit would serve to ensure that adequate attention is devoted to this important element and as a warm-up for the circuit.

When the circuit is to be designed for sport class members, an individual athlete, or an athletic team, the most important factor is the demands of the sport—the cardiovascular, metabolic, and motor fitness elements necessary for the successful performance of that sport. The teacher or coach must, therefore, first analyze the sport and decide which elements can best be developed through use of a circuit. Preseason circuits for school and college teams where conditioning may have to be done in an informal and an unsupervised fashion should be simple and emphasize those muscle groups most important to the upcoming sport season. In-season circuits can add basic individual skills at which the participants are proficient. Off-season circuits are generally more like an overall fitness circuit—designed to maintain baseline fitness.

Basketball, for example, demands a solid foundation of aerobic endurance training, a high ability to produce energy anaerobically, and large elements of agility, strength, power, and muscular endurance. Thus, a series of circuits might be constructed as follows:

Preseason. Run approximately 100 yards between each of the following stations:

1. Abdominal curls
2. Rope jumping
3. Push-ups
4. Bench stepping
5. Wrist rolling—up and down with a weight
6. Vertical jumps
7. Squeezing a tennis or rubber ball
8. Toe raises

In-season (early and for only moderately skilled individuals). Run one complete lap of the court plus the distance to the next station between each of the following exercises:

1. Side sliding (set lines), 6 executions
2. Wall passes (specify type), 10 executions
3. Rope jumping, 50 executions
4. Dribbling—width of court and back, 4 executions
5. Vertical jumps (set goal), 10 executions

In-season (late and/or more highly skilled and conditioned individuals). Run a complete lap of the court plus the distance to the next station between each of the following exercises:

1. Suicide drill—from the end line forward and backward sprints to
   a. foul line
   b. center line
   c. opposite foul line
   d. opposite end line
2. Zig zag dribble drill—switching hands, 2 executions
3. Ball handling drill—passing around body, 10 executions each
   a. overhead
   b. waist
   c. legs—figure 8
4. High-low slide drill along wall—guarding stance, hands touching tape marks at varying heights as the individual moves sideways

5. Controlled dribble drill, 10 executions of each of the following:
   a. right hand
   b. left hand
   c. from knees—right hand and left hand
   d. seated—right hand and left hand
   e. lying down—right hand and left hand
   f. reverse to a standing position
6. Stutter step and backward diagonal sliding—half court, 10 executions on each corner
7. Wall rebound—throws basketball against the wall, jumps to catch it, throws it back up before landing, and catches the ball again, 10 executions

Participants

The number, age, sex, and physiological condition, and sometimes the skill level, of the individuals who are to utilize the circuit must next be considered. Circuits can accommodate large groups of people, both sexes, most ages, and many conditions, but the activities must be appropriate. The two in-season basketball circuits show how this may be taken into consideration.

Facilities and Equipment

In theory the facilities and equipment factor should really be of little importance. However, in practice limitations are often at least temporarily imposed by the equipment and space available. Circuits can be adapted to just about any size area ranging from small all-purpose rooms where jumping rope or bench stepping might have to be substituted for running laps between stations, to a track or large playing field where distance between stations can be such as to tax the participants. Different surfaces can be easily accommodated. One special form of the circuit, the parcours or exercise trail, utilizes pathways of several miles that generally wind through natural wooded areas. With proper lighting these courses can be used at night as well as during the day.

Equipment is the more limiting factor—particularly if one wishes to include weight training in the circuit. The general guidelines must be that there is sufficient equipment available so that no waiting occurs at any station, that no time is lost adjusting equipment, and that people don't have to use weights or other equipment that are inappropriate for their present condition.

In outdoor situations, such as with the parcours, the equipment must also be of the type that can stand the rigors of the climate without constant maintenance. Lead pipes, telephone poles, and railroad ties make excellent materials for these stations.

Selection of Exercises

According to Sorani (1966), the exercises selected for inclusion in a circuit should be based upon the preceding three factors in addition to adhering to the following guidelines:

1. The exercises should be strenuous. The basic principles behind a circuit are overload and progression, and every exercise should contribute to these within each individual's ability and fitness level.

2. The exercises should be simple. Although basic instructions or pictures should be posted at each station, participants should not have to devote a considerable amount of time in understanding complicated movements. Time and intensity are the essence of a circuit, not fine controlled movements. Individuals tend to perform difficult moves in the easiest manner possible when speed is involved, and improper performance of complicated moves is often of little benefit and in certain cases can be harmful. Everyone should be familiar with the exercises before beginning.

3. The exercises should be standardized. Obviously, the only way to see true progression during a training program is by performing the same activities in exactly the same way. In addition, the standardized way is generally the safe way.

4. Safety hazards must be eliminated. Any exercise improperly or carelessly performed has a potential for injury. However, if proper care is taken, the risk of bodily injury can be minimized. Any activities rated as high risk should be avoided. Dangerous obstructions and slippery surfaces should be eliminated.

5. All parts of the body should be exercises. This will help the individual to maintain an overall balance between varying parts of the body and between antagonistic muscles. The sequence of the exercises within the circuit should be such that successive stations do not emphasize the same muscle groups. This will avoid undue fatigue that reduces the individual's capacity for work and may predispose the person to injury.

6. Workouts should be relatively brief. The time available for the circuit to an extent limits the number of different exercises that can be included. Generally, from five to 20 minutes are considered sufficient to achieve a good workout; ten exercises can generally be completed during this time span.

Time

Time is an extremely important factor in circuit training. It can be used at least in three ways:

74

1. As the criterion of overload and progression. In this instance the total time it takes for an individual to complete a given number of trips (usually two or three) around the circuit is noted. This is then reduced by one-quarter to one-third in order to establish a "target time." When the individual has adapted and achieved the target time, progression by additional overload is instituted. This is the "traditional" use of time in a circuit.

2. As the length of time spent at each station. For example, each individual may spend 30 seconds or one minute at each station of a circuit. In this case a count is kept of the number of repetitions of each exercise that the participant has completed. On a given signal everyone moves to the next station. Any type of signal can be used, from the typical whistle to segments of music—when the music stops, everyone rotates.

3. As the length of time spent in completing the circuit. In this case the total time to be devoted to the circuit is set, and the participants are instructed to cover as many stations as possible within the time limit. For instance, both of the in-season basketball circuits outlined earlier were intended to be completed in this way. They were used in a physical education class where it was desirable to supplement the students' condition and teach some aspects of conditioning in a minimal amount of time. Five minutes were allotted in each case. The first circuit could easily be completed in that time with several stations being repeated. The second circuit was beyond the reach of all but the best class members in that time. In a situation such as this, it is imperative to ensure that students start at a different station on successive days so that they get the benefit of a workout at all stations. Another possibility is to adjust the number of repetitions at each station or to delete one or more of the stations. However, if the best students are to be conditioned, a large number of stations may be needed. This form of circuit is probably the least traditional and it is somewhat more difficult to individualize.

PROCEDURES AND TECHNIQUES

Once the stations in the circuit have been determined, the training dosages must be set and the technique for progression established.

Setting the Initial Load

1. It is possible for the instructor or coach to arbitrarily designate how many repetitions are to be completed at each station. The number chosen is thus based on the instructor's knowledge of the group and prior groups under similar circumstances.

A more flexible version of this technique is for the instructor to set several different levels each of which is progressively more difficult. Students can then do one of three things:

    a. choose the level they think appropriate

    b. begin at a given level based upon one's initial fitness status

    c. begin at the lowest level

In the latter case, if on the first day some students easily complete the circuit, they would move up a level the next day the circuit is run. This process would be continued until each individual finds a proper level.

The aforementioned parcours exercise trail utilizes this type of load setting. Generally, three levels of fitness are dealt with—beginning, intermediate, and advanced. A large sign posted at each station describes the exercise and indicates the number of repetitions to be completed at each fitness level.

2. In order to individualize the load more definitely, the obvious technique is to test each person on each exercise in the circuit. Two possibilities exist:

    a. all-out maximal tests for each exercise

    b. all-out maximal test for the number of repetitions that can be performed during a given time period—for example, 30 seconds or one minute.

In both cases the exercises should be performed in the same order in which they will be done in the circuit. Between 60 and 90 seconds rest is allowed between each all-out testing bout. It is not necessary to be consistent as to a maximal or timed maximal bout within the same circuit.

If two laps of the complete circuit are to be run, the total number of repetitions at each station is reduced to two-thirds for each lap. If three laps are to be completed, the maximal repetitions are reduced to one-half for each lap. For example:

Station	Maximal Repetitions	2-Lap Dosage	3-Lap Dosage
Sit-ups	30	20	15
Push-ups	10	7	5
Vertical jumps	18	12	9

After the number of repetitions per station has been established, it is then necessary to measure the total time for completion. As previously indicated, the "target time" is computed by reducing the initial time by one-quarter or one-third. The choice may depend upon the starting level of each individual. Those in the poorest condition will generally show the greatest amount of improvement and thus should have the greater reduction in time.

Target times are advisable but not essential. Some people may simply wish to strive for the fastest possible time and not be "limited" by a target. For the type of circuit in which a set time limit is given at each station, the number of repetitions of each exercise is the changing variable and as such is obviously not predetermined.

Progression

Progression in circuit training can be achieved by a variation in the total amount of work completed, the rate at which the work is performed, or the total amount of time allotted for completing the work.

1. Increases in the total amount of work can be accomplished in three ways:
    a. An additional lap of the circuit can be run. This is a reasonable choice only if the initial task had been a two-lap circuit. Doing more than three laps can get very boring and may actually become counterproductive in terms of motivation.
    b. Additional repetitions of each exercise can be added. In this case increases of one or two repetitions per station are sufficient, for with the completion of two or three laps such an increase adds greatly to the total amount of work performed.
    c. The activity can be modified to a more strenuous form. Variations of the common calisthenics are well known. For example, progression in the sit-up might go as follows:
       1. abdominal curl
       2. bent knee sit-up
       3. sit-up with knees bent and feet elevated
       4. the addition of 5- or 10-pound weights to any of the above versions (a little thought will allow the coach or instructor to modify almost any exercise)
2. The rate of work must be increased (a) if the number of repetitions is increased but the target or allotted time remains the same, or (b) if a further reduction in the target time is set as a goal for the same number of repetitions.
3. Time can be varied by the reduction of the target time as mentioned before. However, if the technique of covering as many stations as possible in a set period of time is used, then an increase in the total time is necessary. For instance, going from five to seven minutes, or from seven to ten minutes.

ADVANTAGES AND DISADVANTAGES

Circuit training is a very sound system of conditioning with far more advantages than disadvantages.

Advantages

Advantages of circuit training include the following:

1. Circuits are very adaptable.
   a. They can be constructed to fit just about any age and either sex.
   b. Activities can be chosen for inclusion to fit a wide range of objectives and needs.
   c. Small or large numbers can be accommodated with individualization possible for each participant. If large groups are involved, it is best to divide the group into smaller units, one of which is assigned to each station as a starting point.
   d. Facilities and equipment can be quite minimal or very extensive.
   e. A wide range of time limits or requirements can be easily accommodated.

2. The application of physiological principles forms the basis of circuit training.
   a. Overload is inherent in the multiple lap or all-out timed bouts, despite the fact that the individual is working at a submaximal load at any given point in the multiple-lap system.
   b. Individualization is relatively easy.
   c. Adaptation and progression are assured if the individual adheres to the prescribed routine.
   d. Maintenance can be accomplished once individual goals have been achieved.
   e. Specificity is accomplished by selecting exercises to meet pre-determined objectives.

3. Students can gain fundamental knowledges in the science of training and conditioning by applying these physiological principles during circuit training.

4. Motivation is provided by pre-established goals (target times) or by charting the number of repetitions or stations completed per unit of time.

5. Self-testing is possible and evaluation can occur with each workout.

6. Circuits provide a high intensity workout in a relatively short period of time. This type of training provides continuous activity that stresses the cardiovascular as well as the muscular system.

7. Circuits can be utilized as the means of conditioning or supplemental to other techniques such as long distance or interval running.

8. Circuits can be set up temporarily for short-term use or for almost permanent use such as in the form of parcours trails in a park or recreational area.

Disadvantages

Disadvantages of circuit training include:

1. Flexibility exercises do not constitute a part of the conditioning program.
2. No allowance or time period for warm-up and cool-down is included in the circuit. These must be added.
3. Students should be continually monitored so that all exercises are performed correctly.
4. Individuals finish at widely different times. The inconvenience of this can be minimized if the circuit is run at the end of the class or practice.
5. If the system of maximal repetitions per unit of time is utilized, participants must carry cards for recording their scores or have partners do the recording for them. In addition, running laps between stations gives the faster students a longer rest period before beginning the next bout.

REFERENCES

Annarino, A. A. 1972. *Developmental Conditioning for Physical Education and Athletics.* St. Louis: C. V. Mosby.

Hockey, R. V. 1973. *Physical Fitness: The Pathway to Healthful Living.* 2nd ed. St. Louis: C. V. Mosby.

Johnson, P. and D. Stolberg. 1971. *Conditioning.* Englewood Cliffs, N.J.: Prentice-Hall.

Novich, M. M. and B. Taylor. 1970. *Training and Conditioning of Athletes.* Philadelphia: Lea and Febiger.

Sorani, R. 1966. *Circuit Training.* Dubuque: Wm. C. Brown.

7

Fartlek

John T. Powell

The Fartlek or "speed play" system of training can best be defined as a Swedish method based on running long distances with free, untimed variations of pace. In discussing the Fartlek system, Stampfl wrote:

> It is best used over undulating country that encourages a natural change of pace up and down hills, interspersed with long, flat stretches. It is most effective when the pace is varied frequently from short, sharp sprints to long, easy jog-trots, with occasional fast quarter-miles and sustained efforts over distances ranging from half a mile to a mile (Stampfl 1956, p. 159).

Gosta Holmer, then Chief National Track Coach of Sweden, was mainly responsible for the development of the Fartlek system. He discussed this development in an address made to the Amateur Athletic Association.

> I returned to Sweden some 25 years ago, after a spell of four years working as a sports reporter in Finland where I had every opportunity to study the training methods of Paavo Nurmi. I was left with the thought that it was necessary for Sweden to evolve a scheme of training that would be in accord with the national characteristics and scenery of our country.
>
> Then, one day, whilst watching my children at play, I realized they had the key to training. The children sitting upon the grass playing would suddenly jump up and rush to their mother, and after a few minutes, run quietly to their play. Then, a little later, jump up again, rush to some other spot in the garden, and after a moment or two run back. They did not walk anywhere but always ran at varying speeds. This is the law of nature for training, and the children develop their hearts, lumgs and bodies by these natural bursts of activity and periods of relaxed exercise. In appreciation of this fact, I named my method of training "speed play" — in Swedish, "Fartlek" (Tomlin 1951, p. 24).

TECHNIQUES

Holmer classified the schedule of training for a runner into four progressive periods of activity: (1) conditioning period (3½ months), walking, easy running, and indoor gymnastic exercises; (2) preseason (1 month), running work and Fartlek with some speed training; (3) early competitive season (1½ months), training as above with the addition of one competition each week; and (4) competitive season (2 months), amount of training dependent upon the amount of racing (Tomlin 1951).

The Fartlek portion includes some variation of the following:

1. walking five to ten minutes for warming up, followed by gymnastic exercises
2. easy jogging five to ten minutes
3. wind sprints ten to 100 yards for five to ten minutes
4. jogging five to ten minutes
5. uphill running 220 to 440 yards at three-quarters speed
6. easy running ten minutes
7. even speed running at a pace less than running pace—one-half mile 15 seconds less; 1 mile 30 seconds less (Tomlin 1951).

Holmer generally recommends that Fartlek training be employed twice each week during early season training and once per week during competitive periods.

Alford (1950) has provided specific sample workouts for Fartlek. Several such samples are as follows:

1. ½ *miler*—about three miles Fartlek: one mile slow plus 100 yards medium pace—about mile speed—and 880 yards slow plus 200 yards medium pace plus 880 yards slow, then 100 yards medium pace plus 440 yards slow and 50 yards fast stride at about ½ mile speed and then 880 yards slow.

   1 miler—about four miles Fartlek: one mile slow plus 100 yards medium pace plus 880 slow, then 200 yards medium pace and 880 yards slow plus 440 medium pace and one mile slow plus 220 yards medium pace and 880 slow.

   3 miler—about five miles Fartlek: one mile slow plus 200 yards medium pace plus 880 slow and 440 medium pace, plus one mile slow and 220 fast stride plus one mile slow. Finish with ten minutes exercise.

2. ½ *miler*—about three miles Fartlek: 880 yards slow plus 200 medium pace plus 880 yards slow, then 100 yards fast stride plus 440 yards slow, then 50 yards fast stride and 880 slow 110 fast stride plus 880 yards slow and 220 at medium pace and 880 yards to finish.

   1 miler—about four miles Fartlek: 880 yards slow plus 200 medium pace plus 880 yards slow and 440 yards medium pace, then one mile slow plus 440 medium pace plus 200 fast stride and 880 yards slow.

   3 miler—about five miles Fartlek: one mile slow plus 440 yards medium pace, then 880 yards slow and 440 medium pace, then one mile slow pace and 200 fast stride plus 880 slow followered by a 440 medium pace and a mile slow to finish.

ADVANTAGES

The advantages of the Fartlek system include the following:

1. Fartlek allows the runner to use personal initiative and intelligence; to learn to evaluate own abilities.
2. Fartlek is refreshing and relieves the monotony of running around the track.
3. Cross-country running gives less jar to the leg muscles than running on a track.
4. Fartlek allows for a more strenuous workout than the usual round-the-track workout.
5. Fartlek workouts tend to be more mentally invigorating, leaving the athlete with feelings of success and well-being.
6. Fartlek provides a basis on which to build more stamina and some speed. By its emphasis on pace variation, it introduces the runner gradually to the more exacting forms of interval training.

DISADVANTAGES

The disadvantages of the Fartlek system include:

1. Fartlek provides no direct supervision.
2. The individual tends to be neglected in the Fartlek group.
3. Fartlek may be a slow method of developing runners.
4. Since the runner varies the pace without reference to fixed distances and a stopwatch, it is useless in teaching pacing.
5. Race tactics and team organization cannot be developed through Fartlek.
6. The soft, uneven surfaces over which most Fartlek workouts are run is not conducive to the development of high speeds.

UTILIZATION

Despite these disadvantages, Fartlek can be successful in developing outstanding runners. Gundar Haegg of Sweden, who held the world record for the mile, grew up in the Swedish countryside where he trained in the woods, by the lakes and up and down the hills near his home. He never trained on a track because he felt such training was monotonous. Haegg maintained that by going to a track only to race, he was more inspired by the occasion. He disliked formality in training and set himself no pre-arranged running exercises or timed distances. He relied entirely on how he felt from day to day.

Haegg trained in all types of weather and frequently pushed himself very hard, and although he was often tired after an outing, he was usually eager to run again the next morning. When the snow was thick during the winter, he trained five or six times a week along ski trails. Starting with walks and slow runs, he covered at least three miles per day, building up over the weeks to run through deep snow, which often severely taxed him. Later, when snow had disappeared, he began the speeding-up period, running over the soft pine needles that cover the floors of the Swedish woods. At this stage of the training, he began by running six miles easily and then, after a week or two, introduced fast stretches of 200 to 800 yards, gradually lengthening the spurts and shortening the easy running periods as he felt his physical condition was improving. When the competitive season began, he raced only when he felt ready and, at first, against easy opposition and over short (1,500-meter) distances. During the season he trained lightly, relying on frequent competition to keep him highly trained. In 1942, he raced 34 times in 14 weeks, breaking ten world records (Dyson 1954).

REFERENCES

Alford, J. W. 1950. Suggested training schedule for beginners to middle distance. *The Athlete*, 5, 87.

Doherty, J. K. 1951. Attitude and fatigue in distance running. *The Athlete*, 7, 100.

Doherty, J. K. 1953. *Modern Track and Field*. New York: Prentice-Hall.

Dyson, G. H. G. 1954. Modern approach to distance running. *The Modern Athlete*, 2, 17-18.

Miller, R. I. 1952. *Fundamentals of Track and Field Coaching*. New York: McGraw-Hill.

Stampfl, F. 1955. *Franz Stampfl on Running*. London: H. Jenkins.

Tomlin, S. A. 1951. Running training in Sweden. *The Athlete*, 6, 24.

8

Interval Training
Edward L. Fox

Among the factors responsible for the lowering of world records in track and swimming events over the last 30 years is the improvement in training methods.

Refinement of one such method, interval training, has probably produced more successful athletes than has any other system of training. Although originally developed primarily for track and swimming athletes, the interval training system can easily be utilized by coaches and athletes of a variety of sports.

As the name implies, interval training is a system of physical conditioning in which the body is subjected to regularly repeated bouts of exercise interspersed with periods of relief. Light or mild exercise usually constitutes the relief interval.

INTERVAL TRAINING TERMS

The following terms are used in describing the interval training system:

1. Training. An exercise program to develop an athlete for a particular event. It involves developing energy capacity as well as skill of performance.

2. Work interval. That portion of the interval training program consisting of the high-intensity work effort; for example, a 200-meter run at a prescribed time.

3. Relief interval. The duration between work intervals and sets.

4. Rest-relief interval. A relief interval consisting of very light activity such as walking or flexing the arms or legs.

5. Work-relief interval. A relief interval consisting of mild to moderate exercise such as rapid walking and jogging.

6. Work-relief ratio. A ratio relating the durations of the work and relief intervals. For example, a work-relief ratio of 1:2 means that the duration of the relief interval is twice that of the work interval.

7. Set. A group of work and relief intervals; for example, six 200-meter runs at a prescribed time and work-relief ratio.

8. Repetition. The number of work intervals within a set. Six 200-meter runs would constitute one set and 6 repetitions.

9. Training time. The rate (speed) at which the work is to be performed during the work interval; for example, each 200-meter run might be run in 30 seconds.

10. Training distance. Distance of the work interval; for example, 200 meters.

11. Frequency. Number of training sessions per day and/or per week.

12. Interval training prescription. Contains necessary information concerning an interval training workout. It includes number of sets and repetitions, training distance and time, and time of the relief interval. As an example, one set from a prescription for a running program would be:

$$\text{Set 1} \qquad 6 \times 200 \text{ at } 0:30 \ (1:30)$$

where: 6 = number of repetitions
     200 = training distance in meters*
   0:30 = training time in minutes and seconds
 (1:30) = time or relief interval in minutes and seconds

THE ENERGY SYSTEMS

Various activities have specific demands for energy. For example, sprinting requires a large energy output over a short period of time. Conversely, running a marathon requires a large energy output over a long period of time. Appreciation of the objectives of training programs requires a basic understanding of energy systems in man.

Adenosine triphosphate, or more simply ATP, is the immediate source of energy for any muscular activity. ATP is stored in skeletal muscle in limited amounts and replenished, as needed, from the chemical breakdown of other substances also stored in the body. There are basically three ways in which ATP can be supplied to the skeletal muscles. Two of these methods are anaerobic, which do not require the presence of oxygen, whereas the third source is aerobic, requiring oxygen to manufacture ATP.

ATP-Pc System

For brief bursts of high energy output (e.g., up to 10 seconds such as sprinting 100 meters), ATP is immediately available from muscular stores and from phosphocreatine (PC), a substance also normally stored in skeletal muscles. Properly prescribed training programs may be expected to increase the stores of ATP and PC. The disadvantage of this system is that the total amount of stored ATP and PC, even following training, is very small.

The Lactic Acid System

When stored ATP and PC are substantially reduced, additional short-term ATP energy is made available from the anaerobic breakdown of glycogen (stored

---

* The equivalent distances in yards for 50, 100, 200, 400, 600, 800, 1000, 1210, and 2400 meters are 55, 110, 440, 660, 880, 1100, 1320, and 2640, respectively.

carbohydrate) to lactic acid. ATP for high-intensity activities lasting from one to three minutes can be supplied by the lactic acid system. Training programs can also increase productivity of ATP from this system thereby increasing the performance potential for activities lasting one to three minutes in duration. A disadvantage of this system is the accumulation of lactic acid in muscles and blood, causing fatigue.

The Oxygen System

ATP is continually being manufactured from the energy released from the breakdown of food nutrients (principally carbohydrates and fats) by a process requiring oxygen. This process, which permits ordinary activity without discomfort or fatigue, is also the basis for meeting increased demands for energy in athletic events of long duration, for example, in running the marathon or playing soccer or lacrosse or other "endurance" sports. Here, too, proper training can lead to increases in the aerobic (oxygen) capacity.

In summary, ATP can be supplied to the skeletal muscles in three different ways: by the ATP-PC system for short, high-intensity activities; by the lactic acid system for intense activities of intermediate length; and through the aerobic system for the long-term, low-intensity activities.

TECHNIQUES

Determining the Predominant Energy System

As indicated, the energy system most used during specific activities depends on the time and rate of energy expenditure demanded by the activity. Therefore, one of the principles involved in the development of any training program is to first identify the energy systems most used in the sports activity in question. For example, to improve performance in the marathon, the training program must develop the aerobic system, whereas to improve the performance of a sprinter, the anaerobic systems must be developed.

Selecting the predominant energy system used during the marathon or sprinting is relatively easy. However, for the majority of sports activities, the task is more difficult. Therefore, guidelines for estimating the emphasis that should be placed on improving the energy systems during interval training are presented in Table 8.1. The table was constructed by analysis of each sport activity with regard to the position played and the time required for performance. The percentages are not exact, but estimates. Accurate laboratory assessment of the interaction of the energy systems for various sports activities is not only difficult, but not necessary for training purposes.

Selecting the Type of Work for the Work Interval

As much as possible, the type of work performed during the work interval of the interval training program should include the same groups and same movement

Table 8.1

Various Sports and Their Predominant Energy Systems*

Sports or Sport Activity	% Emphsis According to Energy Systems		
	ATP-PC and LA	LA-O_2	O_2
1. Baseball	80	20	—
2. Basketball	85	15	—
3. Fencing	90	10	—
4. Field Hockey	60	20	20
5. Football	90	10	—
6. Golf	95	5	—
7. Gymnastics	90	10	—
8. Ice Hockey			
a. forwards, defense	80	20	—
b. goalie	95	5	—
9. Lacrosse			
a. goalie, defense, attack men	80	20	—
b. midfielders, man down	60	20	20
10. Rowing	20	30	50
11. Skiing			
a. slalom, jumping, downhill	80	20	—
b. cross-country	—	5	95
c. pleasure skiing	34	33	33
12. Soccer			
a. goalie, wings, strikers	80	20	—
b. halfbacks, or link men	60	20	20
13. Swimming and diving			
a. 50 yds., diving	98	2	—
b. 100 yds.	80	15	5
c. 200 yds.	30	65	5
d. 400, 500 yds.	20	40	40
e. 1500, 1650 yds.	10	20	70
14. Tennis	70	20	10
15. Track and field			
a. 100, 220 yds.	98	2	—
b. field events	90	15	—
c. 440 yds.	80	15	5
d. 880 yds.	20	65	15
e. 1 mile	20	55	25
f. 2 miles	20	40	40
g. 3 miles	10	20	70
h. 6 miles (cross country)	5	15	80
i. marathon	—	5	95
16. Volleyball	90	10	—
17. Wrestling	90	10	—

* Modified from Fox and Mathews (1974, p. 184).

patterns as those employed during actual performance of the sports skill in question. For example, track athletes should use running; swimmers, swimming; rowers, rowing; cyclists, cycling; and so on.

Intensity of the Work Interval

The proper intensity of the work interval can be estimated in two ways:

1. One method, which is perhaps the more accurate, is based on the heart rate response during the work interval. Table 8.2 gives target work interval heart rates for men and women of different ages. If the heart rate is below this limit, the work load is too easy; if above this limit, the work is probably too hard. The heart rate during the work interval can be estimated by counting the pulse for six or ten seconds immediately after the work interval and multiplying by ten or six, respectively, to convert to beats per minute.

Table 8.2
Target Work Interval Heart Rates for Men and
Women of Different Ages*

Age (years)	Heart Rate (beats per min)
Under 20	190
20-29	180
30-39	170
40-49	160
50-59	150
60-69	140

* From Fox and Mathews (1974, p. 46).

2. The intensity of the work interval can also be estimated from performance times as indicated in Table 8.3. This method is most useful with running and swimming programs. As an example of how to use this table, if a person can run 50 meters from a running start in 6 seconds, the training time for that training distance would be $6 + 1.5 = 7.5$ seconds. For work intervals utilizing 400-meter runs, if the athlete can run 1,600 meters in 5 minutes (300 seconds), then the training time for each 400-meter run would be $75 - 4 = 71$ to $75 - 1 = 74$ seconds (the average time for each 400-meter segment of a 5-minute, 1,600-meter run is 75 seconds). For this same athlete, the training time for a training distance of 1,200 meters would be $75 + 3 = 78$ or $75 + 4 = 79$ seconds.

Number of Repetitions

The number of repetitions of the work interval determines the length of the workout. A total of between 2.5 and 3.0 kilometers (1.5 to 2.0 miles) will usually be necessary to bring about maximal benefits. For example, if 200-meter repeats are used as the training distance, 12 to 16 repetitions would be necessary.

Duration of the Relief Interval

There are two ways to determine the duration of the relief interval.

1. Recovery heart rate. Recovery heart rate following the work interval is a good indicator as to when the next repetition or set is to begin. Recommended heart rate levels between repetitions and sets for both sexes of various ages are given in Table 8.4. Pulse rate, as before, can be determined periodically throughout the relief interval.

Table 8.3
Guidelines for Determining a Sufficient Work Rate
for Running and Swimming Interval Training Programs
Based on Performance Times*

Training Distance (meters)		Work Rate
Run	Swim	
50	15	1½ seconds slower than best
100	25	3 times from moving
200	50	starts
400	100	1 to 4 seconds faster than average 400-meter (run) or 100-meter (swim) while doing best times in 1,600-meter (run) or 400-meter (swim)
600-1210	150-300	3 to 4 seconds slower than average 400-meter (run) or 100-meter (swim) while doing best times in 1,600 meter (run) or 400 meter (swim)

*Modified from Fox and Mathews (1973, p. 49).

Table 8.4
Heart Rate Levels Between Repetitions and Sets
for Both Sexes of Various Ages*

Age (years)	Heart Rate (beats per min)	
	Between Repetitions	Between Sets
Under 20	150	125
20-29	140	120
30-39	130	110
40-49	120	105
50-59	115	100
60-69	105	90

* From Fox and Mathews (1974, p. 60).

2. Work-relief ratio. Since it is sometimes not convenient to use heart rate as a guide for determining the duration of the relief interval, the work-relief ratio, as described earlier, can be used. This will allow sufficient time for the heart rates to recover to or near the values given in Table 8.4. Usually, with longer training distances (e.g., 800 meters and over), a 1:1 or 1:½ work-relief ratio is used; with middle training distances (400 to 600 meters) a 1:2 ratio is used; and with shorter distances, a 1:3 work-relief ratio is prescribed.

Type of Relief Interval

Rest-relief intervals should be used with interval training programs designed to modify the ATP-PC system. The reason for this recommendation is that during rest-relief intervals, ATP and PC are restored to the muscles and thus can provide the energy required for subsequent work intervals. When the lactic acid system is to be modified, work-relief intervals should be used. In this case, mild work will inhibit or partially block complete restoration of ATP and PC in the muscles. In turn, the lactic acid system rather than the ATP-PC system is used during subsequent work intervals. Therefore, a rest-relief interval should be used in this case.

Frequency of Training

Seven- or eight-week interval training programs with two workouts per week have been shown to be as effective in improving the oxygen system, as have 13-week programs administered four days per week (Fox et al. 1975b; Lesmes et al. 1978). However, other training benefits have been shown to be further enhanced the longer and more frequent the program.

Interval Training for General Fitness

Interval training may be used by nonathletes for improvement in general fitness. For the majority of people, particularly adults, improvement in cardiorespiratory fitness is the major need. Therefore, the oxygen (aerobic) system is the energy system most necessary to improve. The principles involved in designing such a program are the same as for the endurance athlete. The major differences in interval training programs designed for athletes and nonathletes will be in the absolute intensity, frequency, and perhaps the overall length of the program.

SUMMARY

In order to write an interval training prescription, the following steps should be taken:

1. Determine which energy systems need to be increased (Table 8.1).
2. Select the type of activity to be used during the work interval.
3. Develop the training prescriptions based upon the information provided in Tables 8.5 and 8.6 relative to the major energy systems to be improved. The

number of repetitions and sets, the work-relief ratio, and the type of relief interval are given in the tables. For any activity selected for the work interval, the training times given in Table 8.5 (second column) can be used. However, if the activity is either running or swimming, it is more convenient to use training distances as shown in column two or Table 8.6.

4. Provide for an increase in intensity throughout the training program.

Table 8.5
Pertinent Information for Writing Interval
Training Prescriptions Based on Training Times*

Major Energy System	Training Time (min:sec)	Repetitions Per Workout	Sets Per Workout	Repetitions Per Set	Work-Relief Ratio	Type of Relief Interval
ATP-PC	0:10	50	5	10		Rest-Relief (e.g.,
	0:15	45	5	9		walking, flexing)
	0:20	40	4	10	1:3	
	0:25	32	4	8		
ATP-PC-LA	0:30	25	5	5		Work-Relief (e.g.,
	0:40-0:50	20	4	5	1:3	light to mild
	1:00-1:10	15	3	5		exercise, jogging.)
	1:20	10	2	5	1:2	
LA-O$_2$	1:30-2:00	8	2	4	1:2	Work-Relief
	2:10-2:40	6	1	6		
	2:50-3:00	4	1	4	1:1	Rest-Relief
O$_2$	3:00-4:00	4	1	4	1:1	Rest-Relief
	4:00-5:00	3	1	3	1:½	

* Modified from Fox and Mathews (1974).

Table 8.6
Pertinent Information for Writing Interval
Training Prescriptions Based on Training Distance*

Major Energy System	Training Distance Yards Run	Swim	Repetitions Per Workout	Sets Per Workout	Maximal Reps Per set	Work-Relief Ratio	Type of Relief Interval
ATP-PC	55	15	50	5	10	1:3	Rest-Relief
	110	25	24	3	8		(e.g., walking, flexing)
ATP-PC-LA	220	55	16	4	4	1:3	Work-Relief
	440	110	8	2	4	1:2	(e.g., light to mild exercise, jogging)
LA-O$_2$	660	165	5	1	5	1:2	Work-Relief
	880	220	4	2	2	1:1	Rest-Relief
O$_2$	110	275	3	1	3	1:½	Rest-Relief
	1320	330	3	1	3	1:½	

* Modified from Fox and Mathews (1974).

EXAMPLE PROGRAMS

The following examples of interval training programs are designed to improve primarily the lactic acid and oxygen systems. The training times are for unconditioned men and women between the ages of 18 and 21 years. More example programs can be found in the book by Fox and Mathews (1974).

Males

Day 1	Set 1	4 × 200 at Easy (1:3)*
	Set 2	8 × 100 at Easy (1:3)
Day 2	Set 1	2 × 400 at Easy (1:3)
	Set 2	8 × 100 at Easy (1:3)
Day 3	Set 1	2 × 400 at Easy (1:3)
	Set 2	6 × 200 at Easy (1:3)
Day 4	Set 1	1 × 800 at Easy (1:3)
	Set 2	6 × 200 at Easy (1:3)

Week 2

Day 1	Set 1	2 × 800 at Easy (1:3)
	Set 2	2 × 400 at Easy (1:3)
Day 2	Set 1	6 × 400 at Easy (1:3)
Day 3	Set 1	3 × 800 at Easy (1:3)
Day 4	Set 1	1 × 2400 at Easy

Week 3

Day 1	Set 1	2 × 600 at 2:15 (4:30)**
	Set 2	2 × 400 at 1:20 (2:40)
Day 2	Set 1	4 × 200 at 0:38 (1:54)
	Set 2	4 × 200 at 0:38 (1:54)
	Set 3	4 × 200 at 0:38 (1:54)
Day 3	Set 1	1 × 800 at 3:00

Week 4

Day 1	Set 1	3 × 600 at 2:10 (4:20)
	Set 2	3 × 400 at 1:20 (2:40)
Day 2	Set 1	4 × 200 at 0:38 (1:54)
	Set 2	4 × 200 at 0:38 (1:54)
	Set 3	4 × 200 at 0:38 (1:54)
	Set 4	4 × 200 at 0:38 (1:54)
Day 3	Set 1	2 × 800 at 2:55 (2:55)
	Set 2	2 × 400 at 1:20 (2:40)

*Work-relief ratio
**Minutes:seconds

Week 5

Day 1	Set 1	4 × 600 at 2:05 (4:10)
	Set 2	2 × 600 at 1:20 (2:40)
Day 2	Set 1	4 × 200 at 0:37 (1:51)
	Set 2	4 × 200 at 0:37 (1:51)
	Set 3	4 × 200 at 0:37 (1:51)
	Set 4	4 × 200 at 0:37 (1:51)
Day 3	Set 1	2 × 800 at 2:55 (2:55)
	Set 2	2 × 400 at 1:20 (2:40)

Week 6

Day 1	Set 1	4 × 600 at 2:00 (4:00)
	Set 2	2 × 400 at 1:18 (2:36)
Day 2	Set 1	4 × 200 at 0:36 (1:48)
	Set 2	4 × 200 at 0:36 (1:48)
	Set 3	4 × 200 at 0:36 (1:48)
	Set 4	4 × 200 at 0:36 (1:48)
Day 3	Set 1	2 × 800 at 2:50 (2:50)
	Set 2	2 × 400 at 1:18 (2:36)

Week 7

Day 1	Set 1	2 × 800 at 2:45 (2:45)
	Set 2	2 × 400 at 1:16 (2:32)
Day 2	Set 1	4 × 200 at 0:35 (1:45)
	Set 2	4 × 200 at 0:35 (1:45)
	Set 3	4 × 200 at 0:35 (1:45)
	Set 4	4 × 200 at 0:35 (1:45)
Day 3	Set 1	1 × 1210 at 4:30 (2:15)
	Set 2	2 × 1000 at 3:40 (1:50)

Week 8

Day 1	Set 1	2 × 800 at 2:40 (2:40)
	Set 2	2 × 400 at 1:16 (2:32)
Day 2	Set 1	4 × 200 at 0:34 (1:42)
	Set 2	4 × 200 at 0:34 (1:42)
	Set 3	4 × 200 at 0:34 (1:42)
	Set 4	4 × 200 at 0:34 (1:42)
Day 3	Set 1	1 × 1210 at 4:24 (2:12)
	Set 2	2 × 1000 at 3:40 (1:50)

Females

Week 1

Day 1	Set 1	4 × 200 at Easy (1:3)*
	Set 2	8 × 100 at Easy (1:3)
Day 2	Set 1	2 × 400 at Easy (1:3)
	Set 2	8 × 100 at Easy (1:3)
Day 3	Set 1	2 × 400 at Easy (1:3)
	Set 2	6 × 200 at Easy (1:3)
Day 4	Set 1	1 × 800 at Easy
	Set 2	6 × 200 at Easy (1:3)

Week 2

Day 1	Set 1	2 × 800 at Easy (1:3)
	Set 2	2 × 400 at Easy (1:3)
Day 2	Set 1	6 × 400 at Easy (1:3)
Day 3	Set 1	3 × 800 at Easy (1:3)
Day 4	Set 1	3 × 800 at Easy (1:3)

Week 3

Day 1	Set 1	2 × 600 at 2:45 (5:30)**
	Set 2	4 × 100 at 0:25 (1:15)
Day 2	Set 1	6 × 200 at 0:45 (2:15)
	Set 2	6 × 100 at 0:25 (1:15)
Day 3	Set 1	6 × 200 at 0:45 (2:15)
	Set 2	6 × 100 at 0:25 (1:15)

Week 4

Day 1	Set 1	4 × 200 at 0:45 (2:15)
	Set 2	8 × 100 at 0:25 (1:15)
	Set 3	10 × 50 at 0:10 (0:30)
Day 2	Set 1	2 × 600 at 2:45 (5:30)
	Set 2	3 × 200 at 0:45 (2:15)
	Set 3	3 × 200 at 0:45 (2:15)
Day 3	Set 1	4 × 200 at 0:45 (2:15)
	Set 2	4 × 200 at 0:45 (2:15)
	Set 3	8 × 100 at 0:25 (1:15)

*Work-relief ratio
**Minutes:seconds

Week 5

Day 1	Set 1	4 × 200 at 0:45 (2:15)
	Set 2	8 × 100 at 0:25 (1:15)
	Set 3	10 × 50 at 0:10 (1:30)
Day 2	Set 1	2 × 600 at 2:45 (5:30)
	Set 2	3 × 200 at 0:45 (2:15)
	Set 3	3 × 200 at 0:45 (2:15)
Day 3	Set 1	4 × 200 at 0:45 (2:15)
	Set 2	4 × 200 at 0:45 (2:15)
	Set 3	8 × 100 at 0:25 (1:15)

Week 6

Day 1	Set 1	4 × 200 at 0:42 (2:06)
	Set 2	8 × 100 at 0:22 (1:06)
	Set 3	8 × 100 at 0:22 (1:06)
Day 2	Set 1	2 × 600 at 2:40 (5:20)
	Set 2	8 × 100 at 0:22 (1:06)
	Set 3	8 × 50 at 0:08 (0:24)
Day 3	Set 1	2 × 800 at 4:00 (4:00)
	Set 2	8 × 50 at 0:08 (0:24)
	Set 3	8 × 50 at 0:08 (0:24)

Week 7

Day 1	Set 1	2 × 600 at 2:40 (5:20)
	Set 2	6 × 100 at 0:22 (1:06)
	Set 3	6 × 100 at 0:22 (1:06)
Day 2	Set 1	4 × 200 at 0:42 (2:06)
	Set 2	4 × 200 at 0:42 (2:06)
	Set 3	4 × 200 at 0:42 (2:06)
Day 3	Set 1	8 × 100 at 0:22 (1:06)
	Set 2	8 × 100 at 0:22 (1:06)
	Set 3	8 × 100 at 0:22 (1:06)

Week 8

Day 1	Set 1	2 × 600 at 2:35 (5:10)
	Set 2	6 × 100 at 0:20 (1:00)
	Set 3	6 × 100 at 0:20 (1:00)
Day 2	Set 1	4 × 200 at 0:40 (2:00)
	Set 2	4 × 200 at 0:40 (2:00)
	Set 3	4 × 200 at 0:40 (2:00)
Day 3	Set 1	8 × 100 at 0:20 (1:00)
	Set 2	8 × 100 at 0:20 (1:00)
	Set 3	8 × 100 at 0:20 (1:00)

REFERENCES

Fox, E. L. 1975. Differences in metabolic alterations with sprint versus endurance interval training programs. In *Metabolic Adaptation to Prolonged Physical Exercise,* H. Howald and J. Poortmans (eds.). Basel: Birkhauser Verlag.

Fox, E. L. 1977. Physical training: Methods and effects. *Orthopedic Clinics of North America,* 8, 533-548.

Fox, E. L. 1979. *Sports Physiology.* Philadelphia: W. B. Saunders.

Fox, E. L., R. L. Bartels, C. E. Billings, D. K. Mathews, R. Bason, and W. M. Webb. 1973. Intensity and distance of interval training programs and changes in aerobic power. *Med Sci Spts,* 5, 18-22.

Fox, E. L., R. L. Bartels, C. E. Billings, R. O'Brien, R. Bason, and D. K. Mathews. 1975. Frequency and duration of interval training programs and changes in aerobic power. *J Appl Physiol,* 38, 481-484.

Fox, E. L., R. L. Bartels, J. Klinzing, and K. Ragg. 1977. Metabolic responses to interval training programs of high and low power output. *Med Sci Spts,* 9, 191-196.

Fox, E. L., J. Klinzing, and R. L. Bartels. 1977. Interval training: Metabolic changes as related to relief-interval heart rates of 120 and 140 beats per minute. *Fed Proc,* 36, 449.

Fox, E. L. and D. K. Mathews. 1974. *Interval Training: Conditioning for Sports and General Fitness.* Philadelphia: W. B. Saunders.

Fox, E. L., D. C. McKenzie, and K. Cohen. 1975. Specificity of training: Metabolic and circulatory responses. *Med Sci Spts,* 7, 83.

Fox, E. L., S. Robinson, and D. L. Wiegman. 1969. Metabolic energy sources during continuous and interval running. *J Appl Physiol,* 27, 174-178.

Lesmes, G. R., E. L. Fox, C. Stevens, and R. Otto. 1978. Metabolic responses of females to high intensity interval training of different frequencies. *Med Sci Spts,* 10, 229-232.

Mathews, D. K. and E. L. Fox. 1976. *The Physiological Basis of Physical Education and Athletics.* 2nd ed. Philadelphia: W. B. Saunders.

McKenzie, D. C., E. L. Fox, and K. Cohen. 1978. Specificity of metabolic and circulatory responses to arm or leg interval training. *Eur J Appl Physiol,* 39, 241-248.

9

Jogging

William J. Bowerman

In recent years, jogging has become an increasingly popular exercise routine in which periods of slow running, or jogging, are alternated with periods of walking. The combination provides moderate but effective exercise for the entire cardiovascular system as well as the muscles involved. It can easily be adapted to fit the needs and changing abilities of a wide range of individuals by adjusting the distance covered and/or the pace.

Physicians often recommend jogging for postcardiac patients, diabetics, or others who need therapeutic exercise. Former athletes ready to retire from competition find it a good way to continue to be physically active but on a reduced scale. Some people use jogging intermittently to train or "tune up" for anticipated periods of extra exertion such as weekends of hunting or skiing.

But jogging is most popular with the thousands of average, middle-aged to older adults who have found this a pleasant, efficient way to exercise regularly. For many it has proved to be an antidote for problems common in today's relatively sedentary society—problems such as tension, unnecessary worry or nervousness, excess body weight, boredom, sluggishness, insomnia, or persistent tiredness.

Other exercises practiced with equal moderation and regularity would probably be as helpful, but few offer such a combination of advantages as jogging. Because it is a comprehensive exercise, workouts of not more than 20 to 30 minutes every other day (three or four times a week) are usually sufficient to maintain a satisfactory level of fitness. However, the routines are so flexible that they can be adjusted to fit most individuals, terrains, and climates. Jogging requires no elaborate facility, expensive equipment, or special skill.

If there is any "secret" to successful jogging, it lies in knowing how much is necessary to attain and then maintain a person's desired fitness level without undue strain or discomfort. It is helpful, therefore, for beginners without backgrounds in physical training to have a physician, physical educator, coach, or other professional observe and give advice. Such leaders can often be found in schools, YMCA's, athletic clubs, recreation departments, or adult education programs. There are a number of books dealing with jogging, and articles continually appear in popular magazines as well as professional journals that provide advice for beginners as well as information to both lay people and professionals.

There is nothing difficult or even new about the technique of jogging. In a stricter sense of the word than is used elsewhere in this article, jogging simply means to proceed at a "jog" or "jog-trot," a gait natural to human beings, generally at a speed of eight minutes per mile or slower. It was probably used rather extensively by our primitive ancestors to stalk game, and it has always been a favorite of children.

The present popularity of jogging in the United States may have received considerable impetus from its earlier popularity in New Zealand. In 1962, Bill Bowerman, then track coach at the University of Oregon, took a relay team to that country to challenge its world-record holding team. Among other things, Bowerman was impressed with the fitness of the general population. He saw not only children, but men and women of all ages jogging in the cities, villages, and countryside. Crowds gathered in parks on weekends for friendly competition. Joining the fun, as the story goes, Bowerman was shocked to find himself out-jogged by people ten to 15 years older.

Competitive by nature and interested in fitness by profession and training, Bowerman put himself on a jogging program patterned after systems used by successful runners, but slightly less vigorous. In six weeks he discovered that he had lost two inches around his waist and felt better than he had for years. When this experience was mentioned to newsmen and, in turn, reported by them, there was a surprising, spontaneous response. Inquiries poured in from people eager to learn how to satisfy their needs for exercise.

In order to provide responsible answers and help more people enjoy the benefits of jogging, Bowerman organized some experimental programs. When interest continued to grow, the programs were expended. With the help of Dr. Waldo F. Harris, a cardiologist, and other technical assistants, groups of postcardiac patients, overweight people, and apparently "normal" men and women were monitored and tested before, during, and after jogging programs. Instructions for following similar programs based on the research of Bowerman and Harris were published (1967). The following recommendations are adapted from their work. These recommendations are abbreviated, and anyone about to embark upon a jogging program should devote further study to the subject.

RECOMMENDATIONS FOR JOGGING

1. Before starting a jogging program, the individual should have a physical examination. This is especially imperative for anyone over 35 years of age or with a known history of serious illness or disability.

2. Jogging should be regular. The Bowerman-Harris theory advocates jogging every other day with a lesser amount of exercise on the alternate days. For instance, a person who jogs comfortably for 20 minutes on Monday, Wednesday, and Friday, should do light bending and stretching exercises or

take brisk walks for not more than ten minutes on Tuesday, Thursday, and Saturday. On Sunday, depending on personal preference, the jogger may take a longer hike, an easy jog, play a favorite active game, or rest completely. The Saturday and Sunday routines may be reversed if desired.

3. A particular time should be chosen for workouts. This should be an hour that is convenient. Experience has shown that early morning joggers tend to be more persistent than others.

4. A comparatively easy way to tailor the jogging program to individual needs is through a series of "test efforts" at the beginning of each two-week period through the first three months. A test effort consists of timing or measuring the distance that can be jogged without gasping for breath or feeling painfully tired. This jog "interval" is followed by walking for the same distance or time. If sufficiently "recovered" after the walk to repeat the jog interval, the jogger continues to repeat the same intervals of jogging and walking for the total time or distance to be covered in the workout that day, and also in each workout thereafter for two weeks or until the next test effort.

   A beginner (anyone who has not been exercising regularly for a year or more) will probably not be able, and should not in any case, jog more than 50 meters for the first test effort. If the person is unable to recover sufficiently while walking the same distance, a lesser distance should be adopted for the pattern or schedule during the first two weeks.

   Likewise, the beginner, whether the interval is 20 or 50 meters or any intervening distance, should limit the total distance covered during the first week to not more than one-half mile. If this amount of exercise is perfectly comfortable, the total distance covered may be increased to one mile the second week without changing the length of the jog-walk intervals.

   After two week, the test effort should be repeated and the distance jogged during the following two weeks should be increased to the amount that is comfortable according to the test. The total distance covered in each workout may be increased by one-quarter to one-half mile over the total distance covered in the workouts for the previous two weeks. Neither the length of the jog-walk intervals nor total distance covered should be increased during any given two-week period. It may, however, be decreased should there be any discomfort. If any muscle soreness results from jogging, the exercise should not be stopped but reduced in amount or vigor until the soreness is gone.

5. Should the program be interrupted because of cold, illness, or any other interference, it should not be resumed at the level of interruption. Rather, if the lay-off has been for ten days, a schedule accomplished at least ten days prior to the lay-off should be chosen for the fresh start and then increased, as usual, according to the test efforts.

6. At the end of three months if progress has been uninterrupted, most people will be on schedules that should be appropriate for the maintenance of permanent levels of fitness. Jogging 4 to 5 kilometers, 2½ to 3 miles, or 20 to 30 minutes every other day are considered good average amounts for a maintenance program. By this time, however, joggers should also be experienced enough to assess their own needs and rely on their own feelings for guidance. They should also be convinced of the value of exercise.

7. Finally, some miscellaneous recommendations, if followed, should facilitate the jogging program. Loose, comfortable clothing appropriate to the weather should always be worn. If the exercise is to be on pavement, gravel, and hard or rough surfaces, shoes must not only be comfortable but well cushioned. If groups of people jog together they should be of approximately the same levels of ability. Competition is discouraged.

Jogging should be gradually progressive. Each individual will probably experience certain times when progress seems particularly rapid or slow. But no one should be discouraged while on a "plateau," nor tempted to overdo at a time when the exercise seems easy. The jogger's motto, borrowed from Arthur Lydiard, New Zealand's famous track coach, should be: Train, don't strain!

REFERENCES

Bowerman, W. J. and W. F. Harris. 1967. *Jogging.* New York: Grossett and Dunlap.

Clarke, H. H. 1977. Jogging. *Research Digest,* Series 7, No. 1.

Donaldson, R. 1977. *Successful Jogging.* Washington, D.C.: Consumer Information Center.

Nelson, C. B. 1969. *Radioelectrocardiographic Analyses of Postcardiac Subjects Following Periods of Training.* Doctoral dissertation, University of Oregon.

Sheehan, G. A. 1975. *Dr. Sheehan on Running.* Mountain View, Ca.: World Publications.

Wooten, E. P. 1967. Cut in recovery heart rate seen in women's jog program. *Medical Tribune,* August 17.

10

Long Slow Distance Training

Patricia J. McSwegin

Long slow distance training, or "L.S.D." as it is commonly known, is a training method in which long slow aerobic runs are used to improve cardiovascular fitness. Runs of two to five times racing distance at a pace of seven to eight minutes per mile are the key elements for improving both performance and physical fitness by increasing the runner's ability to transport and use oxygen (Mathews and Fox 1976). The basic principles of the long slow distance method can be employed by participants in any endurance-type activity but presently are used almost exclusively by long distance runners (Higdon 1977a).

Although the L.S.D. method has been advocated in various forms since early in the 1900s, it did not reach international prominence until the success of three New Zealand runners in the 1960 Olympic Games. The surprising victories of Snell (800 meters) and Halberg (1000 meters) and the third place finish of Magee (marathon) focused world attention on their coach, Arthur Lydiard, and his training regimen. Thus Lydiard, who had been extolling the merits of L.S.D. style training since the mid-1940s, gained the attention and respect of the running world (Higdon 1977b).

Aware of the direct relationship between cardiovascular fitness and performance in endurance events, Lydiard makes optimal cardiovascular fitness the principal goal of his training method. He employs long, moderately paced aerobic runs as an effective means of gradually improving cardiovascular fitness while avoiding the destructive effects of anaerobic work. Lydiard's runners complete 100 miles per week with most of those miles logged over natural terrain at paces ranging between 5½ to 7 minutes per mile. Neither the absolute time nor the distance covered is considered as important as maintaining a steady state when running. A runner should be able to run each mile at the same rate, a rate at which the person's ability to process oxygen fulfills the aerobic needs of the activity. Having to slow down in order to complete a run is an indication that the pace is too fast—that is, so fast that the metabolic cost of the exercise exceeds the oxygen supply. The pace and distance should be strenuous enough to cause sweating and tiredness, but not too difficult as to cause exhaustion (Lydiard 1970).

According to Hans Selye, a Canadian physician, every individual has a finite amount of energy to use in adapting to stress. Because even the simplest activities in the life process itself are stressful, the human organism continually expends energy until the moment of death. Those who learn to work most efficiently get the greatest return for the amount of energy expended (Selye 1974). Lydiard, recognizing that aerobic work is far more efficient than anaerobic work, advocates aerobic runs as an economical means of building a stronger cardiovascular foundation without squandering adaptational energy. Because anaerobic activity depletes the body's energy reserves, Higdon (1977a) has concluded that the speed and strength gained through this effort is soon off-set by the runner's increased susceptibility to injury, illness, and fatigue.

Selye's theory further influenced Lydiard to plan workouts according to a "hard-easy" schedule. Even the best conditioned athletes alternate days of hard workouts with days of relatively easy workouts. In this way, the runner's body is given the time necessary to recover from and adapt to the overload imposed by a particularly long or relatively fast workout (Bowerman and Harris 1976; Lydiard 1970; Osler 1967; Van Aaken 1976). Overload, a necessity for effective training, can be imposed by increasing the time, distance, or pace of a run, but it should not be so intense as to deplete the runner of energy reserves. Lydiard's runners never attempt heavy exertion until they feel fully recovered from previous workouts. By trial and error, Lydiard (Higdon 1977b) discovered that his top runners could increase their running speeds with about four to five weeks of speed training before the anaerobic work began to adversely affect general conditioning. Signs of fatigue, illness, or injury signal the time to cease anaerobic work and return to long, slow running. East German scientists and coaches actually monitor levels of blood lactic acid in order to provide an objective determination as to when an individual has recovered from a particular effort (Higdon 1977b). Lactic acid produced by anaerobic work must be removed by aerobic processes before the athlete is considered fully recovered.

Although Lydiard insists on 100 miles per week for his top runners, other proponents of L.S.D. (Henderson 1969; Osler 1967; Van Aaken 1976) suggest that the total mileage is not as important as the quality of each workout. In accordance with the hard-easy principle, it is genrally agreed that completing a very long slow run (15 to 20 miles) one day followed by a much shorter (but slightly faster) run the next day is more effective in conditioning the cardiovascular system than merely running medium distance very slowly every day (Higdon 1977b; Lydiard 1970; Osler 1967; Van Aaken 1976). For instance, it seems to be better to run 20 miles one day and 10 miles the next rather than 15 miles each day. For a beginner, the hard-easy schedule might call for 15 minutes of slow running one day followed by an attempt to run or even run/walk for 30 minutes the following day (Lydiard 1970).

As the cardiovascular condition improves, distances are lengthened and/or training pace is increased. Because a more efficient CV system supplies the muscles with more oxygen at a lesser energy cost, it is possible for a runner to continue to function aerobically while running faster. This increase in the speed one can sustain aerobically affects endurance performance positively.

Lydiard recommends training at a pace that keeps the heart rate below 150 beats per minute. He suggests that one should feel "pleasantly tired" after each workout and warns runners to "Train, don't strain" (Lydiard 1970). Runners should learn to judge for themselves if the level of activity is too intense. Persistent muscle soreness, nagging injuries, inability to sleep, irritability, frequent illness, and a general feeling of tiredness are indications of overexertion (Lydiard 1970; Osler 1975; Van Aaken 1976).

As early as the 1920s Arthur Newton suggested a training procedure similar to L.S.D. Although Newton himself did not start training until he was nearly 40 years old, he attained international racing caliber through a regular program of long slow running (Henderson 1970). Track coaches ignored his advice, however, just as they ignored the proposals of Van Aaken and Lydiard in the 1940s. Both Van Aaken and Lydiard published books describing the fallacies of too much anaerobic training and extolling the advantages of aerobic training. However, the success of runners such as Emil Zatopek, who trained by repeatedly running fast over short distances, continued to make interval training the most popular training method through the 1950s. This anaerobic-type training remained popular, particularly after two West German physiologists, W. Gerschler and H. Reindell, formulated specific guidelines for its use. Unfortunately, many advocates of interval training tended to ignore the numerous miles Zatopek spent running gently through woods and across the countryside. They focused solely on his interval track sessions—several repetitions of short, hard dashes, each followed by a recovery interval (Henderson 1970; Higdon 1977a).

L.S.D. WORK-OUTS

As mentioned previously, the current popularity of L.S.D. training is a direct result of the success of the New Zealand Olympians of 1960. Under the guidance of their coach, Lydiard, they trained basically through long moderate runs daily. However, recognizing that aerobic running fails to stimulate the speed and neuromuscular coordination needed for racing, Lydiard carefully prescribed anaerobic workouts in the six to ten weeks preceding their major competition. A typical anaerobic workout for the L.S.D. adherent resembles a basic interval training workout, but differs in frequency and duration. Because anaerobic benefits are quite costly in terms of adaptational energy, the L.S.D. trainee limits them to two to three per week and follows each by one to two days of long slow running to assure complete recovery. These speed workouts quickly bring the runner to peak condition and prepare the competitor for maximal performance (Lydiard 1970).

Both Van Aaken (1976) and Lydiard (1976) emphasize the necessity for some type of anaerobic or "tempo" runs to stimulate speed development prior to important racing events. Tempo runs are a series of fast-paced but not maximal effort strides over 50 to 100 yards. Van Aaken advises daily use of tempo runs, while Lydiard schedules more extensive use of interval work into his training six to ten weeks prior to major competition. The peak condition generated by a few weeks of anaerobic effort lasts only eight to twelve weeks, after which the runner's performance declines (Lydiard 1970; Osler 1967). According to Osler (1967), the competitor must then return to aerobic training for recovery and resumption of cardiovascular improvement or risk serious injury as well as prolonged decline in performance.

Van Aaken (1976), who is closely associated with the progress of women's marathoning both as a coach and as a race promoter, summarizes the essential elements of L.S.D. training in his motto: "Run slowly, run daily, drink moderately, and don't eat like a pig." He contends that a heart rate of 130 beats per minute is sufficient to stimulate CV improvement. Harold Norpoth, a student of Van Aaken and silver medalist in the 1964 Olympic 5000-meter race, did 90 percent of his training at a heart rate of 110 and 150 beats per minute. Though basically in agreement with Lydiard, Van Aaken does not feel it necessary to run 100 miles per week nor does he encourage specific hill training. Both agree that the heart rate target is merely a guide and not a rigid requirement. They are more concerned that each individual work hard enough to experience tiredness, but not so hard as to suffer from fatigue. The actual pace and distance run during each workout is entirely dependent upon each runner's own level of fitness and particular goals. Long and slow for one individual might be too long and fast for another (Van Aaken 1976).

Lydiard's advice to beginning runners is to jog slowly each day until comfortably able to complete 15 minutes of running daily. The runner is then ready to undertake the second stage of training as outlined by Lydiard (1970). The second stage requires 15-minute runs on Monday, Wednesday, Friday, and Sunday with 30-minute runs on Tuesday, Thursday, and Saturday. Although six to eight weeks are suggested to complete this stage, individual runners will vary according to their abilities. It is most important to progress gradually, always running well within one's own aerobic capacity. Pace and distance will increase as conditioning occurs.

Runs of 15 minutes continue on Mondays, Wednesdays, and Fridays in the third stage, but overload is provided by running for 30 minutes on Tuesdays and Sundays and for a full hour on Thursdays and Saturdays. If one's goal is simply to improve and maintain general physical fitness, habitual use of stage two schedule is probably adequate. Completion of stage three provides the runner with a strong foundation for sustaining more vigorous training needed for competition.

A 30-minute run is scheduled for each Monday, Wednesday, Friday, and Sunday during stage four. An hour run is Tuesday's goal with runs of 1½ hours on Thursday and 2 full hours on Saturday, completing the weekly schedule. The fifth stage calls for a 5-mile run to replace the 30-minute run of stage four, and runs of 10, 12, and 15 miles replacing runs of 1, 1½, and 2 hours. Again pace is determined by individual ability—as aerobic condition improves so should the pace of each run.

The five-stage schedule outlined above is the basic plan of L.S.D. training for an entire year as well as over a period of several years. Joggers and competitive runners alike follow the same general pattern of workouts. Competitive runners must, however, augment the basic program with a limited amount of anaerobic work for eight to twelve weeks prior to major competition. During that period, L.S.D. training actually becomes a carefully controlled mixture of aerobic running and interval training. The following schedule is an example of how Lydiard prepares a marathoner during the ten weeks preceding a key race:

Weeks 1-4

Monday	220 yards (¼)* 10-20×
Tuesday	15 miles (½)
Wednesday	3 miles (¾)
Thursday	18 miles (¾)
Friday	880 yards (½) 3×
Saturday	20 miles (¼)
Sunday	15 miles (¼)

Weeks 5-9

Monday	2 miles (50 yard dashes)
Tuesday	6 miles (½)
Wednesday	15 miles (½)
Thursday	3 miles (¾)
Friday	220 yards (½) 6×
Saturday	20-26 miles (¼)
Sunday	15 miles (¼)

Week 10

Monday	880 yards (50 yard dashes)
Tuesday	1 hour jog
Wednesday	1 hour jog
Thursday	½ hour jog
Friday	½ hour jog
Saturday	The Race

Another source of information on L.S.D. has been published by Osler (1967). His booklet contains an excellent discussion on how to properly mix aerobic and anaerobic training plus comments on why anaerobic work (or in his terminology, "sharpening") is necessary, how to sharpen, and when to do so. Osler emphasizes two basic facts that should be incorporated into any training schedule: (1) purely aerobic training affects the cardiovascular system gradually

---

*   The fraction indicates intensity of effort to be used. Consult Lydiard (1970, pp. 19-20) for "Tables of Effort."

over many months and through several years; (2) properly used anaerobic workouts can help an athlete to safely reach peak performance only once or twice a year. Therefore, aerobic work is used throughout the year to develop a strong cardiovascular system. Only after the cardiovascular system is strong can anaerobic or sharpening work be added to quickly, but safely, bring the runner to peak condition for maximal performance. Sharpening is accomplished by adding a series of short fast repetition runs to the basic L.S.D. workout for six to ten weeks prior to important races. The speed induced through this type of work can be maintained safely during training for only two to three months.

Osler (1967) defines long slow running as a pace that is well within the individual's own capacity held steadily over a distance that does not bring on exhaustion. The benefits are an increase in general health as well as improved cardiovascular fitness while conserving energy and reducing risks of injury. The disadvantage is an inability to stimulate the gains in muscle strength and neuromuscular coordination needed for racing. Sharpening is done by inserting short (50- to 200-yard) fast dashes and 880-yard build-ups into regular slow runs two or three times per week for six to ten weeks before major competition. The 880-yard build-ups are particularly important in providing the runner with experience in feeling the race pace and learning to relax while running fast. Sharpening develops muscle strength and speed but quickly exhausts energy reserves, exposing the runner to injury and illness. Part II of Osler's book (1967) outlines base conditioning through a series of short, medium, and long runs all at approximately a seven-minute-per mile pace or whatever is comfortable for the individual. This slow aerobic training lays the base upon which sharpening builds speed.

RESULTS

Although running magazines contain numerous personal accounts (Henderson 1974; Owens 1975; Romero 1975) of fantastic results brought about through either fast-paced, high-intensity interval training or by slow and easy aerobic training, it is probable that most successful racers train using a combination of the two methods (Atkins 1971; Hagerman 1974; Henderson 1974; Lydiard 1970; Osler 1967; Pate 1976; Van Aaken 1976). Using the Bloom High School distance trackmen as subjects, head coach Steve Miller and his associate Richard Holloway (1976) studied the results of one mixture of long slow distance, interval, and speed running. The L.S.D. runs were relaxed, easy 5 to 18 miles at a 6- to 8-minute-per-mile pace. These slow runs accounted for most of the training mileage during the first six weeks of the 15-week experimental period and were continued to a lesser degree throughout. Intervals were repetition runs of 220 to 3300 yards at race pace. Interval training was most heavy during the middle three weeks and then tapered off. Speed runs of 220 to 1320 yards at faster than race pace were concentrated into the last six weeks of the season. Personal best times were most evident in the last six weeks as compared to very few personal bests achieved in weeks four to nine. These results tend to support the practice of inserting anaerobic speed work over an aerobic base established by L.S.D. in order to safely achieve maximal performance.

SUMMARY

Van Aaken's (1976) advice to "Run slowly, run daily, drink moderately, and don't eat like a pig" encompasses not only the physiological aspects of L.S.D., but suggests a whole way of life. Regular adherence to a daily schedule of long slow running appears to develop far more than mere cardiovascular fitness; it would seem to help one to learn self-discipline, to adapt phychologically as well as neuromuscularly to daily stresses, and to maintain optimal body weight. Even those trainees who never run a race achieve victory through beneficial gains in health and well-being.

REFERENCES

Atkins, O., N. Cirulnick, and B. Carman. 1971. Training for the long run. *Runner's World,* 6, 20-22.

Bowerman, W. and W. Harris. 1976. *Jogging.* New York: Grosset and Dunlap.

Hagerman, F. 1974. Training for oxygen shortage. *Runner's World,* 9 (4), 28-29.

Henderson, J. 1969. *Long Slow Distance—The Humane Way to Train.* Los Altos: Tafnews Press.

Henderson, J. 1970. *Road Racers and Their Training.* Los Altos: Tafnews Press.

Henderson, J. 1974. Are long runs needed? *Runner's World,* 9 (6), 23.

Higdon, H. 1977a. Lydiard looks at the running world. *Runner's World,* 12(9), 44-47.

Higdon, H. 1977b. Thoughts from Arthur Lydiard. *Runner's World,* 12(9), 28-33.

Holloway, R. and S. Miller. 1976. The mix of endurance, pace and speed. *Runner's World,* 11(1), 30-31.

Lydiard, A. 1970. *Jogging the Lydiard Way: Anaerobic vs. Aerobic.* United States Track and Field Federation.

Mathews, D. and E. Fox. 1976. *The Physiological Basis of Physical Education and Athletics.* 2nd ed. Philadelphia: W. B. Saunders.

Osler, T. 1967. *The Conditioning of Distance Runners.* Long Distance Log Publication.

Osler, T. 1975. Training to new peaks. *Runner's World, 10(5), 20-23.*

Owens, J. 1975. Put "stress" in every jog. *Runner's World,* 10(4), 32.

Pate, R. 1976. Conditioning without crashing. *Runner's World,* 11(7), 37-39.

Romero, J. 1975. Take every other day off. *Runner's World,* 10(4), 30-31.

Selye, H. 1974. *Stress Without Distress.* New York: J. B. Lippincott.

Van Aaken, E. 1976. *Van Aaken Method.* Translated by G. Beinhorn. Mountain View, Ca.: World Publications.

11

Low, Middle, and High Gear Continuous Rhythmical Activity

Thomas K. Cureton, Jr.

The low, middle and high gear program of rhythmical activity consists of an exercise series combining calisthenics and endurance activities in such a way that six major components of motor fitness (agility, balance, flexibility, muscular endurance, power, and strength) and cardiovascular or organic fitness are all stressed and enhanced in each workout in gradual, progressive sessions of relative strenuousness.

LOW GEAR

The low gear program consists of two to three months of light exercises emphasizing flexibility and rhythmical and endurance exercises at a slow pace with deep breathing timed properly with the exercises. The daily routine includes a mile walk that is gradually increased to two miles. After the walk, calisthenic exercises such as push-ups, sit-ups, squat jumps, and leg raises are done. After several weeks, one minute of jogging in place is interspersed between the calisthenics. If possible, swimming should be included and students should work up to a point where they can swim continuously for ten minutes.

MIDDLE GEAR

When the intensity of the low gear program is approximately doubled, it may be called middle gear. Very frequently, low gear work is then used for 15 to 20 minutes of warm-up. Middle gear stresses longer work with less rest, faster work bouts, repetitive strength work, and repetitive power work. The minimum objective is one hour of continuous exercise five days a week. A one-hour workout per week is suggested. Middle gear work generally extends for about six months.

HIGH GEAR

Doing as well as possible in any exercise or in any game is called high gear work. It may be competing in a game itself. The minimum objective is three two-hour workouts per week sandwiched between days of one-hour workouts. One day per week is set aside for rest. Two typical high gear routines include:

1. Run 200 yards, walk 100 yards. Repeat 15 to 20 times. Add a 350-yard all-out run. Run one mile or 15 minutes in place.
2. Swim 100 yards, walk a lap around the pool deck. Repeat 10 to 20 times.

IMPLEMENTATION

The low, middle, and high gear plan can be implemented and utilized in a number of ways.

Nonstop Circular Work

Nonstop circular work is for the gymnasium under a leader, as a demonstration, or as an introductory pattern for people of any age starting physical work. It is like "Follow the Leader." Informal flow in a single, double, or triple grouping is satisfactory as long as individuals are spaced widely enough apart so as not to collide. Warm-up and cool-down generally occur progressing around the outside of the gymnasium floor, while the heavy load central portion of the workout is circular in that the students form an inward facing circle, standing and facing the instructor. The instructor is in the center of the circle so that all students are in view of the instructor. During this peak load period, calisthenics are performed for 15 seconds to one minute involving all major muscle groups in the body. Jogging in place occurs between successive calisthenic movements. An example of this type of workout follows:

General plan of the workout. 55 to 70 minutes, 200 to 500 kcal expenditure, gradually progressing with the passage of weeks.

I. Warm-Up: 20 minutes

Activity	Laps	Variation
Walk	1	
Jog	1	swinging arms
Walk	1	
Jog	2	pull, pull, swing arms
Walk	1	
Skip	1	shake out arms and legs
Walk	1	
Jog	3	stretch arms overhead

Sideways skip	1	arms swinging across body, reverse
Walk	1	1, 2, 3 kick leg to opposite arm
Jog	4	
Walk	1	stretch arms overhead

Transition to heavy work

Run	1	pull, pull, swing
Walk	1	straights and widths respectively
Sprint and jog	2	stretch arms overhead
Walk	1	breathe deeply
Run	2	
Walk	1	
Sprint	1	

II. Main Body of Activity: 20 to 30 minutes, 15 seconds to one minute each

Body Part	Exercise
Neck	Rotation and stretching with alternative directions
Arms	Front crawl
	Back crawl
	Butterfly with knee flexion, add hops
	Pump, pump, swing, arch, arch, add hops
	Extended rotation (criss cross movements)
	Extended circumduction, forward, backward
	Push-ups
Waist, Lateral Flexion	4 count toe touch
	Trunk twisting
	4 count bend and bob, forward, side, back, side
	Palms to floor, circle around head
Abdominals	Single leg pumps
	Lie flat, contact small of back to floor, stretch with arms overhead
	V-sit 6 counts
	Curls
Legs	Side leg raises, left and right
	Track start position, stretch, pump
	Vertical jumps

Single leg raises
Squat thrusts
4 count jumping jacks
Upside down bicycle
Spread eagle, lying on back floot to opposite arm

Back   Flutter kicks, lie on stomach, hands under thighs
                  Swan, trunk extension backward

III. Tapering Off: Recovery, stimulate breathing, 15 to 20 minutes

Activity	Laps	Variation
Walk	1	pump, pump, swing arms, breathe deeply
Jog	1	slowly
Skip	1	slowly
Walk	1	hold breath for 20 paces
Jog	1	
Walk	1	hold breath for 30 paces
Walk	1	hold breath for 40 paces

Diver's stance on tip toes   30 sec., eyes closed
Tip-up   10 sec
Breath-holding   sitting, 30 sec after 3 deep breaths

Another variation of this type of activity is to integrate the calisthenics and endurance work.

Course of Progressive Rhythmical, Non-Stop Exercises.

This program is intended as a formal class under the direction of a trained leader. The course is divided into 22 lessons and generally runs from six to nine months. As with nonstop circular work, the intensity progresses gradually within each session and over months. Suggested frequency varies from three times per week for the beginning levels to six for the upper levels. The sessions start at 30 minutes and progress to 90 minutes or more. One example each of a low, middle, and high gear workout is presented (Cureton, 1973).

Example 1. 30-Minute Low-Gear Workout
I. Warm-up exercises (about 5 minutes)
    a. Walk and jog several laps around the gym. Swing arms in full circles while walking.
       Breathe deeply.

II. Shoulder, Arm and Chest Exercises (about 8 minutes)
   a. Cross-body double arm circles (1 minute)
   b. Crawl strokes, forward (1 minute)
   c. Crawl strokes, backward (1 minute)
   d. Circling one arm backward, then the other (1 minute)
   e. Arm swinging, forward and backward in opposition (1 minute)
   f. Butterfly arm strokes (1 minute)
   g. Simultaneous arm flexions (1 minute)
   h. Jumping jacks (1 minute)
III. Waist Exercises (about 4 minutes)
   a. Cross-body floor touches (2 minutes)
   b. Waist bends and rotations (2 minutes)
IV. Abdominal, Back and Lateral Thigh Exercises (about 10 minutes)
   a. Alternate knee-bend kicks (1 minute)
   b. Side leg kicks (1 minute)
   c. Flutter kicks (2 minutes)
   d. Forward bends, sitting (1 minute)
   e. Trunk bends (1 minute)
   f. Sitting tucks (1 minute)
   g. Chest lifts (1 minute)
   h. Leg lifts (1 minute)
   i. Sit-ups (1 minute)
V. Leg and Feet Exercises (about 5 minutes)
   a. Skip-kicks in place—forward (1 minute)
   b. Skip-kicks in place—sideways (1 minute)
   c. Toe-push-ups (1 minute)
   d. Walking on outside of feet (1 minute)
   e. Hopping on alternate feet (1 minute)

Example 2. 60-Minute Middle-Gear Workout
I. Warm-up Exercises (about 20 minutes)
   a. Run two laps around gym, then walk two.
   b. Run four laps around gym, then walk two.
   c. Run six laps around gym, then walk two.
   d. Run eight laps around gym, then walk two.
   e. Run ten laps around gym, then walk two.
II. Free Exercises
   1. Arm and Shoulder Exercises (about 6 minutes)
      a. Crawl strokes, forward (2 minutes)
      b. Crawl strokes, backward (2 minutes)
      c. Cross-body double arm circles (2 minutes)
   2. Trunk Exercises (about 9 minutes)
      a. Torso rotation, sitting (3 minutes)

    b. Sit-ups (1 minute)

    c. Sitting tucks (1 minute)

    d. Leg spread (2 minutes)

    e. Torso rotation, standing (2 minutes)

III. Individual Circuit Training (about 20 minutes)

    Station 1 Alternate-side leg lifts

    Station 2 Push-ups

    Station 3 Sitting tucks

    Station 4 Vertical jumps

    First round of stations—do each exercise 10 times, run one lap around the gym between each exercise.

    Second round of stations—do each exercise 15 times, run one lap around the gym between each exercise.

    Third round of stations—do each exercise 20 times, run one lap around the gym between each exercise.

    Walk, stretch and breathe to recover.

IV. Repeat Exercises 1 and 2 above (optional)

V. Repeat Individual Circuit Training (optional)

VI. Tapering-Off Exercise (about 5 minutes)

    a. Walk around gym (5 minutes)

       stretch, shake, breathe deeply

Example 3. 90-Minute High-Gear Workout

I. Warm-up Exercises (about 20 minutes)

    a. Run two laps, walk one.

    b. Run four laps, walk one.

    c. Run six laps, walk one.

    d. Run eight laps, walk one.

    e. Run ten laps, walk three laps, then breathe, shake, and stretch.

II. All-Out Exercises (about 30 minutes)

    These exercises are to be performed at top speed and to the limits of strength and endurance. Walk one lap around the gym between each exercise, breathing deeply, shaking, and stretching.

    a. V-Sits

    b. Alternate-side leg lifts

    c. Chest lifts

    d. Agility run

    e. Jumping Jacks

III. Outdoor Running Exercise (about 7 to 13 minutes)

    a. Run down a flight of stairs, out the door and for about 600 yards

    b. Reverse direction, run back inside and up the stairs. Repeat.

IV. Relaxation Exercises (about 4 minutes)

    a. Jog two laps

    b. Walk two laps
V. All-Out Exercises (about 10 to 30 minutes)
    a. Repeat Section II.
VI. Tapering-Off Exercises (about 5 to 15 minutes)
    a. Jog 5 laps slowly
    b. Walk 5 laps slowly
    c. Jog 1 lap slowly
    d. Walk, breathing deeply, stretching until recovered.

Home Exercise Program

The home exercise program is presented in depth elsewhere (Cureton 1973) but also follows a general pattern of low, middle, and high gear for progressive intensity and difficulty. Each exercise session consists of two 30-minute periods. The first is composed of calisthenics intended for warm-up; the second is devoted to endurance activities. Five minutes are devoted to each exercise or group of exercises during the warm-up period.

VARIATIONS

Almost an infinite number of variations on any of the above programs are possible, provided the following six basic principles are adhered to:

1. *Never start a workout fast nor end it fast.* Exercise must be given through progressive overloading. Put on the pressure and take it off. As the individual increases in endurance, step up the pace.

2. *Warm up* the group before moving to vigorous and strenuous exercises and taper off at the end of the workout.

3. *Increase the amount and strenuousness of exercises gradually.* Regulate the dosage as the individual or group's physical condition improves.

4. *Give individuals an opportunity to recuperate between exercises* by slowing down the pace and exercising different muscles and parts of the body. Do not stop the exercise routine until the time is up.

5. *Assign plenty of deep-breathing exercises* and have the participants swing their arms when walking and practicing their breathing.

6. *Make the middle portion of the exercise period the peak period.* Work the session up to the peak slowly in the beginning and gradually slow the pace down as the workout draws to a close.

    Some of the more popular and effective variations are (1) a water workout utilizing calisthenics and endurance swimming; (2) partner exercises that are generally designed for strength and muscular endurance in which two individuals of about the same weight work together—one holding, carrying, pushing, or pulling the other; (3) medicine ball drills; (4) obstacle course or steeplechase runs; and (5) machine drills using a bicycle ergometer, treadmill, Universal gym, Nautilus, minigym, or rowing machine.

REFERENCE

Cureton, T. K. 1973. *Physical Fitness and Dynamic Health.* 2nd ed. New York: Dial Press.

12

The Royal Canadian Air Force 5BX and XBX Exercise Plans

William A. R. Orban

The 5BX physical fitness plan, which was specifically designed for fighter pilots of the Royal Canadian Air Force, has characteristics of universal appeal and potential benefit to the general public and, as such, has been expanded into a program for women, widely circulated, and widely utilized. In addition to incorporating all the basic principles of training, the plan is simple and includes a built-in self-assessment of personal progress on a day-to-day basis. The 5BX plan is intended for males, the XBX plan for females. Neither plan requires any knowledge of exercise programs or principles of training; all exercises are fully illustrated and explained in detail. The programs are designed to be followed, with no special equipment, in one's home or place of work.

5BX

The five basic exercises (one flexibility exercise, one sit-up exercise, a back-arch exercise, a push-up exercise, and running in place) provide a balanced and complete physical fitness development. The plan produces a training stimulus on all the large muscles as well as the cardiopulmonary system of the body. It consequently develops both muscular and organic power in 11 minutes per day.

The plan consists of six charts each with 12 levels. Each level indicates the number of exercise repetitions to be performed within the specified time limits.

In order to provide a progressive training stimulus for increasing work capacity, progression within each chart is provided by an increased number of repetitions of the same exercise. Progression from one chart to the next is accomplished by modifying the corresponding exercise of the previous chart so as to increase the work output demand. This occurs by increasing the effort required by the body for that exercise. For example, in chart 1, push-ups are performed with the knees on the floor, and in chart 2, this same exercise is performed with the feet on the floor.

WORKOUT TYPE

A workout consists of performing each of the exercises at the same level in the allotted time; they should be performed in the order given, completing the number of repetitions in the time set for each exercise.

For example, if one wishes to perform level B- in chart 3, one would do the following exercises as described below:

1. Stand with feet astride, extend arms upward, touch toes, and bend backward 29 times in two minutes.
2. Lying on back, knees slightly bent, hands behind the head, sit up to a vertical position 26 times in one minute.
3. Lying on front, hands interlocked behind the back, arms straight, lift head, shoulders, chest and legs as high as possible 37 times in one minute.
4. Lying on front, palms flat on the floor under the shoulders, push up 18 times in one minute.
5. Stationary run—lifting feet approximately 4 inches off the floor, do "half knee bends" after each 75 completed steps to a total of 490 steps in 6 minutes.

XBX

The XBX plan for women, developed primarily through the work of Norman Ashton, follows the same basic format. Ten basic exercises are included, and these are aimed at developing the waist, hips, legs, ankles, and cardiovascular system (running in place).

The plan consists of four charts each with 12 levels. As with the 5BX, each level indicates the number of exercise repetitions that are to be performed within the specified time limits for a total exercise time of 12 minutes.

SPECIAL CONSIDERATIONS

If the instructions are followed rigidly, physical capacity will be increased progressively without discomfort or injurious effects. However, like any physical activity, harmful effects may result if certain precautions are not observed. Although the charts are designed to provide a physical rating scale, caution should be employed in using them exclusively for this purpose. This rating scale is best used to measure progress in the achievement of physical capacity by following the plan. Each level should, therefore, be regarded as another rung attained in climbing the ladder of improved physical fitness.

Because there exists a great deal of variation in the ability to perform these exercises, some individuals may encounter undue difficulty in completing a particular exercise as required. It is suggested that if a level is completed as instructed for all but one exercise, one should advance to the next level without penalty.

Running on the spot has caused discomfort and lower limb soreness that can be avoided. Running on a resilient surface will help a great deal, but at the same time the action of the legs should be one of lifting the feet off the floor rather than pounding them on it.

STRENGTHS AND WEAKNESSES OF THIS WORKOUT TYPE

The research on which the 5BX plan is based was conducted on 110 young college males who were undergoing summer military service. The purposes of the research were to:(1) select exercises that could be employed in a progressive manner; (2) determine the range of repetitions for each exercise; and (3) validate the effectiveness of the plan.

The exercises were selected on the basis of simplicity and adaptability to modification. Repetition distributions and degree of difficulty were analyzed to provide the progression of a given exercise in one chart and the smooth progression of the modified exercise in the subsequent chart. Because of the small sample, however, the repetitions for the exercise skewed positively. Consequently, it has been found that some individuals could not perform the required number of repetitions in some of the exercises. Following the establishment of the levels and the charts, small samplings of fit military men of various ages were utilized to establish the desired levels of the plan for different ages.

Independent research has generally confirmed the progressive nature of the plan by means of increased energy cost of the levels progressing through the charts. Other studies have indicated that moderate fitness changes can be produced in following this plan. It should be noted, however, that the plan provides minimal benefits because of the limited duration of each workout.

SAMPLE WORKOUT

The selection of the level at which one beings the plan is critical if smooth progression is to be made without discomfort or strain. If one is to err, the error should be made on the lower level side. A schedule indicating the desired level for each age is provided in the published booklet, available at most bookstores. This should serve as a guide to determine the starting point for a given individual. A completely sedentary person should start about 24 levels below the maintenance level indicated for the person's age classification. If the exercises at this level cannot be completed comfortably within the required time, one should go to a lower level the next day. This should be repeated until all the exercises can be performed as indicated. When a selected starting level is performed without any strain at all, the same procedure should be followed in reverse. The optimum starting level is the one at which a person can perform all the exercises in the allotted time with relative ease.

EIGHT-WEEK WORKOUT OUTLINE

Once the starting level has been selected, the rate of progression to subsequent levels is critical, particularly in the first three or four weeks. If stiffness and soreness are to be avoided, the initial rate of progression must be restrained and slow. Muscle soreness and stiffness are warning signs that one has either started at too high a level or is progressing too rapidly. When this occurs, the individual should either revert to a lower level or stay at the same level for three or four days before proceeding to the next. This kind of holding pattern, particularly in the first three or four weeks, is very important. After this period, one should proceed to the succeeding level when each level can be performed satisfactorily.

REFERENCES

Alexander, J. F. et al. 1963. An evaluation of the 5BX program of exercises by certain physiologic responses to a treadmill test. *J Spts Med Phys Fit*, 3, 259.

Brown, S. R. et al. 1966. A metabolic evaluation of 5BX program using closed circuit respirometry. *Abstracts of C.A.H.P.E.R.*, 1(1), May 8-9.

Dhanaraj, V. H. 1974. The effects of yoga and the 5BX fitness plan on selected physiological parameters. Doctoral dissertation, University of Alberta.

Hoops, D. D. 1964. The contributions of the Canadian 5BX plan on the physical fitness of adult men. Master's thesis, University of Illinois.

Landry, F. 1966. Illustration du coût energetique du programme d'entraînement 5BX. Paper read at the 34th Annual Congress of L'ACPAS, Québec, Québec.

Stallman, R. K. 1963. The metabolic cost of the 5BX plan for physical fitness. Master's thesis. University of Illinois.

ENVIRONMENTAL ASPECTS OF PHYSICAL PERFORMANCE

Introduction

It is well known that extremes in environmental variables affect physical performance. In this section, the various environments in which humans participate in physical activity are described and d ntent othe sction is to provide the reader with basic information regarding the physiological responses of the resting and active human body to the variables described. A better understanding of these environmental variables and of the body's physiological responses to them will enable physical educators, coaches, and athletes to prepare more adequately for physical performance under adverse conditions. Better preparation should lead to the prevention of injury or illness often associated with such performance.

Several papers address the problems of heat stress and heat injury under varying conditions involving high heat and/or high humidity at sea level and high altitude. The first chapter, written by Wells, not only provides information on human adaptation to heat stress, but also "sets the stage" for later papers dealing with cold stress. A moderately theoretical approach is taken in that paper. Next, environmental and performance guidelines for activity in hot environments are provided by Haymes and Buskirk.

The third chapter, prepared by Herbert, describes how and why performance declines with water deficit. Although water balance is mentioned in other papers in this section, this particular paper deals with the problem in considerable detail.

Haymes examines the physiological effects of a cold envirionment upon physical performance and points out the metabolic and circulatory responses to exercise performed in cold air and cold water. In the next paper Kinnear provides specific information on the etiology, prevention, and field treatment of such cold injuries as hypothermia and frostbite.

The immediate and long-term effects of hypobaric atmospheres—moderate and high altitudes—on physical performance are considered by Howley, who discusses training at moderate altitudes as well as adaptations made by high altitude residents. Next, Kinnear and Evans outline those mountaineering procedures one should adopt in order to avoid mountain (or high altitude) sickness. O'Shea then provides environmental and performance guidelines for avoiding dehydration and heat stress at high altitudes.

The effects of adverse environmental variables such as temperature (whether hot or cold) and pressure (whether too much or too little) have long been with us. The problem of air pollution is a relatively modern problem—or at least one that has only been recently recognized. It is unfortunate that the air we breathe is becoming more and more "polluted" despite many of the safeguards employed by industry today. The last paper in the section, by Raven, not only presents current information regarding the effects of carbon monoxide, sulfur oxide, and photochemical oxidents on physical performance, but points out some means by which people can minimize these effects in terms of performance.

CLW

Section Editor

Dr. Christine L. Wells is an associate professor in the Department of Health and Physical Education at Arizona State University. Her teaching responsibilities are in the areas of exercise physiology and environmental aspects of human physical performance. Previously, Dr. Wells directed the applied physiology and human performance research laboratories of Dalhousie University and Temple University. She received her B.S. from the University of Michigan, M.S. from Smith College, and Ph.D. from Pennsylvania State University. She also completed two years of postdoctoral studies and research at the Institute of Environmental Stress at the University of California at Santa Barbara.

Dr. Wells is a Life Member of AAHPERD, a fellow of the Research Consortium of AAHPERD, and a fellow of the American College of Sports Medicine. She is past-president of the Research Consortium.

Besides publishing more than 20 articles on physiological responses to heat exposure, Dr. Wells has a recreational interest in environmental matters. She is an avid hiker, backpacker, environmentalist, and photographer. She has hiked the deserts and mountains of California, Arizona, and New Hampshire. On August 6, 1976, she climbed the summit of Mt. Rainer in a snowstorm. Some 18 hours later she arrived at the Phoenix, Arizona airport, where it was 106° F.

13

Physiological Effects of a Hot Environment upon Physical Performance

Christine L. Wells

Unlike many lower animals, the human is able to maintain a relatively constant deep internal temperature over a wide range of environmental conditions. Because of this ability, the human is called "a regulating organism" as opposed to "a conforming organism" (Prosser 1961), a homeotherm or warm-blooded animal, as opposed to an exotherm.

It is often forgotten that the so-called normal human body temperature is made up of many temperatures oscillating in a more or less regular pattern around an average value usually assumed to be 37°C. Temperatures of deep internal organs such as the metabolically active tissues of the heart, brain, liver, and kidney are usually higher than temperatures in the periphery. With heavy muscular exercise, of course, peripheral muscular tissue temperatures rise, blood flow patterns change, and metabolic heat is distributed more extensively throughout the body. Skin surface temperatures also vary widely and are dependent upon such factors as skin blood flow pattern, ambient temperature, local radiant heat load, and evaporation of sweat and surface moisture.

The regulation of body core temperature (usually assessed as oral, esophageal, or rectal temperature) is usually considered an important matter for survival. The lowest human core temperature reported was a temperature of 13°C (60°F) during which respiration equalled three per minute. A core temperature of 42°C (108°F) is often fatal, but 43°C (110°F) has been tolerated for a few hours on several occasions (Folk 1974). Heavy physical exercise has been known to elevate body core temperatures to 40°C (104°F) or slightly higher, even in a cool environment.

Human body temperatures seem to oscillate in a circadian (about 24 hours) rhythm. Several distinct circadian rhythms have been noted with the predominent pattern a low early morning—high late afternoon variation. This pattern corresponds to the usual lightness-darkness cycle and also to the usual cycle of metabolic activity (Luce 1971). In addition to the usual circadian variation, the female has a tendency toward a slightly higher core temperature during the second half of her monthly menstrual cycle. The temperature rise is thought to be the anabolic effect of progesterone, but no mechanism for this has been described.

THEORY OF TEMPERATURE REGULATION

Thermal regulating mechanisms in the human body involve a series of dynamic processes under the apparent control of the hypothalamus, the organ sometimes referred to as "the human thermostat" (Benzinger 1963). As is shown in Fig. 13.1, this organ, located at the base of the brain stem just above the optic nerve, acts as a *sensor,* an *integrator,* and a *controller* of a huge system standing ready to either increase or decrease the body's ability to conserve or dissipate heat. The hypothalamus senses deep body temperatures itself and/or receives input from other central thermoceptive areas regarding deep body temperatures. Deep "core" receptors other than the hypothalamic thermoceptive area have been postulated but never located in humans. Peripheral thermoreceptors (i.e., warm and cold receptors) have been located in the skin, but there is considerable disagreement as to their role in generalized thermoregulation. It is claimed by some that these body surface thermoreceptors simply send information to the cerebral cortex regarding the degree of heat (or cold) of the skin and hence provide our *thermal sensation.* Without this mechanism, of course, we would be unable to *feel* the heat of the sun or the cold surface of a rock. Some theoretical models for temperature regulation give these skin receptors an important role in sensory input to the hypothalamus while others do not (Benzinger et al. 1963; Hardy 1965, 1967). Gisolfi and Robinson (1970a, 1970b) and Robinson (1972)

Fig. 13.1 The role of the hypothalamus.

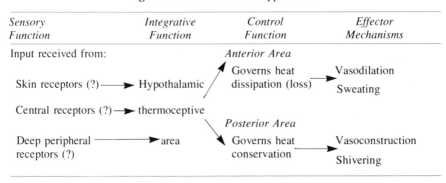

Sensory Function	Integrative Function	Control Function	Effector Mechanisms
Input received from:		*Anterior Area*	
Skin receptors (?) ⟶ Hypothalamic		Governs heat dissipation (loss)	Vasodilation Sweating
Central receptors (?) ⟶ thermoceptive		*Posterior Area*	
Deep peripheral receptors (?) ⟶ area		Governs heat conservation	Vasoconstriction Shivering

have suggested that additional information may come from peripheral thermoreceptors located in the deep veins that drain working musculature. They provide some interesting evidence for their claim, but the matter is far from resolved.

In some way, the hypothalamus receives and integrates information regarding the temperatures of the body. The prevalent theory is that the sensory information received is compared to a "set point temperature," which is approximately 37°C for humans (Hardy 1965, 1967). If the "integrated information" reveals that the body temperature is above the set-point, then neural discharge from the anterior area of the hypothalamus is increased and various effector mechanisms that aid in the dissipation of heat from the tissues, such as vasodilatation and sweating, are initiated. If, on the other hand, the integrated sensory information is determined to be below the set-point, then neural discharge from the posterior area of the hypothalamus is increased and effector mechanisms aiding heat conservation, such as vasoconstriction and shivering, are initiated. These two regulating areas are interconnected so that the stimulation of one control area inhibits the activity of the other. Consequently, we never shiver and sweat at the same time.

To summarize this brief review of a very complicated mechanism, one can assume that the control center for thermoregulation has a "set-point" somewhat similar to a room thermostat, and that physiological responses are made to minimize the deviation of the actual body temperatures from that set-point. The set-point need not be absolutely constant and, indeed, does change under many physiological and environmental conditions. Hence we have the diurnal and menstrual oscillations mentioned previously, and the elevated body temperatures of exercise. Fever is a disruption of the system whereby the set-point is elevated above its usual daily range by some pyrogenic agent that affects the hypothalamus directly. Various antipyrogenic agents (the most common of which is aspirin) serve to destroy or disarm the pyrogen and restore the "normal" hypothalamic set-point.

AVENUES OF HEAT EXCHANGE

Both physiological response mechanisms and behavioral adaptations to heat and cold are better understood with some knowledge of the physical avenues of heat exchange. A basic physics book should aid in further clarification of these factors if desired by the reader.

Heat exchange by the process of *conduction* (K) involved the direct contact of two surfaces with different temperatures. The transfer of heat energy from one substance to another substance (or adjoining part) is directly related to the temperature gradient or temperature difference (ΔT) between the two substances (or surfaces) and to the coefficient of thermal conductivity (K) or each substance. Substances that conduct heat readily are called *conductors*. Substances that do not conduct heat readily are called *insulators* or nonconductors. Metals are good conductors whereas nonmetals are good insulators. Still air is an excellent insulator, whereas water is an excellent conductor. Consequently, a naked human experiences more thermal stress in 10°C (50°F) water than in 10°C air. Human body fat is a better insulator than is human muscle tissue. Consequently, the fatter the human body, the less heat will be transferred to the environment via conduction while immersed in cold water. The rate of heat exchange via conduction is inversely related to the thickness of the insulating substance. Hence, the greater the layer of still air (as in goose down clothing or the "layer" method of dressing for the cold), or the greater the amount of subcutaneous body fat, the less heat will be lost per unit time. Conduction can be expressed by the following formula (Carlson and Hsieh 1974):

$$K = (k/d)(T_1 - T_2) A_k$$

where K = conduction
  k = coefficient of thermal conductivity of a substance
  d = thickness of a substance
  $T_1 - T_2$ = temperature difference between 2 substances or surfaces
  A_k = area of contact

Convective heat exchange (C) requires the movement (convective current) of a fluid or gaseous medium. Convection can be expressed as follows (Carlson and Hsieh 1974):

$$C = k_c (T_1 - T_2) A_c$$

where C = convection
  k_c = surface coefficient of convective heat transfer
  A_c = the effective area of convective heat exchange

The convective transfer coefficient is a function of convective movement, viscosity, density, and thermal conductivity of the medium. Convective heat exchange occurs whenever warm or cold winds or fluids move across the body surface, or whenever "warmed" blood from metabolically active areas of the body flows past "cooled" blood from the periphery of the body. This latter example is a form of "countercurrent heat exchange" and occurs extensively within the body during exercise. Convective heat exchange is directly related to the temperature gradient between the surfaces as well as to the effective convective current surface area and surface coefficient at each laminar boundary.

Radiation (R) is the exchange of electromagnetic energy particles (photons) from one object to another. The most obvious example of radiative heat exchange is that between the earth and the sun during daylight hours and between the earth and its atmosphere during nighttime hours. Radiation can be expressed as follows (Carlson and Hsieh 1974):

$$R = \sigma \ (\overline{T}_S{}^4 - \overline{T}_R{}^4) \ A_r$$

where R = radiation
 σ = Stefan-Boltzmann Constant = $5.67 \times 10^{-8} \ R \times m^{-2} \times \ ^0K^{-1}$
 $\overline{T}_S$ = average surface temperature
 $\overline{T}_R$ = average radiant temperature
 A_R = effective radiating surface of the animal (m²)

Radiant temperature (T_R) is obtained by measuring the temperature in the interior of an opaque body of uniform temperature (usually a suspended six-inch diameter copper sphere painted black) and is called globe temperature. The black globe represents an "ideal black body," that is, a substance that absorbs all the radiation that falls upon it. The emittance of a black body is by definition equal to 1 in all temperatures. The emittance of a nonblack body varies with temperature. At 35.6°C the emittance for human skin is about 0.99. The human body is very close to an ideal black body. For that reason alone, it is a good idea to be lightly but fully clothed while under a desert sun. White clothing reflects *more* heat and absorbs *less* heat than does human skin.

When water passes from a liquid state to a gaseous state, energy must be supplied. The thermal energy requires is called the *latent heat of vaporization* and is 580 calories for one gram of distilled-deionized water. *Evaporative heat loss* (E) is related to the heat of vaporization and the amount of liquid vaporized (evaporated). In the human body, moisture due to insensible perspiration and thermal and nonthermal (nervous) sweating may be evaporated from the skin. Heat may also be lost due to evaporation from the respiratory tract during respiration.

The amount of heat loss via respiration can be expressed as follows (Adapted from Carlson and Hsieh 1974):

$$E_{Resp} = V_E \ (D_{ex} - \emptyset D_{in})$$

where E_{Resp} = heat loss via the respiratory tract
 V_E = ventilation volume in 1/min
 D_{ex} = density of saturated exhaled air (gm/1)
 D_{in} = density of saturated inhaled air (gm/1)
 $\emptyset$ = fractional relative humidity

The density of saturated air varies with temperature.

The rate of heat loss by evaporation from the skin depends primarily on (1) the rate of evaporation that is dependent, in turn, upon the relative humidity of the surrounding environment and the amount of air movement; (2) the rate of sweat secretion; and (3) the latent heat of evaporation for the sweat secreted (this varies with the electrolyte concentration of sweat).

The rate of heat loss by evaporation from the skin surface may be approximated by (Adapted from Carlson and Hsieh 1974):

$$E_{sw} = 40 \ h_D \ (P_{ws} - \emptyset \ P_{wa}) \ R_w T$$

where E_{sw} = the rate of heat loss from sweating
h_D = transfer coefficient (1/min)
P_{ws} = vapor pressure of water at skin temperature (mm Hg)
$\emptyset$ = fractional relative humidity
P_{wa} = vapor pressure of water at ambient temperature (mm Hg)
R_w = aqueous gas constant
T = average of skin and ambient temperatures (K°)

Usually investigators determine the total amount of water loss by estimating the difference between weight loss (corrected for fluid intake) and the weight of the carbon dioxide produced. A man at rest and comfortably warm will lose water from his respiratory tract and by insensible perspiration at a rate of about 30 grams per hour (Carlson and Hsieh 1974). Higher respiratory rates or low relative humidity may significantly increase this value. High environmental temperatures and/or strenuous exercise accompanied by heavy thermal sweating may increase water losses to greater than 1.5 l per hour.

Metabolic heat production (M), while not really an avenue of heat exchange, is the body's only means of heat production. The metabolic heat load (internal heat load) is the total energy released by anaerobic and aerobic processes and has a considerable magnitude of increase in the human body. It is most often determined by measurement of oxygen uptake, calculation of the respiratory exchange ratio ($R = VCO_2/VO_2$) and multiplication of the appropriate kcal factor by the VO_2 expressed in l/min. For example, if $VO_2 = 3.02$ l per min and $R = 0.89$, then the metabolic heat production equals (3.02 l O_2 per min) × (4.91 Kcal per l) = 14.83 Kcal per min.

Metabolic heat production can also be altered involuntarily by shivering. Shivering may increase metabolic heat production as much as five fold over that of resting metabolism.

Analysis of the factors involved in heat balance is now possibly by the use of the following equation, which is a statement of the law of conservation of energy (sometimes called the Fort Knox equation):

$$M \pm R \pm K \pm C - W \pm S = 0$$

where M = metabolic heat production
R = radiative heat exchange
K = conductive heat exchange
C = convective heat exchange
E = evaporative heat loss
W = work accomplished (negative for work against external forces and positive for work against internal forces)
S = heat storage (negative for heat storage, i.e. body temperature gain, and positive for heat loss)

For an individual at rest, W = 0. If the individual is in a state of thermal equilibrium, S = 0. Thus, with the above serving as a basic framework for our understanding of human temperature regulation, we can now consider the physiological effects of a hot environment upon physical performance.

DESCRIPTION OF A HOT ENVIRONMENT

Individuals participating in physical activities often do so under less than optimal environmental conditions. Late spring, summer, and early fall in the eastern and southern United States are often characterized by air temperatures between 26 to 32 °C (80 to 90°F) with correspondingly high levels of relative humidity. This creates a high effective temperature index (T_{eff}). (See Fig. 13.2)

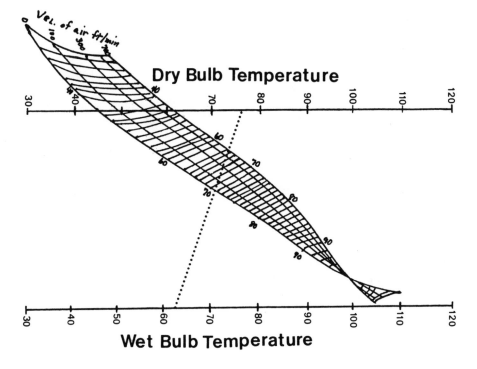

Fig. 13.2 Effective temperature index. Effective temperature is a subjective ''comfort'' index obtained by measuring air temperature (dry-bulb temperature) and wet-bulb tempera-ture (obtained by a thermometer with a wet wick over the bulb). The difference between the two readings constitutes a measure of the dryness or wetness of the air. Dry-bulb and wet-bulb temperatures are most often obtained with a sling psychometer. A ruler is placed on the scale above so as to correspond to the dry-bulb and wet-bulb temperatures obtained. The effective temperature is read from the appropriate middle scale. Note that air speed must be known as well. Redrawn from Yaglou 1968, p. 279. Used by permission.

This type of environment can be extremely stressful during performance of strenuous activity because evaporation of sweat is greatly retarded. As the air temperature reaches into the mid-30°C range (95°F), practically all avenues of heat exchange are nullified in terms of dissipation of internal body heat.

Whenever intense sunlight is present, radiant heat (energy) will place an additional stress upon the human body. The wet-bulb globe temperature (WBGT) was designed specifically for the use of the armed forces for men wearing military uniforms. Dry-bulb (T_{db}), wet-bulb (T_{wb}), and globe temperatures (T_g) are used in the following formula to obtain WBGT outdoors (Minard 1961):

$$WBGT = 0.7 \ T_{wb} + 0.2 \ T_g + 0.1 \ T_{db}$$

Globe temperature is obtained from a thermometer sealed within a six-inch, thin-walled copper sphere painted flat black. The globe is placed in the sun and the thermometer reading is recorded when it has stabilized. The dry-bulb temperature should always be measured in the shade. (See Chapter 14.)

Individuals participating in outdoor activities in much of the western and southwestern United States experience considerable environmental heat load from the sun. Although the relative humidity is considerably lower than in the eastern and southern U.S., the clear skies and hot sun result in a high radiant heat load and, consequently, high globe temperature. In summary, severe environmental heat loads are common in the spring, summer, and fall months in the United States. Physical activity must often be tempered in order to avoid heat injury.

CIRCULATORY RESPONSES DURING EXERCISE IN THE HEAT

The task of maintaining heat balance in the body in a hot environment is borne primarily by the circulatory system. The burden is enhanced with physical activity. The temperatures of the "shell" tissues (tissues in the periphery) vary widely with such environmental variables as air temperature, relative humidity, and radiant heat load, as well as the rate of evaporation of insensible perspiration and sweat. The temperatures of these tissues are also influenced, of course, by the temperatures of the blood flowing through or underlying them.

While precise anatomical lines cannot be drawn between the "core" and the "shell," the former is made up of tissues actively contributing to the production of body heat, while the latter tissues are more superficial. The conductance of heat from the tissues in which it is produced (the core) to the overlying body surfaces (the shell) is largely dependent upon the circulation (Robinson 1968). If thermoregulation is to be maintained, shell temperatures must remain at least 1.2°C (2°F) below core temperatures. Unless such a gradient is maintained, the shell will act as an insulating layer. If this occurs, it will be progressively more difficult to transfer adequate quantities of heat past this barrier into the environment, and the internal body temperatures will rise rapidly (Man, Sweat, and Performance 1969).

Increased blood flow from the interior of the body to the surface layers is brought about by extensive cutaneous vasodilation. Under ordinary circumstances this results in a rise in skin temperature that, in turn, may increase heat loss from the skin by radiation, conduction, convection, and evaporation if sweating is present (Robinson 1968). This mechanism is inadequate under adverse environmental circumstances such as (1) high relative humidity, which decreases the rate of evaporation of sweat; (2) a hot desert wind, which may reverse the convective heat temperature gradient between the skin and the environment; or (3) a high radiant heat load on a clear, hot day, which may reverse the radiant heat gradient between the skin and the environment. Under such conditions, the body may fail to lose body heat via the usual mechanisms of radiation, convection, and evaporation despite enormous efforts on the part of such physiological mechanisms as cutaneous vasodilatation and sweating. The greater the work load, the more serious the consequences.

While extensive vasodilatation increases the effective "heat sink," there are a number of secondary occurrences that affect one's ability to work in the heat. One of the most important of these is the reduction in venous return to the heart and the resultant decrease in stroke volume (Rowell et al. 1966). Even the so-called muscle pump of exercise is less effective than usual since much of the heated blood is shunted away from muscles to peripheral tissues. The reduction in stroke volume is almost immediately apparent in an increase in heart rate. Both rest and exercise in the heat are characterized by high heart rates.

If an increased heart rate cannot offset the lowered stroke volume, then cardiac output drops. If the decline is significant, cardiac insufficiency arises (Robinson 1968). In this event, the circulatory system is faced with a dilemma—whether to serve the metabolically active tissues to the detriment of body temperature regulation or the reverse. The compromise that usually occurs causes the individual to feel weak—a sign of inadequate circulation to the muscles and lowered blood pressure. The individual usually voluntarily stops exercise and seeks a horizontal position in the shade. Occasionally fainting occurs. This situation, which could be exceedingly dangerous to certain individuals, occurs most frequently in the obese, the elderly, the unfit, and those with heart disease.

At the same time that a large blood flow to the skin cools the blood, it supplies the sweat glands with water (Robinson 1968). With exercise in the heat, sweat rate increases almost instantaneously and may reach a level as high as 2.0 1 per hour (Robinson et al. 1945; Horvath and Shelley 1946). The high sweating rates of exercise can be sustained for several hours with adequate fluid replacement (Horstman and Horvath 1972).

There are a number of secondary effects of prolonged and profuse sweating. An initial response to both cutaneous vasodilatation and profuse sweating is a shift of extracellular fluid into the plasma water compartment with a subsequent rise in blood volume (Robinson 1968). Numerous studies have found an increase in blood volume with sudden exposure to hot environments in both acclimatized and unacclimatized men (Robinson 1968; Bazett et al. 1940; Conley and Nickerson 1945; Glickman et al. 1941; Forbes, Hall and Dill 1940). Consequently, with short term exposure hemoglobin, plasma protein and hematocrit values decline, while electrolyte concentrations (Na^+, K^+, Cl^-) increase as a result of blood dilution (Wells and Horvath 1973). Kozlowski and Saltin (1964) suggest that during exercise in the heat there is a significant shift of fluid from the intracellular compartment to the extracellular space. This area of research needs more attention but due to a number of difficulties is not often pursued.

Prolonged exposure to hot environments may result in dehydration, particularly if sweating rates are high and fluid replacement is inadequate. (See Chapter 20.) Dehydration results in body water loss, a decrease in plasma water, a subsequent decrease in blood volume, high heart rates, reduced cardiac output, high surface and internal body temperatures, and reduced sweat rates (Horstmann and Horvath 1972; Robinson 1968; Hertzman and Ferguson 1960; Brown and Sargent 1965). It is evident that dehydration and its consequent reduction of plasma volume would increase circulatory strain and reduce the tolerance of exercising men and women to heat stress.

With profuse and prolonged sweating, electrolyte loss from the sweat may become a matter of significance. However, sweat is more than 99 percent water. Consequently, salt loss is *less* important than many realize.

In most instances, the kidney will adequately conserve electrolytes at the same time that it actively retains body water. On the other hand, under unusual environmental circumstances, unacclimatized individuals with prolonged and profuse sweating may lose considerable amounts of salt (20 grams daily) (Robinson 1968). Electrolyte deficiency may lead to heat cramps, disturbances in cardiovascular function, and heat exhaustion. (See Chapter 14.)

With heat acclimatization, sweat becomes less concentrated. The mechanism by which the sweat gland is better able to conserve electrolytes is not understood, but possibly the hormone aldosterone, from the adrenal cortex, is involved. The normal action of aldosterone involves the conservation of Na^+ by the kidney with the site of action thought to be the renal tubules (Vander et al. 1975).

METABOLIC RESPONSES DURING EXERCISE IN THE HEAT

Early work by DuBois has shown that in fever, the metabolism of a resting man is increased according to Van't Hoff's Law by about 13 percent for each degree centigrade elevation of body temperature (Robinson 1968). Numerous investigations report reduction of metabolism in residents of hot climates, with the change ranging from 6 to 24 percent (Robinson 1968). While some investigators believe these changes are direct alterations in basal metabolic rate, others attribute the reduction to a more complete relaxation of skeletal muscle during the tests. Still others believe that the change may be due to a change in the regulatory activity of the thyroid (Robinson 1968).

In the performance of work, one's oxygen uptake (VO_2) increases in proportion to the intensity of the work until one approaches the maximal level of oxygen consumption. Approximately three-quarters or more of the increased metabolism of exercise takes the form of heat that must be dissipated through the skin and body tissues in order to maintain constant internal (core) temperature (Robinson 1968).

In order for an exercising person to maintain thermal equilibrium, metabolic heat (internal heat load) would have to be dissipated to the environment at the same rate as it was produced. The environmental heat load (external heat load) offers resistance to heat dissipation and will lower the work rate at which the individual can maintain thermal equilibrium.

There is considerable disagreement in the literature as to whether oxygen uptake increases, decreases, or remains unaltered for submaximal work performed in the heat. The matter appears to depend upon a number of factors including the severity of the environment, the duration of work performance, the acclimatization of the subjects, and the degree to which internal temperature is altered.

Robinson et al. (1943) found that metabolism was increased by about 11 percent for each degree centigrade elevation in rectal temperature above control values. Their unacclimatized male subjects walked on a treadmill at 5.6 kilometers per hour at a 5.7 percent grade in 40°C, 23 percent relative humidity. The results confirmed the observations of Dubois' resting men. After acclimatization, when the men were able to perform the same work without a rise in rectal temperature, their metabolism returned to control values.

Consolazio et al. (1963) obtained increased VO_2 values during rest and submaximal bicycle work at 100°F, 30 percent relative humidity, but no differences were found at 70° and 85°F conditions. In three unacclimatized men, Williams et al. (1962) reported lower VO_2 values for submaximal bicycle work in humid heat than in a "comfortable" environment (Teff = 70°F). Rowell et al. (1965, 1966) found VO_2 during submaximal treadmill exercise unaltered by heat. Brouha et al. (1961) reported no changes in VO_2 during submaximal bicycle work in humid heat, but lowered VO_2 in a warm, dry environment. No significant differences in VO_2 were found by Klausen et al. (1967) for submaximal bicycle work performed by seven men in 32°C as compared to 24.8°C Wells and Horvath (1974) reported significantly elevated oxygen requirements during treadmill walking at 50 percent max VO_2 in the heat for untrained and unacclimatized female subjects.

Rowell et al. (1965) and Williams et al. (1962) reported higher lactate and "excess" lactate values for subjects performing submaximal work in the heat. Williams et al. (1962) and Klausen et al. (1967) believed this accounted for the lowered VO_2 they observed for work performed in the heat. The increased acidosis that would result from elevated anaerobic work seems a likely explanation for the increased respiratory drive observed during work in the heat (Wells and Paolone 1977; Wells and Horvath 1974).

Changes in partitional blood flow patterns resulting from thermoregulatory demands would bring about a less efficient blood supply to the working muscles. This offers an explanation for the decreased oxygen extraction reported by Wells and Paolone (1977) during treadmill walking in 40°C. If blood is shunted away from working muscles to subcutaneous and cutaneous regions to dissipate internal heat, the muscles would be left in a state of anoxia and thus forced to work more anaerobically than during work in a neutral environment (Rowell et al. 1966).

SEXUAL DIFFERENCES IN RESPONSE TO HEAT STRESS

There is considerable disagreement regarding the ability of women to work in heat. Generally it has been noted that heart rates of women are considerably higher than those of men performing work in hot environments (Brouha et al 1961; Morimoto et al. 1967; Wyndham et al 1965). However, the most commonly observed difference between men and women in hot environments is that women do not sweat as much as do men even though they have an equal, if not greater, number of heat activated sweat glands (Bar-Or et al. 1968; Brown and Sargent 1965; Hardy 1961; Hertig and Sargent 1963; Kawahata 1960; Morimoto et al 1967; Weinman et al. 1967; Wyndham et al. 1965). Despite the lower evaporative heat losses of women in hot environments, they appear to be as capable of regulating their internal temperatures as are men (Morimoto et al 1967; Weinman et al. 1967; Paolone and Wells 1977). Wyndham et al. (1965) have expressed the opinion that "the male . . . is a prolific, wasteful sweater, whereas the female adjusts her sweat rate better to the required heat loss." Weinman et al. (1967) agreed, suggesting that women might be more efficient regulators of internal temperatures than are men since they achieve the same results with less water loss.

In many studies comparing the performance of men and women in the heat, standardized submaximal work loads were performed regardless of differences in body size, body weight, or physical fitness. Usually the data suggested that the female subjects were less "fit" than the male subjects. This would indicate that the standardized work loads performed would be more difficult for the female subjects than for the males even without an added environmental stressor. Consequently, it is unclear whether the thermoregulatory differences observed occurred because of innate sexual differences or because of variations in physical fitness or training between male and female subjects.

Paolone and Wells (1977) exposed four male and three female subjects to hot environments during which the work stress was related to individual maximal aerobic capacity. This design allows observations of thermoregulatory mechanisms while controlling for variations in levels of fitness between male and female subjects. Responses to "relative work loads" in a neutral environment established baseline measures against which responses to other environments—

warm and hot—were compared. No sexual differences in rectal or skin temperatures were observed. The males had higher heart rates and greater evaporative weight losses during exercise in all environments. The females experienced less severe increases in metabolic requirements during work in the warm and hot environments than did the males. The results of this study—with very few subjects—suggest that physically fit females are capable of working in the heat as well as males when work is relative to individual aerobic capacity. Further study is necessary to verify these results with a greater number of subjects of varying fitness levels, body types, and relative work load levels.

Kawahata (1960) suggested that the sex hormones accounted for observed sex differences in thermoregulatory responses, especially the lower thermal sweat production of women compared to men exposed to equivalent heat stress. He demonstrated that testosterone administration to elderly males produced a sudorific effect, while estradiol was inhibitory to sweating. In women, he compared the time required for onset of sweating at two phases of the menstrual cycle. He found that the onset of sweating was sooner during menstrual flow than during the mid-menstrual phase. Sargent and Weinman (1966), however, were unable to detect significant differences in sweat gland activity during either menstruation or the mid-period of the menstrual cycle.

Wells and Horvath (1973, 1974) reasoned that if the female sex hormones were responsible for lower sweat production in women during thermal stress, then cyclic variations in response to heat exposure should occur during different hormonal phases of the menstrual cycle. Seven subjects with normal menstrual histories were studied in a neutral environment (25°C/78°F, 15 percent RH) and in a hot-dry environment (48°C/118°F, 12 percent RH) at both rest and work during three menstrual phases. During the *flow phase* (first 36 hours of flow) the estrogens and progesterone levels were assumed to be minimal. On the basis of early morning rectal temperature recordings, an interval was selected to represent the *ovulatory phase* for each subject. High levels of estrogens and low levels of progesterone were assumed during this period. The *luteal phase* was the mid-point between expected ovulation and the day of the next expected menstrual flow. High levels of both estrogen and progesterone were assumed during this two-day interval.

No significant differences in rectal or skin temperatures, oxygen consumption, sweating rate, evaporative heat loss, or oxygen pulse occurred with menstrual phase. Luteal phase sweating and evaporative rates (onset of sweating) tended to lag behind values obtained during the other two menstrual phases, but values were essentially equal after 40 minutes of heat exposure. At rest, lower Na^+ and Cl^- losses in total body sweat were observed during the other two menstrual phases. Serum electrolyte concentrations showed little relation to menstrual phase. There was a tendency toward higher resting heart rates and lower resting ventilation volumes during ovulatory phase heat exposures. It was concluded that the few differences occurring with the menstrual phase had minimal influence upon the ability of the female to regulate body temperature when exposed to environmental heat stress (Wells and Horvath 1973, 1974).

ACCLIMATIZATION TO HEAT

Acclimatization to heat occurs when an individual accustomed to working in a moderate temperature environment undertakes multiple exposures to a hot environment. A series of progressive physiological adjustments reduce the strain experienced on the initial exposure to heat and make it possible to work more effectively under conditions that might otherwise be unendurable.

As acclimatization to heat occurs, marked decreases are found in (1) skin and rectal temperatures, (2) heart rate, and (3) electrolyte losses in sweat. Apparently the body becomes more efficient in terms of heat dissipation as sweat production and evaporative heat loss increases significantly and symptoms of heat exhaustion with exercise (dizziness, weakness, and nausea) disappear. Physical work capacity improves as acclimatization progresses and subjects are notably more comfortable as well as more efficient (Buskirk et al. 1965; Cleland et al. 1969; Hertig et al. 1963; Wood and Bass 1960). Not only can performance be improved, but heat disorders can be prevented or reduced by heat acclimatization. (See Chapter 14.)

PERFORMANCE GUIDELINES

Work performance in hot-dry, hot-humid, and even warm-humid conditions can be devastating to the uninitiated. Precautions should be taken to avoid the serious medical problems described in the next chapter, such as heat exhaustion, heat cramps, and heat stroke. Coaches and athletes should be aware that not only can medical problems be avoided but performance can be improved by (1) adequate fluid and electrolyte replacement procedures; (2) becoming accustomed to participation in hot or warm weather (acclimatization); and (3) being aware of the dangers involved with exercise, excessive clothing, and severe heat and/or humidity. These and other environmental and performance guidelines are discussed in the following chapters.

REFERENCES

Astrand, P.-O. and K. Rodahl. 1970. *Textbook of Work Physiology.* New York: McGraw-Hill.

Bar-Or, O., H. M. Lundegren, L. I. Magnusson, and E. R. Buskirk. 1968. Distribution of heat-activated sweat glands in lean and obese men and women. *Human Biol,* 40:235-248.

Bazett, H. C., F. W. Sunderman, J. Doupe, and J. C. Scott. 1940. Climatic effects on the volume and composition of blood in man. *Amer J. Physiol,* 129:68-83.

Benzinger, T. H., C. Kitzinger, and A. W. Pratt. 1963. The human thermostat. In *Temperature: Its Measurement and Control in Science and Industry,* J. D. Hardy (ed.). Vol. 3. New York: Reinhold.

Brouha, L., P. E. Smith, Jr., R. DeLanne, and M. E. Maxfield. 1961. Physiological reactions of men and women during muscular activity and recovery in various environments. *J Appl Physiol,* 16:133-140.

Brown, W. K. and F. Sargent II. 1965. Hidromeiosis. *Arch Environ Health,* 11:442-453.

Buskirk, E. R., H. Lundegren, and L. Magnusson. 1965. Heat acclimatization patterns in obese and lean individuals. *Annals of the N.Y. Acad of Science,* 131:637-653.

Carlson, L. and A. C. L. Hsieh. 1974. Temperature and humidity, Part A: Cold. In *Environmental Physiology,* N. B. Slonim (ed.). St. Louis: C. V. Mosby.

Cleland, T. S., S. M. Horvath, and M. Phillips. 1969. Acclimatization of women to heat after training. *Arbeitsphysiol,* 27:15-24.

Conley, C. L. and J. L. Nickerson. 1945. Effects of temperature change on the water balance of man. *Amer J Physiol,* 143:373-384.

Consolazio, C. F., L. O. Matoush, R. A. Nelson, J. B. Torres, and G. J. Issac. 1963. Environmental temperature and energy expenditure. *J Appl Physiol,* 18:65-68.

DuBois, E. F. 1921. The basal metabolism in fever. *JAMA,* 77:353-355.

Folk, G. E., Jr. 1974. *Textbook of Environmental Physiology.* 2nd ed. Philadelphia: Lea and Febiger.

Forbes, W. H., D. B. Dill, and F. G. Hall. 1940. The effect of climate upon the volumes of blood and of tissue fluid in man. *Amer J Physiol,* 130:739-746.

Fox, E. L. and D. K. Matthews. 1974. *Interval Training.* Philadelphia: W. B. Saunders.

Gisolfi, C. and S. Robinson. 1970a. Central and peripheral stimuli regulating sweating during intermittent work in man. *J Appl Physiol,* 29:761-768.

Gisolfi, C. and S. Robinson. 1970b. Venous blood distribution in the legs during intermittent treadmill work. *J. Appl Physiol,* 29:368-373.

Glickman, N., F. K. Hicks, R. W. Keeton, and M. M. Montgomery. 1941. Blood volume changes in men exposed to hot environmental conditions for a few hours. *Amer J Physiol,* 134:165-176.

Hardy, J. D. 1961. Physiology of temperature regulation. *Physiol Reviews,* 41:521-606.

Hardy, J. D. 1965. The "set-point" concept in physiological temperature regulation. In *Physiological Controls and Regulations,* W. S. Yamamoto and J. R. Brobeck (eds.). Philadelphia: W. B. Saunders.

Hardy, J. D. 1967. Central and peripheral factors in physiological temperature regulation. In *Les Concepts de Calude Bernard sur le Milieu Interieur.* Paris: Masson et Cie, p. 247.

Hertig, B. A. and F. Sargent II. 1963. Acclimatization of women during work in hot environments. *Fed Proc,* 22:810-813.

Hertig, B. A., H. S. Belding, K. K. Kraning, D. L. Batteron, C. R. Smith, and F. Sargent II. 1963. Artificial acclimatization of women to heat. *J Appl Physiol,* 18:383-385.

Hertzman, A. B. and I. D. Ferguson. 1960. Failure in temperature regulation during progressive dehydration. *U.S. Armed Forces Med J,* 11:542-560.

Horstman, D. H. and S. M. Horvath. 1972. Cardiovascular and temperature regulatory changes during progressive dehydration and euhydration. *J Appl Physiol,* 33:446-450.

Horvath, S. M. and W. B. Shelley. 1946. Acclimation to extreme heat and its effect on the ability to work in less severe environments. *Amer J Physiol,* 146:336-343.

Kawahata, A. 1960. Sex differences in sweating. In *Essential Problems in Climatic Physiology,* H. Yoshimura et al. (eds.). Kyoto, Japan: Nankada.

Kozlowski, S. and B. Saltin. 1964. Effect of sweat loss on body fluids. *J Appl Physiol,* 19:1119-1124.

Klausen, K., D. B. Dill, E. E. Phillips, Jr., and D. McGregor. 1967. Metabolic reactions to work in the desert. *J Appl Physiol,* 22:292-296.

Lind, A. R. and D. E. Bass. 1963. Optimal exposure time for development of acclimatization to heat. *Fed Proc,* 22:704-708.

Luce, G. G. 1971. *Body Time.* New York: Bantam Books.

Man, Sweat and Performance. 1969. Becton, Dickinson and Co., Consumer Products Division, P. O. Box 183, Rutherford, N.J.

Minard, D. 1961. Prevention of heat casualties in Marine Corps recruits. *Milit Med,* 126:261.

Morimoto, T., Z. Slobochova, R. K. Naman, and F. Sargent, II. 1967. Sex differences in physiological responses to thermal stress. *J Appl Physiol,* 22:526-532.

Paolone, A. M., C. L. Wells, and G. T. Kelly. 1977. Sexual variations in thermoregulation during heat stress. *Aviation, Space, and Envir Med,* 49:715-719.

Prosser, C. Ladd. 1961. Perspectives of adaptation: Theoretical aspects. In *Adaptation to the Environment, Section 4, Handbook of Physiology,* D. B. Dill (ed.). Washington, D.C.: American Physiological Society.

Robinson, S. 1972. Cardiovascular and respiratory reactions to heat. In *Physiological Adaptations: Desert and Mountain,* M. K. Yousef, S. M. Horvath, and R. W. Bullard (eds.). New York: Academic Press.

Robinson, S. 1968. Physiological adjustments to heat. In *Physiology of Heat Regulation and the Science of Clothing,* L. H. Newburgh (ed.). New York: Hafner.

Robinson, S., E. S. Turrell, B. S. Belding, and S. M. Horvath. 1943. Rapid acclimatization to work in hot climates. *Amer J Physiol,* 140:168-176.

Robinson, S., E. S. Turrell, and S. D. Gerking. 1945. Physiologically equivalent conditions of air temperature and humidity. *Amer J Physiol,* 143:21-32.

Rowell, L. B., J. R. Blackman, R. H. Martin, J. A. Mazzarella, and R. A. Bruce. 1965. Hepatic clearance of indocyanine green in men under thermal and exercise stress. *J Appl Physiol,* 20:384-394.

Rowell, L. B., H. J. Marx, R. A. Bruce, R. D. Conn, and F. Kusumi. 1966. Reductions in cardiac output, central blood volume, and stroke volume with thermal stress in normal men during exercise. *J Clin Invest,* 45:1801-1816.

Sargent, F. II and K. P. Weinman. 1966. Eccrine sweat gland activity during the menstrual cycle. *J Appl Physiol,* 21:1685-1687.

Standards Advisory Committee on Heat Stress, Recommended Standard for Work in Hot Environments. January 9, 1974. *Occupational Safety and Health Reporter,* Bureau of National Affairs.

Vander, A. J., J. H. Sherman, and D. S. Luciano. 1975. *Human Physiology: The Mechanism of Body Function.* 2nd ed. New York: McGraw-Hill.

Weinman, K. P., Z. Slabochova, E. M. Bernauer, T. Morimoto, and F. Sargent, II. 1967. Reactions of men and women to repeated exposure to humid heat. *J Appl Physiol,* 22:533-538.

Wells, C. L. 1977 (Sept.). Sexual differences in heat stress response. *Phys and Sportsmed,* 5:79-90.

Wells, C. L. and S. M. Horvath. 1973. Heat stress responses related to the menstrual cycle. *J Appl Physiol,* 35:1-5.

Wells, C. L. and S. M. Horvath. 1974. Metabolic and thermoregulatory responses of women to exercise in two thermal environments. *Med Sci Spts,* 6:8-13.

Wells, C. L. and A. M. Paolone. 1977. Metabolic responses to exercise in three thermal environments. *Aviation, Space, and Envir Med,* 48:989-993.

Williams, C. G., G. A. Bredell, C. H. Wyndham, N. B. Strydom, J. F. Morrison, J. Peter, P. W. Fleming, and J. S. Ward. 1962. Circulatory and metabolic reactions to work in heat. *J Appl Physiol,* 17:625-638.

Wyndham, C. H., J. R. Morrison, and C. G. Williams. 1965. Heat reactions of male and female Caucasians. *J Appl Physiol,* 20:357-364.

Yaglou, C. P. 1968. Indices of comfort. In *Physiology of Heat Regulation and the Science of Clothing,* L. H. Newburgh (ed.). New York: Hafner.

14

Prevention of Heat Injury

Emily M. Haymes and Elsworth R. Buskirk

Exposure to a warm or hot environment especially when vigorous exercise is involved may result in some form of heat disability. What may appear to be a simple case of dizziness or fainting in the heat (heat syncope) or a heat cramp can actually be a symptom of a more serious disturbance of the thermoregulatory system leading to heat exhaustion and/or heat stroke. Exercise in the heat can be fatal even among young, healthy individuals, as has been observed during military training (Malamud et al. 1946; Minard et al. 1957; Shickele 1947) and football practice (Murphy and Ashe 1965). Recognition of this possibility and an understanding of its prevention are essential for coaches, physical educators, recreators, and trainers who are charged with the supervision of physically demanding activities conducted in warm or hot environments.

THERMAL BALANCE

The major problem in cases of heat injury is the upsetting of thermal balance when heat gain exceeds heat loss. Heat is lost from the body to the environment as long as the skin temperature is greater than the temperature of the air (ambient temperature) and the surrounding environment through four avenues: radiation, convection, conduction, and evaporation. (See Chapter 13.)

Due to the relatively low efficiency of energy turnover by the body, much of the energy released during muscle contraction is converted to heat. The amount of metabolic heat produced is proportional to the work load. (See Chapter 13.) Increases in the rate of energy expenditure necessitate increases in heat loss, primarily through increased evaporation to maintain thermal balance (Nielsen 1938). If the rate of heat loss cannot keep pace with the metabolic heat gain, the body stores heat. Storage of each 0.83 Kcal of heat per kg of body weight results in an increase in body core temperature of 1°C.

Conditions most likely to produce this unfavorable balance between heat gain and heat loss are hot, dry, and warm to hot, humid environments. Because the maximal rate of sweating is limited even in low humidity environments, exercise when the ambient temperature exceeds skin temperature often results in a heat gain greater than the rate of heat loss. The result is heat storage and a rise in body temperature (Wyndham et al. 1965). In a humid environment, not only is evaporation limited but the rate of sweating may actually be depressed by water standing on the skin (Nadel et al. 1971). Since the amount of heat exchange via radiation and convection is independent of work load at a given ambient temperature (Nielsen 1938), an increased metabolic heat load in a humid environment will result in increased heat storage and body temperature.

DEVELOPMENT OF HEAT DISABILITY

As explained by Wells in the preceding chapter, the body responds to heat stress initially by vasodilation of skin arterioles increasing the flow of warm blood from the core of the body to the periphery where the skin is warmed. This increases heat loss through radiation and convection. Sweating commences when the core temperature (sensed in the hypothalamus) rises to a particular point, a variable set point that depends on the type of work and its intensity as well as the ambient temperature (Saltin and Gagge 1971). The increased blood flow to the skin increases the work load of the heart resulting in a greater heart rate and during heavy exercise a redistribution of blood flow away from internal organs to the skin (Rowell et al. 1965). Sweating increases the loss of both water and electrolytes from the body, and when not replaced reduces both plasma volume and total body water. (See Chapter 20.) Prolonged exercise in the heat without water replacement will result in a rise in core temperature due to a reduction in sweating (Pitts et al. 1944).

Heat disorders result from the failure of the body systems for heat loss to appropriately adjust to heat stress. The causes of the most common heat disorders are given in Table 14.1, as well as symptoms and treatment for each.

Certain individuals are more prone to heat disorders than others. In particular, a teacher should be aware of the individual who has not been accustomed to exercise in the heat, one who has recently been ill or recently been immunized (Buskirk and Grasley 1968). The relatively large person appears to be under greater strain in warm environments than individuals of more moderate size (Bar-Or et al. 1969; Robinson 1942), and heat illnesses appear to occur more frequently in obese or overweight individuals (Malamud et al. 1946; Minard et al. 1957; Schickele 1947). The individual who is eager and competes near his maximal capacity constantly must also be watched carefully since this person may ignore the early symptoms of heat disability (Buskirk and Grasley 1968). Both the age and sex of an individual are important in determining tolerance to the heat. Preadolescent children may be more susceptible to heat prostration especially in hot, dry environments (Haymes et al. 1974; Lofstedt 1966; Wagner et al. 1972), and poorly conditioned young women are less tolerant of exercise in both dry (Dill et al. 1973; Lofstedt 1966) and humid heat (Wyndham et al. 1965) than young men. There is also evidence that older men are less tolerant of high temperatures than young men and may acclimatize to heat more slowly (Lofstedt 1966; Wagner et al. 1972). Again, this may be a reflection of a relatively poorer state of physical conditioning among the elderly.

PERFORMANCE GUIDELINES

Prevention of Heat Injury

Heat prostration can be avoided by following a few simple principles outlined by Buskirk and Grasley (1968). Persons who engage in strenuous physical activities, such as athletic teams, should undergo a thorough physical examination and, in the case of activities in warm environments, this should be supplemented by thorough investigation of the history of previous heat illnesses and disorders such as peripheral vascular or sweating defects or problems. An evaluation should also be made of the individual's physical condition as well as the extent of heat exposure and training during the previous month. Heat exposure alone is not sufficient to produce acclimatization to the heat but must be combined with exercise or work in the heat. The amount of conditioning even though not in the heat is also important since some acclimatization occurs through elevation of body core temperature with regular strenuous exercise (Gisolfi 1973; Marcus 1972).

Table 14.1.

Heat Disorders: Treatment and Prevention (Buskirk and Grasley 1968)

Disorder	Cause	Clinical features and diagnosis	Treatment	Prevention
I. Heat cramps	Hard work in heat Heavy and prolonged sweating Inadequate salt intake	Low serum sodium and chloride Muscle twitching, cramps, and spasms in arms, legs and abdomen—usually after mid-day	Severe case: intravenous administration of 500 ml of normal saline Light case; oral administration of saline Rest in cool environment Salt foods used Delay 24 to 48 hrs before reentering hot area	Insure acclimatization Provide extra salt at meals Drink saline when working
II. Heat syncope	Peripheral vasodilation and pooling of blood Circulatory instability & loss of vasomotor tone Cerebral hypoxia Hyperventilation Inadequate acclimatization Infection	Weakness and fatigue Hypotension Increased venous compliance Blurred vision Pallor Syncope Elevated skin and deep body temperatures	Place supine and lower head Rest in cool environment Provide oral saline if conscious and resting Keep record of blood pressure, pulse rate and body temperature	Insure acclimatization Lighten work regimen sudden rise in environmental temperatures or humidity Avoid maintenance of upright static work conditions Comment: Predisposes to heat stroke
III. Water depletion to heat exhaustion	Heavy and prolonged sweating Inadequate fluid intake Polyuria or diarrhea	Reduced sweating, but excessive weight loss Elevated skin and deep body temperatures High hematocrit, serum protein, and sodium Dry tongue and mouth Excessive thirst Hyporexia Weak, disconsolate uncoordinated, and mentally dull Concentrated urine	Bed rest in cool environment Replace fluids by intravenous drip if drinking is impaired, increase fluids to 6 or 8 liters per day Sponge with cool water Provide small quantities of semiliquid food Keep record of body weight, water and salt intake, and body temperature	Provide adequate water Provide opportunity for intermittent cooling and adequate rest

IV. Salt depletion leading to heat exhaustion	Heavy and prolonged sweating Inadequate acclimatization Vomiting or diarrhea	Headache, dizziness, and fatigue Hyporexia Nausea, vomiting, diarrhea Muscle cramps Syncope High hematocrit and serum protein, but low plasma volume Uremia and hypercalemia Low sodium and chloride in sweat and urine	Bed rest in cool environment Replace fluids and salt by intravenous saline drip if drinking is impaired Provide small quantities of semiliquid food Keep record of urinary osmolarity or specific gravity, blood urea, and serum sodium or chloride Keep record of body weight water and salt intake, and body temperature	Provide adequate salt and water, 10 to 15 gms of salt per day may be necessary Provide opportunity for intermittent cooling and adequate rest Insure acclimatization Comment: Develops more slowly (3-5 days) than water depletion heat exhaust
V. Heat hyperpyrexia leading to heat stroke	Thermoregularity failure of sudden onset	General anhidrosis and dry skin Elevated skin and deep body temperatures frequently over 40.5 C (105° F), may have chills Irrational Muscle flaccidity Involuntary limb movements Seizures and coma Spotty cyanosis & ecchymosis Vomiting and diarrhea, frequently with blood Tachycardia and tachypnea	Lower body temperature to 38.9 C (102° F), within 1 hr. with cold rinse or spray (7.2 C (45°F). Use cool air fan or place in ice water bath. Use alcohol rinse if nothing else available Use suction equipment to clear airway and perform tracheotomy if necessary Inject 25-30 mg chloropromazine every 30 minutes Bed rest in cool environment Keep record of skin and deep body temperatures Treat secondary disorders	Insure acclimatization Adapt activities to environment Screen participants with infection or past history of heat illness
VI. Skin lesions	Constantly wetted Overexposure to sun	Erythematous papulovesicular rash Itchy skin Obstruction of sweat ducts	Maintain shaded and dry skin Rest in cool environment	Dry skin when possible and keep shaded Examine skin regularly Provide opportunity for intermittent cooling and adequate sweat free periods

143

Environmental Guidelines

Environmental temperature and humidity should be measured both before and during physical activity periods. A useful and accepted method of evaluating environmental stress is the Wet Bulb Globe Temperature Index (Minard et al. 1957). (See Chapter 13.) This index combines the wet bulb temperature (T_{wb}), a measure of the cooling power of the environment in relation to temperature and air moisture content, with globe temperature (T_g), a measure of the radiation absorbed from the environment, and dry bulb temperature (T_{db}), a measure of air temperature. Since humidity is most important during exercise, the greatest weighting in the index is given to the wet bulb temperature: $WBGT = 0.7\ T_{wb} + 0.2\ T_g + 0.1\ T_{db}$. Instruments are available commercially for evaluating WBGT. Permissible heat exposure limits as outlined by the National Institute for Occupational Safety and Health (1972) are listed in Table 14.2 for occupational exposures (Musacchio 1974). Minard et al. (1957) have suggested training should be modified when the WBGT is 29.4°C (85°F) and suspended when it reaches 31.1°C (88°F). The wet bulb temperature alone can be used as a satisfactory alternative for evaluating the environmental stress.

Table 14.2
Recommendation of OSHA Committee for Heat Stress Threshold
Values for Wet Bulb Globe Temperature °C (°F)

Work Load	Low Air Velocity 1.53 m.sec^{-1} (300 fpm)	High Air Velocity 1.53 m.sec^{-1} (300 fpm)
Light: < 200 kcal.h^{-1}	30.0 (86)	32.2 (90)
Moderate: 201−300 kcal.h^{-1}	27.8 (82)	30.6 (87)
Heavy: > 300 kcal.h^{-1}	26.1 (79)	28.9 (84)

OSHA—Occupational Safety and Health Association.

The American College of Sports Medicine (1975) has issued a position statement on the prevention of heat injuries during distance running. Their recommendations include the following:

1. Distance races (〉 16 kilometers or 10 miles) should not be conducted when the wet bulb globe temperature index exceeds 29°C (82.4°F).

2. During periods of the year when the daylight dry bulb temperature often exceeds 27°C (80°F), distance races should be conducted before 9:00 a.m. or after 4:00 p.m.

3. It is the responsibility of the race sponsors to provide fluids that contain small amounts of sugar (less than 2.5 gm glucose per 100 ml of water) and electrolytes (less than 10 mEq sodium and 5 mEq potassium per liter of solution).

4. Runners should be encouraged to frequently ingest fluids during competition and to consume 400-500 ml (13-17 oz.) of fluid 10-15 minutes before competition.

5. Rules prohibiting the administration of fluids during the first 10 kilometers (6.2 miles) of a marathon race should be amended to permit fluid ingestion at frequent intervals along the race course. In light of the high sweat rates and body temperatures during distance running in the heat, race sponsors should provide "water stations" at 3-4 kilometer (2-2.5 mile) intervals for all races of 16 kilometers (10 miles) or more.

6. Runners should be instructed in how to recognize the early warning symptoms that precede heat injury. Recognition of symptoms, cessation of running, and proper treatment can prevent heat injury. Early symptoms include the following: piloerection on chest and upper arms, chilling, throbbing pressure in the heat, unsteadiness, nausea, and dry skin.

7. Race sponsors should make prior arrangements with medical personnel for the care of cases of heat injury. Responsible and informed personnel should supervise each "feeding station." Organizational personnel should reserve the right to stop runners who exhibit clear signs of heat stroke or heat exhaustion.

Heat Acclimatization

Most heat disorders can be prevented by properly acclimatizing individuals to the heat. This is particularly true of the fall sports that start their seasons near the end of the summer. By starting with short exercise periods in the heat and gradually lengthening practices, appreciable acclimatization can be achieved within seven to ten days, but the process may not be complete for several more days. Murphy and Ashe (1965) emphasize the need for wearing minimal lightweight clothing during acclimatization. Sweating increases during acclimatization and the result is a lower rate of heat storage and core temperature for a given work load. A more efficient distribution of blood flow also occurs with acclimatization (Rowell et al. 1967).

Fluid Replacement

Because body fluids are lost through sweating, fluid replacement should be encouraged during practice sessions, distance races, and any sporting event lasting more than a few minutes. Failure to replace fluids during distance running results in elevated rectal temperatures (Buskirk and Beetham 1960; Costill et al. 1970; Wyndham and Strydom 1969). Most runners will only replace a small fraction of the fluid lost during the race. Administration of fluids during the first ten kilometers of the marathon is prohibited under current international rules. This means the runner will have a large fluid deficit before fluids can be consumed. Rate of gastric emptying is lower than sweat rate, which prevents fluid replacement from keeping pace with fluid loss (Costill et al. 1970). Thirst is also a poor indicator of adequate fluid replacement. Athletes should be encouraged to consume 200 ml (4 oz. of fluid every 15 minutes or 400 ml (8 oz.) every 30 minutes rather than drinking ad libitum (Buskirk and Grasley 1968). The volume consumed should be dependent both on the stressfulness of the environment and the exercise conditions.

Several commercial electrolyte solutions are currently available. These solutions contain sodium, chloride, potassium, and some form of sugar as well as water. Electrolyte drinks containing more than 2.5 gm glucose per 100 ml empty from the stomach more slowly than less concentrated solutions or water (Costill and Saltin 1974). The rate of emptying appears to be controlled by the osmolarity of the stomach content. Solutions empty more rapidly from the stomach if their osmolarity does not exceed 210 mOsm. Temperature of the solution also affects the rate of gastric emptying. Colder fluids (5 to 15°C) empty more rapidly than fluids at body temperature (Costill and Saltin 1974).

Since sweat is hypotonic to plasma and becomes more dilute with acclimatization, it is more important to replace the water lost than the salt. Electrolyte drinks have minimal value in replacing sodium, potassium, and chloride when food and drink are ingested ad libitum even during repeated days of heat exposure (Costill et al. 1975). Sodium and chloride are the major electrolytes lost during sweating while intracellular potassium losses are minimal (Costill et al. 1976). Potassium deficiency has been implicated in heat illnesses (Knochel 1974). Although Consolazio et al. (1963) reported a negative potassium balance when subjects were exposed to the heat for four days, a more recent study has reported positive potassium balance following dehydration (Costill et al. 1975). Potassium deficiency is more likely to occur if a person has had a gastrointestinal disturbance with vomiting and/or diarrhea. Use of salt tablets should be strongly discouraged. Some persons may experience digestive upsets from their use, and many athletes fail to take adequate amounts of water with them. It is more desirable to add salt to the diet by choosing foods with a higher salt content or adding extra salt to food during cooking or at the table.

In sports where large weight losses are expected, such as football, in late summer or early fall athletes should be weighed prior to the start and at the end of each practice. If an athlete continually fails to replace weight lost prior to the start of the succeeding practice, counseling about fluid replacement is needed (Tait et al. 1968.)

Rest

Adequate and frequent rest sessions, preferably in a cool shaded area, are important when exercising on hot days. Care should be taken to avoid hot brick or concrete stadium walls that will radiate heat. Clothing should be loosened during the rest break to create chimney effects to facilitate convective and evaporative heat loss.

Clothing

The amount and type of clothing worn determines the surface area available for heat exchange. Lightweight, loosely fitting clothing provides for more air circulation near the skin and enhances evaporative heat loss. Some clothing is desirable when the globe and ambient temperatures exceed skin temperature and the sun is out, since the clothing cuts down the exposed surface that will gain heat from the environment.

Football uniforms and their underlying padding are a special problem. Not only does the padding decrease the evaporative heat loss, but it also adds to the weight carried by the athlete increasing the metabolic load. The end result is greater heat storage and higher core temperature for the athlete in full uniform compared with one dressed in shorts (Mathews et al. 1969).

Rubber suits and other clothing impermeable to moisture are sometimes used to produce rapid weight loss, especially in wrestling. Although rubber suits can be used as an effective means of acclimatizing athletes to the heat, their use should be avoided for purposes of weight loss because the suits prevent heat loss through evaporation and increase the rate of heat storage. If used during a conditioning program, the rapid rise in body temperature usually results in an earlier curtailment of activity than normally would occur.

Playing Surfaces

The use of artificial playing surfaces has introduced an additional heat stressor. The temperature at the surface of artificial turf may be as much as 22°C (40°F) greater than the ambient temperature at mid-day (Buskirk et al. 1971). This increases the amount of radiation to which the athlete is exposed as well as raising the air temperature immediately above the turf. Surface temperature of the artificial turf can be reduced by irrigation. A rescheduling of activity for the early morning or early evening hours seems advisable during the warmer months of the year.

SUMMARY

Heat disability and deaths due to heat cramps, exhaustion, and stroke among exercising individuals can usually be avoided by (1) recognizing the environmental and physiological factors that combine to produce heat disorders, and (2) instituting proper preventive measures and planning appropriate programs. Methods of prevention include: acclimatization; fluid replacement; frequent rest breaks; proper clothing and protective equipment selection; and regulation of intensity, frequency, and duration of training or conditioning regimens.

REFERENCES

American College of Sports Medicine. 1975. Position statement on prevention of heat injuries during distance running. *Med Sci Spts,* 7, (1) vii-ix.

Bar-Or, O., H. M. Lundegren, and E. R. Buskirk. 1969. Heat tolerance of exercising obese and lean women. *J Appl Physiol,* 26, 403-409.

Buskirk, E. R. and W. P. Beetham. 1960. Dehydration and body temperature as a result of marathon running. *Med Sport,* 14, 2-16.

Buskirk, E. R. and W. C. Grasley. 1968. Heat injury and conduct of athletics. In *Physiological Aspects of Sports and Physical Fitness.* Chicago: Athletic Institute.

Buskirk, E. R., J. L. Loomis, and E. R. McLaughlin. 1971. Microclimate over artificial turf. *Natl Assoc. Coll Dir Athl Quart,* 5, 22-24.

Consolazio, C. F., L. O. Matoush, R. A. Nelson, R. S. Harding, and J. E. Canham. 1963. Excretion of sodium, potassium, magnesium and iron in human sweat and the relation of each to balance and requirements. *J Nutr,* 79, 407-415.

Costill, D. L. and B. Saltin. 1974. Factors limiting gastric emptying during rest and exercise. *J Appl Physiol,* 37, 679-683.

Costill, D. L., R. Cote, and W. Fink. 1976. Muscle water and electrolytes following varied levels of dehydration in man. *J Appl Physiol,* 40, 6-11.

Costill, D. L., R. Cote, E. Miller, T. Miller, and S. Wynder. 1975. Water and electrolyte replacement during repeated days of work in the heat. *Aviat Space Environ Med,* 46, 795-800.

Costill, D. L., W. F. Kammer, and A. Fisher. 1970. Fluid ingestion during distance running. *Arch Environ Hlth,* 21, 520-525.

Dill, D. B., M. K. Yousef, and J. D. Nelson. 1973. Responses of men and women to two-hour walks in desert heat. *J Appl Physiol,* 35, 231-235.

Gisolfi, C. V. 1973. Work-heat tolerance derived from interval training. *J Appl Physiol,* 35, 349-354.

Haymes, E. M., E. R. Buskirk, J. L. Hodgson, H. M. Lundegren, and W. C. Nicholas. 1974. Heat tolerance of exercising lean and heavy prepubertal girls. *J Appl Physiol,* 36, 556-561.

Knochel, J. P. 1974. Environmental heat illness. *Arch Int Med,* 133, 841-864.

Lind, A. R. 1964. Physiological responses to heat. In *Medical Climatology,* S. Licht (ed.). Baltimore: Waverly Press.

Lofstedt, B. E. 1966. *Human Heat Tolerance.* Lund: Berlingska Boktryckeriet.

Malamud, N., W. Haymaker, and R. P. Custer. 1946. Heat stroke: A clincopathologic study of 125 fatal cases. *Milit Surg,* 99, 397-449.

Marcus, P. 1972. Heat acclimatization by exercise-induced elevation of body temperature. *J Appl Physiol,* 33, 283-288.

Mathews, D. K., E. L. Fox, and D. Tanzi. 1969. Physiological responses during exercise and recovery in a football uniform. *J Appl Physiol,* 26, 611-615.

Minard, D., H. S. Belding, and J. R. Kingston. 1957. Prevention of heat casualties. *JAMA,* 165, 1813-1818.

Mitchell, J. W., E. R. Nadel, and J. A. J. Stolwijk. 1972. Respiratory weight losses during exercise. *J Appl Physiol*, 32, 474-476.

Murphy, R. J. and W. F. Ashe. 1965. Prevention of heat illness in football players. *JAMA*, 194, 180-184.

Musacchio, C. 1974 (March), The emerging new OSHA heat stress standard: Could you comply? *Occup Hazards*, 64-67.

Nadel, E. R., J. W. Mitchell, and J. A. J. Stolwijk. 1971. Control of local and total sweating during exercise transients. *Int J Biometeor*, 15, 201-206.

National Institute for Occupational Safety and Health. 1972. Criteria for a recommended standard . . . occupational exposure to hot environments. Washington: U.S. Department of Health, Education and Welfare Document HSM 72-10269.

Nielsen, M. 1938. Die regulation der korpertenperatur bei muskelarbeit. *Skandinav Arch*, 79, 194-230.

Pitts, G. C., R. E. Johnson, and C. F. Consolazio. 1944. Work in the heat as affected by intake of water, salt and glucose. *Amer J Physiol*, 142, 253-259.

Robinson, S. 1942. Effect of body size upon energy exchange in work. *Amer J Physiol*, 136, 363-368.

Rowell, L. B., J. R. Blackman, R. H. Martin, J. A. Mazzarella, and R. A. Bruce. 1965. Hepatic clearance of iodocyanine green in man under thermal and exercise stress. *J Appl Physiol*, 20, 384-394.

Rowell, L. B., K. K. Kraning, J. W. Kennedy, and T. O. Evans. 1967. Central circulatory responses to work in dry heat before and after acclimatization. *J Appl Physiol*, 22, 509-518.

Saltin, B. and A. P. Gagge. 1971. Sweating and body temperatures during exercise. *Int J Biometeor*, 15, 189-194.

Schickele, E. 1947. Environment and fatal heat stroke. *Milit Surg*, 100, 235-256.

Tait, G. T., W. C. Grasely, and E. R. Buskirk. 1968. Simple surveillance records for prevention of heat injury in football: Body weight and environmental conditions. In *Physiological Aspects of Sports and Physical Fitness*. Chicago: Athletic Institute.

Wagner, J. A., S. Robinson, S. P. Tzankoff, and R. P. Marino. 1972. Heat tolerance and acclimatization to work in the heat in relation to age. *J Appl Physiol*, 33, 616-622.

Wyndham, C. H. and N. B. Strydom. 1969. The danger of inadequate water intake during marathon running. *S.A. Med J*, 43, 893-896.

Wyndham, C. H., S. R. Morrison, and C. G. Williams. 1965. Heat reactions of male and female caucasians. *J Appl Physiol*, 20, 357-364.

Wyndham, C. H., N. B. Strydom, J. F. Morrison, C. G. Williams, G. A. G. Bredell, J. S. Maritz, and A. Munro. 1965. Criteria for physiological limits for work in heat. *J Appl Physiol*, 20, 37-45.

15

Water and Physical Performance

William G. Herbert

Water is the most plentiful substance in the human body, constituting more than 63 percent of the total weight in males and 52 percent in females (Pitts 1968). Approximately one-half of this water is distributed intracellularly, where it provides a biochemically active support medium for metabolic reactions. Extracellularly—in blood plasma, interstitial fluid, and lymph—water comprises roughly 20 to 22 percent of body weight and serves as the milieu for transportation of respiratory gases, nutrients, cellular by-products, and metabolic heat (Pitts 1968). With respect to the body exterior, water is a vehicle for elimination of waste through urine, feces, and sweat, and for removal of heat through evaporation of sweat from skin surfaces. Although heat exchanges with the environment also occur via radiation, conduction, and convection, it is chiefly through vaporization from skin surfaces that excess heat is dissipated during vigorous physical performance.

When the deep body temperature is elevated, the thermoregulation center (hypothalamus) elicits a sweating response. Subsequent evaporation from skin surfaces results in highly effective heat dissipation. Sweat rates may exceed 1.8 liters per hour in prolonged heavy exercise (Pugh, Corbett, and Johnson 1967), thereby accounting for heat removal of more than 1000 kcal per hour if all of the sweat is evaporated (Snellen, Mitchell, and Wyndham 1970). Thus the human body is protected from overheating and the central body temperature is regulated below a critical level (41.1°C or 106°F) above which serious injury or thermal death might occur (Pugh, Corbett, and Johnson 1967; Schrier et al. 1971). Unfortunately, evaporative cooling is accomplished at the expense of depleting body water stores (dehydration or hypohydration) and even slight deficits can impair circulation, thermoregulation, and the capability for endurance exercise (Adolph 1947; Costill 1972).

Under normal circumstances, the thirst mechanism is adequate to maintain water balance, particularly when individuals are given opportunity to drink and eat at their leisure. It is generally held that the urge to drink is mediated by the hypothalamus, which is responsive to rising body fluid osmolarity attendant to water depletion (Astrand and Rodahl 1970). This elevated osmolarity also elicits an increased secretion of the antidiuretic hormone (AHD) from the pituitary that, in turn, acts upon the kidney to conserve water by increasing reabsorption through the renal tubules. Since sweat is hypotonic to body fluids, more water than salt is lost through sweating, and blood osmolarity increases. If sufficient water is drunk to replace the losses, body fluids are diluted, osmolarity is reduced and water balance reestablished. Despite this control mechanism, when individuals sweat profusely, they fail to voluntarily replace their losses and dehydration equivalent to five percent of body weight may develop after several hours of activity in the heat (Adolph 1947). If water loss reaches six to ten percent of body weight, the blood becomes concentrated, blood volume is substantially reduced, sweat rates diminish, deep body temperature may rise dangerously high, and dehydration exhaustion is imminent (Adolph 1947).

Water balance problems in sports such as amateur wrestling, football, and distance running have attracted the attention of researchers, physicians, and sports practitioners alike. Position statements have been published by the American College of Sports Medicine (1975, 1976) and the National Research Council (1974) to address the potentially hazardous consequences of dehydration in sports and to suggest guidelines to minimize detrimental performance effects in competitors. The purpose of this chapter is to review the effects of altered body water balance upon physical performance. Specifically, the influences of dehydration, rehydration, and hyperhydration are described in relation to physical performances that commonly involve excessive water losses.

DEHYDRATION

Competitive practices in wrestling, lightweight football, and boxing lead many participants to perform in a dehydrated state. Commonly, lean adolescent wrestlers undergo brief periods of semistarvation and dehydration induced by sweating, diuretics, or laxatives to qualify for competitive classifications that are as far as 15 percent below preseason body weights (Zambraski et al. 1976; Herbert et al. 1977). A considerable degree of these deficits persists during the contest, since drinking is voluntarily curtailed by the wrestlers during the one-to five-hour interval between weight certification and the meet. Although the extent of dehydration arising from a two- to three-day rapid weight loss will vary considerably according to the wrestler's reduction methods, a controlled laboratory investigation of men performing several days of hard work on low water and food intake suggests that more than two-thirds of any such deficit may be due to body fluid losses (Grande et al. 1958). Marathon runners drink so sparingly that weight deficits exceeding five percent frequently arise due to excessive sweating (Pugh, Corbett, and Johnson 1967). Among football players, progressive water loss occurs on the practice field in hot weather even though some fluids are consumed; the heat stroke deaths that occur during late summer practices provide evidence of the tragic manifestations of extreme dehydration and thermoregulatory failure (Murphy 1963; Mathews, Fox, and Tanzi 1969; Ryan et al. 1975).

In a normally hydrated performer, the capacity for exercise is limited primarily by the ability to transport and utilize oxygen in the muscles. In vigorous activities lasting longer than a few minutes, dehydration equivalent to only two percent of body weight can produce noticeable impairments in performance by compromising circulatory and thermoregulatory functions (Pitts, Johnson, and Consolazio 1944; Adolph 1947; Astrand and Saltin 1964; Saltin 1964a, 1964b). These detrimental effects are exaggerated in hot-humid weather (wet-bulb temperature $\geq 78°F$) where conductive and evaporative mechanisms can no longer cool the body. Although the basic factors responsible for reduced performance after dehydration are not clearly understood, experimental evidence suggests at least four possibilities: (1) the capacity to remove body heat is reduced by a diminished blood volume that limits maximal cardiac output and/or peripheral circulation (Adolph 1947; Claremont et al. 1976); (2) central nervous system control of the sweat glands and/or peripheral vasculature is disturbed via thermal or osmolar effects upon the hypothalamus (Senay and Christensen 1965; Ekblom et al. 1970; Nielson 1974); (3) the sweat glands per se fatigue, and subsequently show a diminished capacity to elaborate sweat (Wyndham et al. 1966); and, (4) cellular functions, not exclusively in skeletal muscle, are impaired, which leads to a suppressed anaerobic capacity (Saltin 1964a).

Whatever the ultimate limiting factor, the concomitant reductions in circulating blood volume and intracellular water must play a crucial role. Early investigations by Adolph (1947) indicated that dehydration in the heat reduces the plasma volume roughly twice as much as other body water compartments. Later research by Kozlowski and Saltin (1964) supported this finding for thermal dehydration but suggested that water losses after exercise dehydration were covered largely by extravascular sources. Using improved hematologic measurement methods, Costill and Fink (1974) determined that both thermal and exercise dehydration (four percent of weight) actually diminish the plasma volume to a similar extent (12 percent). Furthermore, Costill, Cote, and Fink (1976), after studying blood, urine, and muscle biopsy parameters, reported that heat-exercise dehydration reduced plasma volume and muscle water approximately 2.4 percent and 1.2 percent, respectively, for each percent decline in body weight. Significant changes in intracellular sodium, potassium, and water were observed in the latter study, but no evidence of impaired cellular membrane function was found in biopsy samples taken 30 minutes after dehydration. If dehydration is induced by taking diuretics, urinary water and Na^+ losses result in plasma volume losses that are nearly twice as great as would occur with a comparable degree of exercise dehydration (Claremont et al. 1976). It has been postulated that water sequestered with muscle glycogen, when released during heavy exercise, might provide a significant water reserve (two to three liters) to offset body fluid losses caused by sweating (Olsson and Saltin 1971). Although some extra carbohydrate intake during the two to three days preceding an endurance performance would seemingly minimize dehydration, experimental evidence clarifying how release of this metabolic water affects body fluids is lacking (Ryan et al. 1975).

The effects of dehydration upon physiological responses to exercise and physical fitness have been studied under a variety of experimental conditions. Dehydration to five percent of body weight caused by passive heat exposure, prolonged heavy exercise, or combinations thereof generally has little effect on oxygen uptake at either submaximal or maximal loads (Saltin 1964a; Saltin and Stenberg 1964; Buskirk, Iampietro, and Bass 1958; Palmer 1968; Herbert and Ribisl 1972a; Greenleaf et al. 1966; Bock, Fox, and Bowers 1967; Craig and Cummings 1966), maximal cardiac output, or heart rate (Saltin 1964a, 1964b; Saltin and Stenberg 1964). In contrast, dehydration beyond two to three percent of weight is associated with marked reductions in blood lactate levels and work time at maximal loads that are particularly pronounced after exercise dehydration (Saltin 1964a, 1964b; Saltin and Stenberg 1964; Craig and Cummings 1966). These findings led Saltin to conclude that cellular level changes are partly responsible for the striking decline in endurance performance following metabolic (exercise) dehydration. Other important manifestations of dehydration seen during exercise at a fixed load include slight declines in both arterial blood pressure and stroke volume of the heart and elevations in heart rate and core temperature (Palmer 1968; Ribisl and Herbert 1970; Craig and Cummings 1966; Saltin 1964a, 1964b; Saltin and Stenberg 1964).

If dehydration exceeds three percent of body weight, linear increments in both heart rate and core temperature are observed in submaximal exercise (Strydom and Holdsworth 1968; Herbert and Ribisl 1972b; Costill and Sparks 1973), and sweat output may fail to increase with elevations in core temperature (Ladell 1947; Hertzman and Ferguson 1960; Ekblom et al. 1970; Senay and Christensen 1965; Strydom and Holdsworth 1968). Maximal isometric strength in various muscle groups is not significantly impaired by water deficits up to five percent of body weight (Saltin 1964a; Tuttle 1943; Ahlman and Karvonen 1961; Singer and Weiss 1968; Greenleaf et al 1966), although significant decrements (= −30 percent) in both static and dynamic muscular endurance of the hand, arm, and leg muscles have been observed by Torranin, Smith, and Byrd (1976) after a four percent dehydrative weight loss. A number of studies dealing specifically with weight reduction in wrestlers (Edwards 1951; Nichols 1957; Elfenbaum 1966; Singer and Weiss 1968) have indicated that between six and nine percent of body weight may be lost through several days of semistarvation-dehydration without detrimentally affecting muscular strength, coordination, or reaction time. Adolph (1947) has shown, however, that after dehydrating by six to ten percent of weight through exercise in the desert, men experienced "dehydration exhaustion," dizziness, and fainting. Buskirk, Iampietro, and Bass (1958) found that although physical training did not prevent impairments after dehydration, it did enable men to tolerate a higher work rate after dehydration than could unconditioned subjects. Heat acclimatization did not further improve their postdehydration performance, however.

Few studies have been done to specifically assess dehydration effects on the physical performance of women. Parallel observations of men and women walking in the desert without water replenishment (Dill, Yousef, and Nelson 1973) suggest that the two sexes respond similarly to dehydration-heat stress by exhibiting roughly the same elevations in heart rate and core temperature during a walking exercise. In an investigation of physically trained women subjects, a heat-exercise dehydration to 3.3 percent of body weight resulted in some deterioration in the cardiovascular responses to tilting and bench stepping, but no decrements occurred in oxygen uptake during submaximal exercise, reaction time, or isometric strength (Greenleaf, Prange, and Averkin 1967). In another study, Byrd and his associates (1977) observed a similar degree of cardiovascular strain during submaximal exercise in men and women subjects after a heat-exercise dehydration, but a slightly reduced capacity for heat dissipation was seen only in the women subjects following a three percent weight loss. With a trend toward greater participation of women in endurance sports, additional study will be necessary to determine if dehydration imposes limitations on performance peculiar to their sex.

WATER CONSUMPTION

Voluntary fluid consumption is effective in partially offsetting body water losses and performance decrements incurred through sweating. In this regard, Strydom and his coworkers (1966) found that ad libitum water intake during a prolonged march (29 km) was associated with lower heart rates, lower rectal temperatures, and fewer drop-outs than were observed in a group of subjects receiving only one liter of water during the march. Despite improved performance in the water drinking group, the thirst mechanism was inadequate to prevent dehydration and their water deficit averaged 2.9 percent of weight at the conclusion of the march. The effects of ad lib fluid consumption have been observed in connection with marathon racing in cool or thermoneutral weather conditions (Pugh, Corbett, and Johnson 1967; Wyndham and Strydom 1969; Magazanik et al. 1974). Collectively, these studies indicated that the majority of competitors undergo voluntary dehydration between two percent and seven percent of body weight, with the most successful runners incurring the larger deficits and exhibiting final rectal temperatures that approach heat-stroke levels (105.6°F). However, individuals who drank sufficiently at water stations to keep their final deficits below three percent showed final rectal temperatures no higher than 102°F (Wyndham and Strydom 1969).

The efficacy of voluntary fluid ingestion has also been investigated in college wrestlers following rapid reduction to a 4.8 percent under competitive conditions (Herbert and Ribisl 1972a). In the five hours between the certification weigh-in and the varsity meet, the athletes ate and drank to reduce their deficit to 2.2 percent. Physical working capacity (PWC--170), measured at the times of weigh-in and just before the meet, showed that partial rehydration was associated with significant improvement in performance, although the PWC-170 was still significantly lower than in a predehydrated control condition.

The value of complete rehydration is clearly evident in studies by Pitts, Johnson, and Consolazio (1944) and Strydom and Holdsworth (1968) wherein ad lib consumption and forced replacement of sweat losses were compared. In the former study, when subjects were made to drink water equivalent to their sweat losses every 15 minutes during prolonged walking in the heat, rectal temperatures remained well below levels observed in water ad lib and no water conditions. The findings of Strydom and Holdsworth are in agreement with those just described.

Dill, Yousef, and Nelson (1973) also provide evidence that dehydration-induced elevations in exercise heart rate and core temperature can be prevented in subjects walking in the desert heat by ingestion of a cold salt solution at seven-minute intervals in amounts to exactly replace sweat losses. Costill, Kammer, and Fisher (1970) utilized a similar feeding schedule to determine the effects of fluid replenishment during two hours of severe aerobic exercise in elite marathon runners. Subjects ingested, on different occasions, either a cold glucose-electrolyte solution, cold water, or no fluids in 100 ml feedings at five-minute intervals during the run until 2000 ml were taken. Exercise in the fluid trials was accompanied by lower rectal temperatures, but heart rate and both pulmonary and metabolic responses were similar in the fluid and no fluid trials. Since sweating rates were equivalent in the fluid and no fluid conditions, lower core temperatures in the fluid trials were possibly due to conductive effects of the cold fluids rather than enhanced heat dissipation.

Palmer (1968), Ribisl and Herbert (1970), and Herbert and Ribisl (1972b) investigated the physiological and performance effects of complete rehydration under conditions pertinent to competitive wrestling. There was good agreement that complete restoration of the cardiovascular response to submaximal exercise can be effected after dehydrations as extensive as seven percent of body weight, if fluid is consumed in quantities to replace the deficit within the five hours prior to competition. Costill and Sparks (1973) compared the rehydrative value of water and a cold glucose-electrolyte solution following a thermal dehydration to four percent of weight. Subjects consumed fluid volumes to replace their deficits within three hours. Neither solution restored blood serum osmolarity or plasma volume to normal levels, and a large diuresis occurred resulting in retention of only 62 percent of the fluid consumed. Submaximal exercise heart rates, however, decreased to predehydration levels by the third hour of rehydration.

Little is known about fluid replenishment needs under conditions where individuals must work in the heat on repeated days. This information is of value to football players undergoing preseason training in the heat of late summer. Costill and coworkers (1975) dehydrated a group of men and women to three percent on five successive days by exercise in the heat; each day the subjects replaced sweat losses with either water or a glucose-electrolyte solution. Consumption of both fluids was associated with a positive electrolyte balance and nearly a ten percent increase in plasma volume after the five-day period. The researchers concluded that under these conditions, a glucose-electrolyte solution offers no advantage over water relative to replacing fluid or electrolyte losses, so long as daily flood and fluid intake are unrestricted. The practical importance of maintaining body water balance in such situations is abundantly clear. Football players, wearing standard uniforms, reduce their evaporative body surface area by up to 50 percent. Consequently, during work in the heat, profuse sweating occurs to compensate for a rising core temperature (Mathews, Fox, and Tanzi 1969). With the great stress imposed on the cardiovascular system to dissipate heat under these conditions, a failure to replenish sweat losses and a cumulative dehydration over successive days of practice could easily lead to heat injury. Although heat retarding effects of wearing a football uniform contraindicate participation with pads when the wet-bulb temperature is above 78°F, free consumption of water during and between practices can minimize the dehydration that otherwise might seriously aggravate the physiological strain associated with participation in the heat.

Since replacement of sweat losses during exercise enhances cardiovascular and thermoregulatory function, there has been some interest in trying to augment these benefits by providing supplemental fluids (hyperhydration) prior to exercise. Blank (1959) gave trackmen approximately 500 ml of water five minutes before performance of a 220-yard dash. As might be expected in an event where performance is influenced more by anaerobic capacity and muscular power than aerobic capacity, the preliminary water consumption had no effect upon sprint times when comparisons were made with control data. Blyth and Burt (1961) examined the effects of a preliminary feeding of one liter of saline plus one liter of water in three normally hydrated subjects upon performance of an exhaustive treadmill run in the heat. The duration of the treadmill run was significantly longer when the individuals performed in a superhydrated condition than when they drank no fluid beforehand. The potential benefit of hyperhydration relative to endurance performance was also studied by Moroff and Bass (1965). Hyperhydration was achieved by administering 2000 ml of tepid water to subjects within 50 minutes before they performed 90-minute treadmill walks in the heat. To prevent dehydration, water was also drunk every 20 minutes throughout the exercise in 300 ml portions. In a second trial, the same subjects exercised without preliminary drinking but received the same amounts of water during work. Comparison of experimental and control responses showed that hyperhydration was associated with significantly lower rectal temperatures, lower heart rates, and higher sweat rates.

In view of the crucial importance of water balance in performances where cardiovascular and thermoregulatory factors may be limiting, the rehydrative qualities of various fluids and the factors that affect their rate of uptake by the body must be considered. Early research by Pitts, Johnson, and Consolazio (1944) was aimed at determining the effects of water, glucose, and salt intake on performance of work in the heat. Comparisons of heart rates, rectal temperatures, sweat losses, and symptoms of subjects measured during work in a 38°C (100°F) room were made with respect to various feeding schedules. Drinking of tap water or saline at a temperature cooler than the environment seemed most beneficial, but administration of glucose or salt in the water offered no additional advantage.

Gastric emptying and intestinal absorption of fluids during one hour of heavy aerobic exercise were investigated by Fordtran and Saltin (1967). In two different trials, either tap water or a solution of 13.3 percent glucose and 0.3 percent sodium chloride was drunk in 150 ml portions at ten-minute intervals concomitantly with exercise until 750 ml were consumed. At an exercise intensity averaging 71 percent of max VO_2 gastric emptying of the fluids was not imparied. Examination of the gastric and intestinal contents after exercise showed that considerably more water than glucose-electrolyte solution was taken up, although 50 gms of glucose were emptied from the stomach during the exercise. It was suggested that the presence of electrolyte in the solution facilitates gastric emptying, whereas glucose has a retarding effect. Nevertheless, addition of small amounts of glucose to a rehydrative solution (2.5 gm per 100 ml) may be advantageous under certain conditions. For example, during extended exercise in a cool environment, a higher priority may be given to supplementing the body's carbohydrate stores rather than maximizing the rate of water uptake. One final study by Costill and Saltin (1974) has considerable impact on rehydration procedures. These investigators varied the solute volume, temperature, osmolarity, and glucose content as well as the intensity of the accompanying exercise to determine conditions for optimizing gastric emptying of fluids. The results showed the rate of emptying to be highest with larger fluid volumes up to 600 ml that were cooler than 35°C, contained little or no glucose, and were consumed during exercise at intensities lower than 70 percent max VO_2.

In summary, water deficit may lead to significant decrements in physical performance, and under certain conditions to serious medical emergencies. Since the thirst mechanism does not always adequately protect the human from water deficit, it is imperative that the recreational participant, the athlete, and the coach be aware of the importance of body water replacement during and following periods of water loss.

REFERENCES

Adolph, E. F., et al. 1947. *Physiology of Man in the Desert*. New York: Wiley.

Ahlman, K. and M. J. Karvonen. 1961. Weight reduction by sweating in wrestlers, and its effect on physical fitness. *J Spts Med Phys Fit*, 1, 58-62.

American College of Sports Medicine. 1975. Position statement: Prevention of heat injuries during distance running. *Med Sci Spts*, 7, vii-ix.

American College of Sports Medicine. 1976. Position stand on weight loss in wrestlers. *Spts Med Bull,* 11, 1-2.

Astrand, P.-O. and K. Rodahl. 1970. *Textbook of Work Physiology.* New York: McGraw-Hill.

Astrand, P.-O. and B. Saltin. 1964. Plasma and red cell volume after prolonged severe exercise. *J Appl Physiol,* 19, 829-832.

Blank, L. B. 1959. An experimental study of the effect of water ingestion upon athletic performance. *Res Quart,* 30, 131-135.

Blyth, C. S. and J. J. Burt. 1961. Effect of water balance on ability to perform in high ambient temperatures. *Res Quart,* 32, 301-307.

Bock, W., E. L. Fox, and R. Bowers. 1967. The effects of acute dehydration upon cardio-respiratory endurance. *J Spts Med,* 7, 67-72.

Buskirk, E. R., P. F. Iampietro, and D. E. Bass. 1958. Work performance after dehydration: Effects of physical conditioning and heat acclimatization. *J Appl Physiol,* 12, 189-194.

Byrd, R., L. Stewart, C. Torranin, and O. M. Berringer. 1977. Sex differences in response to hypohydration. *J Spts Med,* 17, 65-68.

Claremont, A. D., D. L. Costill, W. Fink, and P. Van Handel. 1976. Heat tolerance following diuretic induced dehydration. *Med Sci Spts,* 8, 239-243.

Costill, D. L. 1972. Water and electrolytes. *Ergogenic Aids and Muscular Performance.* W. P. Morgan (ed.). New York: Academic Press.

Costill, D. L., R. Cote, and W. Fink. 1976. Muscle water and electrolytes following varied levels of dehydration in man. *J Appl Physiol,* 40, 6-11.

Costill, D. L., R. Cote, E. Miller, T Miller, and S. Wynder. 1975. Water and electrolyte replacement during repeated days of work in the heat. *Med Sci Spts,* 7, 90.

Costill, D. L. and W. J. Fink. 1974. Plasma volume changes following exercise and thermal dehydration. *J Appl Physiol,* 37, 521-525.

Costill, D. L., W. F. Kammer, and A. Fisher. 1970. Fluid ingestion during distance running. *Arch Environ Hlth,* 21, 520-525.

Costill, D. L. and B. Saltin. 1974. Factors limiting gastric emptying during rest and exercise. *J Appl Physiol,* 37, 679-683.

Costill, D. L. and K. E. Sparks. 1973. Rapid fluid replacement following thermal dehydration. *J Appl Physiol,* 34, 299-303.

Craig, F. N. and E. G. Cummings. 1966. Dehydration and muscular work. *J Appl Physiol,* 21, 670-674.

Dill, D. B., M. K. Yousef, and J. D. Nelson. 1973. Responses of men and women to two-hour walks in desert heat. *J Appl Physiol,* 35, 231-235.

Edwards, J. B., Jr. 1951. A study of the effect of semi-starvation on strength and endurance with reference to college wrestling. Master's thesis, University of North Carolina at Charlotte.

Ekblom, B., C. J. Greenleaf, J. E. Greenleaf, and L. Hermansen. 1970. Temperature regulation during exercise dehydration in man. *Acta Physiol Scand,* 79, 475-483.

Elfenbaum, L. 1966. The physiological effects of rapid weight loss among wrestlers. Doctoral dissertation, Ohio State University.

Fordtran, J. S. and B. Saltin. 1967. Gastric emptying and intestinal absorption during prolonged severe exercise. *J Appl Physiol*, 23, 331-335.

Grande, F., H. L. Taylor, J. T. Anderson, E. Buskirk, and A. Keys. 1958. Water exchange in men on a restricted water intake on a low calorie carbohydrate diet accompanied by physical work. *J Appl Physiol*, 12, 202-210.

Greenleaf, J. E., M. Matter, J. S. Bosco, L. G. Douglas, and E. G. Averkin. 1966. Effects of hypohydration on work performance and tolerance to $+G_l$ acceleration in man. *Aerospace Med*, 37, 34-39.

Greenleaf, J. E., E. M. Prange, and E. G. Averkin. 1967. Physical performance of women following heat-exercise hypohydration. *J Appl Physiol*, 22, 55-60.

Herbert, W. G., C. King, A. Teske, and M. Del Col. 1977. Seasonal changes in physical performance of college wrestlers undergoing repetitive weight reduction. *Med Sci Spts*, 9, 56.

Herbert, W. G. and P. M. Ribisl. 1972a. Effects of dehydration upon physical working capacity of wrestlers under competitive conditions. *Res Quart*, 42, 416-422.

Herbert, W. G. and P. M. Ribisl. 1972b. The effects of three levels of rapid weight reduction and rehydration on plasma volume and cardiovascular performance. *Med Sci Spts*, 4, 59.

Hertzman, A. B. and I. D. Ferguson. 1960. Failure of temperature regulation during progressive dehydration. *U.S. Armed Forces Med J*, 11, 542-560.

Kozlowski, S. and B. Saltin. 1964. Effects of sweat loss on body fluids. *J Appl Physiol*, 19, 1119-1124.

Ladell, W. S. S. 1947. Effects on man of restricted water supply. *Brit Med Bull*, 5, 9-13.

Magazanik, A., Y. Shapiro, D. Meytes, and I. Meytes. 1974. Enzyme blood levels and water balance during a marathon race. *J Appl Physiol*, 36, 214-217.

Mathews, D. K., E. L. Fox, and D. Tanzi. 1969. Physiological responses during exercise and recovery in a football uniform. *J Appl Physiol*, 26, 611-615.

Moroff, S. V. and D. E. Bass. 1965. Effects of overhydration on man's physiological responses to work in the heat. *J Appl Physiol*, 20, 267-270.

Murphy, R. J. 1963. The problems of environmental heat in athletics. *Ohio State Med J*, 59, 799-804.

National Research Council. 1974. A statement by the Food and Nutrition Board on *Water deprivation and performance of athletes*. Washington, D.C.: National Academy of Sciences.

Nichols, H. 1957. The effect of rapid weight loss on selected physiologic responses of wrestlers. Doctoral dissertation, University of Michigan.

Nielsen, B. 1974. Effects of changes in plasma volume and osmolarity on thermoregulation during exercise. *Acta Physiol Scand*, 90, 725-730.

Olsson, K. E. and B. Saltin. 1971. Diet and fluids in training and competition. *Scand J Rehab Med*, 3, 31-38.

Palmer, W. K. 1968. Selected physiological responses of normal young men following dehydration and rehydration. *Res Quart*, 39, 1054-1059.

Pitts, G. C., R. E. Johnson, F. C. Consolazio. 1944. Work in the heat as affected by intake of water, salt and glucose. *Am J Physiol*, 142, 253-259.

Pitts, R. F. 1968. *Physiology of the Kidney and Body Fluids*. Chicago: Yearbook Medical Publishers.

Pugh, L. G. C. E., J. L. Corbett, and R. H. Johnson. 1967. Rectal temperature, weight losses and sweat rates in marathon running. *J Appl Physiol*, 23, 347-352.

Ribisl, P. M. and W. G. Herbert. 1970. Effects of rapid weight reduction and subsequent rehydration upon the physical working capacity of wrestlers. *Res Quart*, 41, 536-541.

Ryan, A. J., D. Costill, C. Gisolfi, R. J. Murphy, and R. L. Westerman. 1975. Round table: Balancing heat stress, fluids and electrolytes. *Physician and Spts Med*, 3, 43-52.

Saltin, B. 1964a. Aerobic and anaerobic work capacity after dehydration. *J Appl Physiol*, 19, 1114-1118.

Saltin, B. 1964b. Circulatory response to submaximal and maximal exercise after thermal dehydration. *J Appl Physiol*, 19, 1125-1132.

Saltin, B. and J. Stenberg. 1964. Circulatory response to prolonged severe exercise. *J Appl Physiol*, 19, 833-838.

Schrier, R. W., H. S. Henderson, C. C. Tisher, and R. L. Tannen. 1971. Nephropathy associated with heat stress and exercise. In *Medicine and Sport (5): Exercise and Cardiac Death*, E. Jokl and S. T. McClellan (eds.). Baltimore: University Park Press.

Senay, L. C., Jr. and M. L. Christensen. 1965. Cutaneous circulation during dehydration and heat stress. *J Appl Physiol*, 20, 278-282.

Singer, R. N. and S. A. Weiss. 1968. Effects of weight reduction on selected anthropometric, physical and performance measures in wrestlers. *Res Quart*, 39, 361-369.

Snellen, J. W., D. Mitchell, and C. H. Wyndham. 1970. Heat of evaporation of sweat. *J Appl Physiol*, 29, 40-44.

Strydom, N. B. and L. D. Holdsworth. 1968. The effects of different levels of water deficit on physiological responses during heat stress. *Int Z Angew Physiol*, 26, 95-102.

Strydom, N. B., C. H. Wyndham, C. H. van Graan, L. D. Holdsworth, and J. F. Morrison. 1966. The influence of water restriction on the performance of men during a prolonged march. *S Afr Med J*, 40, 539-544.

Torranin, D., D. P. Smith, and R. J. Byrd. 1976. The effect of acute dehydration and rehydration on isometric and isotonic endurance. *Med Sci Spts*, 8, 49.

Tuttle, W. W. 1943. The effect of weight loss by dehydration and the withholding of food on the physiological responses of wrestlers. *Res Quart*, 14, 158-166.

Wyndham, C. H. and N. B. Strydom. 1969. The danger of an inadequate water intake during marathon running. *S Afr Med J*, 43, 893-896.

Wyndham, C. H., N. B. Strydom, J. F. Morrison, C. G. Williams, G. A. G. Bredell, and J. Peter. 1966. Fatigue of the sweat gland response. *J Appl Physiol*, 21, 107-110.

Zambraski, E. J., D. T. Foster, P. M. Gross, and C. M. Tipton. 1976. Iowa wrestling study: Weight loss and urinary profiles of collegiate wrestlers, *Med Sci Spts*, 8, 105-108.

16

Physiological Effects of a Cold Environment upon Physical Performance

Emily M. Haymes

Cold environments encompass a broad range of temperatures. For the skier and hiker, the range may span from -40°C to 10°C (-40 to 50°F). For the swimmer, the range may extend between 15°C and 30°C (59-86°F). Many factors influence how a person responds to a particular environmental temperature. For the resting individual with little or no clothing, negative heat balance will occur in a warmer environment than for an exercising person wearing several layers of clothing. The swimmer is placed in a negative heat balance in water temperatures normally found in many outdoor swimming pools.

Heat is lost from the body through convection, radiation and evaporation. In a water environment, conduction also plays a role in heat loss since water conducts heat 25 times better than air.

There are several physiological defense mechanisms that combine to prevent a drop in core temperature during cold exposure. Unfortunately, the cold defense mechanisms do not appear to be as effective as those that prevent an excessive gain in body heat. Therefore, it is sometimes necessary to modify behavior in order to avoid excessive heat loss. The addition of extra layers of clothing or increasing the intensity of exercise can assist the physiological responses to cold. If heat loss becomes excessive, core temperature may drop to dangerously low levels (hypothermia).

PHYSIOLOGICAL RESPONSES TO COLD

There are two main physiological responses to a cold environment: an increase in the thickness of the shell or insulating layers of tissue, and an increase in the metabolic rate. Changes in blood flow distribution are primarily responsible for the changes in the thickness of the shell. Increased vasoconstriction reduces the amount of blood flow to the skin and results in a reduction in heat conduction from the core to the skin surface. Interposed between the skin and muscle is a layer of fat of varying thickness. Fat is an excellent insulator since it receives little blood flow. Both the degree of vasoconstriction and the thickness of the underlying subcutaneous fat layer determine the insulating value of the shell. The insulative value of the tissues (It) is the reciprocal of skin conductance (Ksk) and can be calculated as follows:

$$I_t = \frac{T_c - \overline{T}_{sk}}{E_{sk} + R + C}$$

where T_c = core or internal temperature

T_{sk} = mean skin temperature

E_{sk} = skin evaporative rate

R = heat lost through radiation

C = heat lost through convection.

In addition to vasoconstriction, heat conservation is aided by shunting blood from superficial veins to deep veins located next to arteries. Venous blood flowing toward the core is rewarmed by the warmer blood in the arteries coming from the core through a countercurrent heat exchange (Bazett et al. 1948). This reduces the heat loss to the tissues.

Increased heat production can be accomplished by elevating the metabolic rate through shivering. Shivering may increase the resting metabolic rate by as much as four to five times. An increased metabolic rate without shivering may precede visible shivering in many cases (Pugh 1966b; Smith and Hanna 1974). The exact mechanism responsible for producing nonshivering increases in metabolism is unknown, although increased muscle tonus and increased metabolism of fatty acids are possible reasons.

FACTORS INFLUENCING PHYSIOLOGICAL RESPONSES

The physiological response to cold is affected by several different factors including body fatness, surface area to mass ratio, amount and type of clothing worn, wind, wetness, physical condition, and acclimatization. Metabolic rate and rate of heat loss have been found to be related to thickness of subcutaneous fat (Buskirk et al. 1963; Keatinge 1978; Kollias et al. 1974; Smith and Hanna 1975). Individuals with greater body fat lose heat more slowly and have smaller increases in the metabolic rate when exposed to the cold than individuals with little body fat. The surface area-to-mass ratio also influences the rate of heat loss. Smaller persons, such as children and women, with relatively large surface area-to-mass ratios lose heat at a faster rate than larger persons with similar percentages of body fatness (Kollias et al 1974; Sloan and Keatinge 1973).

Clothing insulation (Icl) depends on the thermal characteristics of the fibers, thickness, and amount of air trapped. It can be calculated as follows (Nishi et al. 1976):

$$I_{clo} = (1/0.155h) (\overline{T}_{sk} - \overline{T}_{cl}) (\overline{T}_{cl} - \overline{T}_a)$$

where I_{clo} = insulation in clo units
$\quad\quad$ h = combined heat transfer coefficient (h = h_c + h_r where
$\quad\quad\quad\quad$ h_c = convective heat loss and h_r = radiative heat loss)
$\quad$ $\overline{T}_{sk}$ = mean skin temperature
$\quad$ T_{cl} = mean clothing temperature

The more intense the exercise, the less clothing insulation necessary to maintain body temperature. For example, the cross-country ski racer working at 15 Mets (15 times the resting metabolic rate) may be comfortably clothed in a standard racing uniform with long underwear (Iclo = approximately 1 clo when the temperature is -20°C (-5°F), while a novice skier working at 6 Mets would need twice as much clothing insulation (2 clo).

The thermal conductance of various fibers determines their effectiveness as insulators. Olfein, a synthetic fiber used in underwear, has a very low thermal conductance and is therefore a good insulator. Wool also has a low thermal conductance and is a good insulator, while cotton is a better conductor and, therefore, a less effective insulator. Insulative value is also dependent on the thickness of the material and the amount of air trapped within the garment and next to the skin, since air is a poor conductor.

Air movement affects the rate of heat lost through convection. Pugh (1966b) found that a 2.5 mph (4 km/hr) wind nearly doubled the rate of heat loss from a resting subject and reduced clothing insulation to about 55 percent of the resting value. Exercise in a 9 mph (15 km/hr) wind at 5°C (41°F) increased heat loss to four times the resting rate and reduced clothing insulation to approximately 25 percent the resting value. In a colder environment (-20°C) a 9 mph (15 km/hr) wind increased the rate of heat loss fourfold during exercise compared to a no-wind exercise situation (Haymes and Dickinson 1979a).

The insulative value of many garments is reduced when they become wet. Wetting can occur due to rain, snow, accidental immersion in water (i.e., falling into a stream or through the ice), or sweating. Exercise in the wind while wearing wet clothing increased the rate of heat lost to five times the resting rate and reduced clothing insulation to 15 percent the resting value (Puch 1966b). Outer garments that repell moisture but allow the skin to breathe are ideal for many outdoor activities such as running and hiking in cold weather. The problem with many waterproof materials is that they do not allow sweat to evaporate from the skin and result in a wet layer of clothing next to the skin and a more rapid loss of body heat.

Physical conditioning appears to reduce the metabolic response to cold (Baum et al. 1976; Keatinge 1961; Kollias et al 1972), although Adams and Heberling (1958) reported an increase in heat production during cold exposure following a three-week physical training program. Elevated muscle temperature and lower skin temperatures have been observed following a conditioning program, suggesting that blood flow is shunted from the skin to the muscles (Buskirk 1978). This has the effect of increasing the tissue insulation.

Living in a cold climate does not necessarily result in acclimatization to cold. The microclimate of the skin may be no different from that found in more temperate climates due to the additional clothing worn. Studies of cold acclimatization have generally compared persons who work outdoors during cold weather with those who remain indoors. Women divers of Korea (ama) have been particularly well studied with respect to cold acclimatization. An increased metabolic rate was found in the ama during the winter (Hong 1973). Thermal insulation appears to be greater for the ama than for nondiving women with similar subcutaneous fat thickness. Lower skin temperatures and higher muscle temperatures were observed during cold water immersion among the women divers compared to nondivers, suggesting a vascular adaptation. However, higher skin temperatures during exercise have been found among outdoor workers than those who habitually remained indoors (Stromme et al. 1963)

Increased skin temperatures, especially hand temperature, would appear to be beneficial when working in the cold. Nerve conduction decreases with cooling and complete nerve block has been observed at skin temperatures below 10°C (50°F) (Vangaard, 1975). Reduced nerve conduction would impair normal motor functions and lead to loss of dexterity and feeling in the extremities.

METABOLIC RESPONSES TO EXERCISE IN THE COLD

During exercise in the cold an increase in the metabolic rate has been observed compared to warmer environments (Nadel et al. 1973; Stromme et al. 1963). Similar observations have been made on subjects wearing wet clothing exercising in the cold (Pugh 1966b). The reason for this increased metabolic rate has not always been apparent since shivering was not visible in some cases.

Increased metabolic rates have also been observed during swimming in cold water at submaximal velocities. This work was generally accompanied by shivering (Nadel et al. 1974). Lower core and skin temperatures were thought primarily responsible for the shivering response. Maximal swimming, however, produced lower maximal oxygen uptakes (max VO_2) in cold water compared to warmer water in lean subjects (Holmer and Bergh 1974; Nadel et al. 1974). In most cases the lower max VO_2 was accompanied by a drop in core temperature (Holmer and Bergh 1974). Hypothermia has been shown to significantly reduce max VO_2 while cycling (Davies et al. 1975). Elevated submaximal and reduced maximal metabolic rates may explain why exhaustion is frequently seen in conjunction with hypothermia.

Holmer and Bergh (1974) also observed lower muscle temperatures (during the maximal swims) in cold water than in warm water. Low muscle temperature could affect the chemical and physical contraction processes.

Even though metabolic rate is increased during submaximal exercise, the core temperature of lean subjects continues to drop in cold water (Holmer and

Bergh 1974). Similar observations have been made during cycling and cross-country skiing. Pugh (1967) found that exercise at work rates below 800 kgm per minute when clothing was wet resulted in a drop in core temperature. Decreases in core temperature during cross-country skiing are partially due to the downhill segments of a course since air velocity is increased during the downhill and relatively little muscular activity is needed (Haymes and Dickinson 1979b). Increasing the metabolic rate (uphill skiing) results in an increase in core temperature. In cold water, however, lean swimmers may not be able to increase the metabolic rate sufficiently, by swimming faster, to offset heat loss (Nadel 1977).

CIRCULATORY RESPONSES TO EXERCISE IN THE COLD

When resting persons are exposed to cold air (50°C/41°F), cardiac output increases, due primarily to increased stroke volume (Raven et al. 1970, 1975). Blood pressure is also elevated during cold exposure, but total peripheral resistance decreases as air temperature decreases (Raven et al. 1975). Epstein et al. (1969) observed no change in cardiac output but an increase in blood pressure during exercise in cold air. Total peripheral resistance and left ventricular minute work were also increased during exercise. Several patients with coronary-artery disease experienced angina while exercising in the cold, which Epstein et al. attributed to the increased oxygen demands of the heart muscle. Little change in heart rate has been observed when exercising in cold air (Epstein et al. 1969; Nadel et al. 1973).

Exercise in cold water is accompanied by a depression in heart rate even though metabolic rate is elevated (Holmer and Bergh 1974; McArdle et al. 1976; Nadel et al. 1974). However, cardiac output is maintained by increasing stroke volume (McArdle et al. 1976). Vasoconstriction of peripheral blood vessels would increase central blood volume, which would enhance venous return. This could explain why stroke volume increases during exercise in the cold. Immersion in water decreases the hydrostatic pressure that could further increase central blood volume and, therefore, stroke volume. The baroreceptors located in the aortic arch and carotid sinus respond to increased blood pressure by reflexly slowing the heart. This is one possible explanation why the heart rate is depressed during exercise in water but not in air.

Another explanation by Davies et al. (1975) centers on exercising subjects who were hypothermic. Heart rate was decreased during both submaximal and maximal exercise in cold air. The administration of atropine, a heart stimulant, increased the heart rate during submaximal exercise, but had little effect on the maximal heart rate. Davies et al. concluded that a lowered core temperature might directly affect cardiac muscle function. Lowered core temperatures are seen more frequently during swimming in cold water than exercise in cold air.

DANGERS OF A COLD ENVIRONMENT

The two major dangers of exercise in a cold environment are (1) failure to maintain body core temperature (hypothermia), and (2) freezing of tissues (frostbite). (See Chapter 17.) Normally, core temperature is well regulated in a narrow zone around 37°C. When heat loss exceeds heat gain, a decrease in core temperature results. As body temperature drops, muscular coordination may be impaired and cold sensations blocked (Vangaard 1975). Collapse and loss of consciousness may follow as core temperature falls below 32°C (90°F) (Taylor 1972). Death from heart failure occurs when core temperature falls in the 26 to 30°C (79 to 86°F) range (Taylor, 1972).

Failure to maintain body core temperature is often associated with exhaustion (Pugh 1966a). Since submaximal metabolic rates are elevated and maximal metabolic rates are reduced when core temperature is lowered (Davies et al. 1975; Nadel et al. 1973), fatigue may occur more rapidly in the cold. Prolonged exercise may result in lowering blood glucose to hypoglycemic levels. Core temperature has been observed to fall during exercise when hypoglycemia has been induced by alcohol consumption (Haight and Keatinge 1973).

The probability of avoiding hypothermia can be improved by selection of proper clothing, carrying extra clothes and food (including sweets), and avoidance of alcohol. Hypothermia is more commonly seen in wet-cold environments than in dry-cold (Pugh 1966a). Since clothing insulation is greatly reduced by wetting, water repellent clothing should be worn or carried in a pack. Heat loss from the heat can be substantial since little vasoconstriction in the head occurs in the cold (Froese and Burton 1957). At a temperature of -4°C (25°F), 50 percent of the resting heat loss occurs through the head (Froese and Burton 1957). Wearing a hat or other head covering can substantially reduce heat loss. Carbohydrate consumption will prevent a fall in blood glucose and core temperature (Haight and Keatinge 1973).

Frostbite most commonly affects exposed skin areas. When the wind chill index, a combination of air temperature and wind speed, falls below -32°C (-26°F) there is increased danger of freezing exposed flesh. In a -12°C (10°F) environment with a 20 mph wind, the wind chill index would be -32°C. Since sensory nerve endings are blocked at low temperatures, no sensations or pain will be felt. Cellular death does not occur until the tissue water crystalizes as ice at -4°C (25°F) (Taylor 1972). Skiers should be particularly aware of the danger of frostbite and check other members of their party for signs of numbness when the wind chill index is in the dangerous range.

REFERENCES

Adams, T. and E. J. Heberling. 1958. Human physiological responses to a standardized cold stress as modified by physical fitness. *J Appl Physiol,* 13:226-230.

Baum, E., K. Bruck, and H. P. Schwennicke. 1976. Adaptive modifications in the thermoregulatory system of long-distance runners. *J Appl Physiol*, 40:404-410.

Bazett, H. C., L. Love, M. Newton, L. Eisenberg, R. Day, and R. Forster, II. 1948. Temperature changes in blood flowing in arteries and veins in man. *J Appl Physiol*, 1:3-19.

Buskirk, E. R. 1978. Cold stress: A selective review. In *Environmental Stress: Individual Human Adaptations*, L. J. Folinsbee et al. (eds.). New York: Academic Press. pp. 249-266.

Buskirk, E. R., R. H. Thompson, and G. D. Whedon. 1963. Metabolic response to cold air in men and women in relation to total body fat content. *J Appl Physiol*, 18:603-612.

Davies, M., B. Ekblom, U. Bergh, and I. L. Kanstrup-Jensen. 1975. The effects of hypothermia on submaximal and maximal work performance. *Acta Physiol Scand*, 95:201-202.

Epstein, S. E., M. Stampfer, G. D. Beiser, R. E. Goldstein, and E. Braunwald. 1969. Effects of a reduction in environmental temperature on the circulatory response to exercise in man. *New Eng J Med*, 280:7-11.

Froese, G. and A. C. Burton. 1957. Heat losses from the human head. *J Appl Physiol*, 10:235-241.

Haight, J. S. J. and W. R. Keatinge. 1973. Failure of thermoregulation in the cold during hypoglycaemia induced by exercise and ethanol. *J Physiol*, 229:87-97.

Haymes, E. M. and A. L. Dickinson. 1979a. Body temperatures during exercise in a cold environment. *Med Sci Spts*, In press.

Haymes, E. M. and A. L. Dickinson. 1979b. Heat loss: clothing and wind. *J U.S. Ski Coaches Assoc*, 2(4):96-103.

Holmer, I. and U. Bergh. 1974. Metabolic and thermal response to swimming in water at varying temperatures. *J Appl Physiol*, 37:702-705.

Hong, S. K. 1973. Pattern of cold adaptation in women divers of Korea (ama). *Fed Proceed*, 32:1614-1622.

Keatinge, W. R. 1978. Body fat and cooling rates in relation to age. In *Environmental Stress: Individual Human Adaptation*, L. J. Folinsbee et al. (eds.). New York: Academic Press. pp. 299-302.

Keatinge, W. R. 1961. The effect of repeated daily exposure to cold and of improved physical fitness on the metabolic and vascular response to cold air. *J Physiol*, 157:209-220.

Kollias, J., R. Boileau, and E. R. Buskirk. 1972. Effects of physical conditioning in man on thermal responses to cold air. *Int J Biometerol*, 16:389-402.

Kollias, J., L. Barlett, V. Bergsteinova, J. S. Skinner, E. R. Buskirk, and W. C. Nicholas. 1974. Metabolic and thermal responses of women during cooling in water. *J Appl Physiol*, 36:577-580.

McArdle, W. D., J. R. Magel, G. R. Lesmes, and G. S. Pechar. 1976. Metabolic and cardiovascular adjustment to work in air and water at 18, 25, and 33°C. *J Appl Physiol*, 40:85-90.

Nadel, E. R., I. Holmer, U. Bergh, P. O. Astrand, and J. A. J. Stolwijk. 1973. Thermoregulatory shivering during exercise, *Life Sciences.* 13:893-989.

Nadel, E. R., I. Holmer, U. Bergh, P. O. Astrand, and J. A. J. Stolwijk. 1974. Energy exchanges of swimming man. *J Appl Physiol,* 35:465-471.

Nadel, E. R. 1977. Thermal and energetic exchanges during swimming. In *Problems with Temperature Regulation during Exercise,* E. R. Nadel (ed.). New York: Academic Press. pp. 91-119.

Nishi, Y., R. Gonzalez, R. G. Nevins, and A. P. Gagge. 1976. Field measurement of clothing thermal insulation. *ASHRAE Trans,* 81:245-252.

Pugh, L. G. C. E. 1966a. Accidental hypothermia in walkers, climbers, and campers: Report to the medical commission on accident prevention. *Brit Med J,* 1:123-129.

Pugh, L. G. C. E. 1966b. Clothing insulation and accidental hypothermia in youth. *Nature,* 209:1281-1286.

Pugh, L. G. C. E. 1967. Cold stress and muscular exercise, with special reference to accidental hypothermia. *Brit Med J,* 2:333-337.

Raven, P. B., I. Niki, T. E. Dahms, and S. M. Horvath. 1970. Compensatory cardiovascular responses during an environmental cold stress, 5°C. *J Appl Physiol,* 29:417-421.

Raven, P. B., J. E. Wilkerson, S. M. Horvath, and N. W. Bolduan. 1975. Thermal, metabolic, and cardiovascular responses to various degrees of cold stress. *J Physiol Pharmacol,* 53:293-298.

Sloan, R. E. G. and W. R. Keatinge. 1973. Cooling rates of young people swimming in cold water. *J Appl Physiol,* 35:371-375.

Smith, R. M. and J. M. Hanna. 1975. Skinfolds and resting heat loss in cold air and water: temperature equivalence. *J Appl Physiol,* 39:93-102.

Stromme, S., K. Lange Andersen, and R. W. Elsner. 1963. Metabolic and thermal responses to muscular exertion in the cold. *J Appl Physiol,* 18:756-763.

Taylor, D. E. M. 1972. Cold survival. *Brit J Spts Med,* 6:111-116.

Vangaard, L. 1975. Physiological reactions to wet-cold. *Aviat Space Environ Med,* 46:33-36.

17

Cold Weather Injuries: Hypothermia and Frostbite

George R. Kinnear

The winter season, with its characteristic drop in temperature, creates ideal conditions for a variety of coldweather activities for the outdoor enthusiast. Unfortunately, too few such individuals possess the necessary knowledge, equipment, and technical skill to deal with the severe conditions that may be encountered. Two of the more insidious problems are hypothermia (often simply referred to as exposure) and frostbite. (See Chapter 16.) These encironmental cold injuries are often associated, but each may occur without the other.

HYPOTHERMIA

The term hypothermia refers to a condition characterized by a gradual lowering of the body's core temperature. Normally, hypothermia occurs slowly. However, it can advance rapidly and, unless arrested, can cause unconciousness and death in less than an hour. Hypothermia has been classified into the following categories: mild—core temperature 35° to 30°C (95° to 86° F), moderate—core temperature 30° to 25°C (86° to 77°F), or profound—core temperature under 25°C (77°F) (Paton 1975). While hypothermia is most prevalent in geographical areas in which the ambient temperature is extremely low, it is not uncommon in regions in which the climate is fair or moderate. Hypothermia has claimed many victims when the ambient temperature is well above freezing (Nourse 1973). In the latter situation, the outdoorsperson may misjudge how easily hypothermia is initiated and becomes more vulnerable than the better prepared cold-weather-conscious person.

Characteristics

Hypothermia manifests itself gradually and may only be uncomfortable in the early stages. An individual suffering from hypothermia normally exhibits a number of characteristics corresponding to reduced internal temperature. Most of these characteristics are detectable to the outdoorsperson who is familiar with hypothermia. Figure 17.1 indicates the characteristics exhibited by an individual digressing from a normal body temperature to an unconscious condition. Ironically, the afflicted person, probably due to a lack of blood flow to the brain, exhibits irrational thinking and does not realize the severity of the problem with initial symptoms. Consequently, the person often does not take precautions to prevent further deterioration. This fact would add credence to the simple yet often violated rule that one should always travel with a partner or group in the outdoors.

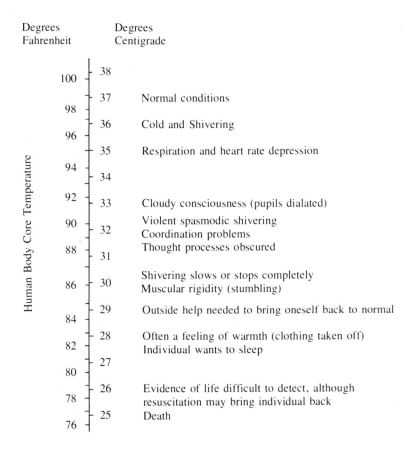

Fig. 17.1 Characteristic stages of hypothermia.

Cause

The etiology of hypothermia is quite simple. It is caused by the body's inability to prevent heat loss and/or to generate enough heat to compensate for body heat loss. The mechanisms involved in maintaining a constant internal temperature are outlined in Fig. 17.2. As illustrated, if the combined effects of factors that decrease heat loss (B) and factors that produce internal heat (C) are not enough to compensate for the loss of body heat via the mechanisms listed (A), the core temperature of the individual will fall. This will continue to occur until the effects of A are reduced or the combined effects of B and C are increased.

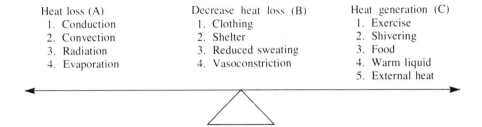

Heat loss (A)	Decrease heat loss (B)	Heat generation (C)
1. Conduction	1. Clothing	1. Exercise
2. Convection	2. Shelter	2. Shivering
3. Radiation	3. Reduced sweating	3. Food
4. Evaporation	4. Vasoconstriction	4. Warm liquid
		5. External heat

Fig. 17.2 Factors in body temperature regulation.

Heat Loss

As Wells pointed out in Chapter 13, an individual can lose heat through conduction, convection, radiation, and/or evaporation. Under normal resting conditions in a comfortable indoor atmosphere, about 40 percent of this loss will be convection, 40 percent by radiation, 20 percent by evaporation, and a negligible amount by conduction (de Vries 1974). When an individual becomes physically active in a cold and windy environment, the actual heat loss by each mechanism increases. The body will lose heat by conduction when it comes in contact with objects colder than itself, such as snow, ice, rock, metal, and air. Radiant heat loss occurs from the body to cooler objects with which it is not in contact, such as clouds, stars, or outer-space. As the layer of warmed air immediately surrounding the body moves and is replaced with cool air, heat is lost via convection. In the outdoors this is manifested in the phenomenon of wind-chill, which can very quickly reduce a warm body to a hypothermic state. Evaporation is an important cooling process during exercise, but excessive sweating may cause a serious heat loss in cold weather. Many persons are hidrotic, and this excessive sweating adds significantly to body heat loss (Ryan 1976). Wet clothing, due to either heavy sweating or to foul weather, will be dangerous in cold, windy environments. Heat is also lost from the evaporative process in respiration and is significantly increased by labored breathing. (See Chapter 13 for further explanation of avenues of heat exchange.)

Prevention of Heat Loss

If an individual exhibits any of the characteristic stages of hypothermia, immediate steps must be instituted to prevent a further reduction of body temperature. The addition of more clothing is the most accepted method of overcoming the ravages of cold, particularly if heat is being lost by the processes of convection and conduction. A clo unit is the amount of clothing normally needed to keep a resting man comfortable at a normal room temperature (see Chapter 16). While sleeping in the outdoors at -40°C (-40°F), about 12 clo units are required, but if the individual is exercising in the same conditions, only about four units are needed (Astrand and Rodahl 1970). The benefit of the heat generated by muscular effort is evident. It is important to remember that clothing is useful only in heat retention and not in heat production. Heat loss can be further reduced by the addition of wind-proof garments to reduce heat lost by wind-chill. Tents, tarps, space blankets, igloos, and snow caves reduce heat loss through radiation and convection.

Since water has a heat-removing capacity over 20 times that of air, wet garments are responsible for "wicking" heat away from the body. The removal of damp or wet clothing and replacement with dry clothing is essential. Clothing becomes wet either by the production of sweat or by contact with fluids such as rain or waterproduced by melting snow. Keeping the body cool and well ventilated while exercising and covered with water-proofed garment in the event of wet weather should ensure that heat loss due to evaporation and conduction is kept to a minimum. Wool and pile are excellent insulators since they do not absorb as much water as do other materials, and they retain much of their insulating qualities even when wet.

For the person who has fallen into cold water, a different approach is necessary in order to preserve the critical core temperature. Hayward, Eckerson, and Collis (1975) have devised a technique called the HELP (Heat Escape Lessening Posture) behavior. In the posture the individual tries to remain motionless while crossing and flexing the legs and placing the hands against the thorax. The head, being a great heat radiator, is kept out of the water. When this position is assumed and the body is nearly motionless, less body heat is lost to the surrounding water. Hence, the individual's body temperature is not reduced as much as it would be if the individual treaded water or used the drownproofing technique.

The body possesses a unique mechanism that assists in reducing heat loss. Peripheral vasoconstriction, which may reduce blood circulation through surface blood vessels as much as a hundredfold, allows the temperature in the skin and extremities to decline sharply while maintaining a warm inner core. The vessels of the head and neck do not possess extensive vasoconstrictive capacity, however (Astrand and Rodahl 1970), and heat is lost from this part of the body even in the hypothermic person. Clothing such as balaclavas or togues and scarves are necessary to reduce massive heat loss from the head and neck during cold exposure.

Subcutaneous fat acts as an excellent insulator. (See Chapters 13 and 16.) Females, due to their higher percentage of body fat, may be more tolerant to cold than their male counterparts (DeVries 1974). Adipose tissue, however, is functional in trapping heat only so long as it is warm. When it becomes chilled, it too draws heat from the inner core (Morehouse and Miller 1976). The continued but temporary fall in core temperature after the body has been removed from a cold environment—often called "after drop"—may be partially explained by a continued loss of heat to chilled inactive fat (Morehouse and Miller 1976).

Heat Generation

The only way to generate additional heat in the body is to increase the metabolic rate. This may be accomplished voluntarily with exercise or involuntarily by shivering. Brisk walking and/or shivering can increase heat production as much as four or five times (Astrand and Rodahl 1970). These processes are not accomplished without fuel, however, and food or liquids must be ingested to provide necessary substrates for the production of the energy required for muscular contraction. Warm foods and liquids have the additional effect of supplying heat to the body beyond their caloric value. Without this necessary energy source a vicious cycle results, for fatigue would eventually occur, and the extent of shivering and/or exercise would decrease. Since digestion and assimilation require time, it is necessary that the outdoorsperson become a constant nibbler, for food may be eaten too late to be of benefit to provide the necessary heat for the hypothermic individual. Foods high in carbohydrates are prescribed for such situations since they are a labile form of energy.

Rewarming

If internal methods of heat generation are not of a magnitude to overcome the effects of heat loss, external heat sources must be utilized. Fires, warmed tents, waterbottles on the body, and even the heat of another body cuddled against the hypothermic victim are all effective in rewarming. The whole process of rewarming, particularly if the individual is in the final stages of hypothermia, is a slow intricate process and unless done correctly can bring death to a subject who could, under correct conditions, recover. The rewarming process, if done in the outdoors where heartbeat analysis, medication, and acid-base balance cannot be monitored, should be done slowly and by initially warming the torso and then the extremities. If cold blood, laden with metabolites from the extremities, is rushed back to the heart, cardiac arrest often occurs (Bangs 1975). This phenomenon is referred to as "rewarm shock." Forcing the individual to walk or massaging the extremities, particularly if the individual is elderly or unfit, produces the same undesirable results as when one attempts to rewarm a hypothermic individual too rapidly. A delicate balance in the speed of rewarming seems to exist, for if rewarming is too slow the victim may not recover.

An individual in the final stages of hypothermia may according to all outward appearances be clinically dead and yet may survive as a result of proper rewarming. Slowed down metabolic processes make it possible for the individual to survive without suffering brain damage. The best field treatment would seem to be to initiate rewarming procedures no matter how hopeless the situation appears. Ward states, "It should be stressed that death may be defined as a failure to survive—apparently dead individuals have recovered." (Ward 1975, p. 316.)

FROSTBITE

Frostbite, the actual freezing of skin and/or underlying deeper tissue as a result of exposure to cold conditions, is often associated with hypothermia. It too manifests itself in varying degrees, based primarily upon the period of contact and the degree of cold exposure. Areas not covered by a layer of subcutaneous tissue, such as fingers and toes, and other normally uncovered areas such as the nose and ears are the most commonly affected sites.

Causes of frostbite extend beyond actual exposure to cold in that such factors as fatigue, lack of food, and dehydration play a role (Nourse 1973). Exposure to high altitude leads to a reduction in peripheral blood flow that may predispose a person to cold injury of this nature (Ward 1975). The genetic make-up of an individual may, however, be the most significant contributing factor, for some people are much more susceptible to the ravages of frostbite than are others (Bangs 1975). Bangs has emphasized the importance of wearing nonconstricting garments in the cold. The foot, because circulation is often impaired by wearing ill-fitting or tightly laced shoes (or too many socks), is particularly vulnerable to frostbite. Keeping the upper leg warm to assist in preventing heat loss from warm blood circulating to a cold foot is a consideration often overlooked when one attempts to keep the foot warm.

Frostbite can actually be thought of as a protective mechanism, for in essence, the body is shutting off the circulation to a part or parts to prevent further heat loss. When an area becomes chilled, small blood vessels become constricted and blood is shifted away from the chilled area via arterialvenous shunts. This mechanism prevents warm blood from being cooled and then returned to central body parts where it could lower the core temperature to a critical level. A life-for-limb trade-off is apparent. Unlike the victim of severe hypothermia, the frostbitten individual usually does not succumb (Clarke, Ward, and Williams 1975). This obviously dictates the order of treatment of the hypothermic and frostbitten person.

Frostnip (First Degree)

The first or least severe form of tissue freezing is called frostnip, in which no permanent damage is done to the tissue. In this condition the skin merely blanches and with immediate warming (even by gently rubbing) it does not progress further. Frequently the individual is not aware of frostnip, and it is often another individual who detects the initial warning signs of trouble.

Superficial Frostbite (Second and Third Degree)

In second degree frostbite, the freezing affects the epidermis of the skin, whereas in the third degree the entire dermis is frozen. These degrees of frostbite are curable without a residual scar, although in some cases surgery may be necessary (Paton 1975).

Deep Frostbite (Fourth Degree)

When underlying tissues such as muscle, bone, and tendon are frozen in addition to the skin, the individual experiences fourth degree frostbite. Ramifications are severe, and the individual may lose appendages, or parts thereof, either because of the need for surgical amputation (usually necessary as a result of persistent gangrene) or because of spontaneous amputation in which the afflicted part sloughs off by itself. Often near normal functioning will return to the area after a period of months, and surgery should usually be delayed as long as possible (Ward 1975).

Immersion Injury (Trench Foot)

A third injury, related to frostbite yet not quite as severe, is referred to as immersion injury (Ward 1975) or trench foot (Hourse 1973). The injury is unique since it may occur on tissue exposed to nonfreezing temperatures (usually below 15°C/59°F). This injury normally affects the feet and may be a problem when they are subjected to cold, wet conditions for a period of six hours or more. The symptoms and treatment of immersion injury are similar to those associated with frostbite. The outdoorsperson, particularly if involved in activities in which the feet are wet, should be aware that problems can develop even when the temperature is quite comfortable.

Treatment

Modern treatment of frostbite involves rapid rewarming without massage. Field treatment should be initiated only if the individual is able to reach medical help without having to use the afflicted area further. Once the area is rewarmed, it must not be used until healing has progressed; otherwise permanent damage may result. Mountaineers have often walked miles on numb, frostbitten feet without any apparent added damage. Thawing the frostbitten extremity, only to have it immediately refrozen, assures more damage than leaving it initially frozen until medical treatment is available.

Field treatment should ideally involve bathing the afflicted area in 45°C water or by hot towels or immersion. Treatment should be accomplished in 30 to 45 minutes. Intense pain always results upon rapid rewarming, but less injury results than if rewarming is slower.

Frostbite, probably because of the associated numbness, is often experienced without the individual realizing it. For these reasons boots should be removed periodically in cold conditions, and the toes checked to ensure that circulation and, hence, warmth are still present.

CONCLUSION

Cold weather environmental injuries are insidious and serious. Prevention in the form of proper clothing, a working knowledge of the causes, symptoms, and treatment of cold weather injuries, a high level of personal fitness, and sound judgment should mitigate complications and ensure that an outdoor experience becomes a unique and enjoyable one rather than a disaster.

REFERENCES

Astrand, P. O. and K. Rodahl. 1970. *Textbook of Work Physiology*. New York: McGraw-Hill.

Bangs, C. 1976. Hypothermia and cold injury. *Off Belay*, 29:2-5.

Clarke, C., M. Ward, and E. Williams (eds.). 1975. *Mountain Medicine and Physiology*. Alpine Club of Canada.

deVries, H. A. 1974. *Physiology of Exercise for Physical Education and Athletics*. 2nd ed Dubuque, Iowa: Wm. C. Brown.

Hayward, J. S., J. D. Eckerson, and M. S. Collis. 1975. Effect of behavioral variables on cooling rate of man in cold water. *J Appl Physiol*, 38, 1073-1077.

Keatinge, W. R. 1969. *Survival in Cold Water*. Oxford: Blackwell Scientific.

Lathrop, T. G. 1973. *Hypothermia: Killer of the Unprepared*. Oregon: Mazamas.

Martin, E. 1973. A killer for all season: Hypothermia. *Wilderness Camping*, 3, 38-41.

Meyer-Arendt, J. 1974 Frostbite—Signs, prevention, and treatment. *Off Belay*, 18, 2-6.

Morehouse, L. E. and A. T. Miller. 1976. *Physiology of Exercise*. 7th ed. St. Louis: C. V. Mosby.

Neuwirth, J. G. 1974. Cold. *Off Belay*, 13, 4-9.

Nourse, A. E. 1973. Cold-weather killers: Hypothermia and frostbite. *Backpacker*, 1, 37-39.

Paton, B. C. 1976. Cold, hypothermia and frostbite. *Proceedings Mountain Medicine Symposium Yosemite*. Yosemite: Charles S. Houston.

Ryan, A. J. 1977. Medical aspects of mountain climbing. *Physician and Spts Med*, 5, 45-60.

Ward, M. 1975. *Mountain Medicine*. London: Crosby, Lockwood, Staples.

18

Effect of Altitude on Physical Performance

Edward T. Howley

In the months prior to the 1968 Olympic Games, some athletes thought their performances would be adversely affected as a result of competing in Mexico City. The reason for such a reaction was the altitude — 2300 m (7400 ft.). While many performances were not equal to the former Olympic standards in these games, not all were below expectations. In fact, some improved. Why? What adjustments does the body have to make in order to exercise at high altitude? Can someone who was born and raised at sea level ever completely adapt to high altitude? Before we can examine these questions, a brief overview of the environmental conditions at altitude will be presented.

Of major importance to performance at altitude is the composition of atmospheric air. The atmospheric pressure at any point on earth is proportional to the weight of the air over that point. This pressure at sea level (SL) is equal to the pressure exerted by a column of mercury one centimeter square and 76.0 centimeters high. As one goes to a higher altitude, the weight of that air column is less and the gas molecules are farther apart, that is, the air becomes less dense. At an altitude of 5600 m (18,400 ft.) the atmospheric pressure is one-half that of SL, and there are half as many molecules of oxygen (and other gases) per unit volume of air. Consequently, to take the same volume of oxygen into the lungs at 5600 m, one would have to breathe twice as much air as at SL. Simply stated, as the altitude increases, the availability of oxygen decreases. In addition to reduced oxygen availability at altitude, the air is dryer and colder, and the ultraviolet radiation is greater. These combined stresses can have dramatic effects on the human body at rest as well as at work. This chapter will deal exclusively with the stress of reduced oxygen availability and athletic performance. (The most common altitudes at which human performance has been studied are 2,300 m (7,400 ft.), 3,100 m (10,200 ft.), 4,000m (13,000 ft.), and 4,540 m (14,900 ft.). For the remainder of this chapter the altitude will be presented in meters.)

In order to discuss the effect of altitude on performance, athletic events will be classified into two broad categories: short-term and long-term activities. In short-term activities, the energy for muscle contraction (adenosine triphosphate or ATP) is provided from that stored or easily produced in the muscle. Oxygen is not required for these energy-producing processes. These short-term activities are sometimes called anaerobic activities, meaning that ATP is produced without oxygen. In long-term activities the energy for muscle contraction is provided primarily by reactions in which oxygen is needed. These long-term activities are sometimes called aerobic activities, indicating that performance is dependent on a continuous supply of oxygen to the tissues. Any reduction in the supply of oxygen to the tissues would be detrimental to the performance of long-term activities.

SHORT-TERM ANAEROBIC PERFORMANCE

The shorter the performance the more an individual relies on energy that is stored or easily produced within a muscle. Consequently, the availability of oxygen from the environment is of little importance in short races, that is, those lasting less than two minutes. Under these circumstances one might predict that performance in short races might not be adversely affected at altitude. In fact, due to the lower density of the air at altitude, less resistance is offered to movement; consequently, performance in these events might be improved (Pugh 1967). This appeared to be the case in Mexico City. Table 18.1 shows the performance in the 1964 (Tokyo) and 1968 (Mexico City) Olympic Games for some short, explosive events. It is clear that not all performances suffer when races are conducted at altitude.

Table 18.1
Comparison of Performances in Short Races in
1964 and 1968 Olympic Games

OLYMPIC	SHORT RACES: MEN				SHORT RACES: WOMEN			
GAMES	100m	200m	400m	800m	100m	200m	400m	800m
1964 (Tokyo)	10.0s	20.3s	45.1s	1m.45.1s	11.4s	23.0s	52.0s	2m.1.1s
1968 (Mexico City)	9.9s	19.8s	43.8s	1m.44.3s	11.0s	22.5s	52.0s	2m.0.9s
% change*	+1.0	+2.5	+2.9	+0.8	+3.5	+2.2	0	+0.2

* + sign indicates improvement over 1964 performance.

LONG-TERM AEROBIC PERFORMANCE

As the duration of an activity increases, more and more of the energy for muscular contraction is derived from processes requiring oxygen. For example, 90 percent of muscular energy is derived from aerobic processes in a 5000-meter race as compared to only 20 percent in a 400-meter race (see Table 18.2; Saltin 1967). It is performance in these longer events, that is, aerobic events, that deteriorates at altitude. Table 18.3 shows the results of some of the longer races in the 1964 (Tokyo) and 1968(Mexico City) Olympic Games.

Table 18.2
The percent of energy derived aerobically and
anaerobically for short and long races

ENERGY SOURCES	DISTANCE IN METERS					
	400	800	1500	3000	5000	10000
AEROBIC PROCESSES %	20	35	60	85	90	95
ANAEROBIC PROCESSES %	80	65	40	15	10	5

Table 18.3
Comparison of Performances in Long Races in the
1964 and 1968 Olympic Games

OLYMPIC GAMES	LONG RACES: MEN					
	1500m	3000m	5000m	10,000m	Marathon	50,000m Walk
1964 (Tokyo)	3m. 38.1s	8m.30.8s	13m.48.8s	28m.24.4s	2h.12m.11.2s	4h.11m.11.2s
1968 (Mexico City)	3m. 34.9s	8m.51.0s	14m.05.0s	29m.27.4s	2h.20m.26.4s	4h.20m.13.6s
% Change*	+1.5	−3.9	+1.9	−3.7	−6.2	−3.6

*+ sign indicates improvement over 1964 performance.

Kipchoge Keino's performance in the 1500-meter run is noteworthy. Not only did he improve the Olympic record set by Herb Elliot in 1960, but the time of 3 minutes, 34.9 seconds is still the Olympic record. His performance stands apart from those in the longer races in which performance decrements of 1.9 to 6.2 percent were observed. His birth and prolonged residence in Kenya, at an altitude similar to that of Mexico City, probably contributed to his outstanding performancer

Maximal Aerobic Power

Why did altitude have such a negative effect on performance in the longer races? The reason is the reduction in available atmospheric oxygen. The effect of this oxygen lack is easily seen when one measures the maximal rate at which a person can produce energy aerobically. This is called maximal aerobic power. The greater the maximal aerobic power the higher is the speed an individual can maintain in the long races. As the maximal aerobic power decreases, the rate at which an individual can run these longer races tends to decrease.

Figure 18.1 shows what happens to maximal aerobic power in trained athletes as they go to higher and higher altitudes. As the altitude increases, the maximal aerobic power decreases. On this basis one might predict that performance in the long races decreases as altitude increases. This appears to be the case (Jokl et al. 1967).

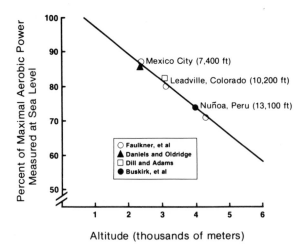

Fig. 18.1 Athletes' maximal aerobic power in differing altitudes.

The Cardiovascular System at Altitude

Maximal aerobic power is more than a measure of the maximal rate at which energy can be produced aerobically. It is also a measure of the maximal rate at which the heart can deliver oxygen enriched blood to active tissues to produce that energy. Could the reduction in maximal aerobic power at altitude be due to a decrease in heart function rather than just a simple reduction in available oxygen? The answer appears to be yes and no, depending on the altitude.

The volume (liters) of blood pumped by the heart each minute is called the cardiac output. Cardiac output is calculated by multiplying the heart rate (beats per minute) times the stroke volume (the volume of blood pumped by the heart per beat). Any decrease in maximal heart rate or maximal stroke volume at altitude would decrease cardiac output and, consequently, the delivery of O_2 to working muscles. In several studies the maximal heart rate was unchanged by exposure to altitudes of 2300 m (Faulkner et al. 1968; Pugh 1967), 3100 m (Grover et al. 1967), and 4000 m (Buskirk et al. 1967).

Studies on the changes in maximal stroke volume at altitude are inconsistent (Kollias and Buskirk 1974). Consequently, it is not possible to make a clear statement about the effect of altitude on maximal stroke volume. If, for purposes of discussion, it is assumed that maximal stroke volume is unaffected by altitude, then one would have to conclude that the maximal cardiac output (the maximal rate at which blood can be delivered to tissues) is unaffected by exposure to moderate altitudes.

Maximal aerobic power is said to be a measure of the maximal rate at which the heart can deliver oxygen to active tissues. If the maximal cardiac output is unchanged by exposure to moderate altitudes, then how could the maximal rate of oxygen transport be decreased? The answer is that the hemoglobin molecule, found in the red blood cell, is transporting less oxygen at altitude.

There is a maximum amount of O_2 that can be bound with hemoglobin. At sea level, hemoglobin is 96 to 98 percent saturated with O_2. With an increase in altitude, the degree to which the hemoglobin molecule is saturated with O_2 declines. At 2300 m, hemoglobin is only 88 percent saturated with O_2, and at 4000 m, only 71 percent saturated with O_2. These values are similar to the values shown in Fig. 18.1 for the decrease in maximal aerobic power with increasing altitude. This is strong evidence that it is the reduction in the saturation of the hemoglobin molecule rather than any decrease in heart function that causes the decrease in maximal aerobic power at these altitudes (Kollias and Buskirk 1974).

The above discussion is based on the observation in several studies that maximal heart rate does not change at moderate altitude. However, some studies have reported a decrease in maximal heart rate at 3100 m (Dill and Adams 1971) and 4300 m (Faulkner et al. 1968) for trained athletes. In these cases the decrease in maximal aerobic power at altitude is due to the combined effects of lower O_2 saturation of the hemoglobin and the lower maximal cardiac output. While there may be some inconsistencies in the observations concerning the maximal heart rate at altitudes below 4300 m, there is little question that maximal heart rate decreases at altitudes above 4300 m.

At 4650 m (15300 ft.), the maximal heart rate was observed to be 33 beats per minute lower than at sea level. At 5800 to 6400 m (19,000 to 21,000 ft.), the value was 47 beats per minute lower than at sea level (Pugh 1964). The result is that maximal aerobic power falls off at an even greater rate than predicted from desaturation of hemoglobin. Work, even light work, at these altitudes is very difficult to perform.

In the previous discussion we dealt with the effect of altitude on maximal performance and maximal aerobic power. The lower O_2 saturation of hemoglobin occurring at altitude also affects the heart rate response to light or moderate work. The oxygen requirement for doing a given rate of work is the same at altitude as it is at sea level (Pugh et al. 1964). Since there is less oxygen contained in each liter of blood at altitude, the heart must beat faster to deliver the same quantity of oxygen to the muscles. Figure 18.2 shows values for the heart rate response for the same oxygen consumption at sea level and at 3100 m altitude for a group of trained runners. It is apparent that even at this altitude marked changes in the heart rate response to light work have occurred.

The Respiratory System at Altitude

As mentioned in the introductory comments, the air at altitude is less dense. In order to transport the same number of oxygen molecules from the air to the lungs at altitude, one must breathe more air than at sea level. The term pulmonary ventilation describes the volume of air (in liters) breathed per minute. It should be no surprise that in order to consume the same volume of oxygen per

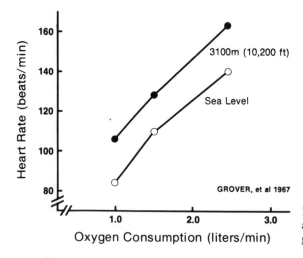

Fig. 18.2 Heart rate response at different altitudes for a group of trained runners.

minute during exercise at altitude, pulmonary ventilation must increase. Figure 18.3 shows this clearly for a group of trained runners tested at sea level and at 3100 m. In Fig. 18.4, data for subject MBG from Pugh's study of exercise at high altitudes (Pugh 1964) are presented. It is apparent that as altitude increases, the pulmonary ventilation must increase to bring the same number of oxygen molecules into the lungs. The ventilation response at these high altitudes is so great that one's ability to do work may be limited by fatigue of the respiratory muscles (Pugh 1964).

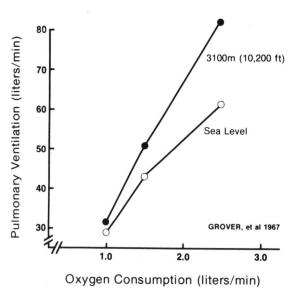

Fig. 18.3 Pulmonary ventilation differences at varying altitudes for a group of trained runners.

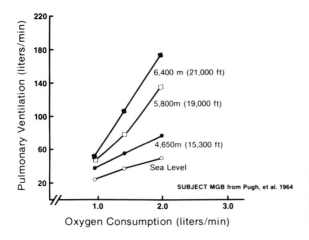

Fig. 18.4 Pulmonary ventilation differences for one subject excercising at varying altitudes.

Observations recorded by Major R. W. G. Hingston in the 1924 assault of Mount Everest are of interest. Above 5800 m (19,000 ft.), "the very slightest exertion, such as the tying of a bootlace, the opening of a rationbox, the getting into a sleeping-bag, was associated with marked respiratory distress." At 8200 m (27,000 ft.) one member of the expedition "had to take seven, eight, or ten complete respirations for every single step forward. And even at that slow rate of progress he had to rest for a minute or two every 20 or 30 yards" (Norton 1925).

Adaptation to Altitude

As described earlier, one of the main factors affecting performance in the distance races at altitude is the incomplete saturation of hemoglobin. Is it possible to compensate for this? The answer is yes.

As a person spends time at altitude, the body responds to the low oxygen pressure (hypoxia) by increasing the production of red blood cells that contain hemoglobin. The results of studies on permanent residents of high altitude show a rather complete compensation for the low oxygen pressure. The hemoglobin concentration of male, sea-level resident in Lima, Peru was found to be 15.6 percent by weight. A value of 21.1 percent was found in males who were permanent residents of Morococha, Peru (4540 m) (Hurtado 1964). The hemoglobin of the sea level resident was 98 percent saturated with O_2, and as a result, 206 milliliters (ml) of oxygen were transported per liter of blood. The hemoglobin of the altitude resident was only 81 percent saturated with O_2, but due to the "extra" hemoglobin, each liter of blood carried 224 ml of oxygen—a value that is about 9 percent greater than that found in sea level residents.

Additional evidence that the adaptation of these altitude residents is complete is found in their maximal aerobic power. Values reported for these altitude residents measured at or above 4000 m are similar to those reported for healthy sea level residents measured at sea level (Mazess 1969; Kollias et al. 1968).

A practical example of this adaptation is found in Captain J. G. Bruce's observations of the Tibetan porters during the 1924 attempt to reach the top of Mount Everest. "The performance of the women are worthy of record. One carried her child of about two years on top of her 40 lb load from 17,500 feet to 19,800 feet, deposited her load there and carried the child back again. She at once expressed her readiness to repeat the journey if necessary" (Norton 1925).

How long does it take to achieve this complete adaptation? This is a difficult question to answer. Some believe that the fully adapted individual must be exposed to high altitude during the growth period in early childhood. A study of altitude residents who had migrated to altitude as children indicated that the maximal aerobic power was highest in those who spent most of their childhood at altitude and lowest in those who had spent only a few years of childhood at altitude (Frisancho et al. 1973).

To determine how complete this adaptation was in the migrants who spent most of their childhood at altitude, measurements of maximal aerobic power were made on these migrants and on permanent altitude residents whose parents were also permanent altitude residents. The values for maximal aerobic power were the same for both groups. Measurements of maximal aerobic power were also made on Peruvian adults who spent their childhood near sea level, and on United States Peace Corps volunteers. These groups lived at altitudes above 3000 m for four months to four years. In contrast to those who migrated to altitude as children, there was no apparent relationship between length of residence and maximal aerobic power. This suggests that for complete adaptation to altitude one must be exposed to the altitude during the growing years.

Training for Competition at Altitude

Several years before the Olympic Games were held in Mexico City it was very clear that performance in the long races would be relatively poor because of the altitude. Many studies were conducted to determine the method and length of time an athlete should train at altitude to minimize the effect of the oxygen lack on performance. The results of these studies were both surprising and interesting.

One of the first surprises was the variability among the athletes in how they responded to altitude. In a study of six world class middle distance runners at 2300 m, the decrement in maximal aerobic power ranged from 8.8 to 22.3 percent on the second day at altitude (Pugh 1967). In a study of six well-trained high school champion runners at 3090m, the decrement in maximal aerobic power ranged from 13.9 to 24.4 percent (Dill and Adams 1971). Finally, in a study of six college runners at 4000 m, the percent decrement in maximal aerobic power ranged from 24.8 to 34.3 on the third day at altitude (Buskirk et al. 1967). With such variability it is understandable that the best runner at sea level may not necessarily be the best at a particular altitude if the person experiences the largest drop in maximal aerobic power. Another interesting observation was the considerable variability among the athletes in how they responded to their stay at altitude. One study reported during a 25-day residence at 2300 m that the improvement in maximal aerobic power ranged from 1 to 8 percent (Pugh 1967). While several studies found a gradual improvement in maximal aerobic power as a result of training at altitude for periods of 10 to 28 days (Balke et al. 1965; Daniels and Oldridge 1970; Pugh 1967; Dill and Adams 1971), other studies did not observe this (Faulkner et al. 1968; Grover and Reeves 1967). Finally, upon return to sea level after training at altitude, some studies reported higher values for maximal aerobic power than were measured before the altitude residence (Balke et al. 1965; Daniels and Oldridge 1970; Dill and Adams 1971). Others found no improvement over the pre-altitude sea level value for maximal aerobic power (Buskirk et al. 1967; Faulkner et al. 1968; Grover and Reeves 1967).

Why was there such variability in response to training at altitude? Several explanations have been offered. If an athlete is not in peak condition before going to altitude, the stress of training and exposure to the low oxygen levels would probably cause greater gains in performance capabilities than might be observed in an athlete who begins altitude training in peak condition. There were some differences from study to study in the physical condition of the participants, so one would have to expect differences in the degree of improvement. A second reason for the differences in studies is found in the altitude at which the study was conducted.

If runners train at high altitude (4000 m), their reduced maximal aerobic power at altitude forces them to train at speeds slower than what they would run at lower altitudes. Such a reduction in the intensity of training could result in the runner becoming relatively "detrained." Consequently, upon return to sea level, performance might not be as good as it was before going to these high altitudes (Buskirk et al. 1967). As an alternative to training at one altitude for prolonged periods of time, one study (Daniels and Oldridge 1970) used a series of short exposures to 2300 m (for 7 to 14 days) with intermittent trips to sea level (for 5 to 11 days). This method provided an opportunity to adapt to the altitude and also to train at "race pace." Detraining should be less likely under such conditions, and as evidence of this, 13 personal best times were recorded by the subjects during the various sea level trips.

It is apparent that regardless of the type and duration of training used to adapt to altitude, most athletes in the middle and long distance races will show a reduction in performance when the races are held at altitude. The only exception might be an athlete who had the good fortune to be born and raised at altitude. This individual, compared to a person born and raised at sea level, would probably not experience the same degree of deterioration in performance in the long races. Kipchoge Keino had this good fortune. He was born, raised, and trained at about 2400 m in Africa. He set a new Olympic record in the 1500 m race at the Mexico City games held at 2300 m.

SUMMARY

Altitude does not have a detrimental effect on all athletic performances. In fact, due to the reduction in the density of the air at altitude, performance in the middle and long distances races is definitely reduced. The energy required for muscular contraction in these long races is derived from cellular processes requiring oxygen. As the altitude increases, performance in the long races declines as a result of a decrease in the ability to transport oxygen. The hemoglobin molecule, found in the red blood cell, is not as saturated with oxygen at altitude compared to sea level. Nature's way to compensate for this reduction in available atmospheric oxygen at altitude is to produce more hemoglobin and red blood cells. This compensation is so complete in the altitude resident that the person has the same capacity to transport oxygen at 4300 m as the sea level resident can at sea level. Sea level residents can make some modest improvements in their ability to transport oxygen at altitude by continuous or intermittent exposures to the altitude. It is clear that hard physical training at altitude is necessary to realize optimum performance in competition held at altitude.

REFERENCES

Balke, B., F. Nagle, and J. Daniels. 1965. Altitude and maximum performance in work and sports activity. *JAMA*, 194, 646-649.

Balke, B. 1968. Variation in altitude and its effects on exercise performance. In *Exercise Physiology*, H. B. Falls (ed.). New York: Academic Press.

Buskirk, E., J. Kollias, R. Akers, E. Prokop, and E. Reategui. 1967. Maximal performance at altitude and on return from altitude in conditioned runners. *J Appl Physiol*, 23, 259-266.

Daniels, J. and N. Oldridge. 1970. The effects of alternate exposure to altitude and sea level on world-class middle-distance runners. *Med Sci Spts*, 2, 107-112.

Dill, D. and W. Adams. 1971. Maximal oxygen uptake at sea level and at 3,090-m altitude in high school champion runners. *J Appl Physiol*, 30, 854-859.

Faulkner, J., J. Kollias, C. Favour, E. Buskirk, and B. Balke. 1968. Maximum aerobic capacity and running performance at altitude. *J Appl Physiol*, 24, 685-691.

Frisancho, R., C. Martinez, T. Velasques, J. Sanchez, and H. Montoye. 1973. Influence of developmental adaptation on aerobic capacity at high altitude. *J Appl Physiol*, 34, 176-180.

Grover, R. F. and J. T. Reeves. 1967. Exercise performance of athletes at sea level and 3,100 meters altitude. In *The Effects of Altitude on Physical Performance*, R. F. Goddard (ed.). Chicago: Athletic Institute.

Grover, R., J. Reeves, E. Grover, and J. Leathers. 1967. Muscular exercise in young men native to 3,100 m altitude. *J Appl Physiol*, 22, 555-564.

Hurtado, A. 1964. Animals in high altitudes: Resident man. In *Handbook of Physiology, Section 4, Adaptation to the Environment,* D. B. Dill (ed.). Washington: American Physiological Society.

Jokl, E., A. Frucht, H. Brauer, D. Seaton, P. Jokl, and E. Simon. 1967. Interpretation of performance predictions for Tokyo Olympic Games, 1964, with extrapolation for 1968. In *The Effects of Altitude on Physical Performance,* R. F. Goddard (ed.). Chicago: Athletic Institute.

Kollias, J., E. Buskirk, R. Akers, E. Prokop, P. Baker, and E. Picon-Reategui. 1968. Work capacity of long-time residents and newcomers to altitude. *J Appl Physiol,* 25, 792-799.

Kollias, J. and E. Buskirk. 1974. Exercise and Altitude. In *Science and Medicine of Exercise and Sport.* 2nd ed. W. R. Johnson and E. R. Buskirk (eds.). New York: Harper and Row.

Mazess, R. 1969. Exercise performance at high altitude in Peru. *Fed Proc,* 28, 1301-1306.

Norton, E. F. 1925. *The Fight for Everest 1924.* New York: Longmans, Green.

Pugh, L. 1964. Animals in high altitudes: Man above 5,000 meters-mountain exploration. In *Handbook of Physiology, Section 4, Adaptation to the Environment,* D. B. Dill (ed.). Washington: American Physiological Society.

Pugh, L., M. Gill, S. Lahiri, J. Milledge, M. Ward, and J. West. 1964. Muscular exercise at great altitudes. *J Appl Physiol,* 19, 431-440.

Pugh, L. 1967. Athletes at altitude. *J Appl Physiol,* 192, 619-646.

Saltin, B. 1967. Aerobic and anaerobic work capacity at an altitude of 2,250 meters. In *The Effects of Altitude on Physical Performance,* R. F. Goddard (ed.). Chicago: Athletic Institute.

19

Altitude Illness

George R. Kinnear and John Evans

Altitude or mountain illness is revealed by a group of symptoms arising mainly from increased altitude and concomitant hypoxic conditions. These symptoms are often merely uncomfortable and only partially debilitating, but in many instances certain types of the malady cause needless and preventable deaths (Houston 1975).

Altitude illness manifests itself in four recognizable ways, often with much overlap. Acute mountain sickness (AMS), high altitude pulmonary edema (HAPE), cerebral edema (CE), and retinal hemorrhage (RH) are currently recognized as distinct problems. With the exception of RH, the hypoxic conditions encountered at medium to high altitudes lead to increased arterial pressure that tends to shift extracellular water in excessive amounts into the brain and lung compartments.

Death may result quickly from both HAPE or CE, but recognition of subtle symptoms in the early stages of these conditions will enable the individual to take preventive measures. Since altitude sickness often begins as low as 5000 feet, Alpine and Nordic skiers, climbers, and ambitious hikers all need an awareness of the cause, symptoms, prevention, and treatment of the illness. Relationships among the illnesses are ill-defined at this time. However, case studies tend to suggest that while the four main types of mountain illness may occur independently of each other, the tendency is for them to occur in conjunction (although possibly in differing degrees). Rennis (1975) believes that AMS is the forerunner to CE. Individuals with severe HAPE are more prone to CE (Hultgren 1976). The reverse may also be true in that Rennie (1975) has observed that the worst cases of CE always exhibit HAPE.

ACUTE MOUNTAIN SICKNESS (AMS)

The mechanism responsible for AMS, although not clearly understood, is outlined in Fig. 19.1. AMS is most apparent in people who go rapidly from low to moderate or high altitude. Although it normally persists for only two or three days (Houston 1975), AMS may recur once the individual moves to a higher altitude. Symptoms of AMS such as headache, nausea and vomiting, shortness of breath, rapid heart rate, poor appetite, and general malaise may be apparent as low as 5000 feet, but generally do not develop at altitudes less than 10,000 feet. Symptoms, although sometimes present immediately upon arrival at altitude, are more commonly delayed one to three days after arrival. Unfortunately, a high level of physical fitness does not prevent AMS (Rennie 1976) nor any of the more serious complications. Some people are more prone to mountain illness than others, and being sick at altitude once may suggest that the individual has a predisposition to become ill again upon returning to altitude.

In an attempt to acclimatize and hence reduce the symptoms of AMS, climbers going to high altitudes have developed techniques that appear to give some immunization. Stage ascents, in which climbers advance slowly, have proven efficacious in dealing with altitude problems. Generally, one day is allowed for every 1000 foot ascent above 10,000 feet; while above 14,000 feet the climber is limited to 500 feet a day. In expedition or siege-type climbing in which three weeks or more may be spent on a mountain, another adage—"climb high, sleep low" is followed. This simply means that the day is spent working at

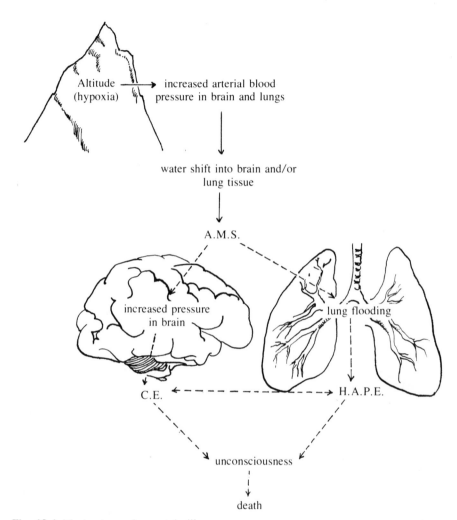

Fig. 19.1 Mechanisms of mountain illnesses.

altitudes higher than where the party will sleep. Climbers will carry one or two loads up a thousand feet and then return to sleep. The next day the process is repeated, sleeping at the point of the previous day's high camp. These techniques are not needed in moderate-altitude climbs of 14,000 to 15,000 feet during which it is possible to ascend and descend in one or two days, and during which relief from the illness occurs upon descending. On higher altitude climbs during which technical difficulties are not present and a rapid descent is possible, the acclimatization guidelines are often violated.

AMS is not fatal, but it may be a precursor to more serious problems. Treatment involves the ingestion of liberal amounts of fluids. Climbers often need an excess of four quarts of water per day (Bowman 1977) in order to avoid dehydration because of excessive water loss. In addition, mild activity, often referred to as"active-rest" (as opposed to complete rest), and aspirin seem to mitigate the symptoms.

HIGH ALTITUDE PULMONARY EDEMA (HAPE)

HAPE is more serious than AMS particularly if technical difficulties or storms do not allow for the rapid removal of a climber to lower altitudes. The mechanism as outlined in Fig. 19.1 results in water collecting in the lungs with the manifestation of symptoms such as extreme shortness of breath, coughing with rales (gurgly breathing), and a frothy pink sputum. These symptoms, often delayed three to five days after arrival at altitude, indicate that action should be taken at once. Time is of the essence for the HAPE victim may expire in a matter of hours after the recognition of the first indication of this illness.

Drugs such as Lasix may bring relief but their use alone is inadequate. The most successful procedure is to transport the affected person as rapidly as possible to a lower altitude. This must be accomplished immediately, even in the face of a storm or nightfall. Complete retreat from the mountain is not necessary, for often a descent of one to three thousand feet will be adequate to bring relief (Hultgren 1976b). The administration of oxygen is of benefit to the HAPE victim but is seldom available or in sufficient quantity to ensure sustained treatment.

CEREBRAL EDEMA (CE)

An increasing amount of water in brain tissue elicits severe headache, hallucinations, stupor, and motor incoordination (ataxia), all indicative that the individual is suffering from CE. Although CE is less common that AMS or HAPE, it can kill the victim within a matter of hours. Treatment is similar to that for HAPE—that is, fast removal to lower altitudes.

RETINAL HEMMORRHAGE (RH)

The manifestation of mountain illness that seems to present the fewest problems, both for immediate and long-term consideration, is retinal hemorrhage. In this condition, the optic nerve is swollen and pressed forward against the brain. There is also a hemorrhaging of the arteries that supply blood to the retina. While the etiology of this condition is not understood, it is believed to be related to exercise, exertion, and altitude (Rennie 1976). Some degree of CE is present in those who experience RH, according to Rennie (1976). Further evidence for such a connection is provided by the fact that those who experience no headache at altitude do not experience RH (Schumacher 1975). Inasmuch as no direct pain emanates from the eyes and because its detection requires special optical instruments, RH often goes undetected. Houston (1975) has reported that probably 20 to 30 percent of all climbers going above 14,000 feet experience some degree of hemorrhage, while other investigators have reported an even higher incidence (Schumacher 1975). Although retinal hemorrhage is not debilitating, it may be an indication that cerebral edema is present. The condition usually subsides within six weeks to three months.

CONCLUSION

Exposure to high altitude, with associated hypoxia, can lead to an abnormal shifting of water in certain body compartments. As with other problems resulting from environmental stress, prevention of altitude sickness should be of primary concern. In those cases in which symptoms of potentially serious disorders develop, there should be immediate and rapid evacuation of the afflicted individuals to lower altitudes.

REFERENCES

Bowman, W. D. 1977. Medical aspects of mountain climbing. *Physician and Sportsmedicine,* 5, 45-68.

Houston, C. B. 1975. High altitude edema. *Summit,* 18,1.

Hultgren, H. 1976a. *Proceedings Mountain Medicine Symposium Yosemite.* Yosemite: Charles S. Houston.

Hultgren, H. 1976b. HAPE: High altitude pulmonary edema. *Off Belay,* 26, 7-10.

O'Shea, J. P. 1977. Medical aspects of mountain climbing. *Physician and Spts Med,* 5, 45-68.

Rennie, D. 1975. High altitude edema—Cerebral and pulmonary. In *Mountain Medicine and Physiology,* C. Clarke, M. Ward, and E. Williams (eds.). London: Alpine Club.

Rennie, D. 1976. Mountain sickness and high altitude deterioration. *Off Belay,* 28, 30-35.

Schumacher, G. A. and J. H. Petajan. 1975. High altitude stress and retinal hemorrhage: Relation to vascular headache mechanism. *Arch Environ Hlth,* 30:217-222.

Ward, M. 1975. *Mountain Medicine.* London: Crosby, Lockwood, Staples.

20

Dehydration and Heat Stress in Mountaineering

John P. O'Shea

Dehydration is a major health problem confronting people engaged in mountaineering related activities. This hazard is most likely to occur in the inexperienced recreational hiker and cross-country skier who may go out for two or three strenuous days without adequate conditioning. For the climber and ski mountaineer who is physically and mentally prepared, dehydration remains a potential problem—but body water losses are usually more adequately controlled. Dehydration alone seldom results in death, but it does create a possibly critical condition when combined with any of the hazards of mountaineering such as storms, heat, cold, precipitation, or avalanche.

Dehydration, an abnormal loss of body fluids, places an extraordinary demand on the cardiovascular system. Depending on environmental circumstances, either hypothermia or hyperthermia may result. At first this seems paradoxical; however, dehydration results in an increase in blood viscosity that greatly impairs circulation. In cold weather, impaired circulation increases the risk of cold injuries—hypothermia and frostbite. Under warm conditions, high body water losses may lead to heat stress injuries such as heat cramps, heat exhaustion, or heat stroke (see Chapter 14).

The human body possesses natural defenses against hot or cold environments (see Chapters 13 and 16). Under most circumstances, these defense mechanisms enable one to perform well in any season of the year provided adequate precautions are taken to ensure proper replacement of body fluids. This chapter reviews some of the current medical and physiological concepts regarding the maintenance of body water and electrolyte balance during mountaineering activities

In a lean 155-pound climber or cross-country skier, total free water equals approximately 40 liters or 57 percent of body weight. Of this total, 15 liters is extracellular or water found in blood plasma and interstitial fluid, while 25 liters is intracellular or water found inside the cells of the body. Intracellular water makes up about 63 percent of the total body water (Guyton 1971). With obesity, the percentage of water in the body may be as low as 45 percent of the body weight. Females tend to have more natural body fat and, therefore, have lower total water ratios per pound of body weight than males. Body water also decreases with age. For example, body water is approximately 60 percent of body weight at age 20, but only 48 percent of body weight at age 55 (Guyton 1971).

The quantity of water required by the body is determined by the amount needed to (1) maintain proper volume and osmotic concentrations in the various fluid compartments, and (2) compensate for water lost by excretion through the kidneys, skin, lungs, and intestines.

Water helps to carry vital electrolytes—sodium, chloride, potassium, magnesium—to all parts of the body and transports waste products out of the body. A disturbance in water balance is usually accompanied by simultaneous changes in electrolyte balance and temperature regulation. Adequate water balance plays an important role in optimal climbing or cross-country skiing performance. Therefore, it is desirable to have an understanding of the primary channels of body water production, intake, and loss in order to maintain a properly hydrated state under adverse environmental conditions.

Body water is derived from drinking water, the water content of food eaten, and the water formed in the oxidation of foods. Metabolic (oxidative water) water is roughly proportional to the caloric value of foods and amounts to 100 to 140 grams per 1000 calories. The possibility of dehydration is enhanced when a large portion of food consists of dried or dehydrated food (the type of food most often consumed by the mountaineer) since a considerable portion of the daily water intake comes from that ingested with regular meals. This must be a consideration on extended expeditions or in situations where water may be in short supply.

Water may be lost from the body in the following ways:

1. *Urinary excretion.* Urinary water loss ranges from 1000 to 2000 ml and averages about 1200 ml daily. It decreases with increased loss of water through the skin, lungs, and intestines. Urinary water volume varies with the diet. A high protein diet results in the formation of large quantities of urea. More urinary water is required for elimination of this substance than when a normal diet is consumed. The kidneys are the primary regulator of salt-water balance.

2. *Pulmonary excretion.* The quantity of water exhaled by the lungs per day averages 400 ml. At higher altitudes where the atmosphere contains little moisture and pulmonary ventilation is markedly increased due to hypobaric-hypoxic conditions, considerably greater quantities of water are exhaled by the lungs. The result is a reduction in the volume of extracellular fluid (pure water volume deficit). Consequently, sodium becomes more concentrated in the extracellular fluid.

3. *Loss from the skin.* Cutaneous evaporation, even when there is no visible sweating (insensible perspiration), averages 1,200 ml per day at sea level. Loss of water from sweating varies from 1 to 14 liters per day with heavy exercise. Prolonged copious sweating may lead to severe dehydration and electrolyte deficiencies. Since the salt content of sweat is less than that of

193

blood, proportionately more water than salt is lost. This causes an increase in the salt concentrations of the blood. Increased salt concentrations of the body fluids leads to the sensation of thirst and reduced urine volume. When a person becomes dehydrated through sweating, the total amount of heat held by the body increases. For every one percent of body weight lost through sweating, the body temperature may increase 0.3 to 0.5°F. This points out the critical need to maintain a hydrated state to avoid heat stress problems while climbing.

4. *Fecal excretion.* Water losses through the feces averages 200 ml per day. This is greatly increased in cases of diarrhea. Mountain sickness may contribute to severe dehydration.

Additional water balance control stems indirectly from the thermal regulatory mechanisms of the hypothalamus. One portion of the hypothalamus directs the retention or conservation of body heat, whereas the other monitors the dissipation of heat by cutaneous vasodilation and sweating (see Chapter 13). This latter function of the hypothalamus indirectly regulates sweat production, sweat concentration, and water balance through hormonal action.

Stimulus for the hormonal activity does not come from heat stress itself, but appears to stem from changes in water and electrolyte balance, which are monitored by the hypothalamus. Mountaineering activities that cause moderate or excessive fluid losses result in an increase in osmotic pressure or a decrease in circulating blood volume. Either situation acts to trigger secretion of the antidiuretic hormone (ADH) from the pituitary gland. This hormone conserves body water by causing an increased reabsorption of water in the kidneys. The ADH system can alter by three to five percent the total quantity of water in the body fluids (Hardy 1965).

The relative concentrations of sodium and potassium in the body fluids have a marked effect on heart and muscle function. Aldosterone, a hormone of the adrenal cortex, plays a major role in regulating sodium and potassium concentrations in the extracellular fluids. Often called the sodium-conserving hormone, aldosterone is stimulated by a change in salt balance. It increases reabsorption of sodium—at the expense of potassium—in both the kidneys and sweat glands. In fact, in its effort to conserve sodium, aldosterone can increase the excretion of potassium to such an extent that a serious deficit may result.

DEHYDRATION

Dehydration occurs when intracellular water shifts to the interstitial spaces. As body water is lost through evaporation and respiration, blood plasma becomes more concentrated. This not only increases blood viscosity, which places an extra strain on the heart and circulatory system, but also increases the osmotic pressure of the plasma. Water then passes *to* the plasma *from* the interstitial fluid. As the interstitial fluid gradually becomes more concentrated, water passes from the adjacent cells across the cell membrane into the interstitial compartment. When this occurs the cell shrinks.

In addition to the concentration difference of water, an electrical difference between fluid compartments occurs with dehydration. As water diffuses across the cell membrane, negatively charged potassium ions go with it leaving an excess of positively charged sodium ions. This altered electrical difference interferes with the transmission of nerve impulses and upsets normal muscle function. Continued dehydration of muscle and nerve cells leads to weakness, cramps, and mental confusion.

Some of the symptoms of dehydration are a rise in body temperature and heart rate, increased thirst, hypotension, and weakness. Part of the elevation of body temperature in dehydration results from the lack of available fluid for sweating. The first sign of intracellular dehydration is severe thirst, which is reflexly initiated by the drying out of the mucous membranes of the mouth and throat. In the dehydrated state, however, thirst is a poor regulator of water intake. By the time people experience severe thirst they usually have at least a two-liter water deficit and are entering an advanced state of dehydration. A thirst center located in the hypothalamus causes the sensation of thirst when the extracellular fluids become hypertonic or decrease in volume through sweating and respiration.

Three levels of dehydration have been identified:

1. *Mild* (1 to 5 percent loss of body weight). Symptoms include thirst, vague discomfort, impatience, nausea, loss of efficiency, and muscle cramps.

2. *Moderate* (6 to 10 percent loss of body weight). Symptoms include dizziness, headache, shortness of breath, tingling of the limbs, absence of salivation, blueness of tongue and lips, inability to walk, and mental impairment.

3. *Severe* (11 to 20 percent loss of body weight). Symptoms include delirium, spasticity of limbs, deafness, dimming of vision, and possibly death.

The net effect of dehydration is a reduction in the physical working capacity of an individual. Fluid loss should not exceed two percent of body weight if performance is to remain optimal.

FLUID AND ELECTROLYTE REPLACEMENT

Water

In assessing long-term water requirements, one should aim at preventing thirst, and promoting a daily (24-hour) urinary output of not less than 600 ml. Because the sensation of thirst may be a poor indicator of water needs, forced drinking while mountaineering is an absolute necessity. The ingestion of small amounts of

Fig. 20.1 Cross-country skiing in the high Cascades of Oregon. Even in the winter dehydration is potential hazard to be avoided in order to maintain maximum physical effenciency.

Fig. 20.2 Packing a heavy load at the 16,000 foot level om Mt. McKinley, Alaska, where the air is thin and the sun hot. These conditions emphasize the critical need to maintain and support water and electrolyte balence.

water at frequent intervals (½ pint every 45 minutes) is recommended. Overall, one must plan for a fluid replacement equal to or nearly equal to the expected water loss under the prevailing weather conditions and the severity of physical activity.

For reference, water balance may be determined in the following manner. On a 3000 calorie diet, approximately 1000 ml of water are ingested with the food, and an additional 300 ml are formed as a by-product of metabolizing the food. At the same time, about 700 ml of water are lost in normal respiration and another 600 ml are lost in feces and urine daily. These quantities balance; what remains to be considered is perspiration, which may be in the four- to eight-liter range when climbing. In addition, respiratory loss when working in the cold or at altitude can amount to 500 ml per hour. This must be offset by drinking an equivalent amount of water.

High altitude climbers and cross-country skiers often experience difficulty in providing sufficient water for drinking and cooking. Water is scarce in extremely cold conditions and also on glaciers and snowfields, making a high performance stove for melting snow an absolute necessity. In mountaineering, unless fluids are within easy reach a mild degree of water depletion will develop. "Voluntary dehydration" is frequently the reason mountaineering expeditions fail to reach the summit of major peaks (18,000 feet or higher).

Sodium

During acclimatization to heat and/or strenuous physical activity, salt requirements are increased due to sweating. After six to ten days of warm weather mountaineering, acclimatization takes place and the salt requirement is reduced to normal levels. This is due to the fact that the concentration of salt in sweat decreases gradually during acclimatization. Whenever unacclimatized mountaineers progressively lose large quantities of salt and water, their physical work capacity is severely impaired. The detrimental effects of progressive salt depletion include a decrease in physical performance, increased body temperature and pulse rate, nausea, muscular weakness, and finally heat exhaustion brought on by circulatory failure. In mountaineering, heat exhaustion usually develops over a five- to seven-day period and is accompanied by profound fatigue and extreme muscle cramping.

Because highly conditioned and heat-acclimatized mountaineers are able to produce large amounts of sweat, they are paradoxically endangered by the capacity to lose larger quantities of sodium than unacclimatized persons. The possible magnitude of sodium losses can be explained as follows. The maximum sweat rate for unacclimatized men is 1.5 liters per hour, while for acclimatized men it is 2.5 liters per hour. The sodium loss for the former group is approximately 100 mEq per liter compared to about 70 mEq per liter for the latter group. Consequently, while the maximum sodium loss is 150 mEq per hour for unacclimatized men, it is 175 mEq per hour for acclimatized men (Knochel 1974). To avoid severe salt losses, salt should be supplemented in the diet in moderation until acclimatization takes place and continued to a lesser degree in cases of prolonged physical activity in hot dry weather. Although the minimal salt allowances have not been established by the National Research Council, five grams per day of salt is a liberal allowance in a temperate environment under conditions of minimal sweating. The need may be as high as 10 to 15 grams per day in a temperate mountaineering environment when the daily fluid intake is close to four liters. On a climb that will be hot and prolonged, it is sound policy to drink as much as possible and to take extra salt with food.

Potassium

Potassium is one of the basic elements of intracellular fluid and is found in great quantities within the cell for enzymatic functions. It is also a very important extracellular fluid constituent as it can influence muscular activity, notably the cardiac muscle, and can affect the excitability of the nerve tissue. Potassium is usually associated with protein in the intracellular water. Under the severe stress of high altitude exposure, a negative nitrogen balance occurs with potassium depletion. This is indicative of body protein catabolism and cellular destruction. Potassium depletion also results from excessive loss through sweating, urine excretion, vomiting, and diarrhea. Potassium excretion is increased during periods of sodium deprivation.

Potassium depletion leads to muscular weakness, reduced reflexes, mental confusion, weak pulse, and fall in blood pressure. The most common symptom of early potassium deficiency is malaise, usually expressed as "just not feeling too well."

Although the traditional procedure of preventing salt depletion is by sodium chloride supplementation, recent research indicates that the indiscriminate use of salt by heat acclimatized climbers could very well lead to serious potassium depletion (Potts 1968). Evidence exists to indicate a direct relationship between potassium depletion and heat illness. Many heat stroke victims suffer from potassium depletion.

High potassium intake, however, can be toxic. Excess potassium in the extracellular fluids causes the heart to become extremely dilated and flaccid and to beat slowly. Elevation of potassium concentration two to three times the normal value usually causes such weakness of the heart that death will result (Dill 1967).

Potassium excretion in sweat and total daily potassium excretion is related to such variables as body temperature, acclimatization to heat, sweat rate, and intensity of physical activity. Potassium loss in sweat during heavy physical activity has been reported to range from 0.5 to 0.8 grams per day (Knochel 1974). There is no question that these losses should be replaced. However, if the climber's diet is providing sufficient potassium there is no need to take a supplement. Normal diets provide a daily intake of between 2.5 and 4.5 grams per day on a 3000 calorie diet. (See Table 20.1 for foods high in potassium.)

HEAT EXHAUSTION

Heat exhaustion is due to inadequacy or collapse of the peripheral circulation resulting from salt-depletion and dehydration (see Chapter 14). Mountaineering

Table 20.1
Sodium and Potassium Content of Foods

High Sodium (125-1000 mg and over per average serving)	High Potassium (300-500 mg per average serving)
Cheese of all kinds	Coffee—instant
Soda and graham crackers	Cocoa
Ketchup and tomato juice	Bran flakes
Cured and canned meats	Graham crackers
Fish	Whole-grain breads and break-
Poultry	fast cereals
Foods made with baking powder	Dried skim or whole milk
or baking soda	Dried or canned fish or shell
Buttermilk	fish
Sauerkraut	Most meats
Celery	Legumes and nuts
Potato chips	Most vegetables
Snack foods	Bananas, dates, oranges,
Salted nuts, popcorn	peaches (dried)
Salted butter, margarine	Prune juice
Dried, cooked legumes	Raisins
Ordinary breads	Raw tomatoes and tomato juice

activities in a hot dry atmosphere can lead to dehydration due to excessive fluid loss through respiration and sweating. Dry air and convective air currents (wind) promote water evaporation from the body.

In treating heat exhaustion, place the victim in a shady, cool place, elevate the feet, and massage the legs. Sprinkle the person with water and cool by fanning. If available, snow packs may be placed on the wrist and heat. The victim should be given a cool *very dilute* salt solution to drink. Upon recovery, a rest of an hour or more is necessary before continuing a climb (Wilkerson 1975).

PREVENTION OF DEHYDRATION AND HEAT ILLNESS IN MOUNTAINEERING

Clothing

Clothing, in addition to proper fluid intake and electrolyte replacement, plays a critical role in avoiding dehydration and heat stress problems. In mountaineering, the primary function of clothing is to serve as an insulator for the thin layer of warm air surrounding the body and to prevent the loss of this air through radiation and convection. On the other hand, it also serves to prevent the body from absorbing environmental heat through radiation and to permit the escape of excess heat generated during strenuous physical activity (see Chapter 14).

To understand how clothing can perform this dual function, one must understand the "layer principle" of dressing for mountaineering. The "layer principle" dictates what will be worn according to the demands of the weather and the level of physical exertion. The layer principle of dressing for mountaineering activities involves wearing three to five layers of lightweight and light colored garments rather than one or two heavy ones. Hence, clothing can be shed or donned as the demands for body heat decrease or increase.

Ski mountaineering with a full pack creates unique clothing problems and so can provide an excellent example of putting the layer principle of dressing to use. While skiing, considerable body heat is generated, and unless this heat can escape, water will collect as condensation on the inner garments and may freeze when one stops. Therefore, a light breathable outer garment must be worn that allows this excess body heat and moisture to escape. The correct layers of clothing for this situation from the skin side out are fishnet underwear, cotton T-shirt, a light wool shirt or sweater, and a lightweight wind parka. The parka is not weatherproof but water repellent to allow condensation to escape and permit proper heat exchange with the environment.

Acclimatization

Any discussion of acclimatization must include reference to the SAID principle (specific adaptation to imposed demands). This principle states that the body adapts specifically to the demands imposed upon it. This principle also implies that these demands must be gradually applied if adaptation is to take place in a safe manner (progressive overload principle).

Physical Conditioning

A critical factor in ability to tolerate the effects of physical work in the heat or cold is one's capacity for performance of muscular work. When speaking of acclimatization to heat or cold we are, in essence, referring to the body's ability to dissipate or to conserve metabolic heat in an efficient manner during mild to strenuous work. One's ability to perform physical work for prolonged periods of time under any climatic condition is directly related to one's physical conditioning. Whether one spends a week or more backpacking or climbing at high altitudes in August or ski mountaineering in January, the level of cardiovascular conditioning must be such that the person can maintain a high level of mental and physical efficiency under stressful environmental conditions.

REFERENCES

Bell, D. R. and J. D. Walters. 1969. Reaction of men working in hot and humid conditions. *J Appl Physiol,* 27, 684-690.

Benzinger, T. H. 1959. On physical heat regulation and the sense of temperature in man. *Proc Nat Acad Sci,* 45, 645-659.

Benzinger, T. H. 1969. Heat regulation: Hemeostasis of central temperature in man. *Physiol Rev*, 49, 671-680.

Bosco, J. S., R. L. Terjung, and J. E. Greenleaf. 1968. Effects of progressive hypohydration on maximal isometric muscular strength. *J Sports Med*, 8, 82-86.

Dill, D. B. and S. M. Horvath. 1967. Sweat electrolytes in desert walks. *J Appl Physiol*, 23, 746-754.

Guyton, A. C. 1971. *Textbook of Medical Physiology*. 4th ed. Philadelphia: W. B. Saunders.

Hammel, H. T. 1968. Regulation of internal body temperature. *Annual Rev Physiol*, 30, 641-649.

Hardy, J. D. 1965. The "set-point" concept in physiological temperature regulation. In *Physiological Controls and Regulation*, W. S. Yamamoto and J. R. Brobeck (eds.). Philadelphia: W. B. Saunders.

Knochel, J. P. 1974. Environmental heat illness. *Arch Internal Med*, 133, 841-864.

Potts, W. T. 1968 Osmotic and ionic regulation. *Annual Rev Physiol*, 30, 73-83.

Stolwijk, J. A. and B. Saltin. 1968. Physiological factors associated with sweating during exercise. *J Aerospace Med*, 39, 1101-1112.

Strydom, N. M. and C. H. Wyndham. 1966. Acclimatization to humid heat and the role of physical conditioning. *J Appl Physiol*, 21, 636-644.

Welt, L. G. 1964. Water balance in health and disease. In *Diseases of Metabolism*, G. Duncan (ed.). 5th ed. Philadelphia: W. B. Saunders.

Wilkerson, J. A. 1975. *Medicine for Mountaineering*. Seattle: The Mountaineers.

21

Effects of Air Pollution on Physical Performance

Peter B. Raven

Within the air surrounding large cities, small amounts of gases and particulates are found that are not the normal constituents of ambient air. These trace gases and particulates are described as pollutants. An air pollution alert (smog episode) usually consists of a combination of two or more pollutants in significantly high levels of concentration expressed as parts per million (ppm) or micrograms per cubic meter ($\mu g/m^3$). Levels of pollutants discussed in this section will be described as ppm because most physiological investigators utilize this terminology; unfortunately, governmental agencies are reporting aerometry data in $\mu g/m^3$. The conversion procedures are outlined in Table 21.1

Table 21.1
Conversions of Pollutant Concentrations

Pollutant	To Convert	To	Multiply By
Sulfur Dioxide (SO$_2$)	mg SO$_2$/m^3 (0°C, at 760 mmHg)	ppm SO$_2$ (vol)	3.5×10^{-4}
	mg SO$_2$/m^3 (0°C, at 760 mmHg)	ppm SO$_2$ (wt)	7.7×10^4
Carbon Monoxide (CO)	1 mg CO/m^3	ppm CO	0.87
Ozone (O$_3$)	1 mg O$_3$/m^3	ppm O$_3$	0.51×10^{-3}

It can be concluded from available reports that there are two forms of smog, and depending upon the pollutant constituents involved, the resultant smog can be generally described as: (1) *reductive,* consisting mainly of carbon monoxide (CO), sulfur oxides (SOx), and particulates usually in combination with high humidities and high or low temperatures; or (2) *oxidant or photochemical,* consisting mainly of carbon monoxide (CO), ozone (O3), nitric oxides (NOx), peroxyacylnitrates (PANs), and particulates usually in combination with high temperatures and low humidities. These combinations occur during periods of air stagnation generally brought about by a thermal inversion, that is when warm air is trapped below cold air.

REDUCTIVE POLLUTANTS

Carbon monoxide (CO) is the most widely distributed and the most commonly occurring air pollutant. Total emmissions of CO to the atmosphere exceed those of all other pollutants combined. Human activities are largely responsible for CO contamination, and technological advances have contributed to the present atmospheric concentrations. Urban levels of CO arise mainly from the incomplete combustion of fossil fuels (gasoline) and other carbonaceous materials such as coal, mineral oils, wood, and tobacco. Worldwide emmissions of CO from technological sources have been estimated to be more than 1.8×10^{11} Kg (200 million tons) annually. In the absence of natural removal processes, this large tonnage would be sufficient to raise the background level of CO 0.03 ppm per year. However, the background levels are not increasing. Therefore, natural processes of removal must be present, although they have not been identified. The primary urban source of CO is the automobile. If Environmental Protection Agency controls on automobiles were not in effect, the actual increase in total emissions in 1985 would double those observed in 1965. It is also predicted that the levels will not be increased significantly in the year 2000 if the EPA controls are maintained despite a predicted increase in population and volume of traffic within the same time period.

Sulfer oxides (SO_x), sulfur dioxide (SO_2), sulfur trioxide (SO_3), and the corresponding acids, sulphurous acid (H_2SO_3), sulfuric acid (H_2SO_4), and salts (sulfites and sulfates), are common atmospheric pollutants arising mainly from combustion processes involving coal and fuel oil. In general, 40 to 80 parts of SO_2 to one part of SO_3 are emitted from fossil-fueled power plants. SO_2 is a nonflammable, nonexplosive, colorless gas that most people can taste as concentrations from 0.3 ppm to 1 ppm in air. In the atmosphere, SO_2 is partly converted to SO_3, H_2SO_4, and its sulfate salts by photochemical or catalytic processes. SO_3 is immediately converted to sulfuric acid in the presence of moisture. These changes are determined by a number of factors including concentration, residence time in the atmosphere, temperature, humidity, intensity and spectral distribution of incident radiation, and the presence of other pollutants such as metal oxides, hydrocarbons, and oxides of nitrogen. Of the total suspended particulates in the air 5 to 20 percent consists of sulfuric acid and other sulfates. These particles reduce the visibility in the atmosphere dependent upon the size and concentration of the particles.

PHOTOCHEMICAL OXIDANTS

The combusion of coal and petroleum products such as natural gas, gasoline, and fuel oil (termed "fossil fuels") is an oxidation-reduction reaction that is responsible for most of the air pollution in urban atmospheres. Since the combustion process is not 100 percent efficient in the production of water and carbon dioxide, the combustion reaction results in by-products such as CO, SO_x, pure fuel, aldehydes, and other hydrocarbons. In addition, small amounts of air are oxidized to nitric oxide (NO). When these by-products are released into the atmosphere, they react together under the influence of sunlight to produce other contaminants quite different from those originally released. During daylight hours NO is rapidly oxidized to nitrogen dioxide (NO_2), SO_2 is oxidized to SO_3, and the hydrocarbons are oxidized to more stable compounds known as aldehydes and ketones. In addition, ozone (O_3) is formed that further reacts to produce complex mixtures of hydrocarbon nitrogen components known as peroxyacylnitrates (PANS). By far the most important photochemical pollutants are NO_2, O_3, and PANS; however, the complex interactions of these compounds is beyond the scope of this chapter.

The other major pollutants, *particulates* and *hydrocarbons,* are associated with the formation of photochemical smog and/or reductive smog, since the techniques required to accurately measure these pollutants in ambient air remain primitive, investigation into their effects on human performance has been minimal. This chapter considers only those pollutants (CO, O_3, SO_2, PAN, and NO_2) and their effects that have been documented in a scientific fashion.

HUMAN PHYSIOLOGICAL RESPONSES TO AIR POLLUTANTS

Carbon Monoxide

By attaching itself to the hemoglobin carried in the red blood cell, and thereby competing with oxygen, CO reduces the oxygen-carrying capacity of the blood. The effect of CO combination with the hemoglobin (COHb - carboxyhemoglobin) is somewhat similar to going to an altitude, where ambient oxygen is reduced, or to anemia, where the number of red blood cells is reduced, thereby lowering the amount of oxygen carried in the blood. In order that a sufficient amount of oxygen is delivered to the active muscles and functioning organs, an adequate blood supply is required along with a sufficient amount of deliverable oxygen. When the amount of oxygen carried by the blood is reduced, then significant reductions in endurance capacity will occur. If the levels of COHb become too high ()20 percent COHb), then clinical symptoms of CO poisoning will be observed.

However, it is extremely unlikely that COHb levels of greater than 15 to 20 percent will be encountered in everyday life, although frequently smokers may have blood levels above 10 percent. The normal level of COHb in the blood of nonsmokers is approximately 1 percent or less. In urban environments, where ambient CO levels may range from 15 to 100 ppm (Wright et al. 1975) the level of COHb in the blood is dependent upon length of time exposed to these levels and the person's ventilation level during the exposure (Forbes et al. 1975; and Peterson and Stewart 1970). Hence, it is common to record levels of COHb in the blood of nonsmokers greater than 5 percent.

Recent investigations (Pirnay et al. 1971; Vogel et al. 1972; Vogel and Gleser 1972; and Ekblom and Huot 1972) into the effects of COHb levels ranging from 7 to 22 percent on maximal performance while inspiring high concentrations of CO (225 to 10,000 ppm) for brief periods of time, have shown that when COHb levels were 15 percent or more, maximal oxygen uptake was reduced 15 percent, maximal heart rate was increased 2 beats per minute, and submaximal ventilation was increased 19 percent. Also, at 20 percent COHb maximal oxygen uptake was reduced 24 percent, no change occurred in maximum heart rate, but a 33 percent increase in submaximal ventilation was found. These changes occurred without alterations in maximal cardiac output (the amount of blood ejected per minute from the heart); therefore, the decrease in maximal oxygen uptake was a direct effect of the replacement of oxygen in arterial blood by CO.

More pertinent to everyday living and its concomitant activities has been the work recently performed at the Institute of Environmental Stress in Santa Barbara (Raven et al. 1974; Drinkwater et al. 1974; Raven et al. 1974; Dahms et al 1975; Horvath et al. 1975). Subjects performed maximal work tasks while breathing air containing 50 ppm, 75 ppm, and 100 ppm CO. Although maximal performance time was significantly reduced when blood COHb levels of nonsmokers exceeded 2.7 percent, maximal oxygen uptake (max VO₂) was unaffected until levels greater than 4.3 percent were attained. The data of these investigations and those previously outlined above indicate that max VO₂ is reduced in a linear fashion with respect to increased levels of COHb in the blood (see Fig. 21.1). In one investigation (Horvath et al. 1975) it was striking to note that following a rapid rise in blood COHb levels to greater than 4.3 percent, max VO₂ was reduced even though the ambient inspired level of CO was only 23.7 ppm, a level far below the initial government health alert level and yet one commonly found surrounding busy roadways.

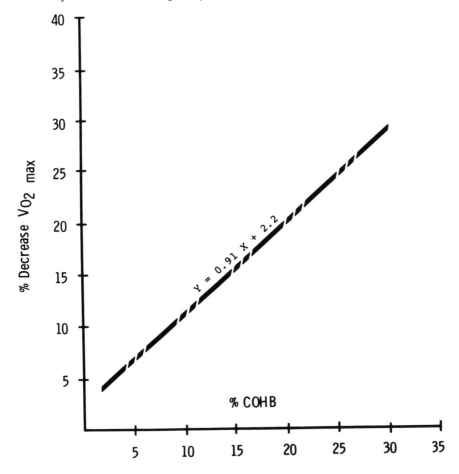

Fig. 21.1 A regression line for the decrease in max VO₂ with increasing levels of carboxyhemoglobin (r = 0.89). Reprinted with permission of the publishers.

When performing submaximal tasks of less than 40 percent maximal capacity, it appears that levels of COHb less than 15 percent have little effect on endurance capacity, energy production, or ventilation; however, submaximal heart rate is increased (Pirnay et al. 1971; Vogel et al. 1972; Vogel and Gleser 1972). Hence, at low work levels the efficiency of muscular exercise is unaffected by CO inhalation (at levels < 15 percent COHb) in that the CO desaturation of the hemoglobin is overcome by the increased circulation. That is, cardiac output is raised by increasing the heart rate and thereby delivering more blood to the working muscles per unit time. However, as the work load increases, significant cardiovascular and lung function changes occur (Vogel et al. 1972; Vogel and Gleser 1972). Primarily these adjustments are accomplished by increasing the ventilation required to obtain a given oxygen uptake. In effect, the ventilatory system becomes less efficient.

The nonsmoker will be severely hampered by exposures to carbon monoxide, especially if their COHb levels are raised above 5 percent. Predictable decrements in maximal performance can be made of COHb levels are available. Unfortunately ambient levels of CO are in no way predictive of COHb levels unless time exposure and ventilatory volume are known. Submaximal performance will not be affected below 15 percent COHb; yet, cognitive functions are affected when COHb levels exceed 5 percent and, therefore, errors in judgment may become apparent as exposure to CO continues. However, it is apparent that physiological effects do occur with levels of COHb less than 15 percent during submaximal work when one investigates diseased populations (Aronow, et al. 1972; Aronow and Isbell 1973; Anderson et al. 1973). In these studies patients suffering from angina pectoris had reduced times to angina pain following the increase in blood COHb to levels ranging from 2.7 to 4.5 percent. In addition, angina pain lasted longer and was more intense the higher the level of COHb.

Sulfur Oxides (SO$_x$)

The pattern of response to different levels of SO$_2$ while at rest is strikingly similar—airway resistance increases rapidly reaching a maximum at four to ten minutes of exposure. Subsequently, a decrease in resistance occurs with continued exposure regardless of SO$_2$ concentrations. However, above 5 ppm SO$_2$ the decreased resistance noted after ten minutes of prolonged exposure is insufficient to return resistance to preexposure levels (Sim and Pattle 1957; Snell and Luchsinger 1969; Frank et al. 1961; Frank 1964). During recovery the resistance to flow remained elevated for 15 minutes or more following exposure to 1 ppm. No effects were observed on respiratory rate, tidal volume, heart rate, and/or other pulmonary measures; hence, it seems that the increased resistance to air flow is primarily due to a bronchoconstriction effect.

During exercise one changes to mouth breathing and bypasses the effective SO$_2$ filters of the nose (Ogura and Harvey 1971); therefore, greater dosages of

SO_2 are delivered to the lung, with concomitant increases in airway resistance being dose related (Salem and Aviado 1961). In addition to causing bronchoconstriction and reduced air flow within the lung, SO_2 will cause a reduction in ciliary clearance of mucus from the lung and further reduce small airway ventilation (Kilburn 1967).

Haldane had suspected that the choking effect of dense fog resulted mainly from sulfate rather than SO_2 (Haldane and Priestley 1935). More recently it has been shown that sulfuric acid and particulate sulfates cause greater airway obstruction than equivalent amounts of SO_2 (Amdur 1971). The effect of SO_2 was potentiated when a liquid droplet aerosol was administered with SO_2 and may be explained by the conversion of SO_2 to sulfuric acid within the droplets. Aerosol interaction and high humidities appear to be a necessary component of SO_2 reactivity; however, little work has been done with these atmospheres during exercise.

Similarly, few experiments have investigated working capacity or submaximal work performance during SO_2 exposures. It was recently shown that pulmonary function was not affected by two hours of intermittent exercise exposure (VE = 20 l per min) to 0.37 ppm pure SO_2; however, no other functional aspects of the human were investigated (Bates and Hazucha 1973). The dose response relationships described above with respect to airway resistance have been developed on resting human subjects. When ambient levels of SO2 are above 1.0 ppm, significant discomfort will occur and will prove detrimental to performance. Also, it is apparent that sulfuric acid aerosol and sulfates are much more detrimental to performance than pure SO_2. Unfortunately, data relating the increased ventilations found during exercise and dose level of these pollutants are not available. Without doubt, if an effect is observed at rest, then it is sure to be present during exercise; however, the degree to which it will impair performance has not been determined.

Ozone

Any athlete who has had the unpleasant experience of performing in high ambient levels of oxidants is subjectively convinced that his/her ability to function at maximal levels is significantly reduced. The athlete often complains of eye irritation (burning sensation and scratchy feelings on the eyeball with significant conjunctivitis), pain sensations below the sternum, chest tightness, dyspnea, and cough with a feeling of nausea sometimes strong enough to produce wretching or the "dry heaves" and, in fact, the person feels totally miserable. (See Fig. 21.2 for an outline of oxidant does/symptom response relationship.)

The primary targets of O_3 action appear to be the lungs and respiratory tract (Stokinger 1954; Trucke 1959). If exposure to low levels of ozone (0.1 to 0.5 ppm) occurs for long periods of time (days and weeks), significant changes in lung function occur even at rest. Decrements in capacity and expiratory flow

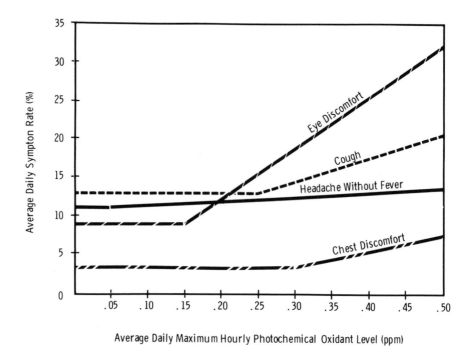

Fig. 21.2 Ambient photochemical oxidants in Los Angeles: Hockey-stick threshold functions. Reprinted from D. I. Hammer et al., *Arch Environ Hlth* 28: 255-260, with the permission of the publishers.

rates have been observed (Stokinger 1965; Goldsmith and Nadel 1969; Young et al. 1969) during acute exposures, suggesting that increased airway resistance may be caused by the bronchoconstriction effect of O_3. One hour of exercise producing ventilations at twice resting levels for periods of exposure lasting two hours have indicated that a dose-response relationship exists, although too few studies have been completed to describe the relationship in the detail that is available for CO (Bates et al. 1972; Bates and Hazucha 1973; Hazucha et al. 1973; Folinsbee et al. 1975; Silverman 1976). However, it appears that above a critical concentration level of 0.37 ppm O_3, decrements in functional parameters of the lung occur in a linear fashion related to delivered dosage of O_3. Simply stated, concentrations of O_3 (above 0.37 ppm) multiplied by the level of ventilation and time of exposure are predictive of lung function decrement (see Fig. 21.3). In addition, maximal aerobic capacity was significantly decreased following two hours of intermittent exercise exposure to 0.75 ppm O_3 (Folinsbee et al. 1977). This decrease in exercise performance was thought to be due to brochoconstriction and pain, which severely limited pulmonary capacity. It was also noted that during O_3 exposures, ventilatory modality is altered. That is, for a given oxygen uptake (work load) the O_3 exposed subject decreases the tidal volume and increases the respiratory rate, producing a relative hyperventilation (Folinsbee et al. 1977). This response will greatly inhibit oxygen transfer at the lung because the proportion of alveolar air being exchanged is reduced; hence, decreases in maximal and submaximal performance will occur. Recently it has been shown that the higher the humidity and temperature, the greater the effect O_3 has on the lung (Folinsbee et al. 1977). Hence, as oxidant pollutant episodes usually occur during high temperature inversions, performance decrements would be expected.

Peroxyacetylnitrate (PAN)

PAN is a minor portion of the total oxidant concentration; however, the mechanisms of action of O_3 and PAN on biological materials are strikingly similar. Early reports concerning the effects of PAN on functional performance were inconclusive. Smith (1965) found that the total oxygen cost of five minutes of light work was increased during 0.3 ppm PAN inhalation, while Holland et al. (1958) observed no effects of photochemical air pollution on metabolic or ventilatory parameters during 30 minutes of exercise. Further work (Drinkwater

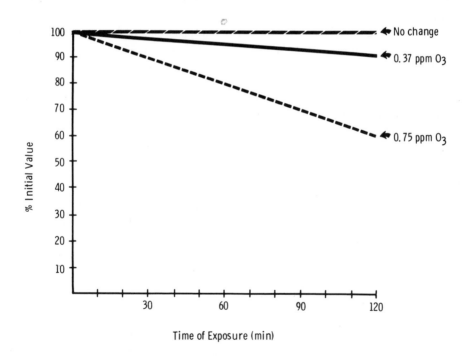

Fig. 21.3 Percent change of mid-maximal flow rate (MMFR) following two hours exposure to 0.37 ppm and 0.75 ppm ozone. Modified from the data presented in Hazucha et al., 1973, with the permission of the publisher.

et al. 1974; Raven et al. 1974a, 1974b) had indicated that 0.24 ppm PAN has little effect on metabolic and cardiopulmonary parameters during maximal work. In fact, neither submaximal nor maximal oxygen uptake was altered. However, following 0.24 ppm PAN exposure for four hours, younger subjects (mean age of 25) who worked at 35 percent of their maximal capacity evidenced significant decreases in lung function (FVC), while lung function of older subjects (mean age 45) was unaffected (Raven et al. 1976). A more extensive study indicated that 0.24 ppm PAN, although subjectively irritating to the eyes and throat, did not compromise the cardiovascular, ventilatory, or thermoregulatory function during four hours of work at 35 percent maximal capacity (Gliner et al. 1975).

Nitrogen Dioxide

The number of industrial exposures of the human to NO_2 have increased greatly, mainly paralleling the increased usage of electricity in the industrial situation, the use of nitrogenous missile fuels, and the agricultural practice of storage of farm produce in silos. However, by far the largest pervasive source of NO_2 in urban communities arises from the exhaust of the internal combustion engine. It has been estimated that this source alone adds 200 to 300 tons of NO_2 to the Los Angeles air daily. Another individual source of NO_2 is cigarette smoke, and this inhaled NO_2 may account for the increased incidence of emphysema among smokers. Emphysema has been experimentally induced with NO_2 in rats. Six different clinical syndromes result from exposures to NO_2 ranging from 0.15 to 0.38 ppm, while the annual average oscillates around 0.02 to 0.05 (Battigelli 1971). The maximal observed peak value was 0.242 ppm (Shy 1970, 1972). Obviously, serious pulmonary disorders are unlikely to be observed as a result of short-term exposures to urban concentrations of NO_2 unless the repeated exposures are additive in their effects. The Air Quality Standard (AQS) of 0.05 ppm each year resulted from the evidence that a greater incidence of bronchitis occurred in infants and children of school age in areas where the mean 24-hour NO_2 concentration varied from 0.063 to 0.083 ppm (Shy 1972). Primary evidence relating urban NO_2 levels and disease states are nonexistent; however, epidemiological data suggesting casual relationships between disease states and ambient pollutant levels remain the bastion of evidence for the setting of the AQS. Specific mechanisms by which these adverse health affects of NO_2 could occur have been developed using animal models. Unfortunately, interspecies differences in response to various levels of NO_2 have only served to further confuse the issue.

Despite the increasing number of investigations utilizing animal models, the only evidence linking urban levels of NO_2 with increased incidence of respiratory infection (Shy 1970, 1972) is the finding that animals exposed to low levels of NO_2 have a lowered resistance to pulmonary infection (Ehrlich 1966; Ehrlich and Henry 1968; Blair et al. 1969; Goldstein 1973.) The irritant effect of NO_2 is possibly explained by its inhibitory effect on microciliary function of the lung

(Battigelli et al. 1966; Dalhamm and Sjoholm 1963; Spritzer et al. 1967) and its probable deep penetration into the lung via synergistic absorption on the surface of particles such as carbon. Only recently has it been observed that long-term exposures of rates to 2.0 ppm NO_2 for nine months produced a significant reduction in lung compliance (Arner and Rhoades 1973), a functional rather than a pathological finding related to possible interference in the lipid content of lung tissue. In the human, inspiration of 5 to 8 ppm NO_2 increased airway resistance. This effect was abolished by the use of antihistamine drugs and suggests that NO_2 stimulates the release of histamine and mediates bronchoconstriction (Nieding and Krekeler 1971).

In conclusion, the experimental exposures of humans to nitrogen dioxide are limited in number and provide a minimal basis for defining critical levels of exposure. There is a noticeable lack of information in the literature about possible interactive effects of such things as age, ambient temperature, humidity, altitude, sex, smoking habits, and exercise. Epidemiological studies of the effect of NO_2 on the human body have concentrated primarily on the relationship between ambient levels and morbidity and mortality rates in selected populations. While there is considerable evidence to indicate that levels below the acute exposure stage do aggravate respiratory disease, the inconsistencies in experimental results are such that specific causative agents and concomitant environmental conditions have not been isolated (Campbell 1969).

PERFORMANCE GUIDELINES

Many recreational and spectator sport activities occur within the areas surrounding major cities where air pollutant levels are found to be at a maximum. For example, the proposed site for the 1984 Olympic Games is Los Angeles, a city renowned for its year-round pollution problems. Wayne et al. (1967) have indicated that track runners performed more poorly when their races were held during days when air pollutant levels were increased. This information is of value to the practitioner, whether a competitor, coach, or leisure-time participant.

How can these problems be overcome in a practical manner? In this section it is intended to outline some personally concluded practical considerations that may prove beneficial to both the high level performer and the leisure time participant.

Generally, pollutant effects are time and dosage dependent. The delivered dosage is dependent upon both ventilation and concentration; hence, the harder one works in a polluted atmosphere, the greater the effect. To maximize performance, the participant should be exposed to the pollutants for the shortest possible time. If participants are scheduled to perform their events in an area where pollutant levels are high on the day of the competition, they should attempt to prepare for the competition in a nonpolluted atmosphere. In the case of carbon monoxide, participants should be removed from exposures to bolus* doses of CO (smoking, motor driven transportation, and urban residence) for at least two or three hours prior to the event. Submaximal performance is not affected below 15 percent COHb; yet cognitive functions and maximal performance are affected when COHb levels exceed 5 percent. Therefore, errors in judgment and a drop in performance may become apparent as the exposure to CO continues.

Oxidant pollutants are more irritating and therefore more psychogenic in their effect than CO. If one feels uncomfortable, the mental drive required to overcome the discomfort takes away from one's participation. Hence, time spent in the polluted atmosphere again is important and should be reduced to a minimum. It appears that populations may have the ability to acclimatize to specific oxidant pollutants at low levels. Continual exposure to low levels of CO and oxidants have apparently made Los Angeles residents less susceptible to the acute effects of oxidant pollutants. Therefore, one could suggest training at times when pollutant levels are highest (i.e., late afternoon). One possible therapeutic agent that may help in more ways than one is vitamin E. In animal studies anti-oxidants such as vitamin E have been shown to protect the organism from lipid peroxydative effects of ozone, thereby reducing the decrement in lung function. Hence, dietary supplements of vitamin E may prove beneficial.

For the leisure-time participant where time of event is not fixed to a schedule, the activities should be performed when pollutant levels are at their lowest. In major urban areas CO had a bimodal peak occurring at 7 to 10 a.m. and 4 to 7 p.m., while oxidants begin to build up in the late morning (11 a.m.) and peak somewhere between 4 to 6 p.m. Hence, for those people wishing to perform daily activities, the early morning (6 a.m.) should prove to be the time when pollutants are at their lowest.

REFERENCES

Amdur, M. O. 1971. Aerosols formed by oxidation of sulfur dioxide. *Arch Environ Hlth*, 23, 459-468.

Anderson, E. W., R. J. Andelman, J. M. Strauch, N. J. Fortuin, and J. H. Knelson. 1973. Effect of low-level carbon monoxide exposure on onset and duration of angina pectoris: A study of ten patients with ischemic heart disease. *Ann Int Med*, 79, 46-50.

Arner, E. C. and R. A. Rhoades. 1973. Long-term nitrogen dioxide exposure. *Arch Environ Hlth*, 26, 156-160.

---

* Bolus dose refers to the sudden inhalation of large concentrations of carbon monoxide, similar to what might happen to a pedestrian crossing a street passing near a badly tuned automobile.

Aronow, W. S., C. N. Harris, M. W. Isbell, S. N. Rokaw, and B. Imparato. 1972. Effect of freeway travel on angina pectoris. *Ann Int Med*, 77, 669-676.

Aronow, W. S. and M. W. Isbell. 1973. Carbon monoxide effect on exercise induced angina pectoris. *Ann Int Med*, 79, 392-395.

Balchum, O. J., J. Dybicki, and G. R. Meneely. 1959a. Measurement of pulmonary resistance and compliance with concurrent tissue radioactive sulfur distribution in dogs inhaling a labeled air pollutant: Sulfur dioxide. *Fed Proc*, 18, 6.

Balchum, O. J., J. Dybicki, and G. R. Meneely. 1959b. Absorption and distribution of $S^{35}O_2$ inhaled through the nose and mouth by dogs. *Am J Physiol*, 197, 1317-1321.

Bates, D. V., G. M. Bell, C. D. Burham, M. Hazucha, J. Mantha, L. D. Pengelly, and F. Silverman. 1972. Short-term effects of ozone on the lung. *J Appl Physiol*, 32, 176-181.

Bates, D. V. and M. Hazucha. 1973. The short-term effects of ozone on the human lung. In *Proceedings of the Conference on Health Effects of Air Pollutants*. Washington: Government Printing Office, NAS/NRC, pp. 507-540.

Battigelli, M. C., F. Hengstenberg, and R. J. Mannela. 1966. Mucociliary activity. *Arch Environ Hlth*, 12, 460-466.

Battigelli, M. C. 1971. *Biological Significance of Nitrogen Oxides in Medical Aspects of Air Pollution*. Detroit: Society of Automotive Engineers, pp. 10-19.

Blair, W. H., M. C. Henry, and R. Ehrlich. 1969. Chronic toxicity of nitrogen dioxide. II. Effects of histopathology of lung tissue. *Arch Environ Hlth*, 18, 186-192.

Campbell, E. J. 1969. Air pollution, weather, and illness in a New York population. *Arch Environ Hlth*, 18, 523-530.

Dahms, T. E., S. M. Horvath, and D. J. Gray. 1975. Technique for accurately producing desired carboxyhemoglobin levels during rest and exercise. *J Appl Physiol*, 38, 366-368.

Dalhamm, T. and J. Sjoholm. 1963. Studies on SO_2, NO_2, and NH_3. Effect on ciliary activity in rabit trachea of single in vitro exposure and resorption in rabbit nasal cavity. *Acta Physiol Scand*, 58, 287-291.

Drinkwater, B. L., P. B. Raven, S. M. Horvath, J. A. Gliner, R. O. Ruhling, N. Bolduan, and S. Taguchi. 1974. Air pollution, exercise and heat stress. *Arch Environ Hlth*, 28, 177-182.

Ehrlich. R. 1966. Effect of nitrogen dioxide on resistance to respiratory infection. *Bacteriol Rev*, 30, 604-614.

Ehrlich, R. and M. C. Henry. 1968. Chronic toxicity of nitrogen dioxide. I. Effect on resistance to bacterial pneumonia. *Arch Environ Hlth*, 17, 860-865.

Ekblom B. and R. Huot. 1972. Response to submaximal and maximal exercise at different levels of carboxyhemoglobin. *Acta Physiol Scand*, 86, 474-482.

Folinsbee, L. J., F. Silverman, and R. J. Shephard. 1975. Exercise responses following ozone exposure. *J Appl Physiol*, 38, 996-1001.

Folinsbee, L. J., F. Silverman, and R. J. Shephard. 1977. Decrease of maximum oxygen uptake following exposure to ozone. *J Appl Physiol*, 42, 531-536.

Folinsbee, L. J., S. M. Horvath, P. B. Raven, J. F. Bedi, A. R. Morton, B. D. Drinkwater, N. N. Bolduan, and J. A. Gliner. 1977. Influence of exercise and heat stress on pulmonary function during ozone exposure. *J Appl Physiol*, in press.

Forbes, W. H., F. Sargent, and F. J. W. Roughton. 1945. The rate of carbon monoxide uptake by normal men. *Am J Physiol*, 143, 594-608.

Frank, N. R., M. O. Amdur, J. Worcester, and J. L. Whittenberger. 1961. Effects of acute controlled exposure to SO_2 on respiratory mechanics in healthy male adults. *J Appl Physiol*, 17, 252-258.

Frank, N. R. 1964. Studies on the effects of acute exposure to sulfur dioxide in human subjects. *Royal Soc Med Rev*, 57, 1029-1033.

Frank, N. R., R. E. Yoder, E. Yokoyama, and F. E. Speizer. 1967. The diffusion of SO_2 from tissue fluids into the lungs following exposure of dogs to SO_2. *Hlth Physics*, 13, 31-38.

Frank, N. R., R. E. Yoder, J. D. Brian, and E. Yokoyama. 1969. SO_2 (^{35}S labeled) absorption by the nose and mouth under conditions of varying concentration and flow. *Arch Environ Hlth*, 18, 315-322.

Gliner, J. A., P. B. Raven, S. M. Horvath, B. L. Drinkwater, and J. C. Sutton. 1975. Man's physiologic response to long-term work during thermal and pollutant stress. *J Appl Physiol*, 39, 628-632.

Goldsmith, J. R. and J. A. Nadel. 1969. Experimental exposure of human subjects to ozone. *Air Pollution Cont Assoc*, 19, 329-330.

Goldstein, E., M. C. Eagle, and P. D. Hoeprich. 1973. Effect of nitrogen dioxide on pulmonary bacterial defense mechanisms. *Arch Environ Hlth*, 202-204.

Haldane, J. S. and J. G. Priestley. 1935. *Respiration*. London: Oxford University Press.

Hazucha, M., F. Silverman, C. Parent, S. Field, and D. V. Bates. 1973. Pulmonary function in man after short-term exposure to ozone. *Arch Environ Hlth*, 27, 183-188.

Holland, G. J., D. Benson, A. Bush, G. Q. Rich, and R. P. Holland. 1958. Air pollution simulation and human performance. *Am J Pub Hlth*, 58, 1684-1691.

Horvath, S. M., P. B. Raven, T. E. Dahms, and D. J. Gray. 1975. Maximal aerobic capacity at different levels of carboxyhemoglobin. *J Appl Physiol*, 38, 300-303.

Kilburn, K. H. 1967. Cilia and mucus transport as determinants of the response of lung to air pollutants. *Arch Environ Hlth*, 14, 77-91.

Kleinerman, J. and C. R. Cowdrey. 1968. The effect of continuous high level nitrogen dioxide on hamsters. *Yale J Biol and Med*, 40, 579-590.

Nieding, G. Von and H. Krekeler. 1971. Pharmakologische beeinflussung der akuten NO_2 - wirkung auf die lungfuncton von gesunden and kraken mit einer chronischen bronchitis. *Int Arch Arbeitsmed*, 29, 55-63.

Ogura, J. H. and J. E. Harvey. 1971. Nasopulmonary mechanics - experimental evidence of the influence of the upper airway upon the lower. *Acta Oto-Laryngologica*, 71, 123-132.

Peterson, J. E. and R. D. Stewart. 1970. Absorption and elimination of carbon monoxide by inactive young men. *Arch Environ Hlth*, 21, 165-171.

Pirnay, F., J. Dujardin, R. Deroanne, and J. M. Petit. 1971. Muscular exercise during intoxication by carbon monoxide. *J Appl Physiol,* 31, 573-575.

Raven, P. B., B. L. Drinkwater, R. O. Ruhling, N. Bolduan, S. Taguchi, J. Gliner, and S. M. Horvath. 1974a. Effect of carbon monoxide and peroxyacetylnitrate on man's maximal aerobic capacity. *J Appl Physiol,* 36, 288-293.

Raven, P. B., B. L. Drinkwater, S. M. Horvath, R. O. Ruhling, J. A. Gliner, J. C. Sutton, and N. W. Bolduan. 1974b. Age, smoking habits, heat stress and their interactive effects with carbon monoxide and peroxyacetyl-nitrate on man's aerobic power. *Int J Biometeor,* 18, 222-232.

Raven, P. B., J. A. Gliner, and J. C. Sutton. 1976. Dynamic lung function changes following long-term work in polluted environments. *Environ Res,* 12, 18-26.

Salem, H. and D. M. Aviado. 1961. Inhalation of sulfur dioxide. *Arch Environ Hlth,* 2, 656-662.

Shy, C. M. 1970. The Chattanooga school children study: Effects of community exposure, and results of ventilatory function testing. *J Air Pollution Cont Assoc,* 20, 539-581.

Shy, C. M. 1972. The Chattanooga school children study: Effects of community exposure to nitrogen dioxide. II. Incidence of acute respiratory illness. *J Air Pollution Con Assoc,* 20, 582-610.

Silverman, F., L. J. Folinsbee, and R. J. Shephard. 1976. Pulmonary function changes in ozone. Interaction of concentration and ventilation. *J Appl Physiol,* 41, 859-864.

Sim, V. M. and R. E. Pattle. 1957. Effects of possible smog irritants on human subjects. *JAMA,* 165: 1908-1913.

Smith, L. E. 1965. Inhalation of the photochemical smog compound peroxyacetylnitrate. *Am J Pub Hlth,* 55, 1460-1468.

Snell, R. E. and P. C. Luchsinger. 1969. Effects of sulfur dioxide on expiratory flow rates and total respiratory resistance in normal human subjects. *Arch Environ Hlth,* 18, 693-698.

Spritzer, A. A., J. A. Watson, and J. A. Auld. 1967. Mucociliary clearance rates: Deposition and clearance in the tracheobronchial tree of rats. *Arch Environ Hlth,* 15, 39-42.

Stokinger, H. W. 1954. Ozone toxicity: Review of literature through 1953. *Arch Indus Hygiene & Occupat Med,* 9, 366-378.

Stokinger, H. W. 1965. Pollutant gases. In *Handbook of Physiology-Respiration,* W. O. Fenn and H. Rahn (eds.). Washington: Am Physiol Soc, Vol. II, Sect. 3, pp. 1067-1086.

Thomas, H. V., P. K. Mueller, and R. L. Lyman. 1968. Lipoperoxidation of lung lipids in rats exposed to nitrogen dioxide. *Science,* 159, 532-634.

Trucke, R. 1951. Toxicity of ozone. *Arch Maladies Prof Hyg & Toxicol in Ind,* 12, 55-58.

Vogel, J. A., M. A. Gleser, R. C. Wheeler, and B. K. Whitten. 1972. Carbon monoxide and physical work capacity. *Arch Environ Hlth,* 24, 198-203.

Vogel, J. A. and M. A. Gleser. 1972. Effect of carbon monoxide transport during exercise. *J Appl Physiol,* 32, 234-239.

Wayne, W. S., P. S. Wehle, and R. E. Carroll. 1967. Oxidant air pollution and athletic performance. *JAMA*, 199, 151-154.

Wright, G. R., S. Jewezyk, J. Onrot, P. Tomlinson, and R. J. Shephard. 1975. Carbon monoxide in the urban atmosphere. *Arch Environ Hlth*, 30, 123-129.

Yokoyama, E., R. E. Yoder, and N. R. Frank. 1971. Distribution of ^{35}S in blood and its excretion in urine of dogs exposed to [35]SO_2. *Arch Environ Hlth*, 22, 389-395.

Young, W. A., D. B. Shaw, and D. V. Bates. 1964. Effect of low concentrations of ozone on pulmonary function. *J Appl Physiol*, 19, 765-768.

NUTRITIONAL ASPECTS OF PHYSICAL PERFORMANCE

Introduction

Over the course of time athletes have utilized a variety of nutritional practices in attempts to improve their physical performance capacity. Since the various nutrients in foods provide energy and regulate many physiological processes essential to increased work capacity, there is some theoretical basis linking dietary modification to improvement in athletic performance. Hence, research scientists have been investigating the effect of the various nutrients upon physical performance for nearly 80 years.

The purpose of this section of the ENCYCLOPEDIA is to present basic information relative to various nutritional practices and their influence upon physical performance. This information may be of value in assisting coaches, trainers, and athletes to understand nutritional principles applied to physical and athletic performance.

In the first paper, Wingard discusses the essential nutrients necessary in the diet of the athlete, and Haymes, in the second paper, stresses the special dietary needs of female athletes. The general recommendation of these papers is that the athlete basically needs only a balanced diet. Williams then discusses why, contrary to this general recommendation, myths and misconceptions permeate the field of athletic nutrition.

Energy and its proper utilization is a major key to success in athletics. Three papers cover this topic. Fox discusses general energy sources during rest and exercise, Van Handel explores the role of glucose, and Hultman covers the technique of glycogen loading.

In the next paper, Williams provides an overview of vitamins, one of the most abused nutrients in athletics. The next four papers deal with specific vitamins. Williams reviews the limited research with vitamins A and D, while Shephard analyzes the literature relative to vitamin E. The B vitamins are discussed by Williams, and Van Huss reports on vitamin C.

Patton then presents a brief treatise on electrolyte solutions as they may influence performance. Haymes explores the role of iron as a supplement to the athlete's diet.

The next four papers deal with the topic of body composition and weight control. Katch and McArdle discuss the importance of body composition analysis and present some simple body composition procedures. Oscai then presents the health hazards associated with obesity, followed by McArdle and Katch's paper on the role of diet and exercise in weight control programs. Zambraski concludes this series of papers with a discussion of the problems of rapid weight reduction techniques.

The final two chapters are concerned with two drugs that are ingredients in commonly consumed beverages. Williams explores the role of alcohol on physical performance, while Van Handel provides some interesting viewpoints on caffeine as an ergogenic acid.

MHW

Section Editor

Dr. Melvin H. Williams is currently a professor of physical education at Old Dominion University in Norfolk, Virginia. A graduate of East Stroudsburg State College, Dr. Williams also holds the M.Ed. degree from Ohio University and the Ph.D. degree from the University of Maryland. He was an instructor at the latter institution and also taught and coached at the senior high school level in Reading, Pennsylvania.

Dr. Williams has authored two textbooks dealing with the effects of drugs and nutrition on physical and athletic performance. In addition, he has published more than 20 articles in a wide range of professional journals and has presented some 15 papers at professional mettings. He is a member of the AAHPERD, NCPEAM, Virginia AHPER, and New York Academy of Science. Dr. Williams is a Fellow in the American College of Sports Medicine and twice has been named as Eminent Scholar by the Old Dominion University Board of Visitors.

22

Essential Nutrients in the Diet of the Athlete

Harold E. Wingard

The body can synthesize thousands of different substances that are required for growth, development, energy, and optimal health. However, in order to meet the demands of the body, food, water, and oxygen must be ingested. A nutrient is the chemical substance found in foods that can be utilized by the human body through anabolic or catabolic processes to release energy, provide materials for building and maintenance of body tissue, or supply substances that act in regulating body processes. All nutrients can be placed in one of the following six general classes: carbohydrates, fats, proteins, minerals, vitamins, and water.

The Four Basic Food Groups were set up by the United States Department of Agriculture to classify foods on the basis of similar nutritive composition. One of the basics of good nutrition is eating a variety of foods from the four basic groups and consuming sufficient fluids to meet one's energy and fluid requirements. No single food group provides all of the essential nutrients, but a specific number of servings from each group should be consumed daily. Four servings from the bread and cereal group, four servings from the vegetables and fruit group, two servings from the meat group, and three glasses of milk taken daily provide at least a major portion of the needed vitamins, minerals, and proteins.

Most nutritionists agree that there is little difference in most nutrient requirements between athletes and nonathletes. However, there may be a significant difference in individual caloric requirements depending on the caloric cost of the activity in which the athlete engages. These portions may be supplied by extra amounts of the foods listed in the four food groups. Additional foods such as candy, cakes, and other pastries high in caloric value, but which contribute very little else to the diet, may also be used to supplement the added portions from the four groups on a limited basis.

CARBOHYDRATES

Carbohydrates are composed of carbon, hydrogen, and oxygen atoms, and always have twice as many hydrogen as oxygen atoms. The main function of carbohydrates is to supply energy for the body. Each gram of carbohydrate contains approximately four calories, and during metabolism carbohydrates are completely oxidized to carbon dioxide and water. Typically, diets in the United States consist of approximately 46 percent carbohydrate, 42 percent fat, and 12 percent protein. The Senate Select Committee on Nutrition and Human Needs recommends dietary goals of 58 percent carbohydrate, 12 percent protein, and 30 percent fat (United States Department of Agriculture 1977a). The National Research Council (1974) has not set a Recommended Dietary Allowance for carbohydrates; therefore, variance can be made in combinations with fats to meet one's total energy expenditure.

All carbohydrates are sugars, disaccharides, or polysaccharides formed from the combination of many sugar groups. There are three groups of carbohydrates that are most important in the diet: (1) monosaccharides or the simple sugars of glucose, fructose, and galactose; (2) disaccharides or the double sugars of sucrose, maltose, and lactose; and (3) polysaccharides or the starches, dextrine, glycogen, cellulose, and hemicelluloses.

Foods of plant origin are the number one source of carbohydrates. Potatoes, peas, beans, corn, pears, pineapple, raisins, and cereal grains such as oats, corn, wheat and rice are some examples of foods rich in carbohydrates. Most plant foods such as grains, legumes, fruits, and vegetables contain starch and cellulose. Starch must be broken down in the body to the simpler sugars before they can be utilized. Cellulose is also a polysaccharide, but is much more resistant to the digestive process than the starches and sugars. Cellulose, the fibrous parts of plants, serves to give body to the food and provide stimulation of the digestive tract.

Carbohydrate digestion begins in the mouth by the starch-splitting action of ptyalin secreted from the salivary glands. Action of the carbohydrate-splitting amylase is inactivated as the food reaches the stomach because of the hydrochloric acid produced from the cells lining the stomach. The major portion of carbohydrate digestion takes place in the small intestine by the catabolic action of pancreatic amylase. Starch is hydrolyzed to maltose, and some of the disaccharides maltose, sucrose, and lactose are split into their respective monosaccharides glucose, fructose, and galactose for absorption by the small intestine. Nutritional research has demonstrated that the major portion of hydrolysis of the disaccharides takes place within the mucous membranes of the walls of the small intestine after absorption. These walls contain many disaccharide-splitting enzymes and are capable of preparing monosaccharides from the disaccharides to be secreted into the portal bloodstream. Monosaccharides, once they have been absorbed, are carried to the liver through the portal circulation. In the liver, fructose and galactose are converted into glucose to be utilized for cellular energy, the main function of glucose.

The liver cells release glucose into the bloodstream for energy as required. Excess glucose is converted into glycogen and stored in the liver and skeletal muscle tissue in an insoluble state to be converted back to glucose as the energy need arises. This storage process continues until the storage capacity is reached and then excess glucose is converted into fat and stored in that form. The optimal blood sugar level of 80 to 100 mg of sugar per 100 ml of blood is controlled by the conversion of glycogen to glucose and the release of glucose into the bloodstream by the liver.

Synthesis of glucose from glycogen may take place in the muscle tissue to restore the high-energy compounds of adenosine triphosphate and creatine phosphate that provide energy for strenuous muscular activity. Restoration of the high energy state of muscle tissue is obtained through the oxidation process of glucose inside the muscle cell itself, as well as the concurrent oxidation of fatty acids by muscle tissue. Thus, carbohydrates are truly essential to the diet of the athlete to provide needed energy for training. This essential need for intake of foods containing carbohydrates is proportional to the total amount of energy expended by the athlete.

FAT

Although carbohydrates generally make up the majority of a person's energy supply, fats also play a central role in the energy supply for the body. The human body has a very limited capacity to store carbohydrates in the form of glycogen; however, its ability to store fat is less limiting. As the glycogen storage reaches capacity, glycogen is converted into fat and stored in the adipose tissue. Ingesting protein and fat in excess of one's caloric expenditure will also result in the conversion of this excess to adipose tissue. If carbohydrates are absent from the diet or if insufficient amounts of carbohydrates are ingested, body fat and body protein are broken down and utilized for energy. The National Research Council has not set recommendations for daily allowances because fat can be synthesized from carbohydrates and proteins.

Fats serve a variety of functions in the body. They supplement carbohydrates in protecting protein from being burned as fuel for energy. Body fat provides physical protection for various body organs. Fat in the digestive system aids in the absorption of the fat-soluble vitamins as well as providing a satiety value.

Fats have a higher ratio of hydrogen to oxygen than either protein or carbohydrates; therefore, fats have a greater potential to furnish more energy than equal weights of carbohydrates or protein. In fact, fat has more than twice the caloric value of either of the other energy nutrients. Caloric values per gram that are generally acceptable are: protein, 4; carbohydrates, 4; and fats, 9.

Fats may be either solids or liquids and are usually referred to as fats if in solid state and oils if in the liquid state. They contain one or more fatty acids that are chains of carbon and hydrogen atoms. Typically, fats or oils consist of three fatty acids and one glycerol molecule. They are often referred to as triglycerides because a fatty acid containing 4 to 20 carbon atoms is chemically attached to each of the three carbon compounds of the glycerol molecule.

The glycerol part of the chemical structure of fat remains constant, but the fatty acids vary with respect to the number of carbon atoms in the chain and their relationship to bond with adjacent carbons. A saturated fatty acid is void of double bonds in the carbon chain and contains a full quota of hydrogen ions. Unsaturated fatty acids are those with one or more double bonds in the carbon chain that are capable of absorbing additional hydrogen atoms. Monounsaturated fats can absorb two additional hydrogen ions, whereas polyunsaturated fats are capable of absorbing four or more.

The body tissue is capable of synthesizing sufficient amounts of most of the fatty acids needed for health with the exception of linoleic acid. According to the National Research Council (1974), linoleic and arachadonic fatty acids must be ingested as part of the diet; however, it is now believed that only linoleic acid is essential as arachadonic acid can be manufactured in the body from linoleic acid if vitamin B_6 and pantothenic acid are present.

Vegetable oils such as olive, soybean, coconut, cottenseed, peanut, corn, and safflower are usually in liquid form and referred to as unsaturated fats. Most fats of animal origin such as milk, butter, lard, fatty meats, egg yolks, and cheese are saturated fats. For example: one pat of butter contains 2.5 gm of saturated fat; one cup of whole milk contains 5.1 gm of saturated fat; one ounce of cream cheese contains 6.2 gm of saturated fat; and a 3.1 ounce cooked lamb chop, lean and fat, contains 14.8 gm of saturated fat. Athletes must be aware of the fact that many "high protein" foods are also high in fat content. A broiled ground beef patty for example, contains 185 total calories of which 92 are of protein and 93 are of fat origin.

Although the National Research Council (1974) has not provided a Recommended Daily Allowance (RDA) for fats, fat in a person's diet should not exceed 35 percent of the total calories ingested. In fact, many nutritionists recommend that people in the United States should attempt to keep the fat content in the diet within a 20 to 25 percent range of the total caloric intake.

Cholesterol, a fatlike steroid substance, is widely distributed in animal bodies, especially in the blood, nerve tissue, and bile. Cholesterol is supplied in the diet only from foods of animal origin; however, cholesterol can be synthesized in the body from acetyl CoA, which can be derived endogenously from carbohydrates and fats. Although there is great interest in reducing the cholesterol intake as a preventative measure against cardiovascular disease, cholesterol has many important functions in the human body. It is a precursor of sex hormones, adrenal hormones, and bile acids. Cholesterol is an important part of certain organs, such as the coverings for nerve fibers, and it facilitates the absorption of fatty acids from the intestines. Vitamin D is also produced in the body from a cholesterol derivative.

Digestion of fats starts in the esophagus as pharyngeal lipase comes in contact with the masticated fat. Hydrolysis begins in the throat and continues in the stomach where gastric lipase is released and a small amount of triglycerides is broken down into free fatty acids, monoglycerides, and diglycerides. Digestion and absorption take place primarily in the small intestines. Steapsin, or pancreatic lipase, is the active enzyme for fat digestion in the small intestines, which hydrolyzes fats into simple glycerides, fatty acids, and glycerol.

Bile, discharged from the liver and gallbladder into the intestines, acts to emulsify fats and is essential in the absorption of fatty acids into the mucosal cells. Most of the fatty acids and glycerol are absorbed into the lacteals as a milky emulsion called chyle. Only about 30 percent of the hydrolyzed fat is absorbed into the capillaries.

During metabolism of fats, which takes place in the liver and muscle tissue, each fatty acid is broken down to acetyl CoA, a two-carbon compound. This acetyl CoA may then be oxidized via the citric acid cycle and utilized for energy or be used to resynthesize fatty acids.

Glycerol metabolism on the other hand is different from fatty acid metabolism. Glycerol can be phosphorylated in the liver and converted into glucose. Glycerol metabolism becomes merged with carbohydrate metabolism, but the amount of glucose synthesized by this process is trivial.

Fat is synthesized in the liver, adipose tissue, and mammary glands and stored as adipose tissue. The fat deposited as adipose tissue is primarily in the form of triglycerides. The amount of fat deposited correlates with the amount of fat ingested and energy expended.

PROTEINS

Proteins are complex molecules constructed of many amino acids linked together in peptide bonds that serve as essential constituents of every living cell. Amino acids and nitrogen are provided in food protein to synthesize body protein and other tissue constituents. They are the only class of energy nutrients that contain nitrogen plus carbon, hydrogen, and oxygen. An amino group (NH_2) and a carboxyl group (COOH) are present in each protein molecule, but the molecular structure may vary with respect to the following: total number of amino acids, proportions of amino acids, kinds of amino acids, and their sequence on the amino acid chain.

Of the 22 naturally occurring amino acids known, eight are essential for adult humans: isoleucine, leucine, lysine, methionine, phenylalanine, threonine, tryptophan, and valine. Histidine is essential for children, but probably not for adults who are in good health. "Essential" amino acids are those that cannot be synthesized in the body and must be supplied by food in the diet. All other amino acids are referred to as "nonessential" because they can be synthesized in the body if they are not contained in the diet.

The human body has a duel requirement for protein. A minimum amount of the essential amino acids is required for growth and maintenance of health. Second, a minimum amount of amino nitrogen must be provided to maintain the body's nitrogen equilibrium. Sufficient amounts of protein must be present to equal the total nitrogen utilized by the body in the anabolic processes of body protein development. During the constant process of protein breakdown and synthesis, nitrogen balance is reached when the total nitrogen intake equals the total nitrogen waste output.

The principal functions of protein in the body are to serve as the basic structure of most body tissue, including enzymes, antibodies, hormones, genes, hemoglobin, and other plasma proteins. A secondary function of protein is to serve as an energy source. Certain uses of amino acids have priority over others, and the demand for energy takes top priority in metabolism. If carbohydrate and fat consumption do not meet the energy requirements, amino acids are catabolized and utilized as a source of energy.

The National Research Council (1974) has set an RDA for protein based upon an average need of 0.47 gm/kg of body weight with a 30 percent coefficient of variation increasing the value to 0.6 gm/kg. A correction factor for the 75 percent efficiency of utilization for mixed protein increases the RDA to 0.8 gm/kg of body weight per day. The allowances are shown for infants, children, males and females in Table 22.1

Protein quality differs due to the presence of the number and amount of each of the various essential amino acids. In order for amino acids to be utilized for protein synthesis in the cells of the human body, all of the amino acids from which the protein is to be constructed (directed by the DNA in the cell) must be present at the same time.

Generally, vegetable proteins are less complete in amino acids than protein from animal origin and are therefore considered inferior to animal protein. Animal protein contains all the essential amino acids. A rule of thumb to remember is that tryptophan, methionine, and lysine are three amino acids frequently lacking in sufficient quantity in protein of vegetable origin. Therefore, vegetarians (Vegans) must be assured they get all of the essential amino acids in the proper quantities by ingesting vegetables that supplement each other in amino acids. Time of ingestion (consuming all essential amino acids at one setting) is very important also because there is no physiological capability to store individual amino acids to be used for synthesis later. As protein synthesis occurs, all needed amino acids must be present to form their link in the chain as designated by the coded information from DNA.

Most people in the United States consume more protein than they actually need. Generally there are two reasons for this: (1) people have access to an abundant supply of protein, and (2) protein, an expensive nutrient, is often respected as an "extra special" health food. Protein utilization has been regarded as the most important nutrient among athletes for many years because of its relationship to muscle tissue and power. However, there does not appear to be any evidence in nutritional literature that shows a nutritional benefit can be gained by consuming protein in excess of the RDA in healthy individuals. On the other hand, there does not seem to be evidence that excess amounts of protein in the diet are harmful. One must remember, however, that excess protein as well as excess carbohydrates and fats can indeed mean excess calories. If an excess amount of amino acids exists after the anabolic needs of the body are met, these amino acids will be deaminated and converted to fat, which will eventually be stored if the body's caloric energy need is exceeded.

Digestion of protein beings in the stomach with a gradual degradation of large protein molecules to proteoses and some peptones. The gastric enzyme pepsin, which breaks proteins to short chains of amino acids, and rennin, which is a milk-curdling enzyme, are secreted by the zymgenic cells of the stomach. Hydrochloric acid is also secreted by the gastric mucosa to provide an optimal acidic pH of 1.5, which is required in order for pepsin to digest protein. Casein, the principal protein in milk, is split into soluble paracasein by rennin in the stomach. The remainder of protein digestion takes place in the small intestine.

In the intestines, several enzyme secretions contribute to the completion of protein digestion. Trypsin, an active enyzme formed from the precursor trypsinogen secreted by the pancreas, splits proteins into polypeptides. Chymotrypsin, also secreted from the pancreas, aids in the breakdown of the proteoses to dipeptides. Three more enzymes (carboxypeptidase, a pancreatic secretion; and aminopeptidase and dipeptidase, intestinal secretions) complete the breakdown of peptones, polypeptides, and dipeptides to single amino acids for absorption.

Although there is a wide difference in the absorption rate of the various amino acids, approximately 90 percent of the amino acids derived from the food protein is selectively absorbed into the bloodstream. The amino acids are transported to the liver; some are retained by the liver, and others are placed in general circulation to be carried to all body tissue. The liver serves to synthesize, from the amino acid pool, a wide spectrum of amino acids for plasma protein and tissue utilization.

Proteins may also enter the pathway of carbohydrate or ketone body metabolism where the amino acids are transformed, via a deamination process, and broken down into the ultimate end products of carbon dioxide, water, heat, and energy. The nitrogen containing part of the amino group is removed and forms ammonia; the ammonia is then immediately converted to urea to be eliminated from the body.

There is a constant flux between protein breakdown and synthesis of protein in the human body. As long as the relationship between the anabolic and catabolic processes are equated, a nitrogen balance will be maintained. When total catabolism exceeds total anabolism, a negative nitrogen balance will be reached and body protein will be utilized to meet the body's needs. This situation will occur under two circumstances: (1) the food protein intake is

Table 22.1

Food and Nutrition Board, National Academy of Sciences—National Research Council
Recommended Daily Dietary Allowances* Revised 1974

Designed for the maintenance of good nutrition of practically all healthy people in the U.S.A.

| | | | | | | | | Fat-Soluble Vitamins | | | |
| | Age | Weight | | Height | | Energy | Protein | Vita-min A Activity | | Vita-min D | Vita-min E Activity** |
	(years)	(kg)	(lbs)	(cm)	(in)	(kcal)†	(g)	(RE)‡	(IU)	(IU)	(IU)
Infants	0.0-0.5	6	14	60	24	kg × 117	kg × 2.2	420•	1,400	400	4
	0.5-1.0	9	20	71	28	kg × 108	kg × 2.0	400	2,000	400	5
Children	1-3	13	28	86	34	1,300	23	400	2,000	400	7
	4-6	20	44	110	44	1,800	30	500	2,500	400	9
	7-10	30	66	135	54	2,400	36	700	3,300	400	10
Males	11-14	44	97	158	63	2,800	44	1,000	5,000	400	12
	15-18	61	134	172	69	3,000	54	1,000	5,000	400	15
	19-22	67	147	172	69	3,000	54	1,000	5,000	400	15
	23-50	70	154	172	69	2,700	56	1,000	5,000		15
	51+	70	154	172	69	2,400	56	1,000	5,000		15
Females	11-14	44	97	155	62	2,400	44	800	4,000	400	12
	15-18	54	119	162	65	2,100	48	800	4,000	400	12
	19-22	58	128	162	65	2,100	46	800	4,000	400	12
	23-50	58	128	162	65	2,000	46	800	4,000		12
	51+	58	128	162	65	1,800	46	800	4,000		12
Pregnant						+300	+30	1,000	5,000	400	15
Lactating						+500	+20	1,200	6,000	400	15

* The allowances are intended to provide for individual variations among most normal persons as they live in the United States under usual environmental stress. Diets should be based on a variety of common foods in order to provide other nutrients for which human requirements have been less well defined. See test for more detailed discussion of allowances and of nutrients not tabulated.

† Kilojoules (kj) = 4.2 × kcal.

‡ Retinol equivalents.

• Assumed to be all as retinol in milk during the first six months of life. All subsequent intakes are assumed to be half as retinol and half as β-carotene when calculated from international units. As retinol equivalents, three fourths are a retinol and one fourth as β-carotene.

** Total vitamin E activity, estimated to be 80 percent as a-tocopherol and 20 percent other tocopherols. See text for variation in allowances.

†† The folacin allowances refer to dietary sources as determined by *Lactobacillus casei* assay. Pure forms of folacin may be effective in doses less than one fourth of the recommended dietary allowance.

‡‡ Although allowances are expressed as niacin, it is recognized that on the average 12 mg of niacin is derived form each 60 mg of dietary tryptophan.

•• This increased requirement cannot be met by ordinary diets; therefore, the use of supplemental iron is recommended.

inadequate for the body's needs, or (2) the energy requirement for the body is not met by intake of adequate amounts of carbohydrates and fats.

In brief, athletes as well as nonathletes must ingest sufficient amounts of protein to provide enough of the essential amino acids needed by the body. Partaking of food sources of animal origin is the easiest way to assure sufficient amounts of the essential amino acids are ingested. Sufficient amounts of protein

Table 22.1

Water-Soluble Vitamins							Minerals					
Ascorbic Acid (mg)	Folacin†† (ug)	Niacin‡‡ (mg)	Riboflavin (mg)	Thiamin (mg)	Vitamin B6 (mg)	Vitamin B12 (ug)	Calcium (mg)	Phosphorus (mg)	Iodine (ug)	Iron (mg)	Magnesium (mg)	Zinc (mg)
35	50	5	0.4	0.3	0.3	0.3	360	240	35	10	60	3
36	50	8	0.6	0.5	0.4	0.3	540	400	45	15	70	5
40	100	9	0.8	0.7	0.6	1.0	800	800	60	15	150	10
40	200	12	1.1	0.9	0.9	1.5	800	800	80	10	200	10
40	300	16	1.2	1.2	1.2	2.0	800	800	110	10	250	10
45	400	18	1.5	1.4	1.6	3.0	1,200	1,200	130	18	350	15
45	400	20	1.8	1.5	2.0	3.0	1,200	1,200	150	18	400	15
45	400	20	1.8	1.5	2.0	3.0	800	800	140	10	350	15
45	400	18	1.6	1.4	2.0	3.0	800	800	130	10	350	15
45	400	16	1.5	1.2	2.0	3.0	800	800	110	10	350	15
45	400	16	1.3	1.2	1.6	3.0	1,200	1,200	115	18	300	15
45	400	14	1.4	1.1	2.0	3.0	1,200	1,200	115	18	300	15
45	400	14	1.4	1.1	2.0	3.0	800	800	100	18	300	15
45	400	13	1.2	1.0	2.0	3.0	800	800	100	18	300	15
45	400	12	1.1	1.0	2.0	3.0	800	800	80	10	300	15
60	800	+2	+0.3	+0.3	2.5	4.0	1,200	1,200	125	18+••	450	20
80	600	+4	+0.5	+0.3	2.5	4.0	1,200	1,200	150	18	450	25

appear to be about 12 percent of the total caloric intake per day. There is no substantial evidence showing any beneficial physiological gain for healthy athletes that exceed the 12 percent recommendation.

VITAMINS

Vitamins are a group of organic compounds essential in the diet in small quantities for normal growth, maintenance of health, and reproduction. Vitamin requirements vary from person to person according to the individual's sex, rate of metabolism, age, place of living, food eaten, and physical activities. Humans must have most of their vitamins supplied in the diet. Most foods contain a good supply and variety of vitamins, but no one food contains all of the needed vitamins in sufficient amounts to maintain positive health. Since vitamins are found in varying quantities in food, it is important that a person's diet be varied. One vitamin cannot replace another missing vitamin because each vitamin has its own specific function. They do, however, function together to regulate biological processes.

Vitamins are not energy nutrients, but their enzyme and coenzyme activities are a vital part of the biological reaction whereby energy is released from carbohydrates, fats, and protein. Vitamins also play an important role in the chemical reaction of transforming nutrients into living matter for growth, maintenance, and reproduction.

Traditionally, vitamins have been classified in two broad categories according to their solubility. Vitamins A, D, E, and K, which are soluble in fats and oils, are called fat-soluble vitamins. These vitamins are absorbed along with dietary fat and can be stored in the body's fat. All other vitamins that are water soluble are called water-soluble vitamins. Included are all the B vitamins and vitamin C. These vitamins cannot be stored by the body in appreciable quantities and therefore should be replaced daily.

A well-balanced diet should contain all of the required vitamins in their proper amounts. A point to remember is that vitamin supplements will not make up for skipped meals because vitamins have no caloric value. Since vitamins are in almost everything a person eats or drinks, an individual on a well-balanced diet will maintain the RDA for positive health. The fact that some foods are richer than others in vitamin content, coupled with the fact that people in the United States have eating habits that are nonconducive to a well-balanced diet, may result in inadequate vitamin consumption: however, vitamin deficiency diseases will only appear after prolonged consumption of a diet deficient in vitamins, and even then the symptoms may be vague and ill-defined.

It is possible to overdose with fat-soluble vitamins, especially A and D. Surplus fat-soluble vitamins accumulate in the fat tissue; therefore, massive doses may result in harmful effects on the body. There is no conclusive evidence of any adverse effect of supersaturation with the water-soluble vitamins.

Advertising has placed vitamins on a "supernatural" plane where the public, including athletes, uncritically accepts the use of vitamins as an ergogenic aid and a preventive or treatment for many human ills. However, there is no substantial evidence to support any value in taking vitamin supplements for the healthy individual.

FAT-SOLUBLE VITAMINS

Vitamin A is derived from preformed retinol and a provitamin Beta carotene. Vitamin A does not occur in plants; however, provitamins of vitamin A do, and every two carotene units consumed would be expected to yield one vitamin A unit in the body. Vitamin A plays important roles in normal vision, development of rhodopsin in the eyes, maintenance of epithelial tissues and normal growth of epithelial cells, growth and development of the skeletal system and teeth, and the functioning of cilia.

The National Research Council (1974) has adopted RDAs ranging from 1400 IU (International Units) for infants to 6000 IU for lactating mothers. The best sources of carotene are deep yellow fruits and vegetables, green leafy vegetables, liver, milk, eggs, and butter.

Vitamin D, the sunshine vitamin, is produced in the body by ultraviolet light shining on the skin. The sebaceous glands secrete 7-dehydrocholesterol onto the skin and as the skin is exposed to sunlight, the provitamin D is converted into vitamin D. Vitamin D is abosrbed into the blood and distributed throughout the body. Vitamin D aids in the utilization and retention of calcium and phosphorus. It also increases the intestinal absorption of calcium and phosphorus. The RDA for infants, children, adolescents, pregnant or lactating women is 400 IU. The vitamin D requirement for all other adults is minimal and not listed. Sources of dietary vitamin D are fortified milk, eggs, fishliver oil, saltwater fish, and liver.

Vitamin E is made up of several viscous oil compounds with alphatocopherol providing the most biological activity. It is an antioxidant that protects natural fats and oils from becoming rencid. Vitamin E also inhibits the oxidation of vitamin A and other fatty acids. The biological function of vitamin E in the human living cell has not been established thus far. Many claims have been made for supplemental use of synthetic vitamin E; however, in light of the fact that clinical or biochemical evidence is absent in regard to the RDAs adopted by the National Research Council as being insufficient, it is assumed that the recommended daily allowance is adequate for the United States population. Wheat germ oils, whole grains, eggs, meats, shortening, margarine, soybean oil, corn oil, and cotten seed oil are all good sources of vitamin E.

Vitamin K is referred to as the "antihemorrhagic vitamin" because it is essential for the synthesis of prothrombin and other blood coagulating protein factors in the liver. Vitamin K is ingested from a widely distributed group of plant foods. Another form of vitamin K is synthesized in the intestinal track by bacteria and stored in the liver; therefore, deficiency is rare in adults. Green leafy vegetables, egg yolk, pork liver and soybean oil are excellent sources of dietary vitamin K.

WATER-SOLUBLE VITAMINS

Thiamine or vitamin B_1 functions as a coenzyme in the conversion of carbohydrate into glucose. It also aids in fat metabolism, digestion, and the conversion of tryptophan to nicotinamide. Allowances for thiamine have been related to carbohydrate metabolism and energy intake. In the United States, deficiencies do occur among adult men and women; however, deficiencies are primarily associated with alcoholics who have poor dietary intake.

The National Research Council (1974) recommends a thiamine allowance for adults of 0.5 mg/1000 kcal with ordinary levels of intake. The minimum that is recommended is a daily intake of 1 mg/day even if the caloric intake is less than 2000 kcal daily. The thiamine allowance for children and teenagers is also 0.5 mg/1000 kcal. Common food sources for thiamine are numerous. Some good sources are lean pork, organ meats, dried beans, peas, peanuts, and enriched cereals.

Riboflavin (B_2), niacin, pyridoxine (B_6), and pantothenic acid all function as part of a coenzyme group in the metabolism of carbohydrates, fats, and proteins. Vitamin B_2 is essential to good vision and healthy eyes and helps to keep the skin around the mouth and lips healthy. Niacin prevents and cures pellagra. It can be synthesized in the body from the amino acid tryptophan in the presence of pyridoxine. Vitamin B_6 facilitates the release of glycogen from the muscles and liver. B_6 also aids in the formation of erythrocytes and antibodies. It also aids in the utilization of energy in the brain and nervous tissue. Pantothenic acid is a constituent of coenzyme A, which is essential in cellular metabolism. Pantothenic acid is necessary for the formation of sterols, fatty acids and cholesterol. Good sources of these B vitamins are liver, meats, whole-grain cereals, enriched cereals, wheat germ, lima beans, eggs, nuts, and corn.

Another water-soluble vitamin essential to human life is folic acid (folacin). The various forms of folic acid are supplied by food sources or synthesized by the intestinal flora. Folic acid is essential for the synthesis of purines and pyrimidines, which are primary constituents of nucleic acids. One of the most important functions of folic acid is the role it plays in the orderly formation of red blood cells. It is effective for treatment of macrocytic anemia. The U.S. RDA's for folacin range from 50 mg for infants to 800 mg for pregnant women. Foods containing good supplies of folacin include liver, yeast, dark green leafy vegetables, nuts, legumes, lima beans, and whole-grain cereals.

Vitamin B_{12} (cyanocobalamin), found exclusively in foods of animal origin, prevents the development of pernicious anemia. Vitamin B_{12} also aids in cellular metabolism and is involved in metabolic activity of nervous tissue. Meat, fish, and milk products are good sources of vitamin B_{12}.

Vitamin C or ascorbic acid has been well documented for its importance as a coenzyme in the human body. Ascorbic acid is necessary for the formation of collagen, the intercellular fibrous tissue. It also plays an important role in the metabolism of amino acids. Vitamin C enhances the absorption of iron from the intestinal wall and influences the formation of hemoglobin. It is essential in the formative stages of bone and tooth development. Ascorbic acid is essential in the prevention of scurvy and is believed to enhance an individual's capacity to heal wounds and fractures. Recommendations for ascorbic acid vary somewhat according to the source cited. The Canadian Dietary Standards and the British Medical Research Council have set the allowance for adults at 30 mg per day. The National Research Council (1974) recommends 45 mg per day for adults; however, the daily allowances vary from 35 mg for infants to 80 mg for the lactating woman. There is no evidence that saturation of body tissue with ascorbic acid is beneficial to health. Like other water-soluble vitamins, excess amounts of vitamin C are excreted in the urine. Good sources of ascorbic acid are citrus fruits, tomatoes, raspberries, cantalopes, strawberries, and green vegetables.

MINERALS

Minerals are the inorganic nutrients that perform two general functions in the human body. They aid in body metabolism in their role as regulators of various biological functions. Secondly, about four to five percent of the total body weight is comprised of mineral elements that function as structural material.

Of the 103 known elements, 16 different minerals are known to be needed by the body. Eleven elements constitute the vast majority of living matter, but only six have an RDA established by the National Research Council (1974).

Two classifications of minerals, based upon the amounts needed in the human body, were used to treat mineral elements by the National Research Council (1974): (1) major mineral elements, those needed in the diet at levels of 100 mg/day or more—calcium, phosphorus, magnesium, sodium, potassium and chloride; and (2) trace elements, those minerals needed in amounts no greater than a few mg/day iron, copper, iodine, fluorine, zinc, chromium, cobalt, manganese, and selenium. Only six of the major and trace elements have an established RDA. They are calcium, phosphorus, iodine, iron, magnesium, and zinc. Of all the mineral elements, the three most likely to be deficient in the American diet are calcium, iron and iodine.

Calcium and Phosphorus

Calcium and phosphorus are the two elements found in greatest abundance in the human body. Some 99 percent of the calcium in the body is in the bones. The remaining is distributed throughout the body tissue and body fluids functioning in a regulatory role for muscle contraction, nerve impulse transmission, and blood clotting.

Phosphorus, in the form of phosphate ions, has a definite relationship with calcium in the formation of teeth and bones. Phosphorus and calcium also play a role in each other's absorption. Absorption is accomplished best when the two elements are present in approximately the same amounts. Nearly 80 percent of the body's phosphorus is found in the skeletal system where it adds rigidity to bone structure. The remaining 20 percent is distributed throughout the body fluid in each cell of the body to aid in cell metabolism.

The RDA for calcium set by the Food and Nutrition Board of the National Research Council (1974) is 0.8 g for children, 1.2 g for teenagers, and 0.8 g for adults. A high calcium intake is needed during puberty for growth and development, but adults only require calcium to maintain the body stores. The RDA for phosphorus is the same as that for calcium for all age groups except the young infant. In early infancy a calcium/phosphorus ratio in the diet of 1.51 is recommended. Milk and cheese are excellent sources of both calcium and phosphorus. Nuts, legumes, and animal meats are also good sources of phosphorus. Green vegetables, salmon, shellfish, and egg yolks are good sources of calcium.

Iodine

Iodine is an essential nutrient with only one known function—the formation of the thyroid hormone, thyroxine. Thyroxine regulates the basal metabolic rate of the individual. The availability of iodine affects the thyroid gland and is the determining factor for the output of thyroid hormone. An iodine deficiency will result in hypothyroidism, a decreased metabolic rate, and eventually a "simple" goiter. The RDA set by the National Research Council (1974) for iodine shows variances from 35 mg in infants to 150 mg in lactating women. Seafoods, vegetables grown in iodine-rich soils, cod-liver oil, and iodized salt are the best sources of iodine.

Iron

Iron, an essential trace element, plays an essential role in oxygen transport and cellular respiration. It is a part of hemoglobin, a hemeprotein component of the red blood cell that transports oxygen to cells, and is present in the intracellular cytochrome system, which aids in the production of energy. In the muscle cells, iron is essential for the manufacture of myoglobin.

Absorption of dietary iron takes place in the intestinal mucosa of the duodenum. When iron is available in the diet, only a small percentage is absorbed as needed to maintain the iron storage state in the body. Although the absorption process of iron is very complex, it appears that the degree of absorption depends upon the current iron balance in the body. There is no excretion mechanism for absorbed iron; therefore, the intestinal mucosa becomes the main control to reject available but unneeded dietary iron.

The National Research Council (1974) set the RDA for infants and children at 10 to 15 mg, for adults at 10 to 18 mg, and pregnant or lactating women at 18 mg. The normal adult woman requires approximately 8 mg/day more iron than the normal adult male to meet the additional needs imposed by menstruation.

In the event of iron deficiency, the blood has a decreased oxygen-carrying capacity that, in turn, reflects on the energy functions of the body. Individuals with iron deficiency feel tired, are weak, and may show abnormal fatigue. Severe blood loss or chronic blood loss may deplete the body's iron stores even though the diet and absorption are adequate. Nutritional habits, such as diets with an inadequate supply of iron, may also be the cause of iron deficiency.

Liver is probably one of the best sources of dietary iron. Other organ meats, iron-enriched flour and cereals, lean meats, molasses, dried beans, nuts, dried fruits, egg yolk, and soybeans are also good sources of dietary iron.

Magnesium

Magnesium is a cofactor in numerous enzymatic reactions essential for normal functioning of nerves and muscles. It is a constituent of bone and soft tissue.

Magnesium is involved in calcium and phosphorus metabolism and in bone building. It is also involved in carbohydrate, fat, and protein metabolism in the transfer of phosphate from adenosine triphosphate to adenosine diphosphate.

Magnesium deficiency may result in muscular excitability, nervousness, and metabolic disturbances. However, since magnesium is supplied in a wide variety of foods of plant origin, a true dietary deficiency of this mineral seems rare. The RDAs for this element range from 60 mg for infants to 450 mg for pregnant or lactating women. All four food groups contribute as a source for some magnesium, but the best source of supply is green leafy vegetables.

Zinc

Zinc, the sixth element with an RDA, is a part of carbonic anhydrase, which is involved with the carbon dioxide exchange between tissue and the blood. It also plays a role in protein and nucleic acid formation as well as being essential for providing release of vitamin A from the liver to maintain normal vitamin A blood levels.

The National Research Council (1974) recommends daily allowances ranging from 3 mg for infants to 25 mg for lactating women. Zinc is present in a variety of foods with the richest sources being oysters, herring, and other fish. In general, diets high in protein of animal origin are good supplies of zinc.

Sodium

Sodium, potassium, and chloride show a high degree of interrelatedness in their essential roles for normal functioning of the body. Sodium is found in the extracellular fluids as the main cation that regulates the osmotic pressure and maintains the acid-base balance in the body fluids. It also serves a role in the electrical potential for nerve-impulse conduction and muscular contraction.

There is no RDA for sodium probably because sodium chloride is present in nearly all foods and the normal intake is between 6 gm and 19 gm daily. However, the National Research Council (1974) recommends one additional gram of sodium chloride for each liter of water taken in excess of a daily four-liter intake of fluid to replace sweat loss.

Potassium

Potassium is the principal cation found in the intracellular fluids, and like sodium, possesses the homeostatic capabilities to control normal levels of body fluid. It affects the excitability of nerve tissue and influences the contractility of skeletal, smooth, and cardiac muscle. Potassium also plays a role in converting glucose to glycogen in the liver and muscle tissue.

There is no RDA for potassium but the dietary need is similar to that of sodium. Potassium is widely distributed in foods and under normal circumstances a potassium deficiency is unlikely. Fruits, vegetables, beef, fish, and lentils are good dietary sources of potassium.

Chloride

Chloride is the most important anion that works with sodium in the maintenance of fluid volume and electrolyte balance. Chloride also has a necessary role in forming the hydrochloric acid of the gastric juice in the stomach. Loss of chloride generally parallels loss of sodium under normal circumstances. There is no known deficiency disease for chloride; sources for dietary intake are salt and foods containing salt.

Other Minerals

Fluoride appears to be essential for healthy bones and teeth, especially providing a resistance to dental caries. It may be found in seafoods and tea. Many communities have fluoridated water supplies containing 1 ppm of fluorine (one part of fluorine per one million parts water).

Copper is an essential part of many enzymes. It plays a role in the production of red blood cells and the absorption of iron to aid in prevention of anemia. Cobalt is a part of vitamin B_{12} and is essential for the activity of several enzymes. Chromium is thought to be essential for glucose metabolism. Manganese is an essential element for the formation of urea. It activates several enzymes in the citric acid cycle. Selenium is thought to be essential to liver function and cellular respiration, but very little is known about a human requirement for this element.

WATER

The need for water has already been discussed thoroughly by Herbert in Chapter 15, Section 2. Water is a nutrient necessary for life. An individual can survive for only a few days without water; a body loss of approximately 20 percent is usually fatal. Water serves several important functions. Essentially it comprises approximately 55 to 60 percent of an individual's total body weight, provides the essential building material for cell protoplasm, acts as a powerful ionizing agent, serves as the medium in which practically all metabolic reactions take place, provides the material for evaporation and temperature regulation of the body, and serves as a vehicle of chemical transport for nutrients, waste, and internal enzymes.

Water requirements for the body depend somewhat on the size of the individual. Water is lost by excretion from the kidneys, perspiration on the skin, small amounts in the stool, and water vapor in the expired air. The average adult loses about two to two and one-half liters per day.

Drinking fluids is the main means of replenishing the water loss. Usually five or six glasses a day will suffice under normal circumstances; however, during heat stress a person may require more fluid. The National Research Council (1974) recommends a daily intake of one milliliter of water for each calorie of food under normal circumstances of light exercise and moderate temperature.

Fluid lost may be replenished by three different sources: fluids ingested, water contained in solid foods, and water produced by the metabolism of foods. Thirst is the earliest and best indicator that the water level in the body is being depleted. Thirst usually will be felt when two percent of the body water weight is lost; therefore, fluid intake is necessary.

The kidney, through a complex functioning system, strives to maintain the normal water level in the body. During the time of water deprivation, the kidneys compensate by excreting a concentrated urine of more solutes and less water. During times of increased body water supply, the kidneys function by eliminating excess water.

REFERENCES

National Research Council: Food and Nutrition Board, Committee on Dietary Allowances. 1974. *Recommended Dietary Allowances.* Washington, D.C.

United States Department of Agriculture: Senate Committee on Nutrition and Human Needs. 1977a. Senate looks at your diet, C.Q. *Weekly Report,* 35, No. 6, 203.

United States Department of Agriculture: Agricultural Research Service. 1977b. Nutritive Value of Foods. *Home and Garden Bulletin,* No. 72.

23

Nutrition for the Female Athlete

Emily M. Haymes

From birth through age ten, the recommended daily dietary allowances are the same for girls and boys (National Research Council 1974). Separate allowances for males ane females are given beginning at age 11. Males will have a larger requirement than females if the need for the nutrient is based on body size or energy expenditure. Iron is the only nutrient needed in greater quantities by the nonpregnant or nonlactating female. The requirements for many nutrients increase during pregnancy and lactation, and these will be discussed as a separate topic.

CALORIC REQUIREMENTS

Females versus Males

The daily caloric requirement for the female is generally smaller than that of the male even though both may be training at the same intensity and for equal lengths of time. There are several reasons why the energy requirements are lower for the female. First, the basal metabolic rate per unit of body size of the female is lower than that of a male. This is thought to be primarily due to the female's larger proportion of fat and smaller proportion of lean body mass compared to the male. Male and female sex hormones may also influence the metabolic rate. Second, after puberty males are on the average larger in body size than females. This not only influences the basal metabolic requirement, but also influences energy expenditure during activity. A 70 kg man will use 76 kcal in walking one mile in 20 minutes while a 58 kg woman would use only 67 kcal covering the same distance at the same pace (Howley and Glover 1974). Howley and Glover did find, however, that females use more calories per kilogram weight than males while walking and running.

Estimating Activity Needs

In order to determine the caloric needs of the athlete it is necessary to estimate the caloric requirement of the activity. The energy requirement of any activity will be influenced by the intensity and duration of training and weight of the individual as well as the type of activity. In Table 23.1 the estimated increase in caloric needs for a variety of activities is presented. The estimates were made for a woman weighing 58 kg. Girls and women weighing less would need fewer calories and those women weighing more than 58 kg would need additional calories. These caloric estimates are in addition to the normal energy allowances: 2400 kcal for girls 11 to 14 years; 2100 kcal for females 15 to 22 years; and 2000 kcal for females 23 to 50 years. For example, a 13-year-old girl who practices basketball one hour per day would need 2850 to 3000 kcal. A 20-year-old college woman who practices field hockey two hours per day would need 3000 to 3300 kcal.

NUTRIENT UTILIZATION

Carbohydrates and Fats

Since females have a higher percentage of body weight as fat and a lower percentage of muscle than do males, the female may be better suited to distance running than the male (Ullyot 1974). Ullyot proposed that women might be more efficient in oxidizing fats than men and thus postpone the utilization of glycogen stores. Unfortunately, most studies of carbohydrate versus fat utilization have used male subjects, so the theory has not been verified. Very few differences

Table 23.1
Estimated Increase in Caloric Expenditure Needed per Hour
for Selected Activities*

Activity	Increase (kcal/hr)
Light	200-300
Archery	
Bowling	
Canoeing (leisurely)	
Diving	
Field Events	
Golf	
Gymnastics	
Softball	
Volleyball	
Moderate	300-450
Badminton	
Canoeing (racing)	
Cycling (leisurely)	
Hiking	
Skiing (downhill)	
Swimming (leisurely)	
Tennis	
Heavy	450-600
Basketball	
Backpacking (with 10 kg pack)	
Cycling (racing)	
Field Hockey	
Lacrosse	
Mountain Climbing	
Running (5 miles or less)	
Soccer	
Skiing (cross country on level)	
Squash	
Swimming (racing)	
Very Heavy	600-1000
Running (6 miles or more)	
Skiing (cross country uphill)	

* Estimates made for a female weighing 58 kg.

have been found in skeletal muscle enzymes of males and female track athletes, suggesting that female athletes are as capable of using glycolytic pathways as males (Costill et al. 1976). Glycogen loading should be as important for the female as the male although her smaller muscle mass will result in less total glycogen stores.

Proteins

The requirement for protein is highest in early infancy and declines with age. This is due to the high rate of tissue growth early in life. The recommended dietary allowance is 1.0 gm protein per kilogram of body weight to 11 to 14 year olds, 0.9 gm protein per kg for 15 to 18 year olds, and 0.8 gm protein per kilogram for those over 19, regardless of sex (National Research Council 1974). After age 14, males usually weigh more than females and therefore require a greater total quantity of protein.

Growing children and adolescents may have a greater need for protein during sports training. Results reported by Parizkova (1973) revealed that the lean body mass of girl gymnasts increased during intensive training even though body weight remained relatively constant. Proteins accounted for only 13 percent of the total caloric intake, but intake averaged 1.7 gm protein per kilogram during the period of intensive training. It has been estimated that a growing athlete may need as much as 2 gm protein per kilogram of body weight (Buskirk and Haymes 1972). If the protein content of the diet amounts to 15 percent of the total caloric intake of 3000 kcal, it would provide 112 gm protein, which should be sufficient for most growing female athletes.

Female athletes who are subjected to repeated bruising or injuries may also have a greater protein requirement. These are most likely to occur in such sports as field hockey, football, rugby, and soccer. Nitrogen excretion increases following injury and these losses must be recovered during the healing process (Guthrie 1975). In growing athletes subjected to trauma, a protein intake of 2.5 gm/kg may be required (Buskirk and Haymes 1972).

VITAMIN NEEDS

Thiamine

The requirement for thiamine is 0.5 mg/1000 kcal intake. Normally women need about 1 gm thiamine per day. Women athletes with increased caloric intakes have a greater need for thiamine. In addition, athletes on high carbohydrate diets also have an increased need for thiamine.

Riboflavin

If greater quantities of energy are used, the requirement for riboflavin is increased. Female athletes consuming 3000 kcal/day need 1.8 mg of riboflavin. The Ten State Nutrition Survey (1972) found that about 50 percent of 15-to-16-year-old females had riboflavin intakes below the recommended dietary allowance. No detrimental effects of a riboflavin deficiency on performance have been documented.

Niacin

With increased caloric intake, female athletes should increase their niacin intake. Nicotinic acid supplements have been found to depress the use of plasma fatty acids during exercise (Bergstrom et al. 1969; Carlson et al. 1963; Jenkins 1965). Since this may result in a more rapid depletion of glycogen stores during exercise, nicotinic acid supplements should be used by athletes only when a niacin deficiency exists.

Pyridoxine

With an increased protein intake it is necessary to increase the pyriodoxine intake. There is evidence that the use of oral contraceptive may result in a greater need of vitamin B_6 (Theuer 1972). Female athletes who are on high protein/low carbohydrate diets or are taking oral contraceptives may need vitamin B_6 supplements.

Folic Acid

Folic acid is necessary in the formation of DNA and indirectly affects the synthesis of proteins, including hemoglobin and enzymes. Most adolescents have a folic acid intake that is less than half the recommended dietary allowance of 0.4 mg per day. Although there is no evidence at the present time that a low intake of folic acid affects physical performance, it frequently results in folic acid deficiency during pregnancy. Oral contraceptives also decrease plasma and red blood cell folate levels (Smith et al. 1975; Theuer 1972). Females are more likely to have low levels of this vitamin.

Other Water-Soluble Vitamins

Recommended dietary allowances for vitamin B_{12} and vitamin C are the same for males and females. There is little reason to believe that the female's needs for those vitamins during physical activity would differ from that of the male except during pregnancy and lactation. Strict vegetarians must supplement their diets with vitamin B_{12}. The need for pantothenic acid and biotin is also thought to be the same for both sexes.

Fat-Soluble Vitamins

Vitamins A, D, E, and K are soluble in fat and fat solvents. All are stored in the body and symptoms of deficiency develop slowly. Recommended dietary allowances for males are slightly higher for vitamin A and E than for females. There is little evidence that the requirements for fat soluble vitamins are increased during physical activity.

MINERAL NEEDS

Macronutrients

Magnesium is the only macronutrient that has a larger recommended dietary allowance for the male than the female. The need for electrolytes, sodium and potassium, increases during training in warm environments. At the present time there is little evidence that the need for macronutrients other than the electrolytes increases during training.

Micronutrients

Iodine is incorporated into the thyroid hormone and is important in regulating the metabolic rate. Males have a slightly larger requirement for iodine than females. There is little evidence that exercise increases the requirement.

Iron

Iron is the only nutrient that is needed in greater quantity by the female than the male. Males and nonmenstruating, nonpregnant females lose about 1 mg iron per day through the urine, feces, and sweat. In addition, females lose iron through the menses. The amount of iron lost per period is quite variable (Beaton et al. 1970; Hallberg et al. 1966). Average iron loss is 0.5 mg/day. Because only 10 percent of the ingested iron is absorbed, 10 times as much iron must be present in the diet. Recommended daily dietary allowances are 10 mg for males and 18 mg for females. Most studies of the iron intakes of girls and women have reported the average iron intake ranges between 10 and 12 mg/day (White 1968).

The low intake of iron suggests that many women may suffer from iron deficiency. Iron in excess of that needed daily is stored in the bone marrow, liver, and spleen. Iron deficiency anemia occurs when these stores have been depleted. One recent survey of the nutritional status of Americans reported that 15 percent of females ages 17 to 44 from low income states, and 10 percent of the females from high income states had hemoglobin concentrations below 12 gm/100 ml blood (Ten State Nutrition Survey 1972). A hemoglobin concentration of 12 gm/100 ml is considered the lower limit of normal for nonpregnant women (Committee on Iron Deficiency 1968).

Iron depletion may occur without symptons of iron deficiency anemia. Decreased iron levels in the plasma and bone marrow are clinical signs of iron depletion. Scott and Pritchard (1967) found that nearly two out of three young women sampled had little or no stainable iron in the bone marrow. About 22 percent of the women ages 17 to 44, with more than 10 gm hemoglobin per 100 ml, had low plasma iron levels (Ten State Nutrition Survey 1972). These results suggest that a fairly large segment of the female population is iron deficient with or without anemia. Women athletes are equally as likely to be iron deficient

(Haymes et al. 1972), while females taking oral contraceptives are less likely to develop iron deficiency (Briggs and Staniford 1969; Burton 1967; Prasad et al. 1975; Smith et al. 1975; Zilva 1969).

There is considerable evidence that anemia has a detrimental effect on physical performance (Davies et al. 1973; Gardner et al. 1977; Sproule et al 1960). (A more thorough discussion on iron supplementation and performance can be found in Chapter 34.) Female athletes should ensure that they receive at least 18 mg of iron daily either through the diet or as supplements.

PREGNANCY AND LACTATION

Many women athletes choose to continue training and competing during the early stages of pregnancy and to begin training again while still lactating. The requirements for a number of nutrients increase during pregnancy in order to support the growth of the fetus. It is recommended that pregnant females increase the amount of protein in their diets as well as vitamins A, C, D, E, thiamine, riboflavin, niacin, B_6, B_{12}, and folic acid. Minerals that should be increased in the diet are calcium, phosphorus, magnesium, iron, iodine, and zinc. In order to ensure adequate quantities it may be necessary to take iron, vitamin D, and folic acid supplements. If, however, the woman drinks milk fortified with vitamin D, she does not need vitamin D supplements. Women should maintain the increased intake of nutrients during lactation and even increase their intake of vitamin A and iodine. Caloric intake should increase 300 kcal during pregnancy and 500 kcal during lactation. The intake of sodium should be maintained or even increased during pregnancy (Guthrie 1975).

SUMMARY

Females generally have smaller nutrient intake needs than males with a few exceptions. Female athletes should increase the caloric content and thiamine and riboflavin intakes of their diets. The requirement for iron is greater for the female than the male and it is important that the athlete receives an adequate amount. During pregnancy and lactation the need for most nutrients increases. Other than these minor deviations, including lower caloric intake needs, the nutritional needs of the female athlete are little different from those of the male.

REFERENCES

Beaton, G. H., Thein, H. Milne, and M. J. Veen. 1970. Iron requirements of menstruating women, *Amer J Clin Nutr*, 23, 275-283.

Bergstrom, J., E. Hultman, L. Jorfeldt, B. Pernow, and J. Wahren. 1969. Effect of nicotinic acid on physical working capacity and on metabolism of muscle glycogen in man. *J Appl Physiol*, 23, 170-176.

Briggs, M. and M. Staniford. 1969. Oral contraceptives and blood-iron. *Lancet*, II, 742.

Burton, J. L. 1967. Effect of oral contraceptives on hemoglobin, packed-cell volume, serum-iron and total iron-binding capacity in healthy women. *Lancet*, I, 978-980.

Buskirk, E. R. and E. M. Haymes. 1972. Nutritional requirements for women in sport. In *Women and Sport: A National Research Conference*. D. V. Harris (ed.). University Park: The Pennsylvania State University.

Carlson, L., R. Havel, and L. Ekelund. 1963. Effect of nicotinic acid on the turnover rate and oxidation of the free fatty acids of plasma in man during exercise. *Metabolism*, 12, 837-845.

Committee on Iron Deficiency. 1968. Iron deficiency in the United States *J Amer Med Assoc*, 203, 407-412.

Costill, D. L., J. Daniels, W. Evans, W. Fink, G. Krahenbuhl, and B. Saltin. 1976. Skeletal muscle enzymes and fiber composition in male and female track athletes. *J Appl Physiol*, 40, 149-154.

Daniel, W. A., E. G. Gaines, and D. L. Bennett. 1975. Dietary intakes and plasma concentrations of folate in healthy adolescents. *Amer J Clin Nutr*, 28, 363-370.

Davies, C. T. M., A. C. Chukweumeka, and J. P. M. Van Haaren. 1973. Iron-deficiency anemia: Its effect on maximum aerobic power and responses to exercise in African males ages 17-40 years. *Clin Sci*, 44, 555-562.

Gardner, G. W., V. R. Edgerton, B. Senewiratne, R. J. Barnard, and Y. Ohira. 1977. Physical work capacity and metabolic stress in subjects with iron deficiency anemia. *Amer J Clin Nutr*, 30, 910-917.

Gershoff, S. N. 1976. Vitamin B_6. In *Nutrition Reviews' Present Knowledge in Nutrition*. 4th ed. New York: The Nutrition Foundation.

Guthrie, H. A. 1975. *Introductory Nutrition*. 3rd ed. St. Louis: C. V. Mosby.

Hallberg, L., A. M. Hogdahl, L. Nilsson, and G. Rybo. 1966. Menstrual blood loss and iron deficiency. *Acta Med Scand*, 180, 639-650.

Haymes, E. M., D. V. Harris, M. D. Beldon, J. L. Loomis, and W. C. Nicholas. 1972. The effect of physical activity level on selected hematological variables in adult women. Paper presented at annual AAHPER convention Houston.

Howley, E. T. and M. E. Glover. 1974. The caloric costs of running and walking one mile for men and women. *Med Sci Spts*, 6, 235-237.

Jenkins, D. 1965. Effects of nicotinic acid on carbohydrate and fat metabolism during exercise. *Lancet*, I, 1307-1808.

National Research Council: Committee on Dietary Allowances. 1974. *Recommended Dietary Allowances*. Washington: National Academy of Sciences.

Parizkova, J. 1973. Body composition and exercise during growth and development. In *Physical Activity: Human Growth and Development*. G. L. Rarick (ed.). New York: Academic Press.

Prasad, A. S., D. Oberleas, K. Y. Lei, K. S. Moghissi, and J. C. Stryker. 1975. Effect of oral contraceptive agents on nutrients: I. Minerals *Amer J Clin Nutr*, 28, 377-384.

Scott, D. E. and J. Pritchard. 1967. Iron deficiency in healthy young college women. *J Amer Med Assoc*, 199, 897-900.

Smith, J. L., G. A. Goldsmith, and J. D. Lawrence. 1975. Effects of oral contraceptive steroids on vitamin and lipid levels in serum. *Amer J Clin Nutr,* 28, 371-376.

Sproule, B. J., J. H. Mitchell, and W. F. Miller. 1960. Cardiopulmonary physiological responses to heavy exercise in patients with anemia. *J Clin Invest,* 39, 378-388.

Ten State Nutrition Survey 1968-1970: IV. Biochemical, V. Dietary. 1972. DHEW Pubs. No. (HMS) 72-8133.

Theuer, R. C. 1972. Effect of oral contraceptive agents on vitamin and mineral needs: A review. *J Reprod Med,* 8, 13-19.

Ullyot, J. 1974. Women's secret weapon: FAT. *Runner's World,* 9, December, 22-23.

White, H. S. 1968. Iron nutriture of girls and women: A review. *J Amer Diet Assoc,* 53, 563-569.

Zilva, J. F. 1969. Oral contraceptives and blood iron. *Lancet,* II, 847.

24

Nutritional Faddism in Athletics*

Melvin H. Williams

Athletes in training for competition are always searching for the ultimate ingredient to give them that extra winning edge over their opponents. Over the years a number of theoretical ergogenic, or work-producing, aids have been utilized in attempts to increase athlete performance capability. Due to the diverse nature of these substances or treatments, various hypotheses have been developed in an attempt to explain the beneficial effects they are alleged to produce. Rationale for their use may be reduced to two categories: (a) the substances may directly influence the physiological capacity of a particular body system that contributes to success in the athletic performance; or (b) the substance may remove psychological restraints that may limit physiological capacity.

There are four different classifications of erogenic aids, grouped according to the general nature of their application. Mechanical ergogenic aids, such as heat, cold, ultraviolet rays, and massage, are used primarily for their theoretical

*   From M. H. Williams. 1976. Nutritional aspects of human physical and athletic performance. Springfield, Illinois: C. C. Thomas

beneficial effects on local or general circulation. Thus, application of heat may serve as a passive form of warm-up and may increase performance due to increased speed of contraction and relaxation of the muscles, and greater efficiency due to decreased muscular viscosity. A second categorization, the psychological ergogenic aids, is best represented by hypnosis. With the proper application of hypnotic suggestion, some say the athlete may remove certain psychic limitations and possibly perform at a higher level.

The pharmacological aids—characterized primarily by amphetamines and anabolic steroids although a number of diverse pharmaceutical agents have been used—have become increasingly more prominent in the athletic scene during the past decade and have prompted athletic governing bodies such as the International Olympic Committee (IOC), International Amateur Athletic Federation (IAAF), National Collegiate Athletic Association (NCAA) and others to proscribe their use in conjunction with athletic events. The term "doping" has been applied to the use of drugs to increase athletic performance, and a number of theories have been advanced relative to their mode of action, dependent, of course, upon the nature of the drug and the type of athletic performance.

The fourth general classification, the nutritional ergogenic aids, is replete with foods, vitamins, minerals, or dietary regimens hypothesized to increase performance either by renewing energy stores in the body, facilitating the biochemical reactions that yield the energy, modifying the biochemical changes contributing to fatigue, or maintaining optimal body weight. Thus, glycogen storage techniques, vitamin supplementation, ingestion of alkaline salts, and protein supplementation may be nutritional techniques associated, respectively, with the four physiological goals listed in the preceding sentence.

Although it is important for coaches, trainers, and others associated with the conduct of athletics to understand the theoretical basis and experimental evidence relative to the usefulness of ergogenic aids or techniques within each of the four general categories, special consideration should be directed towards the nutritive agents and practices, for as J. V. Durnin (1967) has stated, there is still no sphere of nutrition in which faddism and ignorance are more obvious than in athletics. Many athletes still believe there is a special diet or special nutritional ingredient essential to their success.

QUACKERY IN SPORTS

As indicated above, there is still no area of nutrition where faddism, misconceptions, and ignorance are more obvious than in athletics. Why? Durnin (1967) has noted that there are no ordinary foods humans eat that are of any special value or, for that matter, contraindicated in athletic training. He has also emphasized the point that the nutritional requirements for the athlete in training depends upon the same fundamental principles governing human beings in general. Durnin's viewpoint is buttressed by a number of fellow nutritionists, exercise physiologists, and others involved in sports medicine. Ernst Simonson (1951), an international expert in work physiology, concluded that in general, no type of diet supplementation will improve any type of performance in a normal person on a normal diet. J. Williams (1962), the renowned British authority in sports medicine, stated that no specific diet will change a moderately endowed athlete into a champion, but a sound dietary regimen is necessary to produce maximal fitness. Roger Banister (1974), a prominent physician and the first human to break the four-minute mile, indicated that there is no proof that special foods or extra vitamin supplements are necessary as long as athletes eat a well-balanced diet. The National Research Council (1974) noted that even though athletic activity increases energy expenditure, the increased needs for any essential nutrients should be met by the larger quantities of foods consumed, provided they are well-selected. Jean Mayer (1972), an international authority on nutrition and exercise, and a host of other investigators have supported the general concept of these statements. The general consensus is that the athlete, aside from possible increases in caloric intake due to increased energy expenditure, does not need additional nutrients beyond those found in a balanced diet.

Even though these eminent authorities contend that diet manipulation will not enhance athletic performance, some coaches, trainers, and athletes continue to search for the super diet. There are various reasons for their pursuit, ranging from collective food faddism to rather reputable research. The plight of the coach and athlete is to separate fact from fancy and to discern what is quackery from what may possibly be a useful dietary technique. The sports world is replete with nutritional faddism and misinformation that appears to be propagated by coaches, athletes, and the media, thus enticing the gullible athlete to reach for that ultimate ingredient. This is not to say that there are not any important dietary concerns for the athlete beyond the normal diet, for there may be some useful application of selected nutritional techniques to some athletic activities. Nevertheless, nutritional quackery does exist in athletics, and the following paragraphs will attempt to delineate the major reason why.

Olson (1958) described the phenomenon of collective food faddism, in which the general public may pattern food habits after a particular individual. This phenomenon is readily apparent in the sporting world, whereby dietary practices of successful athletes or teams become the *sine qua non* of the aspiring athlete. If a freshman wrestler observes the senior star consume tea laced with honey an hour before his match, there is a strong possibility he will do the same. Some current professional athletes are devoted to organic foods or are vegetarians, and it is assumed that young athletes who emulate these stars may experiment with their diets. Thus, the phenomenon of collective food faddism may be one of the main reasons for unscientific nutritional behavior in sports.

Another reason for food faddism in sports may be due to the directives of those individuals administering a program. Mayer and Bullen (1960) reported that perusal of the daily newspaper, inquiries into university athletic training table practices, and study of the diets of professional and Olympic athletes revealed that a number of team physicians, coaches, and trainers are convinced that there are some very special nutritional factors involved in the preparation of athletes. Krause and Hunscher (1972) indicated that coaches have contributed to the belief that certain foods will enable the athlete to do more and better work, win more medals, or gain greater victories. To document this point, Phil Shinnick (United States Senate 1973), an Olympic contender, testified before a Senate subcommittee that coaches and trainers gave him a list of substances, including vitamins B_{12} and C, that would make him great if he took them.

These sports administration personnel may have obtained their nutritional information from respected journals, which have in some cases published research indicative of an ergogenic effect of some particular ingredient, or a review by some authorities recommending some specific diet modifications for athletes. Simonson (1971) has severely criticized some of the research done in this area, noting that in one rather uncontrolled study the authors indicated that one of the properties of orange juice provided resistance to fatigue. Simonson noted that such uncritical claims are unfortunately abundant in the literature dealing with nutrition and performance. Recent Russian researchers (Ranson 1973) have claimed that athletes need special food supplements. The translation of their research has indicated that enrichment of the diet may regulate and activate biochemical reactions in a desired direction and, therefore, increase the efficiency of the athlete. According to the researchers, due to the high stress on athletes' bodies, especially in endurance events, they require additional vitamin B complex and vitamin C, probably a two-fold increase. They also indicated that vitamin E, wheat germ, wheat germ oil, and citric acid may be essential in the athlete's diet. Cureton (1969a, 1969b) also noted it appears wise for people involved in hard stressful work to use extra B complex and C vitamins, as well as extra fresh, natural, unheated oils such as wheat germ oil. With statements such as these, presented in popular coaching magazines such as *Swimming Technique* and *Athletic Journal,* a coach or athlete might assume that vitamin supplementation and wheat germ oil are essential.

The athlete and coach are also subjected to direct advertisements extolling the virtues of a given product relative to increased performance capacity. For example, a product called "World Champion Protein" has been marketed in Europe, and the box of 250 tablets included a total of 34 gm protein at a cost ten times that of an equivalent amount of milk protein—and no better (Blix 1970). Similar compounds are advertised in the United States. One advertisement suggests that most coaches know the deciding factor in a winning team is often the training diet, and that its super high protein mixture and germ oil concentrate have energizing properties. The Carnation Company advertised one of its products, Carnation Instant Breakfast, in a leading athletic journal. Bold faced type read "High-powered liquid meal increases speed of swimmers," and the remaining content of the advertisement reported that according to their research, the Instant Breakfast produced an "energy edge" and allowed swimmers to beat their own best times. Another company, the General Health and Fitness Corporation, advertised four different products, indicating they could be applied for conditioning athletes to top performance. The four products, Protein Weight Gainer, Protein Powerizer, Protein Energizer, and Protein Slimmer, were designed for specific athletic purposes, as the names imply. Their report indicated that all products had been university tested and implied that they would be effective in improving athletic records. Both the Carnation Company and the General Health and Fitness Corporation indicated that reports of their research were available upon request. Upon receiving and analyzing these reports, the general conclusion is that they would not appear to meet acceptable standards for reporting research dealing with dietary supplements and their role in human athletic performance. According to Clarke (1968), numerous companies have been profiting on the sale of nutritional supplements to athletes. In several instances, the Food and Drug Administration (FDA) has seized food supplements to athletes because of false or misleading advertising. However, although the FDA has taken some action in this area, a number of products still exist on the market.

In summary, although many respected nutritionists indicate that there are no magic nutritional ingredients available that will improve performance of an athlete on a well-balanced diet, reports from other authoritative sources, advice from coaches, the nutritional practices of star athletes, and well-designed product advertisements in major athletic journals all give the impression that certain substances may increase athletic potential.

There exists a variety of reasons why nutritional quackery in sports should be attacked by those individuals responsible for the education of the athlete. First, from a health standpoint, certain complications may arise from the indiscriminant consumption of various nutrients. In one report (United States Senate 1973), a team doctor for the United States Olympic team in 1968 noticed some athletes consuming as many as 10,000 mg vitamin C in one day, with some Olympic athletes experiencing tremendous allergic reactions to vitamins. In the same report, Dr. John Boyer indicated that the combination of large amounts of vitamin D, plus prolonged exposure to ultraviolet light, increases the hazard of vitamin D intoxication. The liberal consumption of salt tablets by athletes exercising in hot environments may predispose them to gastrointestinal disturbances and possible electrolyte imbalance in the body fluids. Also, the athlete may rely on one particular compound to the exclusion of others necessary for a balanced diet, and consequently may suffer nutritionally; this may be particularly true of those athletes who train on extreme restricted diets and utilize dehydration techniques to maintain certain body weights. On an intellectual basis, the particular ingredient the athlete is consuming may have no scientific basis for increasing his or her performance capacity. In addition, the athlete may credit part of his or her success if he or she does win to an extraneous substance, thus depriving his or her ego of the fact that success was due to the natural development of innate resources. Finally, the nutritional ergogenic aids may impose a financial burden on the athlete, as some of the compounds are relatively expensive.

REFERENCES

Banister, R. 1974. Human beings are not the same. *Physician and Sportsmed,* 2, 91-92.

Blix, G. (ed.). 1970. *Food Cultism and Nutrition Quackery: Symposia of the Swedish Nutrition Foundation.* Uppsala, Sweden: Almqvist and Wilksells.

Clarke, K. 1968. Quackery and Sports. *Ohio State Med J,* 64, 913-20.

Cureton, T. 1969a. The diet of schoolboy athletes can be improved. *Athletic J,* 50, September, 71.

Durnin, J. 1967b. Nutritive aspects of physical fitness work. *Swimming Technique,* 6, July, 44-49.

Krause, M. and M. Hunscher. 1972. *Food, Nutrition and Diet Therapy.* Philadelphia: W. B. Saunders.

Mayer, J. 1972. *Human Nutrition: Its Physiological, Medical and Social Aspects.* Springfield, Illinois: C. C. Thomas.

Mayer, J. and B. Bullen. 1960. Nutrition and athletic performance. *Physiol Rev,* 40, 369-97.

National Research Council: Committee on Dietary Allowances. 1974. *Recommended Dietary Allowances.* Washington: National Academy of Sciences.

Olson, R. 1958. Food faddism . . . Why? *Nutr Rev,* 16, 97-99.

Ranson, R. 1973. Nutritional guidelines for athletes. *Swimming Technique,* 10, July, 44.

Simonson, E. 1951. Influence of nutrition on work performance. In *Nutrition Fronts in Public Health.* Nutrition Symposium Series No. 3. New York: National Vitamin Foundation.

Simonson, E. 1971. Nutrition and work performance. In *Physiology of Work Capacity and Fatigue.* E. Simonson (ed.). Springfield: C. C. Thomas.

United States Senate. 1973. *Proper and Improper use of drugs by athletes.* Hearings before the subcommittee to investigate juvenile delinquency. June 18 and July 12-13, 1973. Washington: U.S. Government Printing Office.

Williams, J. 1962. *Sports Medicine.* Baltimore: Williams and Wilkins.

25

Energy Sources During Rest and Exercise

Edward L. Fox

Energy is defined as the ability to perform work, whereas work is defined as a force acting on a body to produce a displacement. For example, lifting a book from your desk to the bookshelf would constitute a given amount of work requiring a certain amount of energy. Energy and work are inseparable. The purpose of this chapter is to understand how the human body produces energy to sustain life and perform work.

THE IMMEDIATE ENERGY SOURCE—ATP

We eat food for energy. However, the immediate energy needed at rest or to perform work does not come directly from the food we eat, but rather from a chemical compound called *adenosine triphosphate* or more simply, ATP. ATP is stored in various quantities in most living cells, particularly in muscle cells. As its name implies, the structure of ATP consists of a complex component called adenosine and three simpler components called phosphate groups. When ATP is chemically broken down—for example, when a phosphate group is removed from the rest of the molecule—between 7 and 12 kilocalories* of energy are liberated. Chemically, this can be represented as:

$$ATP \rightleftharpoons ADP + P_i + Energy$$

We will not need to be too concerned about the by-products adenosine diphosphate (ADP) and inorganic phosphate (P_i), but rather will concentrate on the importance of the energy released. This energy becomes immediately available to support any work required by the cell, such as muscular contraction. In other words, the body's immediate useful supply of energy is that which is released when ATP is broken down to ADP and P_i.

---

*   A kilocalorie (kcal) is the amount of heat energy necessary to raise the temperature of one kilogram of water one degree centigrade.

The Principle of Coupled Reactions

The arrow pointing to the left in the above chemical equation indicates that energy from another source is required in order to resynthesize or put back together the ATP molecule. As we shall soon see, the energy for resynthesizing ATP comes from three different series of chemical reactions that also take place within the body. The energy released from any one of these series of reactions, such as from the breakdown of ingested food, is coupled with the energy needs of the reaction that resynthesizes ATP. In other words, the two series of reactions are functionally linked together such that the energy released by the one is always used by the other. Biochemically, this is referred to as *coupled reactions* and is the fundamental principle involved in the metabolic production of ATP.

In chemical terms, the equations for coupled reactions might look like this:

$$AB \rightleftharpoons A + B + \text{Energy}$$
$$CD \rightleftharpoons C + D + \text{Energy}$$

Compound AB breaks down to its components A and B and energy is released. This energy is then used to form compound CD from its components D and C.

Metabolic Production of ATP

As just mentioned, the energy needed for ATP resynthesis comes from three different series of reactions. Although all three series of reactions take place within the cell, two of them do not require the presence of oxygen and are thus termed anaerobic (without oxygen). The third series of reactions can only operate under aerobic conditions, that is, in the presence of oxygen. During exercise, both the anaerobic and aerobic series of reactions are important sources of ATP energy. However, under resting conditions, only the aerobic series is required.

One of the anaerobic series of reactions is referred to as the *ATP-PC or phosphagen system,* and the other is termed *anaerobic glycolysis* or the *lactic acid (LA) system.* The aerobic source is referred to simply as the aerobic or oxygen system.

The ATP-PC system. PC is an abbreviation for phosphocreatine, a chemical substance closely related to ATP. For example, PC, like ATP, is also stored in muscle cells, and when its phosphate group is removed, a large amount of energy is released (at least 12 kcals). The end products of this breakdown are creatine (C) and inorganic phosphate (P_i). Chemically:

$$PC \rightleftharpoons P_i + C + \text{Energy}$$

The released energy of course is coupled to the energy requirement necessary for the rsynthesis of ATP. In other words, as rapidly ad ATP is broken down during muscular contraction, it is continuously reformed from ADP and P$_i$ by the energy liberated during the breakdown of the stored PC. For every mole* of PC broken down, one mole of ATP can be manufactured. Again in chemical terms:

$$PC \rightleftharpoons P_i + C + \text{Energy}$$
$$ATP \rightleftharpoons ADP + P_i + \text{Energy}$$

The total muscular stores of both ATP and PC (collectively referred to as *phosphagens*) are very small, only about 0.3 to 0.6 of a mole in females and males, respectively. Thus, the capacity or amount of energy possible through this system is quite limited. In fact, if one ran 100 meters as fast as possible, the phosphagen stores in the working muscles would probably be empty by the end of the run. However, the usefulness of the stored phosphagens lies in their rapid availability rather than in their quantity.

Although this is not important at rest, it is extremely important with respect to the kinds of physical activities we are capable of performing. Activities such as sprinting, jumping, swinging, kicking, and other similar movements that require only a few seconds to complete, are all dependent upon the stored phosphagens for their primary energy source. For example, in sprinting 100 meters, it can be estimated from energy cost data (Dill 1965; Margaria et al. 1963) that a total of only 0.43 mole of ATP is required, but at an average rate of utilization of 2.6 moles per minute (Fox 1977). As will be pointed out later, such a power requirement can be met only by the phosphagen system.

Anaerobic glycolysis (the lactic acid system). The term glycolysis means to break down glycogen or glucose, and as mentioned earlier, anaerobic means without oxygen. Thus, as the name implies, in anaerobic glycolysis, glycogen or glucose is broken down without oxygen and energy is released for ATP resynthesis. However, since oxygen is not required, glucose can only be partially broken down with the end product being lactic acid (hence the name, the lactic acid system). When lactic acid accumulates in the muscles and blood to very high levels, temporary muscular fatigue results. This, of course, is a very definite limitation during exercise.

Another limitation that also stems from oxygen not being required is that only a few moles of ATP can be resynthesized during anaerobic glycolysis, as

---

* A mole is the amount of a chemical compound whose weight in grams is equal to its molecular weight. The latter is the sum of all the atomic weights of the atoms making up a compound.

compared to the yield possible when oxygen is present. For example, during anaerobic glycolysis only 3 moles of ATP can be resynthesized from breaking down 180 grams (about 6 ounces) of glucose. As we will soon see, in the presence of sufficient oxygen, the complete breakdown of the same amount of glucose yields 39 moles of ATP.

The summary equations for ATP resynthesis from anaerobic glycolysis are:

$$C_6H_{12}O_6 \rightleftharpoons 2C_3H_6O_3 + Energy$$
(glucose) (lactic acid)

$$3ATP \rightleftharpoons 3ADP + 3P_i + Energy$$

During exercise, the useful ATP production from anaerobic glycolysis is actually less than the 3 moles of ATP shown in the above equation (3ATP). The reason for this is that during heavy exercise, the muscles and blood can only tolerate the accumulation of about 60 to 70 grams of lactic acid before fatigue occurs. If all 180 grams of glycogen were broken down anaerobically during exercise, 180 grams of lactic acid would be formed ($2C_3H_6O_3$). Therefore, from a practical viewpoint, only about 1 to 1.2 moles of ATP can be manufactured from anaerobic glycolysis during heavy exercise before lactic acid in blood and muscle reaches exhausting levels.

Anaerobic glycolysis, like the ATP-PC system, is extremely important during exercise primarily because it also provides a very rapid supply of ATP. For example, exercises that can be performed at a maximum rate for between one and three minutes (such as sprinting 400 and 800 meters) depends heavily upon the ATP-PC system and anaerobic glycolysis for ATP formation. For example, from the energy cost data mentioned above, the amount of ATP required for running 400 meters can be estimated at about 1.7 moles, substantially more than the phosphagen system alone can supply.

The aerobic (oxygen) system. In the presence of sufficient oxygen, the complete breakdown of 180 grams of glucose to carbon dioxide (CO_2) and water (H_2O) yields enough energy to manufacture 39 moles at ATP. These reactions, like the anaerobic reactions, also take place within the muscle cell but are confined to specialized, subcellular compartments called mitochondria. The summary equations for this series of reactions are:

$$C_6H_{12}O_6 + 6O_2 \longrightarrow 6H_2O + 6CO_2 + Energy$$
(glucose)
$$39ATP \longrightarrow 39ADP + 39P_i + Energy$$

Besides the fact that abundant ATP can be resynthesized during aerobic metabolism, notice that no fatiguing by-products are formed. The CO_2 produced freely diffuses from the muscle cell into the blood and is carried to the lung where it is exhaled. The water formed is useful within the cell itself, since the largest constituents of the body (cell) fluids is in fact water.

It should also be pointed out that it requires 6 moles of oxygen ($6O_2$) to break down 180 grams of glycogen. Since one mole of any gas occupies 22.4 liters at standard temperature and pressure, dry (STPD), 6 moles of O_2 = 6 × 22.4 = 134.4 liters. Therefore, 134.4 liters of O_2 are required to resynthesize 39 moles of ATP or 134.4 ÷ 39 = 3.5 liters of O_2 required per mole of ATP synthesized. In other words, any time 3.5 liters of O_2 are consumed, one mole of ATP is aerobically synthesized. At rest, this would take between 10 and 15 minutes. During maximal exercise, however, it would take most of us only about one minute!

Another feature of the aerobic system relates to the type of food required for breakdown. Although the above equation depicts the breakdown of glucose, fats and proteins can also be aerobically broken down to CO_2 and H_2O with energy released for ATP resynthesis. For example, one mole (about half of a pound) of a typical fatty acid such as palmitic acid when broken down to CO_2 and H_2O in the presence of oxygen will yield enough energy to resynthesize 130 moles of ATP as follows:

$$C_{16}H_{32}O_2 + 23O_2 \longrightarrow 16CO_2 + 16H_2O + \text{Energy}$$
(palmitic acid)

$$130 \text{ ATP} \longrightarrow 130 \text{ ADP} + 130 \text{ P}_i + \text{Energy}$$

During rest and exercise, both sugar and fats, but not proteins, are important sources of ATP-yielding energy.

The aerobic system, therefore, is capable of utilizing both fats and carbohydrates for resynthesizing large amounts of ATP without simultaneously generating fatiguing by-products. For this reason, it is the system used under resting conditions. With respect to physical education and athletics, it is also easy to see that the aerobic system is particularly suited for manufacturing ATP during prolonged, endurance-type exercise. For example, during marathon running (26.2 miles or 42.2 kilometers) it is estimated that a total of 150 moles of ATP are required with an average rate of utilization (power) of only 1.0 mole per minute. Such a large, sustained output of ATP energy is possible only because early fatigue can be avoided and large amounts of food (glycogen and fats) and oxygen are readily available.

Summary of the Energy Systems

A summary of the capacity and power capabilities of the three energy systems is contained in Table 25.1. Notice that the capacity and power of all three systems can be improved with physical training.

Table 25.1
Summary of the Capacity and Power
Capabilities of the Three Energy Systems

Energy System	Capacity (Moles ATP) Untrained	Trained	Power (Moles ATP per Min) Untrained	Trained
ATP-PC	0.6	0.78	3.6	4.6
Lactic Acid	1.2	1.8	1.6	2.4
Aerobic	∞	∞	1.0	1.3

THE ENERGY CONTINUUM AND PERFORMANCE

As already emphasized, during exercise the capability of each energy system to supply the major portion of the ATP required is related to the specific kind of activity or event performed. For example, on one end we have the short-term, high-intensity types of activities such as the 100-meter dash where the majority of ATP is supplied by the ATP-PC system. At the other end, the long-term, low-intensity types of activities such as the marathon race are supported almost exclusively by the aerobic system. In the middle is anaerobic glycolysis with the major portion of its ATP production used to support types of activities such as the 400 and 800-meter dashes. Also, "in the middle" are those activities such as the 1500-meter run that require a blend of both anaerobic and aerobic metabolism. The interactions of the energy systems during the performance of selected track events can be illustrated by comparing the energy requirements of these activities, as given in Table 25.2, with the capacity and power characteristics of the three energy systems as given in Table 25.1.

Table 25.2
Total ATP (Capacity) and Rate of ATP (Power)
Required at Rest and During Selected Track Events

Activity	Capacity (Total Moles ATP)	Power (Moles ATP/Min)
Rest (5 mins)	0.36	0.07
100 m sprint	0.43	2.6
400 m sprint	1.72	2.3
800 m run	3.43	2.0
1,500 m run	6.00	1.7
42,200 m (marathon)	150.00	1.0

What has been developed here is the concept of an energy continuum, a continuum relating the way in which ATP is made available and the type of activity performed. Such a continuum is depicted in Fig. 25.1. Notice that all three energy systems contribute ATP during performance of all the activities shown in our example. Also notice that one system usually contributes more (as indicated by the heavier shaded areas) during any given activity than do the other systems. This has real meaning with respect to physical education and athletics. For example, if the predominant energy system for any given activity is developed more so than the other systems, then performance in that particular activity will also be improved. Do you think the performance of a marathon runner would be much improved if only his or her anaerobic systems were developed? The answer, quite obviously, is "no" because the necessary energy to perform the two-and-a-half to three-hour race is supplied predominantly by the aerobic system.

	Lactic Acid System	
	ATP-PC System	
	O₂ System	

ATP-PC System	ATP-PC and LA	LA and O₂ System	O₂ System
Shot put	System	800 m dash	Soccer and lacrosse
100 m sprint	200-400 m sprints	Gymnastics events	(except goalies)
Base stealing	Halfbacks-fullbacks	Boxing (3 min. rounds)	Cross country skiing
Golf-tennis swings	Speed skating	Wrestling (2 min.	Marathon
	100 m swim	periods)	Jogging

Fig. 25.1 The energy continuum. On one end are the short-term, high-intensity types of activities such as the 100 m dash, in which the total ATP required is supplied by the ATP-PC system. On the other hand, the long-term, low-intensity types of activities such as the marathon race are supported by the oxygen system. In the middle is the LA system, with the major portion of its ATP production used to support types of activities such as the 400 and 800 m dashes. (From Fox and Mathews 1974, p. 14.)

As a final consideration, from the relationship between each of the energy systems and performance times, we can construct guidelines from which we can easily determine the predominant energy systems involved in various sports activities. The continuum of performance times can be divided into four distinctive areas, as shown in Table 25.3. The first area would include all activities requiring performance times equal to or less than 30 seconds duration. In such activities, the predominant energy system would be the ATP-PC system. Area 2 would include those activities requiring between 30 seconds and 1.5 minutes to perform. The predominant energy systems in this case would be both the ATP-PC and the lactic acid systems. Thus, to improve performance in these activities, the energy capacity of both systems needs to be increased. Area 3 would take into account those activities requiring between 1.5 and 3 minutes to perform. Here also, as in area 2, there are two major energy systems involved: the lactic acid system or anaerobic glycolysis, and the oxygen system. Again, improving these two energy systems will improve performance in those activities classified in this area. Area 4 represents those activities requiring performance times equal to or greater than 3 minutes in duration. Here the major supply of

ATP will be contributed by the aerobic system, and improvement in this system will assure improvement in performance.

Table 25.3
Four Work Effort Areas with Performance Times,
Major Energy System(s) Involved
and Examples of the Type of Activities*

Area	Performance Time	Major Energy Systems(S) Involved	Examples of Type of Activity
1	Less than 30 seconds	ATP-PC	Shot-put, 100m sprint, base stealing, golf and tennis swings
2	30 seconds to 1½ min.	ATP-PC-LA	200-400 m, sprints, halfbacks, fullbacks, speed skating, 100 yd. m. swim
3	1½ min. to 3 min.	LA and O₂	800 m. dash, gymnastics events, boxing (3 min. rounds), wrestling (2 min. periods)
4	Greater than 3 min.	O₂	Soccer and lacrosse (except goalies), cross-country skiing, marathon run, jogging

* From Fox and Mathews (1974, p. 18)

REFERENCES

Dill, D. B. 1965. Oxygen used in horizontal and grade walking and running on the treadmill. *J Appl Physiol*, 20, 19-22.

Fox, E. L. 1977. Physical training: Methods and effects. *Orthop Clinics N Am*, 8, 533-548.

Fox, E. L. and D. K. Mathews. *Interval Training: Conditioning for Sports and General Fitness*. Philadelphia: W. B. Saunders.

Margaria, R., P. Cerretelli, P. Aghemo, and G. Sassi. 1963. Energy cost of running. *J Appl Physiol*, 18, 367-370.

26

Glucose Utilization During Exercise

Peter J. Van Handel

Catabolism of high-energy phosphates provides the ultimate source of energy required for muscle contraction. Upon initiation of work, the body's stores of the adenine nucleotides (ATP) are rapidly depleted. If muscular work is to be continued beyond a relatively short period, the ATP stores must be replenished. This replenishment is accomplished through a phosphorylation of ADP coupled to anaerobic glycolysis or aerobic oxidation of carbohydrates, fats, and proteins (Fig. 26.1). The roles of the latter two substrates in metabolism are discussed elsewhere in this section. The purpose of this paper is to present a summary of the current understanding of glucose homeostasis and its utilization during exercise.

SOURCES OF GLUCOSE

Liver

Quantitatively, the liver provides the greatest amounts of glucose (Cahill and Owen 1968), though several other tissues such as the kidneys are also capable of limited production (Owen et al. 1969). Hultman and Nilsson (1971) have determined that in normal human subjects, the hepatic glycogen concentration is approximately 50 gm/kg wet tissue. With a liver weight of 1,500 gm, the total glycogen store is about 75 gm and represents about 300 kcal of energy. In the basal state, glycogenolysis (the hydrolysis of glycogen to form glucose) is responsible for about 75 to 80 percent of the hepatic glucose output. The remainder is derived from synthesis of precursors such as lactate, pyruvate, glycerol, and amino acids removed from the blood. Uptake of these precursors increases during endurance work, gluconeogenesis (the formation of glucose from noncarbohydrate sources) then accounting for a greater percentage of hepatic glucose release.

At rest, mobilization of this depot glycogen occurs continuously in order to maintain blood glucose levels. As muscle uptake increases during exercise, the rate of glucose release also accelerates. In both humans (Hultman and Nilsson 1971) and rodents (Baldwin et al. 1973), the liver can be substantially depleted of its glycogen content following endurance exercise of moderate intensity, suggesting that glucose is an important substrate during aerobic work. The stores

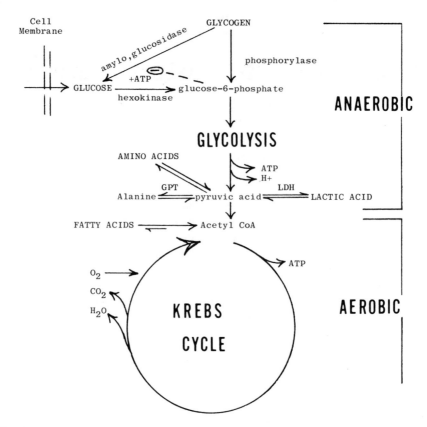

Fig. 26.1 Schematic diagram illustrating the anaerobic and aerobic use of fuels for energy (ATP) production. Glycogen breakdown can provide some free glucose. Fatty acids (FFA) become the preferential fuel during endurance exercise. Training produces adaptations such that FFA use is enhanced at the same work intensity compared to the untrained state.

of glycogen can also be increased above normal levels (supercompensation) by exercise training (Baldwin et al. 1975) and by a carbohydrate-rich diet (Hultman and Nilsson 1971). In addition, training induces adaptations resulting in a conservation of liver glycogen during exercise. The decreased use of carbohydrate by muscle after training is associated with an increased uptake and oxidation of free fatty acids (Saltin and Karlsson 1971). As a result liver carbohydrate is conserved for use by tissues that rely solely on glucose for energy production.

Other "Sources" of Glucose

Skeletal muscle has approximately 9 to 16 gm glycogen/kg wet weight, with values lowest in the arm and shoulder muscles and highest in the lower extremities (Hultman 1967a). Given a total muscle mass accounting for approximately 40 percent of man's body weight, this depot contains an estimated 300 to

400 gm. Although muscle glycogen represents the largest carbohydrate store, its use is thought to be limited to its site since muscle tissue lacks the enzyme glucose-6-phosphatase. In the liver, this enzyme removes phosphate from its substrate creating free glucose, which is then capable of being released into the extra cellular compartment. As a result, while local stores of muscle glycogen can be utilized during exercise, this depot is thought to be unavailable as a source of free glucose for use by other tissues. Bergstrom and Hultman (1967), for example, found that the glycogen content of resting muscle was unaltered in spite of the fact that other muscle groups were exercised to exhaustion.

Theoretically, with high rates of glycogen catabolism during intense muscular work, some free glucose may possibly be released from the exercising muscle into blood (Corsi et al. 1969; Jorfeldt and Wahren 1970). Though quantitatively insignificant, these amounts may help explain some of the divergent results obtained for glucose uptake based on blood flow and A-V differences across the exercising muscle. This may be especially relevant when dealing with relatively small amounts of muscle mass, such as human forearm studies. A possible mechanism of this glucose release lies in the nature of glycogen breakdown. (See Fig. 26.1.) Glycosyl units are converted to glucose phosphate which is not subsequently hydrolyzed since skeletal muscle lacks glucose-6-phosphatase. The debranching of glycogen, however, forms free glucose. At low rates of glycogenolysis, the free glucose is rapidly phosphorylated by the hexokinase reaction. During intense exercise with rapid glycogen degradation, large amounts of free glucose are formed at a time when the hexokinase reaction may be inhibited due to accumulated glucose-6-phosphate (Corsi et al. 1969; Rose and O'Conell 1964) and possibly by low ATP levels. It is conceivable that under these conditions glucose transport may actually proceed from the muscle cell to the extracellular space.

An additional small amount of free glucose is also available. In the human this amounts to approximately 20 gm, but is unevenly distributed and limited to extracellular water and the intracellular compartment of the liver cell.

In summary, the liver and muscle glycogen depots and the blood glucose pool are the quantitatively important sources of carbohydrate. The degree to which each of these depots acts as an energy source during exercise depends upon a number of factors including the type and duration of exercise, the initial level of the stores, and the nutritional status and fitness level or work capacity of the organism. It is important to emphasize that in total, the carbohydrate depots represent a relatively small fraction of the energy stores available in the human body—that is, less than 2000 kcal versus an estimated 140,000 kcal as adipose triglycerides and plasma lipids.

UTILIZATION OF GLUCOSE DURING MUSCULAR WORK

Since muscle tissue accounts for a significant proportion of total body oxygen consumption even at rest, its energetics is a major factor limiting work capacity.

A large number of studies have attempted to describe and quantify the nature and source of substrates used by muscle for energy production. The discussion following here is not meant to be comprehensive but merely representative of studies conducted on the role of blood glucose in muscle metabolism. These studies have used a wide variety of techniques including muscle biopsies, isotopic tracers, organ or tissue blood flow, and arteriovenous concentration differences in isolated perfused muscle systems or intact organisms, as well as indirect estimations of substrate utilization via respiratory measures. In addition, work tasks vary as to the species, age, and sex of the subjects.

Problems related to these differences can make interpretation and comparison of data difficult. As an example, the supply of blood-borne substrates is related both to their concentration and the rate of flow to the muscle. Rates of transport, the conversion of labeled substrates to CO_2, and the production and uptake of tracers are usually studied with appropriately placed catheters. The contribution of glucose to total oxidative metabolism can be misinterpreted because of isotopic exchange reactions, under- or overestimation of blood flow, or "storage" of the label in metabolic intermediates. Moreover, these observations have been made at varying intervals in the postabsorptive state. As the transition from fed to fasting proceeds, biochemical and hormonal changes occur by which the body's fuel supplies are regulated and maintained to meet energy expenditures. Since this transition may last several days in the human, exercise studies after 8 to 12 hours of fasting, for example, involve two superimposed conditions: (1) the transition from fed to fasted state, and (2) the response to the stress of exercise. Any comparison of results, therefore, has to be viewed with these qualifications in mind.

It is also important to distinguish between the response to intense anaerobic work of short duration as opposed to that occurring during endurance exercise. It can be stated that in the former, the ability to work is not limited by the delivery of substrates to the cell. Rather, performance in these activities (sprinting, for example) is dependent upon intracellular ATP, CP (creatine phosphate), and glycogen levels, and the capacity to tolerate an accumulation of glycolytic waste products such as lactic acid. As the intensity of exercise decreases and duration increases, the delivery of glucose (and free fatty acids) becomes more critical.

Short-term, Intense Exercise

In the 1930s Christensen and his coworkers attempted to relate the capacity for work to the utilization of energy supplies. Based on the respiratory exchange ratio they suggested that during intense muscular work, carbohydrate provided most, if not all, of the substrate for energy metabolism (Christensen and Hansen 1939b, 1939c). Subsequent work has shown that the muscular carbohydrate depots are readily available and provide the immediate source of energy as the initial levels of ATP and CP are used. Biopsy studies of muscle glycogen utilization have provided the direct evidence for this observation (Hultman

1967a, 1967b). Glycogen content, however, may vary and is influenced by previous exercise, the level of training and the dietary status of the individual. For example, a work/high-carbohydrate-diet regimen can result in a supercompensation of glycogen stores (Bergstrom et al. 1967). Recently Conlee and others (1976) concluded that skeletal muscle exhibits a diurnal variation in glycogen content that appears to be related to food consumption.

In spite of the fact that there is a normal variation in muscle glycogen content, these depots are more than adequate to meet the demands for substrate at near maximal workloads in normal subjects. Studies by Saltin and Karlsson (1971) on leg muscle glycogen utilization during bicycle ergometer work at relative loads from 30 to 120 percent maximum VO₂ illustrate this point (Fig. 26.2). At the heaviest work loads (90 and 120 percent of max), more than 10 percent of the glycogen store was used per minute. At exhaustion, however, there was ample glycogen remaining in the quadriceps. At lower work loads (70 to 80 percent max) exhaustion did coincide with muscle glycogen values approaching zero.

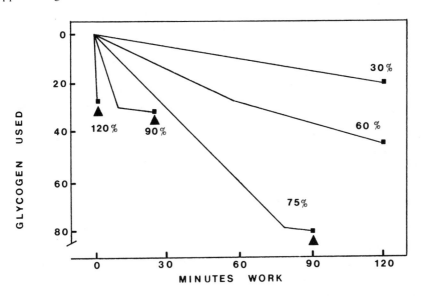

Fig. 26.2 Quadriceps glycogen depletion (mM glucose units/kg) during cycling at 30, 60, 75, 90, and 120% of max. VO₂ max. ▲ indicates exhaustion. During intense exercise (90 and 120%), exhaustion occurred in spite of ample stores of glycogen. (From Saltin 1971, p. 289. Used by permission of Plenum Publishing Corporation.)

It appears, therefore, that under normal conditions at maximal or near maximal work loads, the muscle's endogenous stores of carbohydrate (glycogen) are adequate to meet the demands for energy. Other factors are responsible for the fatigue reported at the termination of exercise (Costill et al. 1971a; Karlsson and Saltin 1970; Keul 1975; Taylor 1975). With lowered glycogen levels, however, work time may be reduced and tolerance for intense exhaustive exercise compromised. Costill and others (1971a) found, for example, the capacity for exhaustive work following an endurance run that reduced glycogen content was progressively lowered on each of three successive days.

Several studies have attempted to quantify the amount of blood glucose taken up and oxidized at maximal work loads. Saltin and his coworkers (1974) studied glucose uptake by the leg at rest and during one maximal work and five submaximal loads. Glucose uptake was related to work intensity and could account for up to 25 percent of the total energy output. At the heaviest workloads (90 and 120 percent max) uptake was 25 to 35 times that observed at rest. Based on glycogen utilization and concomitantly observed VO_2 and R values, the relative contributions of glucose, glycogen, and fat were estimated. At above 50 percent maximum VO_2, carbohydrate was the dominant fuel, but glucose uptake during very heavy work seemed to be quantitatively of minor importance. A similar conclusion was reached by Keul based on his studies of athletes during intense exercise (Keul, Doll, and Keppler 1972).

In contrast to the observation that muscle glycogen is the predominant fuel at high relative work loads, Wahren and coworkers (1971) have suggested that blood glucose is the major carbohydrate oxidized during heavy leg ergometer exercise. A-V differences and substrate exchange across the leg and splanchnic vascular bed were observed at 400, 800, and 1200 kgm/min (VO_2 = 1.0, 1.7, and 2.4 liters/min). Glucose uptake by the leg increased sevenfold after 40 minutes of light work to ten- to twentyfold at moderate-heavy exercise. At the heaviest load, this uptake could account for 28 to 37 percent of the total substrate oxidized by the leg and 75 to 89 percent of the estimated carbohydrate oxidation.

The basis for this rather large discrepancy in estimated percentage of glucose contribution is unclear. It can be pointed out, however, that estimates of substrate utilization based on R and VO_2 values under the nonsteady state conditions of heavy exercise may be misleading. On the other hand, there are methodological problems when measuring small A-V differences; it is assumed that all the venous outflow is accounted for, that there are no arterial shunts, that estimates of blood flow are accurate, and that there is no release of free glucose from muscle. Perhaps most important is the assumption that subcutaneous and nonexercising leg muscle tissues do not contribute significantly to the arterial-venous glucose differences. It should also be mentioned that while Wahren and his colleagues considered the exercise at 1200 kgm to be "heavy," VO_2, RQ, and heart rate data suggest that the work has less than approximately 80 percent of maximum VO_2.

Endurance Exercise

As the intensity of work decreases, exercise can be continued for a longer time (Fig. 26.2) and the importance of oxidative energy production increases. The muscle becomes more dependent on the delivery of substrates from the blood. Under these conditions, glucose uptake and oxidation seem to follow a triphasic pattern. During the more anaerobic initial stages of exercise in both rodents (Baldwin et al. 1973) and humans (Bergstrom and Hultman 1967), endogenous muscle glycogen provides most of the substrate and is rapidly depleted. As exercise continues, the rate of glycogen utilization slows while the rate of glucose uptake increases. Wahren and others (1971) have estimated that at this point glucose may contribute as much as 90 percent of the total carbohydrate oxidized in leg exercise. FFA levels increase concurrently, and they soon become the predominant fuel for muscular work (Keul 1975; Paul and Holmes 1975). At the same time, the contribution of blood glucose falls as does the rate of muscle glycogen catabolism. There is, however, some controversy as to the extent of glucose contribution. In contrast to the large percentage of oxidation as described by Wahren and his associates, Young and others (1967) found that based on isotopic determination of glucose uptake and use in prolonged exercise (treadmill walking), only 17 percent of the total CO_2 production was derived from glucose.

Chapler and Stainsby (1968) have also found high rates of glucose uptake and oxidation for an *in situ*, stimulated gastrocnemius-plantaris preparation in dogs. Conversely, Costin and his associates (1971), using an *in situ* isolated gracilis preparation and stimulatory rates similar to those of Chapler and Stainsby, found that glucose uptake could only account for about 10 percent of the carbohydrate utilization, the values about one-third those of Chapler and Stainsby. These differences can perhaps be attributed to differences in fiber type and contractile mechanics of the respective muscles. Other studies on exercising canines (Issekutz et al. 1966; Issekutz et al. 1967; Paul et al. 1966) also suggest that no more than 10 to 15 percent of energy expended by muscular contraction is supplied from plasma glucose. As pointed out by Paul and his coworkers (1966), studies on the uptake and oxidation of substrate by intact animals during exercise show that plasma glucose oxidation represents a minor portion when compared to the participation of plasma free fatty acids.

Despite the discrepancies between these studies, there is no doubt that glucose is an important substrate during endurance exercise. This is perhaps best illustrated by the exercise studies on subjects with McArdle's syndrome (Pernow et al. 1967; Porte et al. 1966). Due to enzyme deficiencies, these individuals are incapable of breaking down muscle glycogen. Upon initiation of even light work, they experience extreme muscular fatigue with associated tachycardia and hyperventilation disproportional to the imposed work stress. No lactate accumulation occurs, and the capacity to exercise can be prolonged by infusing glucose.

Hermansen and his associates (1967) have indicated that during prolonged heavy work, the human body utilizes approximately 3 gm of carbohydrate per minute. If a substantial portion of this carbohydrate is blood glucose, then liver stores may be substantially depleted thereby challenging blood glucose homeostasis. During endurance exercise, total glucose turnover does increase (Reichard et al. 1969), and therefore an augmented hepatic production is required (Rowell et al. 1965) to maintain arterial blood glucose concentration. Since hepatic stores are limited, significant decreases in glycogen content occur with endurance exercise (Balwin et al. 1973; Hultman and Nilsson 1971). Though glycogenolysis accounts for a substantial portion of this hepatic glucose output, gluconeogenesis from lactate, pyruvate, glycerol, and other precursors such as alanine (Ahlborg et al. 1974; Felig and Wahren 1971) increases so that the arterial glucose concentration is maintained or even increased during very strenuous exertion. Thus, hypoglycemia during exercise is rare, though sometimes observed in marathon runners (Costill 1972; Costill and Fox 1969; Levine et al. 1924) and those participating in other very long endurance contests.

It appears, however, that exhaustion in these situations may be due to the simultaneous depletion of skeletal muscle glycogen. For example, Costill (1977) has recently observed that ingestion of glucose some 30 to 45 minutes prior to exercise results in a significant increase in blood glucose and insulin values. This is followed by a rapid decrease in glucose to very low values within 15 to 20 minutes after starting work. (See Fig. 26.3.) In spite of hypoglycemic values in some subjects during this trial, the fatigue reported was no different from that for the other trials where blood glucose was normal.

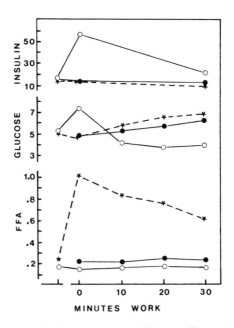

Fig. 26.3 Blood insulin (μ IU/ml), glucose and FFA (mm/liter) values at rest and during 30 minutes of exercise at 70% of max. VO2. Trials were designed such that exercise was initiated with normal (control/fasting) blood parameters (●), or with elevated FFA (fatty meal and heparin) (*) or glucose/insulin values (o). Ingestion of the glucose (75 gm) prior to exercise (~45 min) did not subsequently spare muscle glycogen utilization during work but did result in hypoglycemic glucose values in some subjects.

INGESTION OF GLUCOSE SOLUTIONS DURING ENDURANCE EXERCISE

The depletion of muscle glycogen and/or hypoglycemia are thought to contribute to the fatigue resulting in termination of prolonged exercise (Ahlborg et al. 1967; Bergstrom et al. 1967; Pernow and Saltin 1971). During work of this nature, especially in hot environments, sweat losses may also be high, resulting in dehydration and hyperthermia. Based on these considerations, glucose/electrolyte solutions are commonly ingested during endurance work in an attempt to (1) replenish the lost water, and (2) provide carbohydrate for nerve and muscle energy demands. The benefits of water replacement are well recognized and include a reduction of internal temperature and maintenance of plasma volume. Both factors contribute to the prevention of circulatory collapse. The carbohydrate, however, alters the osmotic properties of the solution and may reduce the gastric emptying of water (Hunt 1961; Hunt and Pathak 1960), an important consideration with dehydration and impending heat stress. Thus, the practical benefits of carbohydrate feedings as related to the maintenance of blood sugar or to oxidative metabolism are less clear. For example, although glucose feedings have been shown to enhance endurance capacity under hypoglycemic conditions (Christensen and Hansen 1939a), there is some question as to the fractional contribution of exogenous carbohydrate to metabolism in exercising men (Costill et al. 1973) when muscle glycogen stores are adequate.

Ingestion of large quantities of glucose before exercise seems unwise in that a response similar to that observed during glucose tolerance tests may result (Fig. 26.3). The rapid increase in blood glucose causes a correspondingly marked increase in insulin release. The presence of large quantities of insulin when carbohydrate absorption is complete may then result in additional glucose removal from the blood. Thus, glucose levels may rapidly fall below normal levels (Costill et al. 1977; Orent-Keiles and Hallman 1949), thereby accelerating the onset of neuromuscular fatigue. It should be pointed out that a long delay between glucose ingestion and the onset of exercise may be the critical factor. If exercise is started before the insulin response to glucose occurs, it may inhibit the subsequent hypoglycemic effects.

Recent studies have also focused on ingestion of carbohydrate solutions during endurance exercise. Ahlborg and Felig (1976) observed subjects during four hours of ergometer exercise at about 30 percent of maximum VO_2. After 90 minutes of exercise they ingested a 200 gm (30 percent) glucose solution. A different control group followed the same protocol without glucose ingestion. They concluded that ingestion of the glucose solution (1) augmented uptake and oxidation of glucose by the legs, (2) decreased fat mobilization, (3) augmented glucose escape from the liver with decreased gluconeogenesis, and (4) resulted in a retention of half the ingested glucose in the splanchnic bed.

While of scientific interest, the practical significance of these data as pertaining to athletic performance remains to be elucidated. The osmotic properties of a 30 percent solution are such that gastric emptying, would have been markedly inhibited (Hunt 1961; Hunt and Pathak 1960). In their studies on factors limiting gastric emptying, for example, Costill and Saltin (1974) found that 15 minutes after ingestion of a 10 to 15 percent glucose solution, the volume remaining in the stomach was always equal to or greater than the volume ingested. They also found that in the first 15 minutes following the feedings, the quantity of glucose emptied seemed to be unrelated to the glucose content of the drink. Approximately 10 gm were absorbed from each of the solutions. Ahlborg and Felig's subjects exercised at roughly 30 percent maximum VO_2. Studies on distance runners and other endurance athletes have shown that they can function in excess of 75 percent max for an entire race (Costill and Fox 1969; Wyndham et al. 1969). At this work intensity, digestion is retarded, gastric emptying is slowed, and the ingested solution stays in the stomach longer (Costill and Saltin 1974; Fordtran and Saltin 1967). It is apparent, therefore, that a high glucose content combined with heavy work drastically limits gastric emptying of water.

Commercially available glucose/electrolyte drinks contain considerably less glucose, ranging from 1 to 6 percent, while soft drinks contain about 10 percent glucose. The former empty rapidly compared to soft drinks or other glucose solutions more concentrated than 10 percent and thus would provide needed water (Fig. 26.4). The sensation of "fullness" is also not present after ingestion. Glucose levels may be only transiently elevated, and the contribution of the ingested load to oxidative metabolism is minimal.

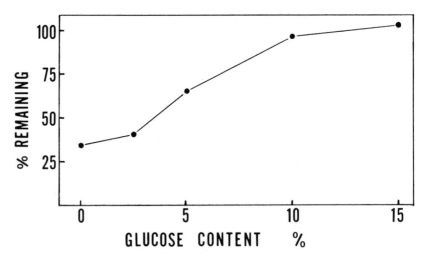

Fig. 26.4 Percent of a 400 ml solution remaining in the stomach 15 min. after ingestion. The solution contained 0, 2.5, 5.0, 10.0, and 15% glucose. The lower the concentration of glucose, the faster the solution empties.

For example, we have observed that subjects ingesting either a 2.5 percent or a 10.6 percent glucose solution (10 and 42.4 gm) after two hours of cycling (50 percent VO_2 max) oxidized less than 10 percent of the glucose in an additional hour of work (Van Handel 1975). The more concentrated drink did provide a greater fraction of the blood glucose, but the feedings only transiently reversed a decreasing trend in blood glucose levels seen throughout the three-hour exercise task. On the other hand, FFA levels rose continuously throughout exercise and were unaffected by the feedings. Based on R and VO_2 measures, it was estimated that free fatty acids continued to be the major source of fuel for muscle metabolism (Fig. 26.5).

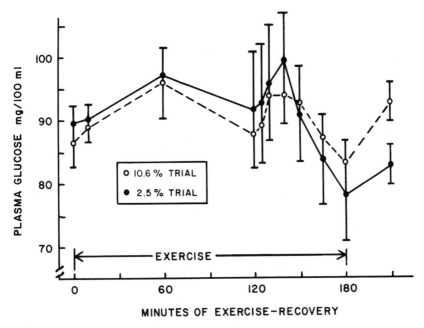

Fig. 26.5 Blood glucose was only transiently affected by ingestion of either a 2.5% or a 10.6% glucose solution after 2 hours of an exercise task at 50% max. VO_2. R, VO_2 and $^{14}CO_2$ data suggested that FFA were the major substrate oxidized as less than 10% of the ingested ^{14}C glucose was recovered as $^{14}CO_2$.

The practical benefits of ingesting a concentrated versus a weak glucose solution during moderate to heavy work remain to be seen. However, solutions containing one to three percent glucose empty nearly as rapidly as water but do not contribute substantially to maintenance of blood sugar levels or to oxidative metabolism. More concentrated solutions (ten percent glucose) empty more slowly, contribute significantly to blood glucose levels, but still are not oxidized to a great degree. Such drinks may be of value under conditions of thermal stress and dehydration when both water and some glucose are desirable. Highly concentrated solutions may indeed elevate blood sugar levels and increase the fractional contribution of glucose to oxidative metabolism (Ahlborg and Felig 1976). This adjustment, however, seems to be at the expense of FFA oxidation. It has been suggested that glycogen catabolism may take place at the same rate irrespective of the quantity of glucose delivered to the cell (Bergstrom and

Hultman 1967). This point deserves some consideration since glycogen sparing is a major result of enhanced fat oxidation and occurs both as a result of training (Baldwin et al. 1975) and with artificially elevated FFA levels (Costill et al. 1977; Rennie et al. 1976). Since muscular fatigue at workloads of approximately 60 to 80 percent max VO_2 is associated with glycogen depletion, sparing of this substrate via elevated FFA oxidation may significantly enhance or prolong performance.

Based on the forecited observations, several recommendations can be stated regarding the ingestion of exogenous carbohydrate for use as an aid to performance.

1. During work of 60 to 90 minutes duration or less, it is unlikely that glucose feedings are necessary. Hepatic stores of glycogen are sufficient to cover the demands for glucose of both muscle and nervous systems. This assumes that both liver and muscle glycogen depots are at least normal. Administration of glucose when these stores are depleted is known to enhance performance.

Fluid feedings under these conditions should contain minimal amounts of carbohydrate (five percent solution) so that gastric emptying of water is optimized. During work in the heat, sweat losses may far exceed the capacity to deliver water to the circulation and thus limit performance capacity. Impending circulatory collapse rather than hypoglycemia or depletion of muscle glycogen may be the limiting factor for work tolerance.

2. Glucose feedings during exercise of longer duration may enhance work ability, again if hypoglycemia is present. Ingestion of large amounts of glucose will significantly elevate blood glucose levels and provide a substantial proportion of oxidized substrate. In terms of gastric emptying, delivery of water, and glycogen sparing, however, this practice may not be advantageous. Small volumes of a low concentration solution (five percent glucose) ingested periodically seem to provide adequate glucose for the maintenance of blood sugar levels while at the same time not inhibiting the release, uptake, or oxidation of free fatty acids. It is interesting to note that training results in an increased use of free fatty acids during work at the same intensity, thus preserving carbohydrate stores. Attempts to alter this metabolic adaptation by ingesting large amounts of carbohydrate seems unwise.

SUMMARY

Blood glucose provides a relatively small but important fraction of the total substrate oxidized during work. During endurance exercise, hypoglycemia may result in muscular and/or nervous system fatigue as the rate of liver glucose production cannot match the rates of muscle/nervous system uptake and catabolism. In this instance, supplemental carbohydrate feedings can enhance performance. Since gastric emptying of water may be of importance, the fluids ingested should be low in carbohydrate content and of small volume as opposed to the ingestion of a highly concentrated solution. Training-induced adaptations occur so that during prolonged work, muscle catabolizes more free fatty acids, at the same time conserving liver and muscle glycogen stores. As a result, blood glucose levels may be less subject to severe alterations and muscle glycogen spared for use when the inevitable increase in work intensity occurs during the final sprint to the finish.

REFERENCES

Ahlborg, B., J. Bergstrom, L. Ekelund, and E. Hultman. 1967. Muscle glycogen during prolonged physical exercise. *Acta Physiol Scand,* 70, 129-142.

Ahlborg, G., P. Felig, L. Hagenfeldt, R. Hendler, and J. Wahren. 1974. Substrate turnover during prolonged exercise in man: Splanchnic and leg metabolism of glucose, free fatty acids and amino acids. *J Clin Invest,* 53, 1080-1090.

Ahlborg, G. and P. Felig. 1976. Influence of glucose ingestion on fuel-hormone response during prolonged exercise. *J Appl Physiol,* 41, 683-688.

Astrand, P. O., I. Hallbock, R. Hedman, and B. Saltin. 1963. Blood lactates after prolonged severe exercise. *J Appl Physiol,* 18, 619-622.

Baldwin, K. M., J. S. Reitman, R. L. Terjung, W. W. Winder, and J. O. Holloszy. 1973. Substrate depletion in different types of muscle and in liver during prolonged running. *Amer J Physiol,* 225, 1045-1050.

Baldwin, K. M., R. H. Fitts, F. W. Booth, W. W. Winder, and J. O. Holloszy. 1975. Depletion of muscle and liver glycogen during exercise. Protective effect of training. *Pflugers Arch,* 354, 203-212.

Benade, A. J., C. H. Wyndham, C. R. Jansen, G. G. Rogers, and E. J. deBruin. 1973. Plasma insulin and carbohydrate metabolism after sucrose ingestion during rest and prolonged aerobic exercise. *Pflugers Arch,* 342, 207-218.

Bergstrom, J., L. Hermansen, E. Hultman, and B. Saltin. 1967a. Diet, muscle glycogen and physical performance. *Acta Physiol Scand,* 71, 140-150.

Bergstrom, J., and E. Hultman. 1967b. A study of the glycogen metabolism during exercise in man. *Scand J Clin Lab Invest,* 19, 218-228.

Cahill, G. F. and E. O. Owen. 1968. Some observations on carbohydrate metabolism in man. In *Carbohydrate Metabolism and Its Disorders,* F. Dickens, P. Randle, and W. Whelan (eds.). New York: Academic Press.

Chapler, C. K. and W. M. Stainsby. 1968. Carbohydrate metabolism in contracting dog skeletal muscle in situ. *Amer J Physiol,* 215, 995-1004.

Christensen, E. H. and O. Hansen. 1939a. IV. Hypoglykamie, Arbeitsfahigkeit und Ehrnahrung. *Skand Arch Physiol,* 81, 172-179.

Christensen, E. H. and O. Hansen. 1939b. Respiratorischer quotient und O_2-aufnahme. *Skand Arch Physiol,* 81, 180.

Christensen, E. H. and O. Hansen. 1939c. Zur methodik der respiratorischen quotient-bestimmungen in ruhe und bei arbeit. *Skand Arch Physiol,* 81, 137-171.

Conlee, R. K., J. J. Rennie, and W. W. Winder. 1976. Skeletal muscle glycogen content: Diurnal variation and effects of fasting. *Amer J Physiol*, 231, 614-618.

Corsi, A., M. Midrio, and A. L. Granata. 1969. In situ utilization of glycogen and blood glucose by skeletal muscle during tetanus. *Amer J Physiol*, 216, 1534-1541.

Costill, D. L. 1972. Physiology of marathon running. *JAMA*, 221, 1024-1029.

Costill, D. L. and E. L. Fox. 1969. Energetics of marathon running. *Med Sci Spts*, 1, 81-86.

Costill, D. L., R. Bowers, G. Branam, and K. Sparks. 1971a. Muscle glycogen utilization during prolonged exercise on successive days. *J Appl Physiol*, 31, 834-838.

Costill, D. L., K. Sparks, R. Gregor, and C. Turner. 1971b. Muscle glycogen utilization during exhaustive running. *J Appl Physiol*, 31, 353-356.

Costill, D. L., A. Bennett, G. Branam, and D. Eddy. 1973. Glucose ingestion at rest and during prolonged exercise. *J Appl Physiol*, 34, 764-769.

Costill, D. L. and B. Saltin. 1974. Factors limiting gastric emptying during rest and exercise. *J Appl Physiol*, 37, 679-683.

Costill, D. L., E. Coyle, G. Dalsky, W. Evans, W. Fink, and D. Hoopes. 1977. Effects of elevated FFA and insulin on muscle glycogen usage during exercise. *J Appl Physiol*, 43, 695-699.

Costin, J. C., B. Saltin, N. S. Skinner, and G. Vastagh. 1971. Glucose uptake at rest and during contraction in isolated dog skeletal muscle. *Acta Physiol Scand*, 81, 124-137.

Felig, P. and J. Wahren. 1971. Amino acid metabolism in exercising man. *J Clin Invest*, 50, 2703-2714.

Fordtran, J. S. and B. Saltin. 1967. Gastric emptying and intestinal absorption during prolonged severe exercise. *J Appl Physiol*, 23, 331-335.

Hermansen, L., E. Hultman, and B. Saltin. 1967. Muscle glycogen during prolonged severe exercise. *Acta Physiol Scand*, 17, 129-139.

Hultman, E. 1967a. Muscle glycogen in man determined in needle biopsy specimens. Method and normal values. *Scand J Clin Lab Invest*, 19, 209-217.

Hultman, E. 1967b. Studies on muscle metabolism of glycogen and active phosphate in man with special reference to exercise and diet. *Scand J Clin Lab Invest*, 94 (Suppl 19), 1-63.

Hultman, E. and L. H. Nilsson. 1971. Liver glycogen in man. Effects of different diets and muscular exercise. In *Muscle Metabolism During Exercise*, B Pernow and B. Saltin (eds.). New York: Plenum Press.

Hunt, J. N. 1961. The osmotic control of gastric emptying. *Gastroenterology*, 41, 49-51.

Hunt, J. N. and J. D. Pathak. 1960. The osmotic effects of some simple molecules and ions on gastric emptying. *J Physiol (Lond)*, 154, 254-269.

Issekutz, B., H. I. Miller, and K. Rodahl. 1966. Lipid and carbohydrate metabolism during exercise. *Fed Proc*, 25, 1415-1420.

Issekutz, B., P. Paul, and H. I. Miller. 1967. Metabolism in normal and pancreatectomized dogs during steady-state exercise. *Amer J Physiol*, 213, 857-862.

Jorfeldt, L. and J. Wahren. 1970. Human forearm muscle metabolism during exercise. V.

Quantitative aspects of glucose uptake and lactate production during prolonged exercise. *Scand J Clin Lab Invest*, 26, 73-81.

Karlsson, J. and B. Saltin. 1970. Lactate, ATP and CP in working muscle during exhaustive exercise in man. *J Appl Physiol*, 29, 598-601.

Keul, J., E. Doll, and D. Keppler. 1972. *Energy metabolism of human muscle*. Baltimore: University Park Press.

Keul, J. 1975. Muscle metabolism during long-lasting exercise. In *Metabolic Adaptation to Prolonged Physical Exercise*. J. Poortmans and H. Howald (eds.). Basel: Birkhauser Verlag.

Levine, S. A., B. Gordon, and C. L. Derick. 1924. Some changes in the chemical constituents of the blood following a marathon race. *JAMA*, 28, 1778-1779.

Orent-Keiles, E. and L. F. Hallman. 1949. US Dept Agr Circ No. 827.

Owen, O. E., P. Felig, A. P. Morgan, J. Wahren, and G. F. Cahill. 1969. Liver and kidney metabolism during prolonged starvation. *J Clin Invest*, 48, 574-583.

Paul, P., B. Issekutz, and H. I. Miller. 1966. Interrelationship of free fatty acids and glucose metabolism in the dog. *Amer J Physiol*, 211, 1313-1320.

Paul, P. and W. Holmes. 1975. Free fatty acid and glucose metabolism during increased energy expenditure and after training. *Med Sci Spts*, 7, 176-184.

Pernow, B., R. Havel, and D. B. Jennings. 1967. The second wind phenomenon in McArdle's Syndrom. *Acta Med Scand* (Suppl 472), 294-307.

Pernow, B. and B. Saltin. 1971. Availability of substrates and capacity for prolonged heavy exercise in man. *J Appl Physiol*, 31, 416-422.

Porte, D., D. Crawford, D. Jennings, C. Aber, and M. McIlroy. Cardiovascular and metabolic responses to exercise in a patient with McArdle's Syndrome. *New Eng J Med*, 2751, 406-412.

Reichard, G. A., B. Issekutz, P. Kimbel, R. C. Putman, N. J. Hochella, and S. Weinhouse. 1961. Blood glucose metabolism in man during muscular work. *J Appl Physiol*, 16, 1001-1005.

Rennie, M. J., W. W. Winder, and J. O. Holloszy. 1976. A sparing effect of increased free fatty acids on muscle glycogen content in exercising rat. *Biochem J*, 156, 647-655.

Rose, I. A. and E. L. O'Conell. 1964. The role of glucose-6-phosphate in the regulation of glucose metabolism in human erythrocytes. *J Biol Chem*, 239, 12-17.

Rowell, L. B., E. J. Masoro, and M. J. Spencer. 1965. Splanchnic metabolism in exercising man. *J Appl Physiol*, 20, 1032-1037.

Saltin, B. and J. Karlsson. 1971. Muscle glycogen utilization during work of different intesities. In *Muscle Metabolism During Exercise*, B. Pernow and B. Saltin (eds.). New York: Plenum Press.

Saltin, B., J. Wahren, and B. Pernow. 1974. Phosphagen and carbohydrate metabolism during exercise in trained middle-aged men. *Scand J Clin Lab Invest*, 33, 71-77.

Taylor, A. W. 1975. The effects of exercise and training on the activities of human skeletal muscle glycogen cycle enzymes. In *Metabolic Adaptation to Prolonged Physical Exercise*, J Poortmans and H. Howald (eds.). Basel: Birkhauser Verlag.

Van Handel, P. J. 1975. Uptake and utilization of exogenous glucose during endurance exercise. Doctoral Dissertation, Kent State University.

Wahren, J., P. Felig, G. Ahlborg, and L. Jorfeldt. 1971. Glucose metabolism during leg exercise in man. *J Clin Invest,* 50, 2715-2725.

Wyndham, C. H., N. B. Strydom, A. J. Van Rensburg, and A. J. S. Benade. 1969. Physiological requirements for world class performances in endurance running. *S A Med J,* 43, 996-1002.

Young, D. R., R. Pelligra, J. Shapira, R. R. Adachi, and K. Skrettingland. 1967. Glucose oxidation and replacement during prolonged exercise in man. *J Appl Physiol,* 23, 734-741.

27

Glycogen Loading and Endurance Capacity

Eric Hultman

In the middle of the 1960s, the muscle biopsy technique was introduced enabling direct measurements of the glycogen stores in the muscles (Bergström and Hultman 1966, 1967a; Hultman 1967a, 1967b). Using this technique researchers showed that the glycogen store in the muscle could be varied with the diet, and also that there was a close relationship between the muscle glycogen content and the capacity for bicycle exercise. It was also shown that a combination of hard (glycogen depleting) exercise and carbohydrate-rich diet could increase the local glycogen stores by two to three times the normal value with a corresponding increase of endurance capacity (Bergström and Hultman 1966; Bergström et al. 1967). Christensen and Hansen (1939) observed that the blood glucose concentration at the end of hard exercise was decreased when a carbohydrate-free diet was given before the exercise period. This was possibly due to an insufficient store of carbohydrate in the liver, but no measurements were done at that time. Subsequently, however, it has been shown using a needle biopsy technique to obtain liver samples that the liver glycogen content is extremely sensitive to the composition of diet, and also that the liver glycogen store is continuously utilized both at rest and during exercise (Hultman and Nilsson 1971, 1973; Nilsson and Hultman 1973).

Since 1967 many athletes have utilized the method of increasing the muscle glycogen stores in order to increase endurance capacity. Many of these have been successful, others not. In the following, some theoretical and practical considerations concerning glycogen loading and endurance capacity will be presented. (For an earlier summary of these results see Bergström and Hultman 1972.)

In discussing glycogen loading and endurance capacity it is necessary to define first at which work loads glycogen degradation meets the required capacity as an energy delivering process, and second when the size of the glycogen store is limiting for the time the work can be continued. Increases of the glycogen store will increase endurance capacity only when the following two criteria are met: (1) the exercise necessitates the use of glycogen as an energy source, and (2) the exercise is such that the entire glycogen store is utilized.

The maximum rate of utilization of a certain fuel for muscle contraction is determined by the activity of the required enzymes. The maximum activity of these enzymes will limit the power delivered from an energy substrate. Estimates of the maximum power available from different fuels in muscle tissue have been made by McGilvary (1975). Maximum power was calculated as the maximum amount of high energy phosphates ($\sim$P) that could be generated per gram muscle per second. His estimates were as follows:

One:

$$\text{ATP, PCr} \longrightarrow \text{ADP, Cr}$$

Max. rate of degradation: $1.6 - 6 \ \mu\text{mol} \sim \text{P} \cdot \text{gm}^{-1} \cdot \text{sec}^{-1}$
Amount available: $24 \ \mu\text{mol/gm}$ muscle

The figure $1.6 \ \mu\text{mol} \sim \text{P} \cdot \text{gm}^{-1} \ \text{sec}^{-1}$ was calculated from experiments in Margaria's laboratory (Margaria et al. 1964; Di Prampero 1971; Di Prampero et al. 1973). The higher value of $6 \ \mu\text{mol}$ is close to the maximum velocity of creatine kinase in human muscle (Kleine 1967) and is in line with previously published estimates of human muscle power (Fletcher and Lewis 1959; Wilkie 1960; Davies 1971). The amount of $\sim$P available in human muscle tissue was first determined by Hultman and others (1967).

Two:

$$\text{Glycogen} \longrightarrow \text{lactate}$$

Max. rate of $\sim$P generation: $1.0 - 1.5 \ \mu\text{mol} \cdot \text{gm}^{-1} \cdot \text{sec}^{-1}$
Amount available: $240 \ \mu\text{mol/gm}$ muscle

Maximum power from glycolysis was calculated from data of Margaria and others (1964) to be of the order of $1.0 \ \mu\text{mol} \cdot \text{gm}^{-1} \cdot \text{sec}^{-1}$. According to McGilvary (1975) the value should theoretically be 50 percent higher. Studies from our laboratory of maximum glycolysis rate during isometric contraction at a load of 90 percent of the subject's maximum voluntary contraction force indicated values up to 1.4 μmol $\cdot$ gm^{-1} $\cdot$ sec^{-1} (Bergström et al. 1971) and were thus close to the theoretical value suggested by McGilvary. The amount of glycogen available was calculated as 90 percent of the normal store, that is, 85 μmol glucose units per gm muscle (Hultman 1967a).

Three:

$$\text{Glycogen} \longrightarrow CO_2 + H_2O$$

Max. rate of $\sim$ P generation: 0.5 μmol $\cdot$ gm$^{-1}\cdot$sec^{-1}
Amount available: 3000 μmol/gm muscle

The calculation of maximum power from glycogen oxidation to CO_2 to H_2O assumes an oxygen uptake and utilization of 3 liters per minute by 30 kg of muscle and yield of 6.17 mole of active phosphate per mole of oxygen. The limiting factor for the rate of glycogen oxidation is mitochondrial electron transport determined by the availability of oxygen or by the maximum velocity of the transfer mechanism.

Four:

$$\text{Fatty acids} \longrightarrow CO_2 + H_2O$$

Max. rate of $\sim$ P generation: 0.24 μmol $\cdot$ gm$^{-1}\cdot$sec^{-1}
Amount available: *not limiting*

The maximum power output from oxidation of fatty acids was calculated from studies by Pernow and Saltin (1971). The lower rate of $\sim$ P generation from fatty acid oxidation compared to oxidation of glycogen must be due to a limiting step before acetyl-CoA-formation and not to the mitochondrial electron transport.

Based on the above calculations of maximum power output from different fuels, during exercise with a power output of more than 1.5 μmol of active phosphate per gram muscle per second, the glycolysis rate is insufficient to cover the energy needs and the result is a continuous decrease of active phosphates. The end point of such work is not determined by the glycogen store, but by the lack of high energy phosphates. In the range of power output between 0.24 and 1.5 μmol of active phosphate gm^{-1} $\cdot$ sec^{-1}, the utilization of the local glycogen store or of glucose delivered via the blood can theoretically cover the need for ATP resynthesis; glycogen or glucose availability is thus a prerequisite for the exercise performance at these work loads. Below that range of power output (0.24 μmol $\cdot$ gm^{-1} $\cdot$ sec^{-1}), FFA oxidation is sufficient to meet the energy needs, and the glycogen store is no longer a limiting factor for performance.

UTILIZATION OF WHOLE GLYCOGEN STORE DURING EXERCISE

The entire glycogen store should be usable during the work performance. Glycogenolysis and glycolysis during muscle contraction are initiated by calcium release and the rate is thereafter determined by the composition of the adenine nucleotide store, that is, high ATP content during rest inhibits glycolysis while increased ADP and AMP content produced during muscle contraction stimulate glycolysis and oxidative phosphorylation. The choice of substrate used for ATP resynthesis is determined by the relative concentrations of the adenine nucleotides. The greater the decrease in ATP (with corresponding increase in ADP and AMP), the more powerful substrate is utilized. If oxidative capacity is sufficient to meet the energy needs, the entire glycogen store may be used. If, on the other hand, oxidative capacity is too low for production of the required energy (e.g., more than 0.5 μmol of active phosphate $gm^{-1} \cdot sec^{-1}$) then glycolysis is further stimulated by increased ADP and AMP, and the result is an excess formation and accumulation of lactate. Together with lactate the cell accumulates an increasing amount of hydrogen ions, which decreases intracellular pH. A low intracellular pH is inhibitory for glycolytic enzymes and diminishes the glycolytic rate (Trivedi and Danforth 1966; Ui 1966). This will further increase ADP and AMP content and decrease ATP. At a certain level of the ATP/ADP ratio the amount of energy delivered from ATP splitting will no longer be sufficient for continuation of the contraction at the preset load. Excessive lactate formation will, therefore, inhibit the continued use of glycogen at a sufficiently high rate and the entire glycogen store will not be used under these circumstances. The practical consequence of these mechanisms are that the local use of the glycogen store during exercise is limited to work loads and exercise routines where the intramuscular accumulation of lactate is kept to a minimum. Examples of this are where the work load is sufficiently low as to enable the energy demands to be met by the oxidation of glycogen to CO_2 and H_2O, and in situations that enable the major fraction of the lactate formed to be transported away from the working muscles (e.g. during intermittent exercise or when only a small fraction of the total muscle mass is employed).

The glycogenolysis rate and the use of the glycogen store during bicycle exercise sustained at different intensities were studied by Saltin and Karlsson (1971). Some results from their study are summarized in Table 27.1. The results from this study show that about 85 percent of the glycogen store in the quadriceps femoris muscle was used during exercise at a work load of 75 percent of the subject's maximum oxygen uptake capacity. Work loads in which most of the glycogen store is used range from 60 to 95 percent of max VO_2. At work loads higher than 95 percent of max VO_2, glycogenolysis rate is high at the beginning of the exercise, but is inhibited during continued exercise due to decreasing cellular pH, and the total glycogen store cannot be utilized. At work loads lower than 60 percent of max VO_2 other energy substrates are used such as free fatty acids. Thus, only part of the glycogen store was broken down during a two-hour exercise period at work load of 50 percent of max VO_2 or lower (see Table 27.1).

Table 27.1
Work Load and Muscle Glycogen
Utilization During Bicycle Exercise

Work load % of VO₂max	120	100	75	50	25
Glycogen degradation rate mmol glucose units kg⁻¹·min⁻¹	6	3.4	1.4	0.6	0.2
Work time min	5	15-20	80-90	120*	120*
Utilized glycogen store % of total	20	35	85	45	15

* Subject not exhausted.

GLYCOGEN UTILIZATION AND MUSCLE FIBER COMPOSITION

Different fiber types exist in the muscle. In human muscle these are predominantly fast-twitch white fibers and slow-twitch red fibers (Gollnick et al. 1972). The fast-twitch white fibers have a high glycogenolytic and a relatively low oxidative capacity, while in the red fibers the oxidative capacity is higher (Dubowitz and Brooke 1973; Essen et al. 1975; Harris et al. 1976). In muscles from other species, two types of fast-twitch fibers are recognized, one with high and one with low oxidative capacity (Peter et al. 1972). The fibers with low oxidative capacity are recruited only in very intense exercise and are then rapidly depleted of glycogen. At lower work loads only the fibers with high oxidative capacity are recruited. The white glycolytic fibers can, however, be used at the end of a prolonged exercise when the oxidative fibers are depleted of glycogen (Armstrong et al. 1975). In human muscle the recruitment pattern is not so clear, but with short lasting bouts of dynamic exercise at a supramaximal load, glycogen depletion is more pronounced in white fibers than in red (Gollnick et al. 1975; Edgerton et al. 1975). The same is found during isometric contraction with loads exceeding 20 percent of maximum voluntary contraction force (Gollnick et al. 1975). After prolonged exercise with work loads using less than 100 percent of the subject's max VO_2, the glycogen store in the red fibers can be completely depleted of glycogen while ample amounts are still left in the white fibers (Saltin 1975). In this situation the force developed in the muscle will rely on glycogen degradation in the white fibers and the utilization of blood-born glucose and FFA as fuel in the red fibers. Since the maximum power output from utilization of these substrates in the red fibers is lower, the total power output will decrease and the subject cannot continue the exercise at the preset load, that is, the subject is "exhausted" before all glycogen is utilized.

The composition of muscle as regards the relative content of the fiber types varies between individuals. The oxidative capacity of the fibers can be increased by physical conditioning (Gollnick et al. 1973; Varnauskas et al. 1970; Henriksson and Reitman 1976). The rate of glycogen use and the degree to which the store can be used during exercise at a certain work load will thus vary between individuals and is dependent on the overall metabolic profiles of the working muscle.

MUSCLE GLYCOGEN STORE IN RELATION TO DIET

The size of the glycogen store in muscle varies between different muscle groups. In the quadriceps femoris muscle, which is the most widely studied, the mean value is about 85 mmol glycosyl units per kg muscle. In nonathletes the deltoid muscle has a 20 percent lower glycogen content (Hultman 1967a), and the rectus abdominus muscle also has a lower content (Nichols 1958). In athletes using preferentially the arm muscles, the glycogen content is higher. As mentioned earlier, the glycogen store in skeletal muscle is not used or only marginally so during rest or at low work loads, such as during ordinary office work. Thus, only small variations in the glycogen content were observed during a day with normal food intake and without excessive work (Hultman 1967a). During starvation the muscle glycogen degradation rate is about 5 μmol glucosyl units per kg muscle per min if only office work is performed. The same glycogen degradation rate was found when the diet consisted of fat and protein without carbohydrate. A carbohydrate-rich diet, on the other hand, was found to increase the glycogen store though the rate of increase was only about 5 to 10 μmol glucosyl units per kg muscle per min (Hultman and Bergström 1967; Hultman et al. 1971). The practical consequences are that carbohydrate starvation during one week without hard exercise decreases the muscle glycogen content by about 40 percent, while a carbohydrate-rich diet gives a corresponding increase.

MUSCLE GLYCOGEN SYNTHESIS AFTER DEPLETION

After glycogen depleting exercise, glycogen synthesis shows a completely different pattern. Both during complete starvation and during intake of a carbohydrate-free diet, glycogen is synthesized in the depleted muscle. The rate of synthesis is low, however, about 5 μmol per kg muscle per minute. Conversely, if the diet given is rich in carbohydrate the rate of synthesis is increased ten times to about 40 μmol glucosyl units per kg per minute (Hultman et al. 1971). It has also been observed that not only is the rate increased but also that glycogen synthesis continues even when the normal level of glycogen synthesis rate is maintained for three to four days after the depleting exercise and the glycogen level is two to three times the normal content. This effect occurred only locally in the glycogen depleted muscles and was not generalized through-out the whole body. Other muscles in the same man showed no overshoot in glycogen content (Bergström and Hultman 1966) (see Fig. 27.1 and 27.2). The biomechanical mechanism responsible for this local overshoot in muscle glycogen content is not known.

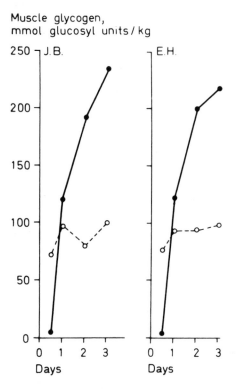

Fig. 27.1 Glycogen content in worked (-●-) and nonworked (-o-) leg during 3 days of carbohydrate-rich diet. One leg of each subject exercised to glycogen depletion in the morning of day 0. The exercise was performed on a bicycle ergometer with one subject on each side of the bike. Biopsies were obtained in both legs after the "one-leg" exercise period and again after one, two and three.

MUSCLE GLYCOGEN AND BICYCLE EXERCISE

To elucidate the relation between the muscle glycogen content and the capacity for bicycle exercise, two experiments were performed. In the first series the muscle glycogen was varied by diet (normal mixed, carbohydrate-rich, and carbohydrate-poor) and the endurance capacity for bicycle exercise was measured (Bergström et al. 1967). Exhaustive exercise was performed three times within a three-day interval. Due to the composition of diet given between the exercise tests, the glycogen content before the start of muscle exercise varied from a

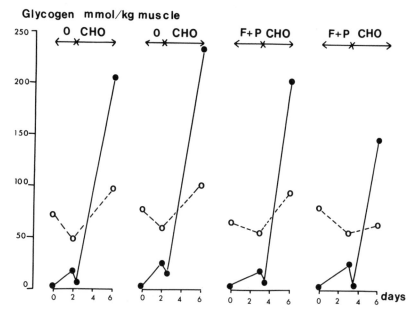

Fig. 27.2 Effect of starvation, carbohydrate-free, and carbohydrate-rich diets on muscle glycogen concentration in quadriceps fermoris muscle of four normal subjects. Exercise with one leg was performed immediately before the first biopsies. After two days of starvation or three days of carbohydrate-free diet, respectively, further exercise with same leg was performed. Thereafter a carbohydrate-rich diet was given. (Work leg—solid line; "rest" leg—broken line.)

0 = starvation

CHO = carbohydrate-rich diet

F + P = carbohydrate-free diet (fat + protein)

minimum value of 25 mmol glucose units per kg to a maximum of 300 mmol per kg after carbohydrate-poor and carbohydrate-rich diets, respectively. Figure 27.3 shows that the endurance time varied in the same way maximally from 30 minutes after the fat and protein diet to about 300 minutes after the carbohydrate-rich diet. *It is thus possible to greatly change a subject's endurance capacity by changing the diet from carbohydrate-poor to carbohydrate-rich after glycogen depleting exercise.* However, along with the changes in muscle glycogen there will also be a change in the liver glycogen store. This is discussed in the next section.

The second series of experiments was designed to assess reliably and objectively the time of fatigue in a subject and to exclude all variables other than muscle glycogen content that might be contributory to fatigue (Hultman and Bergström 1973). The subjects first performed an exhausting exercise with one leg each and were thereafter fed a carbohydrate-rich diet for three days. This resulted in each subject having one leg with an abnormally high muscle glycogen

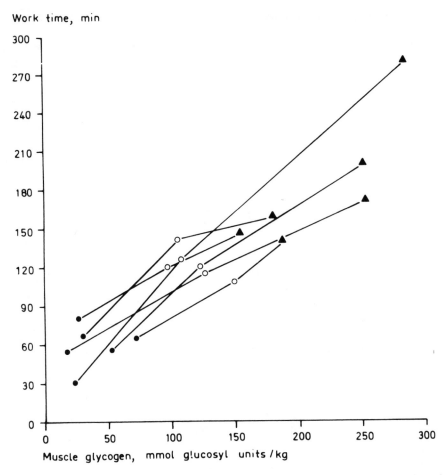

Work time, min

Muscle glycogen, mmol glucosyl units / kg

Fig. 27.3 The relation between initial glycogen content in quadricepts femoris muscle and maximum work time. Each line represents one subject working at a load corresponding to 90 percent of maximum 02 uptake. The different levels of glycogen were achieved by varying the diet during three days between the exercise tests.

○ = normal mixed diet
● = carbohydrate-free diet
▲ = carbohydrate-rich diet

content and the other leg with a normal content. The subjects then worked on a bicycle ergometer equipped with pressure sensitive sensors on the pedal plates, making possible to register when the pressure on one of the pedals decreased indicating a reduction in work force being applied by that leg. The test subjects were surprised to experience tiredness in only one leg, the leg that had not been exercised previously and that had the lower but normal glycogen content before the exercise. This experiment made it possible to determine objectively the point when the supply of energy substrate in the leg was insufficient to meet the energy needs for muscle contraction at the preset load. At the same time other parameters were measured, such as lactate accumulation, glycogen degradation rate, and active phosphate content in muscle. The glycogen degradation rate was the same in both legs even though one leg started with a glycogen content of about 85 mmol glucose units per kg and the other with about 240 mmol. At the end of the exercise one leg had about 20 mmol glucose units left and the other 180 mmol. No differences were found in phosphorylcreatine or ATP content or in lactate accumulation in the two legs with different glycogen contents. The only difference between the two legs was the glycogen content at the point of exhaustion (Hultman and Bergström 1973)

GLYCOGEN LOADING—BENEFITS AND RISKS

It is clear that excessive muscle glycogen loading can be achieved by first emptying the muscle glycogen store completely and thereafter treating the subject with a high carbohydrate intake for three to four days. It is important that the depleting exercise is of the same type as the exercise in which the endurance capacity is intended to be increased by loading. As discussed previously, the exercise must be of a type in which the glycogen store is limiting for the endurance capacity. This is especially the case in sports where a high energy output continues over a long period of time, such as long distance running, cross-country skiing, bicycle racing, canoeing, and many team sports. It should be borne in mind, however, that glycogen loading also increases the water and electrolyte contents of the muscle. If the amount of active muscles during an exercise is about 20 kg, the total store of glycogen in the working muscle is about 1600 to 1700 mmol glucosyl units. An increase by 200 percent in these muscles would mean 3300 mmol glucose units more. This is the same as about 0.6 kg of glycogen. Together with each kilogram of muscle glycogen, 3.4 liters of water are stored (Bergström et al. 1973). This means an increase in the above example of 2.0 liters of water and a total increase in body weight of 2.6 kg. Such a local increase in glycogen and water in the muscles can make them stiff and clumsy and may even hamper certain types of exercise.

LIVER GLYCOGEN

Two mechanisms are available for glucose production by the liver: glycogenolysis, in which the liver glycogen store is utilized; and gluconeo-genesis, in which glucose is synthesized from blood-borne substances such as lactate, pyruvate, glycerol, and some amino acids. Of these two mechanisms for glucose production, glycogenolysis is energetically the more efficient. At high work loads with long duration the size of the liver glycogen store can, therefore, be of importance for blood glucose homeostasis. *With decreasing blood glucose levels the limitation for endurance exercise is set by the central nervous system since the glucose supply may be insufficient for the energy metabolism in the brain.*

Size of Liver Glycogen Store and Its Relation to Composition of Diet

The liver glycogen store at rest varies considerably with the composition of diet. In one study, after a normal mixed diet the liver glycogen content was on average 270 mmol glucose units per kg liver with a range of 87 to 460 mmol (Nilsson 1973). Assuming a mean liver weight of 1.8 kg, the total store thus corresponds to about 500 mmol glucose units. If the diet regimen is changed to a carbohydrate-free diet with normal caloric intake, then the glycogen content in liver decreases rapidly within 24 hours to about ten percent of the normal glycogen store, or 60 mmol in the whole liver. When this diet regimen is continued the low glycogen content persists. Figure 27.4 and Table 27.2 illustrate that a change of the diet to the same caloric intake of carbohydrate-rich food results in a very rapid increase of the liver glycogen store to double the normal content, or about 900 mmol totally (Nilsson and Hultman 1973; Nilsson et al. 1973).

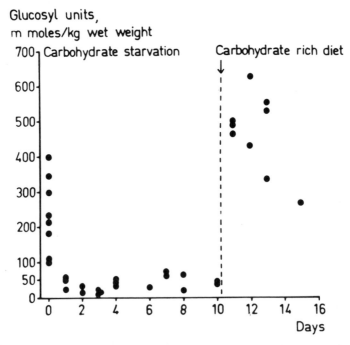

Fig. 27.4 Liver glycogen content in the postabsorptive state, before and during prolonged starvation or supply of carbohydrate-poor diet followed by carbohydrate refeeding. Glycogen content was determined in liver biopsy specimens obtained with the Menghini technique.

284

Table 27.2

Glycogen Store and Glucose Metabolism in Liver at Rest
in Relation to Preceding Diet*

	Glycogen Content mmol/1.8 kg Liver		Glucose Release mmol/min
	Mean	Range	Mean ± SE
After mixed diet	500	160-830	0.87 ± 0.058
After CHO-poor diet, 1-10 days	60	20-130	0.30 ± 0.031
After CHO-rich diet, 1-5 days	900	480-1120	0.95 ± 0.061

* Diet period prior to liver glucose metabolism was three to four days.

The liver glycogen store is utilized at rest at a rate of about 0.54 mmol glucose units per minute. This is about two-thirds of the whole glucose production by the liver, the remaining one-third being derived from gluconeogenesis (Nilsson and Hultman 1973; Nilsson et al. 1973). During exercise glucose release from the liver is increased. At low work loads glucose release is doubled but at higher work loads the increase can amount to four to six times the resting value. The mechanism by which glucose is produced by the liver varies with the work load. At low work loads and during very prolonged exercise periods, a considerable part of the released glucose is derived via gluconeogenesis. At higher work loads and when the liver glycogen stores are normal, most of the released glucose is produced from glycogen degradation (Hultman and Nilsson 1971, 1973). It can easily be calculated that with a normal glycogen content of about 500 mmol glucose units and a glycogen degradation rate of about 2.5 mmol per minute, the glycogen store would be sufficient to provide the required amount of glucose for about 200 minutes. However, at high work loads other factors will limit the endurance time to less than 200 minutes; therefore, a normal liver glycogen content will, in fact, be sufficient to provide all the necessary glucose for working muscle and at the same time for other obligatory glycolytic tissues in the body. This means that the blood sugar content will be stable during even hard exercise periods with durations of two to three hours.

If the carbohydrate content in the diet the day before a hard exercise is low, then the glycogen content in the liver can be as low as 60 mmol glucose units totally. In this situation the liver glycogen store will theoretically suffice for exercise periods of 15 to 20 minutes only assuming the same rate of glycogen degradation, i.e. 2.5 mmol per minute. In this situation there is a change in the mechanism of glucose production by the liver (Hultman and Nilsson 1973). Most of the glucose produced is derived from uptake of gluconeogenic substrates, especially lactate (see Table 27.3). The liver is thus capable of changing the metabolism when the glycogen content is low so that glucose production can continue by means of gluconeogenesis. This process is, however, energy consuming and requires oxygen. This necessitates an increase in oxygen uptake by the liver (Hultman and Nilsson 1973) and must be compensated for by a lower oxygen utilization by working muscle or a higher total oxygen uptake. The gluconeogenic process is not always rapid enough to provide the glucose needed at high work loads, and the result is a decreasing blood glucose level. Blood glucose values as low as 2 mmol per liter have been observed during hard exercise.

Table 27.3

Splanchnic Carbohydrate Metabolism at Rest and During Exercise
after Different Diets

Metabolite Shift Mean Values mmol/min	Carbohydrate Rich Diet		Carbohydrate Poor Diet	
	Rest	Work	Rest	Work
Glucose production	0.92	2.59	0.77	1.99
Lactate uptake	0.25	0.29	0.13	2.14
Pyruvate uptake	0.02	0.02	0.03	0.11
Glycerol uptake	0.04	0.04	0.11	0.13
a-amino acid uptake	0.61	0.07	0.80	0.50
Alanin uptake	0.13	0.04	0.18	0.14
Urea production	0	0.03	0.30	0.27
Oxygen uptake	2.43	2.70	2.44	4.46
Total glucose production mmol		57.55		49.50
Total uptake of metabolites mmol		9.0		72.2
Total calculated maximal gluconeo-genesis mmol		4.5		36.1
Calculated glycogenolysis mmol		53.0 (8.6 gm)		13.4 (2.2 gm)

* The splanchnic carbohydrate metabolism during rest and exercise was measured by liver vein catheterization technique in two subjects. One subject was given carbohydrate-rich diet for three days before the exercise test, the other carbohydrate-free. Glucose release from the liver was measured as well as uptake of gluconeogenic substrates. Maximum glucose production from gluconeogenesis was calculated from uptake of substrates. The difference between maximum gluconeogenesis and hepatic glucose release is given as glycogenolysis. Metabolite shift was determined as mmol/min, but the glucose production from different sources was also calculated for the whole work period (25 min).

LIVER GLYCOGEN AND ENDURANCE CAPACITY

The dependence upon the liver glycogen store for endurance capacity is exemplified in Fig. 27.5, showing the blood sugar content in a man working at the same work load after three different diets: carbohydrate-rich, normal mixed, and carbohydrate-poor (Bergström et al. 1967). All work was performed until exhaustion. After the carbohydrate-rich diet no change in blood sugar occurred during the work period. After mixed diet, blood sugar decreased at the end of work, but after termination of exercise the blood sugar immediately returned to the normal value. Conversely, after the carbohydrate-poor diet blood glucose markedly dropped to 2 mmol per liter of blood, and restoration after termination of exercise was slow. The subject had to stop the work period due to dizziness and headache. Thus, it seems reasonable that at periods with hard, prolonged exercise the liver glycogen store can be limiting for performance capacity. This limitation is seen in sports such as marathon running, cross-country skiing, canoeing, bicycle racing, and possibly in team sports such as soccer and ice-hockey. In most of these sport events the glucose need will be met if the subject has been supplemented with a normal carbohydrate intake the day before the sport performance. Only at very prolonged exercise periods or repeated bouts of hard work is an increased intake of carbohydrate on the day before the performance necessary. On the other hand, an abnormally low intake of carbohydrate the day before a sport performance can seriously decrease the athlete's endurance capacity.

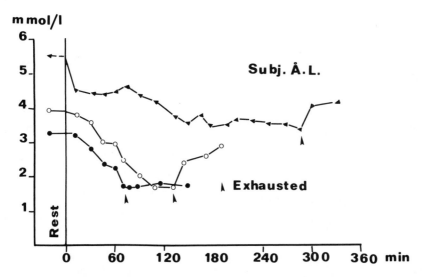

Fig. 27.5 Blood glucose concentration at rest and during exhaustive exercise in one subject with different diets for three days between exercise tests.
▲ = carbohydrate-rich diet
○ = normal mixed diet
● = carbohydrate-free diet

In many published studies where the intention has been to change the muscle glycogen content, the liver glycogen stores have also been changed. Thus, it can be difficult to evaluate which of these two effects is the more important. It seems reasonable that glycogen loading of skeletal muscle for increasing the endurance capacity should be utilized only in a limited number of sport situations when local increase in muscle glycogen is really necessary and the side effects are negligible. The liver glycogen content on the other hand can easily be kept high by sufficient carbohydrate intake on the day before an endurance event. This treatment is without known side effects.

SUMMARY

The two glycogen stores of importance for endurance capacity are those in skeletal muscle and in the liver. The muscle glycogen store is of importance for work with an intensity close to the maximum oxygen uptake and utilization capacity. At such work loads muscle glycogen is the most efficient substrate and the whole glycogen store can be utilized. The endurance capacity will then be related to the size of the muscle glycogen stores.

Increases of the local glycogen store can be achieved by first emptying the muscles by exhaustive exercise and thereafter providing a carbohydrate-rich diet for the next three to four days. During these days no hard exercise should be performed. Only those muscles first depleted of glycogen will be glycogen loaded by the carbohydrate-rich diet. Remember that glycogen loading will increase the weight of the muscles by stored glycogen and water.

The liver glycogen store is utilized to provide blood-borne glucose. During prolonged periods of exercise, blood sugar decreases can limit endurance capacity if the liver glycogen stores are insufficient. The liver glycogen store changes rapidly with diet. A carbohydrate-free diet empties the store within 12 hours while the store is refilled within the same time if a carbohydrate-rich normocaloric diet is given. Thus, for prolonged hard exercise of more than 20 to 30 minutes duration, muscle glycogen loading may be an advantage. To achieve this the athlete should first perform a glycogen depleting exercise, and this should be followed by three days during which a carbohydrate-rich diet is eaten. Glycogen loading of the liver—which is probably advantageous in most sport situations—is easily achieved within a single day if a carbohydrate-rich diet is given.

REFERENCES

Armstrong, R. B., C. W. Saubert, W. L. Sembrowich, R. E. Shephard, and P. D. Gollnick. 1975. Glycogen depletion in rat skeletal muscle fibers during exercise. In *Metabolic adaptation to prolonged physical exercise. Proceedings of the second international symposium on biochemistry of exercise Magglingen*, H. Howald and J. R. Poortmans (eds.). Basel: Birkhäuser Verlag.

Bergström, J., G. Guarnieri, and E. Hultman. 1973. Changes in muscle water and electrolytes during exercise. In *Limiting factors of physical performance. International Symposium at Gravenbruch 1971*, J. Keul (ed.). Stuttgart: Georg Thieme.

Bergström, J., R. C. Harris, E. Hultman, and L. O. Nordesjö. 1971. Energy rich phosphagens in dynamic and static work. In *Muscle metabolism during exercise. Advances in experimental medicine and biology*, Vol. II, B. Pernow and B. Saltin (eds.). New York: Plenum.

Bergström, J., L. Hermansen, E. Hultman, and B. Saltin. 1967. Diet, muscle glycogen and physical performance. *Acta Physiol Scan*, 71, 140-150.

Bergström, J. and E. Hultman. 1966. Muscle glycogen synthesis after exercise. An enhancing factor localized to the muscle cells in man. *Nature* (London), 210, 309-310.

Bergström, J. and E. Hultman. 1967a. A study of the glycogen metabolism during exercise in man. *Scand J Clin Lab Invest,* 19, 218-228.

Bergström, J. and E. Hultman. 1967b. Synthesis of muscle glycogen in man after glucose and fructose infusion. *Acta Med Scand,* 182, 93-107.

Bergström, J. and E. Hultman. 1972. Nutrition for maximal sports performance. *JAMA,* 221, 999-1006.

Christensen, E. H. and O. Hansen. 1939. Arbeitsfähigkeit und Ernährung. *Skan Arch Physiol,* 81, 160-171.

Davies, C. T. M. 1971. Human power output in exercise of short duration in relation to body size and composition. *Ergonomics,* 14, 245-256.

di Prampero, P. E. 1971. The alactic oxygen debt: Its power, capacity, and efficiency. *Adv Exptl Biol Med,* 11, 371-382.

di Prampero, P. E., L. Peeters, and R. Margaria. 1973. Alactic O_2 debt and lactic acid production after exhaustion exercise in man. *J Appl Physiol,* 34, 628-632.

Dubowitz, V. and M. H. Brooke. 1973. Muscle biopsy: A modern approach. In *Major problems in neurology,* Vol. 2. London: W. B. Saunders.

Edgerton, V. R., B. Essén, B. Saltin, and D. R. Simpson. 1975. Glycogen depletion in specific types of human skeletal muscle fibers in intermittent and continuous exercise. In *Metabolic adaptation to prolonged physical exercise. Proceedings of the second international symposium on biochemistry of exercise Magglingen,* H. Howald and J. R. Poortmans (eds.). Basel: Birkhäuser Verlag.

Essén, B., E. Jansson, J. Henriksson, A. W. Taylor, and B. Saltin. 1975. Metabolic characteristics of fibre types in human skeletal muscle. *Acta Physiol Scand,* 95, 153-165.

Fletcher, J. G. and H. E. Lewis. 1959. Photographic methods for estimating external lifting work in man. *Ergonomics,* 2, 114-115.

Gollnick, P. D., R. B. Armstrong, B. Saltin, C. W. Saubert, W. L. Sembrowich, and R. E. Shephard. 1973. Effect of training on enzyme activity and fiber composition of human skeletal muscle. *J Appl Physiol,* 34, 107-111.

Gollnick, P. D., R. B. Armstrong, C. W. Saubert, K. Piehl, and B. Saltin. 1972. Enzyme activity and fiber composition in skeletal muscle of untrained and trained men. *J Appl Physiol,* 33, 312-329.

Gollnick, P. D., K. Piehl, J. Karlsson, and B. Saltin. 1975. Glycogen depletion patterns in human skeletal muscle fibers after varying types and intensities of exercise. In *Metabolic adaptation to prolonged physical exercise. Proceedings of the second international symposium on biochemistry of exercise Magglingen,* H. Howald and J. R. Poortmans (eds.). Basel: Birkhäuser Verlag.

Harris, R. C., B. Essén, and E. Hultman. 1976. Glycogen phosphorylase activity in biopsy samples and single muscle fibres of musculus quadriceps femoris of man at rest. *Scand J Clin Lab Invest,* 36, 521-526.

Henriksson, J. and J. S. Reitman. 1976. Quantitative measures of enzyme activities in type I and type II muscle fibres of man after training. *Acta Physiol Scand,* 99, 123-125.

Hultman, E. 1967a. Muscle glycogen in man determined in needle biopsy specimens. Methods and normal values. *Scand J Clin Lab Invest,* 19, 209-217.

Hultman, E. 1967b. Studies on muscle metabolism of glycogen and active phosphate in man with special reference to exercise and diet. *Scand J Clin Lab Invest*, 19, Suppl. 94, 1-63.

Hultman, E. and J. Bergström. 1967. Muscle glycogen synthesis in relation to diet studied in normal subjects. *Acta Med Scand*, 182, 109-117.

Hultman, E. and J. Bergström. 1973. Local energy-supplying substrates as limiting factors in different types of leg muscle work in normal man. In *Limiting factors of physical performance. International Symposium at Gravenbruch 1971*, J. Keul (ed.). Stuttgart: Georg Thieme.

Hultman, E., J. Bergström, and N. M. Anderson. 1967. Breakdown and resynthesis of phosphorylcreatine and adenosine triphosphate in connection with muscular work in man. *Scand J Clin Lab Invest*, 19, 56-66.

Hultman, E., J. Bergström, and A. E. Roch-Norlund. 1971. Glycogen storage in human skeletal muscle. In *Muscle metabolism during exercise. Advances in experimental medicine and biology*, Vol. II, B. Pernow and B. Saltin (eds.). New York: Plenum.

Hultman, E. and L. H. Nilsson. 1971. Liver glycogen in man, effect of different diets and muscular exercise. In *Muscle metabolism during exercise. Advances in experimental medicine and biology*, Vol II, B. Pernow and B. Saltin (eds.). New York: Plenum.

Hultman, E. and L. H. Nilsson. 1973. Liver glycogen as a glucose-supplying source during exercise. In *Limiting factors of physical performance. International Symposium at Gravenbruch 1971*, J. Keul (ed.). Stuttgart: Georg Thieme.

Hultman, E. and L. H. Nilsson. 1975. Factors influencing carbohydrate metabolism in man. *Nutr Metabol*, 18, Suppl. 1, 1-45.

Kleine, T. O. 1967. Enzymmuster und pathologisch veränderte Muskeln des Menschen. *Zeit Klin Chem*, 5, 244-247.

Margaria, R., P. Cerretelli, and F. Mangili. 1964. Balance and kinetics of anaerobic energy release during strenuous exercise in man. *J Appl Physiol*, 19, 623-628.

McGilvary, R. W. 1975. The use of fuels for muscular work. In *Metabolic adaptation to prolonged physical exercise. Proceedings of the second international symposium on biochemistry of exercise Magglingen 1973*, H. Howald and J. R. Poortmans (eds.). Basel: Birkhäuser Verlag.

Nichols, N. 1958. Intracellular glycogen and electrolyte concentration in human skeletal muscle. *Proc Soc Exptl Biol Med*, 97, 363-366.

Nilsson, L. H. 1973. Liver glycogen content in man in the postoperative state. *Scand J. Clin Lab Invest*, 32, 317-323.

Nilsson, L. H., P. Fürst, and E. Hultman. 1973. Carbohydrate metabolism of the liver in normal man under varying conditions. *Scand J. Clin Lab Invest*, 32, 331-337.

Nilsson, L. H. and E. Hultman. 1973. Liver glycogen in man—the effect of total starvation or a carbohydrate-poor diet followed by carbohydrate refeeding. *Scand J Clin Lab Invest*, 32, 325-330.

Pernow, B. and B. Saltin. 1971. Availability of substrates and capacity for prolonged heavy exercise in man. *J Appl Physiol*, 31, 416-422.

Peter, J. B., R. J. Barnard, V. R. Edgerton, C. A. Gillespie, and L. E. Stempel. 1972. Metabolic profiles of three fiber types of skeletal muscle in guinea pigs and rabbits. *Biochemistry,* 11, 2627-2633.

Saltin, B. 1975. Adaptive changes in carbohydrate metabolism with exercise. In *Metabolic adaptation to prolonged physical exercise. Proceedings of the second international symposium on biochemistry of exercise Magglingen 1973,* H. Howald and J. R. Poortmans (eds.). Basel: Birkhäuser Verlag.

Saltin, B. and J. Karlsson. 1971. Muscle glycogen utilization during work of different intensities. In *Muscle metabolism during exercise. Advances in experimental medicine and biology,* Vol. II, B. Pernow and B. Saltin (eds.). New York: Plenum.

Trivedi, B. and W. H. Danforth. 1966. Effect of pH on the kinetics of frog muscle phosphofructokinase. *J Biol Chem,* 241, 4110-4114.

Ui, M. 1966. A role of phosphofructokinase in pH-dependent regulation of glucolysis. *Biochem Biophys Acta,* 124, 310-322.

Varnauskas, E., P. Björntorp, M. Fahlén, I. Prerovsky, and J. Stenberg. 1970. Effects of physical training on exercise blood flow and enzymatic activity in skeletal muscle. *Cardiovasc Res,* 4, 418-422.

Wahren, J., G. Ahlborg, P. Felig, and L. Jorfeldt. 1971. Glucose metabolism during exercise in man. In *Muscle metabolism during exercise. Advances in experimental medicine and biology,* Vol. II, B. Pernow and B. Saltin (eds.). New York: Plenum.

Wilkie, D. R. 1960. Man as a source of mechanical power. *Ergonomics,* 3, 1-8.

28

Overview of Vitamins and Physical Performance*

Melvin H. Williams

Vitamins represent a number of relatively unrelated organic substances that are found in small amounts in many foods. They are essential for the optimal functioning of a number of diverse bodily functions, and since some of these

---

*   From Melvin H. Williams, 1976. *Nutritional Aspects of Human Physical and Athletic Performance.* Springfield, Illinois: C. C. Thomas.

physiological functions are important during increased levels of physical activity, some authorities have contended that vitamin supplementation is necessary in order for the athlete to maximize his or her potential.

There is a necessity for a certain amount of selected vitamins in the diet. Lack of a certain vitamin may cause a deficiency disease. This was a main cause of many disorders in the past, and vitamin deficiency diseases still persist in some parts of the world today. However, in a modern industrial society with a well-balanced diet, outright deficiency diseases are rare. Nevertheless, in a review of studies of vitamin and mineral nutrition in the United States from 1950-1968, Davis and his associates (1969) concluded that a significant proportion of the population examined had intakes below the Recommended Daily Allowances (RDA) and some of the biochemical indices were in the deficient range. They noted also that the dietary habits of Americans have become worse since 1960. Thus, a number of vitamins and mineral supplements have been on the market for years, and vitamin production is a main function of many drug companies.

Vitamin supplements fall into various categories according to their potency. Prescription vitamins are classified as a drug and may only be prescribed by a physician. Over-the-counter vitamin pills include the therapeutic or high potency vitamins, sometimes called megavitamins, and the regular vitamin supplements that supply the daily requirements found essential to man. However, except for persons with special medical needs, the Food and Nutrition Board of the National Research Council (1974) has indicated there is no available scientific justification for recommending the routine use of vitamin supplements. They noted that vitamins and minerals are supplied in abundant amounts by commonly available foods.

Tatkon (1968), in his excellent analysis *The Great Vitamin Hoax,* indicated the American public is being defrauded, for manufacturers and advertisers are implying that our diets are inadequate in vitamins when in truth they are not. He severely criticized the vitamin industry, noting that vitamin supplements have been suggested as cures for medical problems ranging from gall bladder difficulties to gray hair, and that advertisers have perpetuated the myth that many diseases stem from a faulty diet; hence, the conclusion to be inferred is that we are not getting all the vitamins we need.

As vitamins are in almost everything one eats or drinks, the individual on a well-balanced diet will receive the RDA, the amount recommended to maintain a good nutritional state in all healthy individuals. This value is usually larger than the minimal daily requirement (MDR), that amount needed to prevent vitamin deficiency. Many foods today, such as milk and bread, are also fortified with vitamins, thus helping to ensure vitamin sufficiency. The measurements for the RDA are usually expressed as IU (International Units) or USP (United States Pharmacopeia units); both standards are related to the biological activity of the vitamin. Only prolonged exposure to an inadequate diet will cause any of the vitamin deficiency diseases.

According to Tatkon (1968), there are several misconceptions about vitamins of which the general public should be cognizant. Contrary to popular belief, vitamins can be harmful, especially overdosages of the fat-soluble vitamins A and D, which may accumulate in the tissues over a period of time. Secondly, taking vitamins will not make up for a skipped breakfast, for they have no caloric value. Relative to purchasing vitamin supplements, a brand name does not mean a better vitamin. Thus, the cheapest brand should be purchased. In addition, there is no essential difference between a synthetic and natural vitamin, the only difference being the manner of production.

In summary, Tatkon (1968) concluded that vitamin supplements appear to have little or no practical value for the average American, much less for the athletic performer. However, the use of numerous vitamins and minerals as potential ergogenic aids still persists among many world class performers, as well as college and high school athletes.

A number of recent reports have indicated widespread use of vitamin supplementation in the athletic world. One contributing factor may be the fact that while many drugs are illegal, vitamin and mineral supplements are not since they are considered to be foods. Thus, the athlete searching for an ergogenic aid may believe that a particular vitamin or mineral will provide the needed ergogenic effect. Van Huss (1974) cited a report that 84 percent of Olympic athletes used vitamin supplements. In a report to a United States Senate subcommittee studying the role of drugs in athletics, a team physician for the 1968 United States Olympic team reported the widespread use of various food supplements, including multivitamins, vitamin B_{12}, and vitamin E. He also noticed some athletes consuming as much as 10,000 mg vitamin C in one day and receiving injections of 1000 mg vitamin B_{12} an hour before competition (United States Senate 1973). Novich (1973) reported that weight lifters, in conjunction with anabolic steroids, consumed prodigious amounts of vitamin B_{12}, iron, vitamin C, and other vitamins in the B complex family. Talbot (1974), the assistant coach of the Canadian national swim team, indicated he was not aware of a hard training distance athlete who could be successful without vitamin supplementation or some forms of mineral supplements. He did note that he based his comments on personal observations. In an interview with Jim Ryun, a world record holder in the mile run, Maddox (1974) reported that the runner's diet was rather normal, although he did take vitamins C and E.

Some rather authoritative reports recommend the use of vitamin supplements by athletes in training. Even as early as 1922, Sherman and Smith noted that athletes may require additional quantities of vitamins A, B, and C in order to elicit full stimulation of all body secretions and to prevent nervousness. Although Marrack (1948) indicated it is doubtful that athletic performances are improved by vitamins, more recent comments in sports medicine books and athletic journals may imply otherwise. Klafs and Arnheim (1973) noted that extremely demanding endurance activities may increase the normal requirement for vitamin B, vitamin C, and others as much as 15 times, an apparent misinterpretation of

293

the available research. They do note, however, based on their own research and others, that vitamin supplementation will not markedly improve performance unless a deficiency exists. Cureton (1969) also noted that during hard training, the work stress can deplete a number of critical body nutrients, such as vitamins B and C, which should be replaced.

In a translation of Yakovlev's book on Russian experimentation with nutrition and athletic performance, recommendations for increased levels of vitamins B_1, B_6, C, and E were stressed. The Russian researchers indicated that the most effective enrichment of the body included a complex of vitamins: A, B_1, B_2, B_3, B_6, B_{12}, C, D, and E (Unsigned 1971). This viewpoint was recently reiterated by Yakovlev and Rogozkin (1975). Other European reports (Nocker 1970; Prokop 1965; Scheunert and Grafe 1961) recommend vitamin supplements for athletes in different sports.

The use of vitamin supplements by athletes may have some rationale. In 1972, the United States Department of Health, Education, and Welfare completed a ten-state survey and found some problems with several nutrients, mainly deficiencies in iron and several vitamins (White 1974). Williams (1962) indicated that evidence exists that vitamin C and some of the B complex vitamins are not present in sufficient quantities in the normal diet, and Klafs and Arnheim (1973) suggested some athletes may suffer from a vitamin shortage of sufficient degree to lessen their effectiveness. Thus, if the athlete is not on a well-balanced diet, vitamin supplementation may be advisable. However, vitamin supplements are consumed by athletes who are on sound diets with the thought that physiological functions will be improved. Some implications have been suggested by exercise physiologists. Buskirk and Haymes (1972) indicated that if the number of mitochondria in the muscle cells increases with physical conditioning, then additional vitamin cofactor linkages may be necessary to support the increased mitochondrial enzymatic reactions. Some of the B vitamins play important roles in the energy schema in the muscle cell mitochondria. Zauner and Updyke (1973) stated that most endurance athletes take large daily dosages of vitamin C in an effort to stimulate myocardial and skeletal muscle capillarization, with the theoretical beneficial effect of increasing physical efficiency.

Although some contend that vitamin supplementation will enhance athletic performance capacity, available experimental evidence appears to be rather limited. The following four chapters analyze the relevant research regarding the effect of the fat-soluble and water-soluble vitamins upon physical performance.

REFERENCES

Buskirk, E. and E. Haymes. 1972. Nutritional requirements for women in sport. In *Women and sport: A national research conference*. D. Harris (ed.). University Park: Penn State University.

Cureton, T. 1969. The diet of schoolboy athletes can be improved. *Athletic J*, 50, September, 71.

Davis, T., et al. 1969. Review of studies of vitamin and mineral nutrition in the United States (1950-1968). *J Nutr Educ,* 1, Supplement 1, 41-54.

Klafs, C. and D. Arnheim, 1973. *Modern Principles of Athletic Training.* St. Louis: C. V. Mosby.

Maddox, D. 1974. Jim Ryun: Stability and discipline. *Physician and Sportmed,* 2, September, 71-2.

Marrack, J. 1948. The nutrition of athletes: proceedings of the nutrition society. *Brit J Nutr,* 2, 249-73.

National Research Council. Committee on dietary allowances. 1974. *Recommended dietary allowances.* Washington: National Academy of Sciences.

Nocker, J. 1970. Nutrition and performance. *Internist,* 11, 269-73.

Novich, M. 1973. Drug abuse and drugs in sports. *N.Y. State J Med,* 73, 2597-2600.

Prokop, L. 1965. Vitamine und Sportleistung. 1965. *Med u Ernahrung,* 2, 174-76, 199-201.

Scheunert, A. and H. Grafe. 1961. Ernahrung und sport. *Kleine Gesundheitsbucherei,* Heft 15.

Sherman, H. and S. Smith. 1922. *The Vitamins.* New York: The Chemical Catalogue Co.

Talbot, D. 1974. Vitamin supplements are essential. *Sport and fitness instructor.* June. n.v, n.p.

Tatkon, M. 1968. *The Great Vitamin Hoax.* New York: Macmillan.

Unsigned. 1971. Russians research food requirements of athletes. *Swim Tech,* 8, July, 59.

United States Senate. 1973. *Proper and Improper Use of Drugs by Athletes.* Hearings before the subcommittee to investigate juvenile delinquency. June 18 and July 12-13, 1973. Washington: U.S. Government Printing Office.

Van Huss, W. 1974. *Vitamins and performance with emphasis on vitamin C.* Paper presented at National American College of Sports Medicine Meeting. Knoxville, Tennessee.

White, P. 1974. *Let's Talk about Food.* Acton, Mass.: Publishing Sciences Group.

Williams, J. 1962. *Sports Medicine.* Baltimore: Williams and Wilkins.

Yakovlev, N. and V. Rogozkin. *Sports Biochemistry in the Soviet Union.* National American College of Sports Medicine meeting. New Orleans, May, 1975.

Zauner, C. and W. Updyke. 1973. Nutritional and physiological factors limiting performance in humans. *Swim Tech,* 10, July, 61-64.

29

Vitamins A and D*

Melvin H. Williams

Only several studies have been conducted in order to evaluate the roles of vitamin A and D supplementation relative to increasing physical performance capacity, primarily because there does not appear to be any valid theoretical rationale for their increased use among athletes.

VITAMIN A

Vitamin A is an unsaturated alcohol and exists mainly in mammals and saltwater fish as preformed vitamin A, or retinol. Carotene, notably beta-carotene, is found in many fruits and dark green and yellow vegetables; carotenes are readily converted into vitamin A in the human body. Vitamin A deficiency has a profound effect on virtually every organ, and deficiency has been associated with skin lesions, cessation of skeletal growth, and night blindness. However, the store of vitamin A in the liver may meet the demand for years in one who has been well fed. Although vitamin A is associated with a number of bodily functions, except for its role in the visual process, its exact metabolic functions are unknown (White, Handler, and Smith 1973).

Vitamin A is one of the fat-soluble vitamins and hence may be stored in the body for considerable periods of time in contrast to the water-soluble vitamins. Overdosages over a period of time may cause a condition known as hyper-vitaminosis A, characterized by loss of appetite, loss of hair, enlargement of the liver and spleen, swelling over the long bones, and general irritability (Tatkon 1968). White, Handler, and Smith (1973) noted possible limitations to motion with hypervitaminosis A. The 1974 RDA varies by age, but the daily values for the average male are 1000 retinol units or 5000 IU; female values are, respectively, 800 and 4000. Bair (1951) cited a case of vitamin A poisoning in a child who received 240,000 IU daily for three months.

The application of vitamin A supplementation to athletics does not appear to be substantiated upon theoretical or practical bases, although Russian research (Unsigned 1971) has suggested that in sports requiring considerable eye alertness and stress, extra vitamin A is needed. One early experiment exists relative to

---

*   From Melvin H. Williams, 1976. Nutritional Aspects of Human Physical and Athletic Performance. Springfield, Illinois: C. C. Thomas.

vitamin A deficiency upon maximal endurance capacity. Wald and his associates (1942) placed five subjects on a vitamin A deficient diet for six months and then placed them on a vitamin supplement program for six weeks. Physical performance was tested on a treadmill, with a 15-minute warm-up followed by a run to exhaustion. Measures of heart rate, oxygen uptake, lung ventilation, and blood lactate were monitored. For 30 days prior to the initial test, the subjects received a diet with a high level of vitamin A, thus starting the experiment with a high baseline level. In general, during the six months of the vitamin A deficiency, no significant decrements were noted on physiological functions during submaximal or maximal exercise. Endurance capacity was not compromised. However, the authors noted that the plasma vitamin A maintained its initial level throughout the entire experimental deprivation period. In addition, no significant effects were elicited during the six weeks of supplementation.

It would appear that vitamin A supplementation is not necessary in athletes on an adequate diet. Bodily stores are available in short term deficiency periods. There is also the possibility of some pathological disorders due to prolonged overdosage.

VITAMIN D

Vitamin D represents any one of several related sterols that promote calcification in the bones. According to the National Research Council (1974), the main role of vitamin D is to regulate calcium and phosphate metabolism. White, Handler, and Smith (1973) have noted that vitamin D promotes calcium absorption from the intestine, and the physiological results of vitamin D deficiency are mainly derived from a lack of calcium. In reference to humans, vitamin D exists in two forms. D_2, ergocalciferol, is the result of the irradiation of ergosterol. D_3, cholecalciferol, is the naturally occurring compound in the skin, formed by exposure to sunlight. Vitamin D is known as the sunshine vitamin and is present in fish liver oil and milk fortified with vitamin D. Sunlight activates the natural compound in the body. It is also known as the antirachitic vitamin, since it prevents the development of rickets, a bone disorder. DeLuca (1971) has suggested that vitamin D should not be classified as a vitamin, but rather as a hormone due to its role in bone mineralization.

The RDA for vitamin D is 400 IU; deficiency results primarily in the development of rickets. Since vitamin D is fat soluble, overdosages may lead to increased storage in the body, and pathological results have been reported. Tatkon (1968) reported hypervitaminosis D leads to loss of weight, vomiting, nausea, lethargy, and loss of muscle tone. Calcium may be released from the bones to be deposited in the soft tissues such as the wall of the blood vessels and kidneys. White, Handler, and Smith (1973) reported that overdosages of vitamin D may produce demineralization of bones, and multiple fractures may occur even from minimal injury. Boyer (United States Senate 1973) indicated that the combination of large amounts of vitamin D, plus prolonged exposure to ultraviolet light, increases the hazard of vitamin D intoxication. A case of vitamin D poisoning was reported by Weinstein (1953). Seelig (1970) reported more severe possible consequences. He noted that high levels of calcium in the blood, attributed to excess amounts of vitamin D, are associated during damage to the brain resulting in mental retardation and injury to the heart and blood vessels. He noted that one form of mental retardation and one form of congenital heart disease may be related to hypervitaminosis D in pregnant women. Thus, as with vitamin A, there appear to be sound medical reasons not to utilize vitamin D supplementation with healthy individuals.

Application of vitamin D supplementation to athletes appears to have no theoretical basis. The limited research conducted substantiates this statement. In a German report, Seidl and Hettinger (1957) studied six subjects over a two-year period. Although their results indicated an improvement of physical performance through the systematic utilization of ultraviolet rays, the oral administration of vitamin D₃ did not improve performance on the bicycle ergometer. Berven (1963) studied the effect of vitamin D daily supplementation upon the physical working capacity of 60 schoolchildren, ages 10 to 11. Over two years Berven administered 1500 IU of vitamin D at different time periods to some of the subjects and placebo pills to the others. During another phase of the experiment, he gave a single massive dose of 400,000 IU to some of the subjects. The criterion test of physical performance was the PWC-170 test, a submaximal performance test. His results indicated no significant beneficial effects of either the daily supplementation or the single massive dosage of vitamin D.

It would appear that vitamin D supplementation is unnecessary in athletics, and may be potentially hazardous if prolonged overdosage occurs.

REFERENCES

Bair, G. 1951. Chronic Vitamin A poisoning. *J Amer Med Assn, 146, 1573-74.*

Berven, H. 1963. The physical working capacity of healthy children. Seasonal variation and effect of ultraviolet radiation and vitamin D supply. *Acta Pediat,* 148, Supplement 1-22, 1963.

DeLuca, H. 1971. Vitamin D—A new look at an old vitamin. *Nutr Rev,* 29, 179-81.

National Research Council. Committee on dietary allowances. 1974. *Recommended dietary allowances.* Washington: National Academy of Sciences.

Seelig, M. 1970. Are American children getting an excess of vitamin D. *Clin Pediatr* (Phila.), 9, 380-83.

Seidl, E. and T. Hettinger. 1957. Der Einfluss von Vitamin D auf Kraft und Leistungsfahigkeit des gesunden Erwachsenen. *Int Z Angew Physiol,* 16, 365-72.

Tatkon, M. 1968. *The Great Vitamin Hoax.* New York: Macmillan.

Unsigned. 1971. Russians research food requirements of athletes. *Swim Tech,* 8, July, 59.

United States Senate. 1973. *Proper and Improper Use of Drugs by Athletes*. Hearings before the subcommittee to investigate juvenile delinquency. June 18 and July 12-13, 1973. Washington: U.S. Government Printing Office.

Wald, G., L. Brouha, and R. Johnson. 1942. Experimental human vitamin A deficiency and ability to perform muscular exercise. *Amer J Physiol*, 137, 551-556.

Weinstein, A. 1953. Vitamin D poisoning. *J Tenn Med Assn*, 46, 140-42.

White, A., P. Handler, and E. Smith. 1973. *Principles of Biochemistry*. New York: McGraw-Hill.

30

Vitamin E and Physical Performance

Roy S. Shephard

Vitamin E was first discovered by Evans and his associates in 1923. The pure chemical, alpha tocopherol (Fig. 30.), was subsequently isolated from wheat germ oil (Evans et al. 1936), and both the vitamin and a number of less active analogues have now been synthesized. For more than 50 years vitamin E has enjoyed the unusual distinction of being a "vitamin without a disease." The only clinical problems clearly linked to tocopherol deficiency have been anemia and excessive hemolysis of red cells in certain rather specialized populations, including premature infants (Chadd and Fraser 1971), cases of kwashiorkor (Sandstead et al. 1965), badly nourished Ugandan Africans (Leonard and Losowsky 1971), and astronauts subjected to restricted diet, restricted mobility, and high partial pressures of oxygen (Turner, unpublished report, cited by Legge 1971). In several animal species, deficiency of vitamin E has led to sterility in the male and abortion in the female. A further early manifestation of vitamin E lack in the rat has been an increased urinary excretion of creatine and phosphate, with an increase in the metabolism and the oxidation of polyunsaturated fatty acids (Friedman and Mattill 1940; Houchin and Mattill 1942). If ignored, this progresses to a form of muscular dystrophy (Nichoalds et al. 1969; West and Mason 1958) with weakness, fatty degeneration, and fibrosis of the muscles.

Many vitamin preparations have been offered to athletes on very slender evidence, and it was thus almost inevitable that vitamin E should be given to

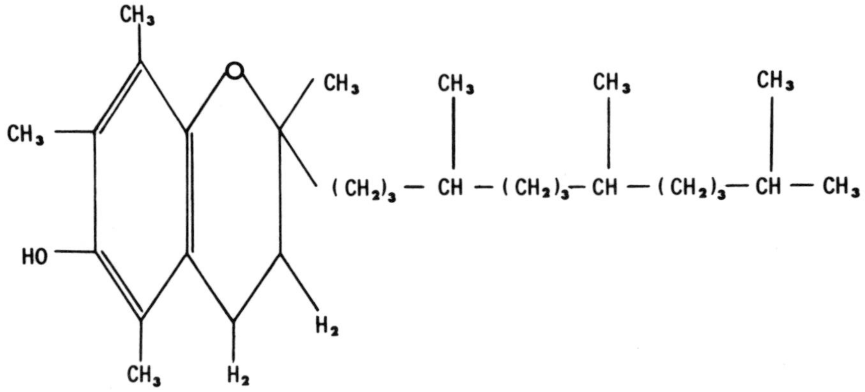

Fig. 30.1 Chemical structure of alpha tocopheral.

longsuffering competitors. Originally, it was administered as wheat germ oil (Cureton and Pohndorf 1955), but more recently the pure compound has been administered in massive doses. Commercial interests have promoted sales to athletes (Shute 1971, 1951), and a recent survey of competitors in the International Masters' Competition (Kavanagh and Shephard 1977) showed that more than 50 percent of participants were taking the vitamin in varying quantities. In the Mexico City Olympics, high doses of vitamin E were widely used in an attempt to compensate for the effects of lowered oxygen pressure (Cooper 1972), and in Munich many Olympic contestants also took vitamin E as an ergogenic acid.

PHARMACOLOGICAL ACTIONS

Vitamin E has been regarded as a pro-oxidant, and in lower doses as an anti-oxidant. The efficiency of oxidative phosphorylation is decreased in vitamin E deficient animals (Carabello et al. 1971; Fedelesova et al. 1971). Abnormalities of phosphate metabolism (Dhalla et al. 1971; Houchin and Mattill 1942; Lu et al. 1941; Mulder et al. 1954) and decreased creatine phosphokinase activity (Fitch and Sinton 1964; Gerber et al. 1964; Read and Nehorayan 1951; Vester et al. 1968) have been described, with associated reductions of ATP production (Fedelesova et al. 1971; Grigoreva and Medovar 1948; Hummel 1948; Lee et al. 1960) and increased levels of lactate and pyruvate (Challa et al. 1971; Hummel 1948). Under such conditions, administration of the vitamin activates the respiratory enzymes of the mitochondria, improving cellular oxygen utilization (Nocker 1964; Houchin 1942; Kaunitz and Papenheimer 1942) and increasing tissue ATP levels (Fedelesova et al. 1972; Matusis 1972). Lack of vitamin E is associated with partial inactivation of the NAD/fifififi/NADP/

succinatecytochrome-c reductase system; this is restored by feeding alpha to-copherol (Grigoreva and Medovar 1948; Bouman and Slater 1956; Donaldson and Nason 1957; Nason et al. 1957), suggesting that the vitamin acts as a cofactor or catalyst in the electron transport chain (Fig. 30.2) just prior to cytochrome-c, possibly stimulating cytochrome-c reductase (Sternberg and Pascoe-Dawson 1959) or succinic dehydrogenase (Houchin 1942; Kaunitz and Pappenheimer 1942).

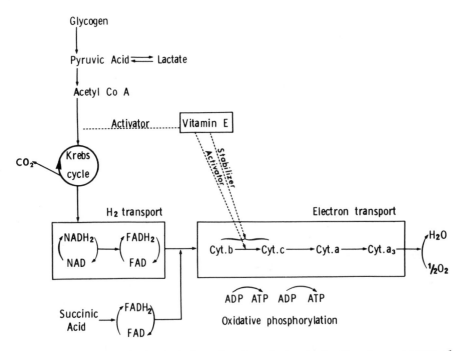

Fig. 30.2 Suggested biochemical sites of action of vitamin E. (Based on concepts of Kobayshi 1974.)

Inefficiency of oxidative phosphorylation during vitamin E depletion is shown by a decreased synthesis of ATP per molecule of oxygen (reduced P/O ratio) (Carabello et al. 1971; Martins 1955; Weinstroke et al. 1955); thus, one further suggested role of vitamin E is that of a stabilizer, maintaining cytochrome-b and cytochrome-c in an optimum juxtaposition for electron transfer (Nason et al. 1957; Keilin and Hartree 1949). There is some suggestion that resting metabolism is increased with vitamin E deficiency, but there is no evidence that additional vitamin E will reduce the energy expenditure of animals given a normal mixed diet. Nevertheless, there have been several reports that the vitamin improves the survival prospects of animals during acute hypoxia (Hove et al. 1945; Kamimura et al. 1962; Telford et al. 1954).

The anti-oxidant effect is also well recognized (Skinner and Parkhurst 1970; Tappel 1962); apparently, the vitamin protects the body against naturally occurring peroxides that would otherwise damage the lipid constituents of cell membranes, thereby causing muscular dystrophies and premature aging. In support of this hypothesis, daily requirements of the vitamin are increased by feeding animals rancid fat and oxidants, but are decreased by provision of the anti-oxidant selenium (Schwarz and Foltz 1957; Schwarz 1960).

Finally, there have been persistent but poorly documented claims that alpha tocopherol has circulatory effects, improving myocardial efficiency (Vaccari 1951), developing, dilating, or preserving capillaires in both skeletal and cardiac muscle (Shute 1951; Telford et al. 1954; Edgerton et al. 1951; Holman 1948; Kamimura and Takahashi 1966) and facilitating diffusion of oxygen to the active tissues (Kamimura et al. 1962). Such changes might contribute to survival under hypoxic conditions and have led to advocacy of vitamin E in the clinical treatment of intermittent claudication (Boyd 1951; Boyd et al. 1953; Leinwand 1948; Livingston and Jones 1958).

DOSAGE

The tocopherols are present in almost all foods, the richest sources being vegetable fats, cereal products, and eggs. A well-balanced western diet provides at least 20 mg per day to a sedentary subject, and an athlete with a high caloric intake may ingest 30 to 100 mg per day.

Early tests of vitamin E supplements used wheat germ oil (Cureton and Pohndorf 1955; Cureton 1954; Cureton 1972). The usual dose was 60 minims, equivalent to about 21 mg of vitamin E. This was less than the normal dietary intake of alpha tocopherol (Cureton 1954; Cureton 1972), and a search was initiated for other active constituents of the wheat germ preparation (Cureton 1972).

One report claiming a positive response to vitamin E supplements (Prokop 1960) used a single dose (1 mg of alpha tocopherol per kilogram of body weight) one hour prior to exercise. Russian authors (Sakaeva and Efremov 1972) have estimated the daily requirements of an athlete at 100 to 150 mg; this dosage is supposedly necessary to prevent a fall in blood and urine levels of vitamin E during hard training. Shute recommends, apparently empirically, that every sportsman should receive 800 IU (660 mg) of alpha tocopherol per day, with a doubling of the amount prior to an important contest; he argues that negative reports are based on inadequate dosage. Fortunately, there seem no dangers from such enthusiasm, as the vitamin is nontoxic even when taken in very large quantities (Hillman 1957).

PERFORMANCE OF ANIMALS

Evidence regarding the effects of vitamin E upon the performance of animals is conflicting. Sato (1963) divided a group of 54 albino rats into three groups—

vitamin E deficient, control (1 mg alpha tocopherol per day), and vitamin E supplemented (20 mg alpha tocopherol per day). Over a 40-day experiment, he found significant differences of swimming time between the three groups, favoring the animals that received the vitamin supplements. Ershoff and Levin (1955) were also able to prolong the swimming times of guinea pigs by use of a diet containing wheat germ oil, but in their studies rats given similar supplements were unaffected.

Consolazio et al. (1964) compared vitamin E in a dose of wheat germ oil (6 minims, 0.4 ml), 0.11 percent octocosanol mixed in a placebo oil, and the placebo oil in three groups of Sprague-Dawley rats. All animals were forced to swim to exhaustion once or twice on two days a week for a total of five weeks, and it was concluded that neither treatment augmented performance relative to the control animals.

OLDER STUDIES IN ATHLETES

Several early studies (Cureton 1954; Prokop 1960; Percival 1951) claimed that administration of vitamin E improved athletic performance. It was also reported that hard training produced a fall in blood and urine levels of alpha tocopherol (Sakaeva and Efremov 1972) and that the ability of horses (Darlington and Chassels 1956) and humans (Percival 1951; MacCarl 1956) to withstand hard training was helped by administration of vitamin E. Unfortunately, much of the positive "evidence" appeared in obscure journals or anecdotal reports. In many instances, contestants and investigators knew the nature of the drug received, and the appraisal of the response was based on rather crude tests.

Prokop (1960) administered a standard dose of vitamin E (1 mg per kg of body weight) to 30 athletes one hour prior to performance of a standard exercise task and claimed that oxygen debt was reduced by seven percent. However, his study has been criticized on three counts: (1) the dose used was too small to anticipate any response, (2) there was failure to allow for a possible training effect during the course of the study, and (3) considerable benefit was apparently derived from the ingestion of the placebo.

In several experiments from Japan, there were rather complicated environmental changes occurring at the same time that vitamin E was given. Aoki et al. (1969) treated eight university long-distance runners with 300 mg of alpha tocopherol every day for 45 days. Their protocol also included one week of altitude training, but at the end of the study the maximum oxygen intake (3.95 liters per minute) was almost identical with the initial value (3.97 liters per minute). Ogawa (1970) also found no change of maximum oxygen intake when skaters were given 300 mg of vitamin E daily for 40 days. However, the final tests were conducted in a cool environment (2.4° C) at an altitude of 1000 meters. Under the latter conditions, control subjects showed a 6.9 percent decrease of aerobic power, and a greater venous blood lactate following all-out bicycle ergometer work. Ogawa thus postulated that the vitamin E had improved the status of his test group. Nagawa et al. (1967) tested 20 excellent long-distance runners at an altitude of 2900 meters. The venous blood lactate was measured immediately and ten minutes after an all-out bicycle ergometer ride. A group that had received 300 mg of vitamin E for 44 days had significantly lower lactate readings than subjects who were given a placebo.

Cureton's laboratory carried out a large number of experiments where wheat germ oil supplements were administered to sedentary volunteers undertaking an endurance training program (Cureton 1972). In general, some benefit was claimed relative to subjects receiving a placebo or no treatment, although there was considerable disagreement on the details of gains between individual reports. As in Prokop's study, the dose used was small (60 minims of wheat germ oil), and Cureton himself now believes the effects were attributable to some constituent of the oil other than alpha tocopherol. Typical positive findings from the Illinois laboratory included a longer maximal running time on the treadmill, a higher T-wave on the electrocardiogram, a lower systolic blood pressure, and a higher Schneider index (Cureton and Pohndorf 1955).

In contrast to these findings, Thomas (1957) gave a large daily dose (450 IU) of alpha tocopherol to 30 athletes for five weeks and found no improvement of cardiorespiratory and motor fitness scores relative to untreated subjects.

RECENT HUMAN TRIALS OF VITAMIN E

Cureton (1972) long maintained that the effects of wheat germ oil were marked only when subjects underwent strenuous training. Sharman and his associates (1971) thus decided to carry out a double-blind trial of vitamin E on two groups of 15 adolescent boys who were undertaking a six-week schedule of training for competitive swimming. The study was well designed in that the subjects were matched for age, ponderal index, and swimming performance, while the use of boarding pupils gave substantial control of diet and other environmental factors.

The tests of cardiorespiratory efficiency and motor fitness were fairly simple-standard lung volumes, a modified Schneider index, a modified Harvard-type step test, breath-holding time, times for a one-mile run and a 400-meter swim, push-ups, pull-ups, and bench presses. Both test and placebo groups showed an improvement of condition in response to training, but there was no evidence of any advantage to the group receiving 400 mg of alpha tocopherol acetate. One possible criticism of the study is that the boys only carried out a moderate intensity of training. Sharman et al. (1975) thus undertook a second double-blind trail, using as their subjects 27 highly trained adolescents who were regularly swimming 40,000 to 50,000 meters per week. Tests were much as in the previous experiment except that the heart rate was also measured at the end of standard bicycle ergometer work. Continued training produced small gains in scores for most tests, but again no significant differences were noted between the placebo group and those receiving 400 mg of alpha tocopherol acetate.

Shephard et al. (1974) decided to carry out the same type of experiment on adults using the much larger doses of alpha tocopherol advocated by Shute (1971), measuring performance by modern physiological tests, and debriefing their subjects with particular reference to their handling of the drug capsules. Their 16 subjects were a team of intercollegiate swimmers covering a training distance of some 20,000 meters per week; in terms of physiological characteristics the group compared favorably with many international competitors (Shephard et al. 1972.) The study commenced in early October and covered 78 to 92 days of intensive conditioning. After completion of the initial laboratory tests, subjects were paired for maximum oxygen intake, body weight, and swimming event. One group was then given a stable natural form of vitamin E (d-alpha tocopherol acid succinate, 400 IU three times per day), while the second group received an identically encapsulated lactose preparation; the code was held by the manufacturer until after completion of the experiment. Diet was unrestricted, but food supplements such as wheat germ oil were prohibited throughout the trial.

Probably because the subjects were initially well trained (maximum oxygen intake 4.5 liters per minute), neither group showed any change of aerobic power over the course of the experiment. However, both groups showed a reduction of maximum heart rate and the slow (lactate) component of the oxygen debt, with a substantial speeding of the heart rate recovery curve. None of these changes differed between test and placebo groups. Muscle strength tended to decline over the three month period of observation, the loss being significant for the placebo but not the experimental group. Rather significantly, the three most successful competitors of the season were from the placebo group. Researchers concluded the vitamin E treated swimmers gained no advantage, with two possible exceptions: (1) they maintained an equality of physiological status in the face of a slightly lighter program (17,229 versus 20,398 meters per week) and (2) there was a suggestion that they lost less muscle protein over the period of intensive training.

The majority of subjects thought that the capsules had not influenced their ability to undertake rigorous training. Ten of the group said their final performance was at the expected level, two (one test, one placebo) believed it was less than expected, two (both placebo) thought it better than expected, and two were undecided. Thirteen of the 16 subjects noticed no effect of the capsules upon appetite, digestion, mood, sleep, muscle soreness, or other subjective complaints. One (placebo) had difficulty in sleeping, one (test) complained of muscle soreness, and one (test) felt complacent and lacking in his usual competitive drive.

Perhaps the most important lesson from the Toronto study was the need for a thorough debriefing of subjects (Shephard et al. 1974). Pill counts were taken at the beginning and end of the trial, and these indicated that some 95 percent of the intended number of capsules had been taken. To avoid conflict with iron therapy, some of the athletes took all three capsules at breakfast and in the event that this was not a fatty meal, absorption may have been somewhat incomplete.

Six of the 16 subjects admitted trying to break the code for the trial; some had opened the capsules and tested the water solubility of the contents, and one enthusiast had even contemplated undertaking a chemical analysis of his preparation. Such observations cast serious doubts on the validity of other supposedly "double-blind" experiments where debriefing was not undertaken, particularly where positive findings were obtained in procedures with a subjective end-point. The secrecy of coding seems a challenge to the ingenuity of the student, and it is doubtful if a full double-blind experiment can be sustained in an undergraduate university setting, except by injection or intragastric feeding of the test drugs.

EFFECTS AT ALTITUDE

Although recent experiments have shown no advantage from vitamin E supplements at normal barometric pressures, one unpublished report (Kobayashi 1974) indicated gains at an altitude of 5000 feet, with further improvement of physiological test scores at a simulated altitude of 15,000 feet. Twelve subjects were given 1200 IU of d-alpha tocopherol succinate or a placebo, according to a crossover design. After six weeks of vitamin treatment there was an increase of maximum oxygen intake (8.9 percent at 5000 ft, 14.2 percent at 15,000 ft), a decrease of oxygen consumption in submaximal work (0 percent at 5000 ft, 7.1 percent at 15,000 ft), and a reduction of oxygen debt (16.5 percent at 5000 ft, 20.1 percent at 15,000 ft). While the subject population was small, and the possibility of code-breaking does not seem to have been checked, these findings are in keeping with previous reports that vitamin E treated animals survive better at altitude (Hove et al. 1945; Kamimura et al. 1962; Telford et al. 1954).

CONCLUSIONS

Despite the enthusiasm of early investigators, the three most recent sea-level trials of vitamin E have yielded essentially negative conclusions. The recent studies used an optimum experimental design, test subjects who were undergoing rigorous endurance training being compared in double-blind fashion with matched subjects who received a placebo. Doses of vitamin E were also much larger than in many early experiments. It is concluded that earlier apparently positive results may have arisen from (1) failure to use a placebo and/or a double-blind protocol, (2) breaking of the double-blind coding, (3) inadequate test procedures, and (4) possibly other active constituents of wheat germ oil. Nevertheless, there remains scope for further testing of vitamin E under conditions of reduced barometric pressure.

REFERENCES

Aoki, J., T. Shimizu, and T. Maeshima. 1969. Effect of vitamin E and C compound as ergogenic acids to physiological responses of male long distance runners in physical training programs. *Bull Sch Phys Ed,* Juntendo University, 12, 14-19.

Bouman, J., and E. C. Slater. 1956. Tocopherol content of heart-muscle preparations. *Nature,* 177, 1181-1182.

Boyd, A. M. 1951. Festival symposium on cardiovascular disease in an aging population. *Brit Med J,* 2, 112-113.

Boyd, A. M., A. H. Ratcliffe, and K. Bloor. 1953. Vitamin E and intermittent claudication. *Lancet,* 1, 491-492.

Carabello, F., F. Liu, O. Eames, and J. Bird. 1971. Effect of vitamin E deficiency on mitochondrial energy transfer. *Fed Proc,* 30, 639.

Chadd, M. A., and A. J. Fraser. 1971. Vitamin E deficiency in premature infants. *Internat J Vit Res,* 40, 604-609.

Consolazio, C. F., L. Matoush, R. Nelson, G. Isaac, and L. Hursh. 1964. Effect of octocosanol, wheat germ oil and vitamin E on performance of swimming rats. *J Appl Physiol,* 19, 265-276.

Cooper, D. L. 1972. Drugs and the athlete. *J Amer Med Assoc,* 221, 1007-1011.

Cureton, T. K. 1954. Effect of wheat germ oil and vitamin E on normal human subjects in physical training programs. *Amer J Physiol,* 179, 628.

Cureton, T. K. 1972. *The Physiological Effects of Wheat Germ Oil on Humans in Exercise.* Springfield, Ill.: C. C. Thomas.

Cureton, T. K. and R. M. Pohndorf. 1955. Influence of wheat germ oil as a dietary supplement in a program of conditioning exercises with middle-aged subjects. *Res Quart,* 26, 391-407.

Darlington, F. G. and J. B. Chassels. 1956. A study on the breeding and racing of thoroughbred horses given a large dose of **α** tocopherol. *The Summary,* 8, 1-25.

Dhalla, N. S., M. Fedelesova, and I. Toffler. 1971. Biochemical alterations in the skeletal muscles of vitamin E deficient rats. *Canad J Biochem Physiol,* 49, 1202-1208.

Donaldson, K. O. and A. Nason. 1957. Inter-relationship between vitamin E and lipid cofactor in the cytochrome C reductase system. *Proc Nat Acad Sci,* 43, 364-369.

Edgerton, M. T., E. M. Hanrahan, and W. B. Davis. 1951. Use of vitamin E in the treatment of keloids. *Plast Reconstr Surg,* 8, 224-233.

Ershoff, B. H. and E. Levin. 1955. Beneficial effects of an unidentified factor in wheat germ oil on the swimming performance of guinea pigs. *Fed Proc,* 14, 431-432.

Evans, H. M., O. H. Emerson, and G. A. Emerson. 1936. The isolation from wheat germ oil of an alcohol **α** tocopherol having the properties of vitamin E. *J Biol Chem,* 113, 319-332.

Fedelesova, M. P., P. V. Sulakhe, J. C. Yates, and N. S. Dhalla. 1971. Biochemical basis of heart function. IV. Energy metabolism and calcium transport in hearts of vitamin E deficient rats. *Canad J Physiol Pharmacol,* 49, 909-918.

Fitch, C. D. and D. W. Sinton. 1964. A study of creatine metabolism in diseases causing muscle wasting. *J Clin Invest,* 43, 444-452.

Friedman, L. and H. A. Mattill. 1940. The oxygen consumption of skeletal muscle from animals deprived of vitamin E. *Amer J Physiol,* 131, 595-600.

Gerber, G. B., T. R. Koszalka, G. Gerber, and L. L. Miller. 1964. Creatine synthesis in perfused liver of vitamin E-deficient rats. *Proc Soc Exp Biol Med,* 116, 884-887.

Grigoreva, V. A. and F. V. Medovar. 1948. Studies on the components of the adenylic system in skeletal and cardiac muscles in experimental muscular dystrophy. *Ukrain Biokim Zhur,* 31, 351-368.

Hillman, R. W. 1957. Tocopherol excess in man. Creatinuria associated with prolonged ingestion. *Amer J Nutr,* 5, 597-600.

Holman, R. L. 1947. Prevention of experimental arteritis in dogs by vitamin E. *Proc Soc Exper Biol Med,* 66, 307-309.

Houchin, O. B. 1942. The in vitro effect of alpha-tocopherol and its phosphate derivative on oxidation in muscle tissue. *J Biol Chem,* 146, 313-321.

Houchin, O. B. and H. A. Mattill. 1942. The oxygen consumption, creatine and chloride content of muscles from vitamin E deficient animals as influenced by feeding α tocopherol. *J Biol Chem,* 146, 301-307.

Hove, E. L., K. C. D. Hickman, and P. L. Harris. 1945. The effect of tocopherol and of fat on the resistance of rats to anoxic anoxia. *Arch Biol Chem,* 8, 395-404.

Hummel, J. P. 1948. Oxidative phosphorylation process in nutritional muscular dystrophy. *J Biol Chem,* 172, 421-429.

Kamimura, M. and S. Takahashi. 1966. Region of skin micro-circulation in which vitamin E acts. Studies on skin temperature and blood volume. *J Vitaminology* (Kyoto), 12, 274-280.

Kamimura, M., S. Takahashi, and I. Henmi. 1962. On the influence of vitamin E on the low oxygen tension tolerance of mice. *Sapporo Med J,* 21, 71-77.

Kaunitz, H. and A. M. Pappenheimer. 1942. Oxygen consumption in vitamin E deficiency. *Amer J Physiol,* 138, 328-340.

Kavanagh, T. and R. J. Shephard. 1977. Characteristics of the Masters' athlete. *Bull NY Acad Sci,* in press.

Keilin, D. and E. F. Hartree. 1949. Activity of succinic dehydrogenase-cytochrome system in different tissue preparations. *Biochemical J,* 44, 205-218.

Kobayashi, Y. 1974. Effect of vitamin E on aerobic work performance in man during acute exposure to hypoxic hypoxia. Ph.D. Thesis. University of New Mexico, Albuquerque.

Lee, Y. C. P., J. T. King, and M. B. Visscher. 1960. Role of certain minerals, vitamin E and other factors in the genesis of myocardial fibrosis in mice. *Amer J Physiol,* 198, 981-984.

Legge, R. F. 1971. Resolving the vitamin E controversy. *Canad. Research & Development,* 1-11, Sept.-Oct.

Leinwand. I. 1958. Dystrophia myotonica complicated by thrombo-angiitis obliterans and pseudo-hypertrophic muscular dystrophy. *NY State J Med,* 48, 1503-1505.

Leonard, P. J. and M. S. Losowsky. 1971. Effect of alpha-tocopherol administration on red cell survival in vitamin E deficient human subjects. *Amer J Clin Nutr,* 24, 388-393.

Livingston, P. D. and C. Jones. 1958. Treatment of intermittent claudication with vitamin E. *Lancet,* 2, 602-604.

Lu, G. D., G. A. Emerson, and H. M. Evans. 1941. Phosphorus metabolism of the musculature of E deficient suckling rats. *Amer J Physiol,* 133, 367-368.

MacCarl, N. 1956. Vitamin E credited as leaf flag tonic-capsules helped Goliat and other vets. *The Sporting News* (St. Louis), 142, Dec., 19.

Martins, C. 1955. Thyroxin and oxidative phosphorylation. *Proc 3rd Internat Congr Biochem* (Brussels), 1-9.

Matusis, L. I. 1971. Effect of administration of alpha-tocopherol to albino rats on changes in content of ATP, ADP, and inorganic phosphorus in the skin and skeletal muscles due to avitaminosis K. Vliianie obogashcheniia organizma belykh krys al'fatokoferolom na K-avitaminozyne izmeneniia soderzhaniia AFT, ADF i neorganicheskogo fosfora v kozhe i skeletnoi muskulature. *Byulletin Eksperimental noi Biologu Meditsiny*, 71, 74-76.

Mulder, A. G., A. J. Gatz, and B. Tigerman. 1954. Phosphate and glycogen determinations in the hearts of vitamin E-deficient rabbits. *Amer J Physiol*, 179, 246-248.

Nagawa, T., H. Kita, J. Aoki, T. Maeshima, and K. Shiozawa. 1967. The effect of vitamin E on endurance. *Bull School Phys Educ*, Juntendo University, 10, 25-31.

Nason, A., K. O. Donaldson, and T. R. Leham. 1957. The role of vitamin E at the enzymatic level. *Trans. NY. Acad Sci*, 20, 27-50.

Nicholalds, G. E., R. R. Jones, J. F. Diehl, and C. D. Fitch. 1969. Vitamin E deficiency and the accumulation of amino acids in skeletal muscle. *J Nutr*, 99, 27-33.

Nocker, J. 1964. *Physiologie der Leibesubungen*. Stuttgart: Ferdinand Enke Verlag.

Ogawa, S. 1970. Effect of vitamin E and vitamin C compound on aerobic physical performance in a cold environment. Report of Sports Science Research, *Jap Amat Sports Assoc*, 1-8.

Percival, L. 1951. Vitamin E in athletic efficiency (preliminary report). *The Summary*, 3, 55-64.

Prokop, L. 1960. Die Wirkung von naturlichem vitamin E auf Sauerstoffverbrauch und Sauerstoffschuld. *Sportarztl Prax*, 1, 19-23.

Read, W. O. and S. Nehorayan. 1959. Effect of vitamin E deficiency on creatine phosphokinase of heart and skeletal muscle. *Amer J Physiol*, 196, 1286-1288.

Sakaeva, E. A. and V. V. Efremov. 1972. Opyt dopolnitel'nogo naznacheniia vitamina e sportsmenam velogonshchikam i lyzhnikam. (Exercise and Vitamin E in cyclists and skiers). *Vest Adad Meditskin Nauk*, 27, 52.

Sandstead, H. H., M. K. Gabr, S. Azzam, A. S. Shunky, R. J. Weiler, D. M. El Din, N. Mokhter, A. S. Prasad, A. El Hifney, and W. J. Darby. 1965. Kwashiorkor in Egypt. II Haematological aspects: The occurrence of a macrocytic anaemia associated with low vitamin E levels and a wide range of serum vitamin B_{12} levels. *Amer J Clin Nutr*, 17, 27-35.

Sato, D. 1963. Effect of vitamin E on swimming performance in rats. *Jap J Phys Fitness*, 11, 151-156.

Schwarz, K. 1960. Factor 3, Selenium and Vitamin E. *Nutr Rev*, 18, 193-197.

Schwarz, K. and C. M. Foltz. 1957. Selenium as an integral part of factor 3 against dietary necrotic liver degeneration. *J Amer Chem Soc*, 79 (2), 3292-3293.

Sharman, I. M., M. G. Down, and N. G. Norgan. 1975. Alleged ergogenic properties of vitamin E. In: *Proceedings of 20th World Congress of Sports Medicine*, A. H. Toyne (ed.). Melbourne: Australian Sports Medicine Federation.

Sharman, I. M., M. G. Down, and R. N. Sen. 1971. The effects of vitamin E and training on physiological function and athletic performance in adolescent swimmers. *Brit J Nutr*, 26, 265-276.

Shephard, R. J., R. Campbell, P. Pimm, D. Stuart, and G. Wright. 1974. Vitamin E exercise and the recovery from physical activity. *Europ J Appl Physiol*, 33, 119-126.

Shephard, R. J., G. Godin, and R. Campbell. 1973. Characteristics of sprint, medium and middle distance swimmers. *Europ J Appl Physiol*, 32, 1-19.

Shephard, R. J., D. Stuart, R. Campbell, G. Wright, and P. Pimm. 1974. Do athletes need vitamin E? *Physician and Sports Medicine*, 2, (9), 57-60.

Skinner, W. A. and R. M. Parkhurst. 1970. Antioxidant properties of alphatocopherol derivatives and relationship of antioxidant activity. *Lipids*, 5, 184-186.

Shute, E. V. 1971. Vitamin E for athletes. Paper presented to First International Congress of swimming coaches in Montreal. *The Summary*, 23, 3-9.

Shute, E. V. 1951. *The Summary*, 3, 77.

Sternberg, J. and E. Pascoe-Dawson. 1959. Metabolic studies in atherosclerosis. I. Metabolis pathway of C^{14} labelled alphatocopherol. *Canad Med Assoc J*, 80, 266-275.

Tappel, A. L. 1962. Vitamin E as the biological lipid antioxidant. *Vitamin Horm*, 20, 493-510.

Thomas, P. 1957. The effects of vitamin E on some aspects of athletic efficiency. Ph.D. Thesis, University of Southern California, Los Angeles.

Vaccari, F. 1951. *Cuore & Circulazione*, 35, 3.

Vester, J. W., G. Sabeh, R. H. Newton, H. B. Finkelhor, C. H. Fetterman, and T. Danowski. 1968. Muscle creatine phosphokinase in primary myopathies. *Proc Soc Exp Biol Med*, 128, 5-8.

Weinstrock, I. M., I. Schoichet, A. D. Goldrich, and A. T. Milhorat. 1955. The effect of vitamin E deficiency on the oxidation of tricarboxylic acid cycle intermediates. *Arch Biochem Biophys*, 57, 496-505.

West, W. T. and K. E. Mason. 1958. Histopathology of muscular dystrophy in the vitamin E deficient hamster. *Amer J Anat*, 102, 323-349.

Wiley, J. F. 1969. Effects of training with and without wheat germ oil on cardiac intervals and other fitness measures of middle-aged men. Ph.D. Thesis. University of Illinois.

31

The B Vitamins*

Melvin H. Williams

There are a number of different organic compounds that help regulate diverse metabolic functions that have been categorized as the B vitamins or the vitamin B complex, including thiamine, riboflavin, niacin, pyridoxine, pantothenic acid, folic acid, cyanocobalamin, and biotin. Although the following are not known as vitamins in the strictest sense of the word, they have been historically grouped with the B vitamins: choline, inositol, and para-aminobenzoic acid. The B vitamins are water soluble; hence, their storage in the human body is not significant.

Olson (1958) has characterized the B complex vitamin as the "great American placebo." However, the use of vitamin B supplementation in athletics has been advocated by several authorities due to the diverse roles of the B vitamins in energy metabolism. The following review is concerned primarily with the published experimental research involving vitamin B supplementation and physical performance.

VITAMIN B₁ (THIAMINE)

Thiamine, vitamin B₁, plays an important role in energy metabolism and the nervous system. A deficiency of thiamine leads to beriberi, a condition rarely seen in the western world except in cases of chronic alcoholism. Thiamine is found in the outer layers of seeds and in other food sources including animal tissues such as meat, fish, poultry, eggs, milk, cheese, whole grain, enriched breads and cereals, dried beans, peas, and all vegetables. The respective RDA for adult males and females is 1.5 mg and 1.1 mg per day.

Early and Carlson (1969) indicated that thiamine may modify physiological processes in order to deter fatigue. Thiamine plays an important role in the oxidative decarboxylation of pyruvate to acetyl CoA for entrance into the Krebs cycle and subsequent oxidation to ATP. If the thiamine level were deficient, the increased demand for acetyl CoA during physical activity would not be met; hence, more pyruvate would be converted to lactic acid, and possible fatigue

*   From Melvin H. Williams, *Nutritional Aspects of Human Physical and Athletic Performance*. Springfield, Illinois: C. C. Thomas, 1976.

would develop. Early and Carlson also noted thiamine deficiency could result in inadequate amounts of succinate, a coingredient of heme. A deficiency in heme would limit the oxygen carrying capacity of the blood. Brozek (1962), analyzing the research reports from the Institute of Nutrition of the U.S.S.R. Academy of Medical Sciences, noted the relationship of thiamine to glucose metabolism, glucose being essential for the optimal functioning of the central nervous system. The need for thiamine replenishment would appear to be dependent upon the daily loss. As related to exercise, the National Research Council (1974) noted that the need for thiamine is dependent upon energy expenditure and is influenced by carbohydrate intake.

Some older sports medicine books have implied that athletes may need 15 times the amount of thiamine in heavy training as at rest. This recommendation is based on an erroneous interpretation and application of the research by Bicknell and Prescott (1953). They reported that the thiamine requirement is proportional to the metabolic rate, and physical exertion can elevate the metabolic rate 15 times. This is not to imply, however, that the athlete needs a 15-fold increase in his/her faily thiamine requirement. It is probably just proportional to the time spent in physical activity. The National Research Council (1974) reports that as energy expenditure is increased during physical activity, the increased needs for thiamine or any other nutrient should be met by the larger quantities of foods consumed, provided that they are well selected.

Since the role of thiamine in energy metabolism was discovered 30 years ago, it has been one of the most studied vitamins in relation to physical performance. Even so, the total number of relevant studies is limited. Many of the studies with thiamine were conducted in association with riboflavin and niacin and are covered in a later section. The following represents the available research dealing with the utilization of thiamine alone.

After reviewing the pre-1939 studies, Boje (1939) contended that there is no value to ingesting extra amounts of thiamine. Throughout the 1940s, several conflicting reports were published. In most cases, experimental methodology was inadequate to validly assess the role of thiamine. With little detail available, Gounelle (1940) reported that the supplementation of diets of bicyclists with vitamin B_1 improved their performance during the Tour de France race in 1939. McCormick (1940) suggested that increased thiamine intake would improve oxygen uptake and sustained physical performance. In an experiment with no controls, no statistical treatment, and tremendous potential for placebo effect, he reported significant gains on an endurance arm-holding test after one week of B_1 supplementation. Karpovich and Millman (1941) replicated McCormick's study with better controls, using pre and posttest scores as well as a control placebo group. The thiamine supplement was 5 mg/day for one week. There was no significant effect of the thiamine on the arm endurance test.

Several other studies during the 1940s centered around the effect of thiamine deficiency upon physical performance. Keys and his colleagues (1943), in four series of complex experiments each 10 to 12 weeks long, studied the effect of controlled thiamine intake upon a number of performance parameters, including strength and responses during brief exhausting work and prolonged severe work. The results failed to indicate, for the period of time studied, any benefit upon the physical performance parameters by an intake of more than 0.23 mg per 1000 calories. One possible limitation would be the fact that the subjects did not appear to work to exhaustion in all tests, and apparently maximal performance capacity was not assessed.

In a later study by Archdeacon and Murlin (1944), three persons were subjected to a moderate exercise work load and a work load to exhaustion on a bicycle ergometer during a period of thiamine deprivation. The subjects were restricted to thiamine intakes of 0.27 mg per day on one diet and 0.15 mg per day on another. The general results reflected a decline in muscular endurance within 10 to 14 days on the deficient diet, increasing back to normal when the vitamins were restored. However, they also noted that the inclusion of B complex vitamins in a diet already adequate in these vitamins did not result in increased muscular endurance. In another study relative to thiamine deficiency in the diet, Tuttle and his colleagues (1949) reported that those subjects who received 2500 calories per day for 45 days, but were getting only .14 mg or less thiamine per day, suffered an increase in reaction time. In this latter case, the results would indicate an adverse effect upon the nervous system rather than the energy-producing aspects.

Although thiamine plays an important role in some metabolic processes associated with energy metabolism and central nervous system functioning, there is no conclusive evidence to support the contention that thiamine intake above and beyond normal RDA will enhance physical performance. Extra amounts are probably not harmful, as they will be excreted from the body.

VITAMIN B2 (RIBOFLAVIN)

Riboflavin, vitamin B2, functions as a coenzyme for a group of flavoproteins concerned with biological oxidations, the most common one being flavin adenine dinucleotide (FAD). Riboflavin is found in liver, yeast, wheat germ, milk, cheese, meats, eggs, and green leafy vegetables. Its role in humans appears to be central to the oxidative reactions occurring in the energy schema of the mitochondria. The RDA for riboflavin has been computed at 0.6 mg per 1000 calories for all persons. The average adult male, with a 3000 calorie diet, would need 1.8 mg per day. Since the National Research Council (1974) reported that there is no evidence that riboflavin requirements are raised when energy utilization is increased, the allowances are intended for individuals engaged in normal activity.

No research has been uncovered studying the role of riboflavin individually during physical exertion. However, studies in conjunction with thiamine and niacin intake are reported in a later section dealing with the B complex.

VITAMIN B₃ (NIACIN)

Niacin, vitamin B_3, is also known as nicotinic acid, nicotinamide, or the antipellagra vitamin. In the foreign literature it is often represented by the symbol PP or pellagra preventive vitamin. Niacin is widely distributed in plant and animal sources, being most abundant in poultry, meats, organ meats, fish, grain products, peanuts, and peanut butter. Milk and eggs are almost completely devoid of niacin. White, Handler, and Smith (1973) indicate it is difficult to assess the human niacin requirement, as it may be synthesized in the body from tryptophan. The RDA is 6.6 mg per 1000 calories.

The major function of niacin is to serve as a component of two important coenzymes concerned with glycolysis, fat synthesis, and tissue respiration. Nicotinamide adenine dinucleotide (NAD) and nicotinamide adenine dinucleotide phosphate (NADP) serve as hydrogen acceptors in the energy schema. According to White, Handler, and Smith (1973), no serious impairment of oxidative reactions have been demonstrated in tissues of niacin deficient animals. Conversely, Bialecki (1962) suggested an increased demand for niacin in physical exertion. With the role that NAD plays in glycolysis, it might be theorized that increased niacin levels might lead to increased anaerobic capacity.

An early report suggested an ergogenic effect of niacin, primarily in anaerobic exercise. Frankau (1943), although primarily studying the effects of multiple-vitamin preparations upon physical performance, did conduct some experiments with niacin alone. The performance task was an agility test similar to a shuttle run with blocks. Subjects were tested 1.5 to 3.0 hours after taking 50 to 100 mg niacin. Highly significant improvements in shuttle run times were noted, and Frankau concluded that niacin, given to fit young men, could result in increased efficiency in severe tests involving coordination and physical effort. However, no statistical analysis was run on the data, and the explicit experimental methodology was not noted. Later Hilsendager and Karpovich (1964) studied the effect of niacin and glycine in combination with niacin upon endurance capacity of 86 subjects as measured by performance on either a bicycle ergometer or forearm ergometer. The dosages consisted of either 750 mg glycine, 75 mg niacin, or a combination of the two. A double-blind placebo experimental design was used with a double-repeated measures application. The data from the well-designed experiment revealed no significant effect of the treatments upon the endurance task.

In experimentation to investigate the acute effects of niacin, Carlson and Oro (1962) found that the plasma-free fatty acids (FFA) decreased within 15 to 30 minutes following administration of niacin. After 60 to 90 minutes, the plasma FFA rose again. Since plasma FFA is a source of energy during prolonged submaximal work, there may be implications relative to niacin supplementation. In a subsequent study, Carlson and his associates (1963) reported that niacin greatly decreased mobilization of FFA into the blood at both rest and during exercise. The rise in the RQ and the fall in the plasma concentration of glucose following the administration of niacin suggests that increased combustion of carbohydrates occurred in association with the decreased availability of energy from FFA. However, the investigators noted that niacin had no effect on the efficiency of work. Jenkins (1965) also noted an increased RQ in subjects exercising for a prolonged period of time following the administration of niacin. Although the plasma FFA levels were changed little during exercise following the niacin, they did not rise as in the control trial; FFA normally rises during exercise. Therefore, the niacin blocked FFA mobilization from the fatty tissues in the body. However, Jenkins noted no difference in energy consumption as calculated from the RQ and oxygen uptake.

Some have contended that the reduction in plasma FFA could contribute to the development of fatigue, since muscle glycogen would be used at a faster rate during prolonged exercise. Bergstrom and his associates (1969) studied the effect of niacin on muscular endurance capacity in two series of experiments. The niacin blocked the release of FFA, thus the muscle used glycogen for its main source of energy. The ability to perform either short-term, near-maximal work or prolonged submaximal work was unchanged after administration of niacin. However, the subjects experienced the work after administration of niacin as heavier and more fatiguing.

Based upon current viewpoints, the use of niacin as an ergogenic food supplement is contraindicated. There is no substantial evidence to support a detrimental effect upon energy metabolism during a deficiency state, and supplementation above normal RDA has not increased endurance capacity.

VITAMIN B6 (PYRIDOXINE)

Vitamin B6 is not a single substance, but rather a collective term for three naturally occurring pyridines—pyridoxine, pyridoxal, and pyridoxamine—that are all metabolically and functionally related. Best sources for vitamin B6 are meats, poultry, fish, potatoes, whole grain products, yeast, eggs, and seeds. The adult RDA is 2 mg per day. Although White, Handler, and Smith (1973) reported that there is no specific disease syndrome associated with a deficiency of B6 in the diet, the National Research Council (1974) noted that depression and confusion may occur in adults, and other disorders such as anemia occur in children. Vitamin B6 plays a central role in the biochemical reactions whereby a cell converts nutrient amino acids into the particular amino acid necessary for the cell's own activities. Buskirk and Haymes (1972) reported that vitamin B6 is important in the formation of hemoglobin, myoglobin, and the cytochromres, all compounds essential to the oxygen transportation and utilization process in the body. In humans, the requirement for B6 also appears to increase when high protein diets are consumed, a finding that may have some implications for athletes on high protein diets. Since B6 is found in meats and other animal products, it may be sufficiently provided if these foods are the source of the high protein diet.

Only one study has been uncovered relative to the effect of vitamin B_6. Lawrence and his colleagues (1975) investigated the effect of 51 mg pyridoxine HCL (vitamin B_6), given daily for a six-month period, on the endurance capacity of trained competitive swimmers. Subjects were matched on age, sex, and swimming ability and assigned to the treatment or a placebo group. A control group also was used. Swimming endurance was measured by performance times in ten intermittent 100-yard swims. The test was administered five times during the conduct of the study. Blood analyses indicated a more saturated B_6 status, but there was no significant effect of the supplementation on swimming performances in comparison to the placebo and control groups.

VITAMIN B_{12} (CYANOCOBALAMIN)

Cyanocobalamin, vitamin B_{12}, is present in all body cells are appears to be essential for optimal functioning. Cobalt is part of its structure. It is found mainly in animal products, meats, cheese, organs, milk, and eggs. One important point is that B_{12} is not found in plant foods, an observation that should be heeded by strict vegetarians. The RDA is 3 mg per day. The average diet contains 5 to 15 mg per day. Although the deficiency of B_{12} may cause several disorders, including some dysfunction of nerve cells, the main effect is pernicious anemia. However, White, Handler, and Smith (1973) noted that pernicious anemia results not from an inadequate ingestion of B_{12}, but rather from an inadequate amount of gastric secretion of the intrinsic factor, which is known to facilitate absorption of B_{12} from the intestinal lumen. Anemia in an athlete would adversely affect endurance capacity, since the decreased amount of circulating red blood cells and hemoglobin would restrict the blood's oxygen-carrying capacity.

The normal individual is more likely to have iron deficiency anemia rather than pernicious anemia. Thus, B_{12} will not benefit the normal athlete; yet Hirata (1973) indicated that vitamin B_{12} injection is a common practice throughout the athletic world. Some athletes have been reported to receive 1000 mg an hour or so prior to competition. The belief probably persists that if a little B_{12} can prevent anemia, a lot will do something magical to increase capacity. Russian researchers (Unsigned 1971) have indicated a need for more research into the application of B_{12} to athletics; however, Montoye and his colleagues (1955) presented some useful evidence. Their experimentation was the only research uncovered relative to the ergogenic application of B_{12}.

Montoye and others (1955) studied the effect of B_{12} supplementation upon performance in a half-mile run. Fifty-one boys, ranging in age from 12 to 17, who were residents of a state institution, served as subjects. Three groups were formed, the experimental group receiving 50 mg B_{12} daily; a placebo and control group were also included in the double-blind study. The subjects were matched on their ability to run the half-mile. During a seven-week period, all boys in the experimental and placebo groups trained one hour daily in their regular physical education class and also ran the half-mile three times per week. Although both groups improved significantly in the half-mile run due to the training program, no significant differences were noted between the groups. In another report, Montoye (1955) noted that in normal young men, B_{12} supplementation has no effect on grip strength, heart rate recovery after submaximal exercise, or maximal performance capacity on a bicycle ergometer. He concluded that there is not sufficient evidence to recommend vitamin B_{12} supplementation as a general practice for athletes.

PANTOTHENIC ACID

Pantothenic acid is a factor of the vitamin B complex, and in the body it is found as a component of acetyl CoA, the intermediate metabolite of carbohydrate and fat metabolism leading to energy release and other essential reactions. It is found in all animal products, eggs, yeast, and whole grains. Its richest source, one of the so-called ergogenic foods, is royal jelly, the nutrition for the queen bee. The RDA is 5 to 10 mg per day. White, Handler, and Smith (1973) note that the nutritional role of pantothenic acid in the human body has not been determined, although its central role as a component of acetyl CoA suggests it may be involved in the energy schema. Early and Carlson (1969) reported that a multiple-vitamin supplement helped reduce exercise fatigue in a hot climate and theorized that part of the effectiveness could be attributed to pantothenic acid. They suggested that a deficiency in pantothenic acid, which might occur through excess sweating, could possibly decrease the availability of substrate for the Krebs cycle, thus shifting the energy production to glygolysis, which is less efficient. However, since there were five other vitamins in their supplement, an ergogenic effect may not be attributed to pantothenic acid per se. Objective data are not available to support the suggestion that supplementation with pantothenic acid will benefit physical performance.

FOLIC ACID (FOLACIN)

Folic acid, or folacin, is involved in growth processes, since it is related to DNA synthesis. Its best source includes organ meats, green vegetables, dry beans, and whole grains. A deficiency may lead to growth failure and anemia. Theoretically, a deficiency in folic acid could handicap an endurance athlete due to anemic effects upon oxygen transport, but no experimental evidence has been uncovered to support this position. Moreover, the effect of folic acid supplementation on physical performance has not been found in the literature.

OTHER B COMPLEX VITAMINS OR FACTORS

Although several other vitamins and related factors in the B complex appear essential to normal human functioning, such as biotin and para-aminobenzoic acid, there is little theoretical or experimental evidence to support their use as supplements to the diet of the athlete.

VITAMIN B COMPLEX SUPPLEMENTATION

In many older reports, due to the close association of many of the vitamins in the B complex, the effect of deprivation or supplementation with selected vitamins in the complex were studied together. As the three principal vitamins in the complex—thiamine, riboflavin, and niacin—are all associated with the energy schema during exercise, they were the primary vitamins investigated as a group.

The effect of a prolonged dietary deficiency in the B complex results in a decreased capacity for endurance exercise. Egana and his associates (1942) studied the effect of a B complex deficient diet upon the exhaustive work capacity of seven healthy physicians over a four-week period. Although other physiological parameters were measured, the main finding was that a shorter run to exhaustion occurred during the period of deficiency. When brewers yeast, high in vitamin B, was included in the diet, the fitness levels returned to normal. Similar findings were reported by Keys and his colleagues (1945) and Berryman and his coworkers (1947).

In general, it may be concluded that a deficiency of the B complex vitamins over a period of time, a few weeks at the most, may lead to decreased endurance capacity. The athlete on a sound diet is not likely to encounter this deficiency. However, there are those who advocate B complex supplementation to the diet of the athlete. The research is contradictory relative to the effectiveness of B complex supplementation to the diet of the athlete.

In an early study, Csik and Bencsik (1927) reported an increase in the working capacity of two subjects who received vitamin B extract over a six-month period. The criterion tests consisted of performances on dynamometers and a treadmill. However, Simonson and his colleagues (1942) studied the effect of vitamin B surplus upon the capacity for dynamic muscular endurance, maximal strength, and other such tests involving function of the central nervous system. For six weeks an experimental group consumed eight tablets per day, each tablet containing 0.75 mg thiamine, 10 mg niacin, 1 mg riboflavin, and 0.03 to 0.04 mg B_6. In comparison to a control group, no difference was noted for the muscular performance tests. Foltz and others (1942) utilized a double work period to exhaustion as a criterion measure for endurance to study the ergogenic effects of a number of the B complex vitamins. Five young men on controlled diet, which was adequate in B vitamins, received intravenous injections of B complex components over a total of 43 trials. In none of the cases was the total work output greater following administration of the vitamins that it was in the control or placebo series.

In a more recent report, Early and Carlson (1969) concluded that vitamin supplementation reduced fatigue that could be induced by loss of vitamins through exercise-induced sweating in a hot environment. They matched 18 high school boys and assigned them to experimental and placebo groups. The criterion tests, a series of ten dashes with a 30-second rest period between successive trials, was administered on days 1, 9, and 15 of the experiment. During days 1 through 9, no vitamin supplement was given, and all boys underwent heavy training to induce sweat losses. During days 9 through 15, the experimental group received a supplement including 100 mg thiamine, 8 mg riboflavin, 5 mg pyridoxine, 25 mg cobalamin, 100 mg niacin, and 30 mg pantothenic acid. Using a sophisticated ANOVA technique with trend analysis, the researchers concluded that the degree of fatigue of the experimental subjects was less than that of the placebo group on the days of vitamin supplementation. They theorized that thiamine and pantothenic acid were the active substances, due primarily to their roles in oxidative metabolism, as discussed previously.

In summary, the available scientific evidence suggests that vitamin B supplementation to an individual already on a balanced diet will not increase physical performance capacity. Nevertheless, the positive findings of Early and Carlson (1969) provide grounds for further research.

REFERENCES

Archdeacon, J. and J. Murlin. 1944. The effect of thiamine deletion and restoration on muscular efficiency and endurance. *J Nutr*, 28, 241-54.

Bergstrom, J., et al. 1969. Effects of nicotinic acid on physical working capacity and on metabolism of muscle glycogen in man. *J Appl Physiol*, 26, 170-176.

Berryman, G., et al. 1947. Effects in young men consuming restricted quantities of B-complex vitamins and proteins, and changes associated with supplementation. *Am J Physiol*, 148, 618-47.

Bialecki, M. 1962. Nicotinic acid after physical exertion. *Pol Tyg Lek*, 17, 1370-75.

Bicknell, F. and F. Prescott. 1953. *The Vitamins in Medicine*. London: Heinemann.

Boje, O. 1939. Doping: A study of the means employed to raise the level of performance in sport. *League Nat Bull Health Org*, 8, 439-69.

Brozek, J. 1962. Soviet studies on nutrition and higher nervous activity. *Ann N Y Acad Sci*, 93, 667-714.

Buskirk, E. and E. Haymes. 1972. Nutritional requirements for women in sports. In Harris, D. (ed.) *Women and Sport: A National Research Conference*. University Park: The Pennsylvania State University.

Carlson, L. and L. Oro. 1962. The effect of nicotinic acid on the plasma free fatty acids. *Acta Med Scand*, 172, 641-45.

Carlson, L., R. Havel, and L. Ekelund. 1963. Effect of nicotinic acid on the turnover rate and oxidation of the free fatty acids of plasma in man during exercise. *Metabolism*, 12, 837-45.

Csik, L. and J. Bencsik, 1927. Versuche die Wirkung von B-Vitamin auf die Arbeitsleistung des Menschen Festzustellen. *Klinische Wochenschrift*, 6, 2275-2278.

Early, R. and B. Carlson. 1969. Water soluble vitamin therapy on the delay of fatigue from physical activity in hot climatic conditions. *Int Z Angew Physiol*, 27, 43-50.

Egana, E., et al. 1942. The effects of a diet deficient in the vitamin B complex on sedentary men. *Am J Physiol*, 127, 731-41.

Foltz, E., A. Ivy, and C. Barborka. 1942. Influence of components of the vitamin B complex on recovery from fatigue. *J Lab Clin Med*, 27, 1396-1399.

Frankau, I. 1943. Acceleration of co-ordinated muscular effort by nicotinamide. *Br Med J*, 2, 601-603.

Gounelle, H. 1940. Action de la vitamine B, dans l'exercise musculaire et la prevention de la fatigue. *Bull Soc Med Hop*, Paris, 56, 255-57.

Hilsendager, D. and P. Karpovich. 1964. Ergogenic effect of glycine and niacin separately and in combination. *Res Quart*, 35, 389-92.

Hirata, I. 1973. Pre-game meals: A discussion. *Swim Tech*, 10, April, 22-24.

Jenkins, D. 1965. Effects of nicotinic acid on carbohydrate and fat metabolism during exercise. *Lancet*, 1, 1307-1308.

Karpovich, P. and N. Millman. 1942. Vitamin B and endurance. *N Engl J Med*, 226, 881-882.

Keys, A. et al. 1943. The performance of normal young men on controlled thiamine intakes. *J Nutr*, 26, 399-415.

Keys, A., et al. 1945. Experimental studies on men with a restricted intake of the B vitamins. *Am J Physiol*, 144, 5-42.

Lawrence, J., et al. 1975. The effect of alpha-tocopherol (vitamin E) and pyridoxine HCl (vitamin B6) on the swimming endurance of trained swimmers. *J Am Coll Hlth Assn*, 23, 219-222.

McCormick, W. 1940. Vitamin B and physical endurance. *Med Record*, 152, 439-442.

Montoye, H. 1955. Vitamin B12: A review. *Res Quart*, 26, 308-313.

Montoye, H., et al. 1955. Effects of vitamin B12 supplementation on physical fitness and growth of young boys. *J Appl Physiol*, 7, 589-592.

National Research Council. Committee on dietary allowances. 1974. *Recommended Dietary Allowances*. Washington: National Academy of Sciences.

Olson, R. 1958. Food faddism . . . why. *Nutr Rev*, 16, 97-99.

Simonson, E., et al. 1942. The influence of vitamin B (complex) surplus on the capacity for muscular and mental work. *J Indust Hyg*, 24, 83-90.

Tuttle, W., et al. 1949. Influence of various levels of thiamine intake on physiologic response. III. Reaction time. *J Am Diet Assn*, 25, 21-27.

Unsigned. 1971. Russians research food requirements of athletes. *Swimming Technique*, 8, July, 59-62.

White, A., P. Handler, and E. Smith. 1973. *Principles of Biochemistry*. New York: McGraw-Hill.

32

Vitamin C

Wayne D. Van Huss

One of the most abused vitamins among athletes is vitamin C. Even though the Recommended Daily Allowance is only 45 mg, some athletes consume as much as 10,000 mg per day.

It is quite clear that a void exists between recommendations and practice. In the following material the evidence regarding vitamin C is examined relative to deficiency, requirements during training programs, above threshold feeding, and revision of the recommendations for athletes.

DEFICIENCY

The vitamin C deficiency studies show a progressive deterioration in work output and ability to perform aerobic work (Crandon, Lund, and Dill 1940; Farmer 1944; DeFelice 1950). In the classic Sheffield study (Medical Research Council 1953) of experimental scurvy, work performance was markedly impaired. The recovery pulse rates three minutes following a standard work test were significantly lower in a group receiving 70 mg of vitamin C daily than in groups receiving 10 mg or none. Vitamin C deficiency is associated with loss of body tone and a drastic reduction of the acid soluble phosphates. Glycogen, total nitrogen, and muscle solids are also reduced. The general weakness and fatigability are attributed to the low levels of creatine phosphate and the interference with its synthesis. In this study, 30 days without ascorbic acid intake were required before signs of scurvy appeared (i.e., petechiae, looseness of gums, etc.). The ingestion of 10 mg of vitamin C daily was sufficient to cure scurvy, and it was from this study that the United Kingdom's requirement of 30 mg daily was derived. There is some conflicting evidence but none of the other studies had the subject control that the British had with their conscientious objectors at Sheffield. There is nothing new here—one would expect impaired performance in the presence of a rank vitamin deficiency.

VITAMIN C REQUIREMENT DURING TRAINING

In this country Henschel and others (1944) found no beneficial effects of high vitamin C intakes on the ability of men to work in hot environment. This study is representative of the American studies in that none has shown enhanced work output in an industrial environment with vitamin C supplementation. Efremove (1960) headed an investigation by the Academy of Sciences in Moscow directed toward recommendations for the daily requirements of vitamin C. Table 32.1 shows her recommendations with those of the United States, United Kingdom, and Yakovlev's (1958) recommendations for work at several energy consumption levels.

Table 32.1
Vitamin C Daily Requirements

U.K.	30 mg		
U.S.	45 mg		
USSR (Efremova 1960)		mg	
Adults			
Light and medium work		100	
Heavy work		150	
Very heavy work		200	
Children			
7 yrs		75	
7-14 yrs		100	
14 yrs		150	
USSR (Yakovlev 1958)			
Energy consumption	3,000-4,500 Cal	14 mg/1000 Cal	
Energy consumption	4,500-5,000 Cal	20 mg/1000 Cal	

Apparently only one study has been conducted on humans in this country concerning vitamin C supplementation during a physical training period. Gey, Cooper, and Bottenberg (1970) reported complete data on 111 experimental subjects who took 1000 mg of ascorbic acid daily and 96 who took a similar appearing placebo. These air force men, mean age of 28, took part in a 12-week training course. At the beginning and end of the course the subjects took the Cooper test to determine how far they could run in 12 minutes. There were no discernible performance differences between the two groups; however, no dietary controls or serum levels were presented.

The Europeans have done considerable research on the vitamin C requirement during training. Of the more than 30 such studies conducted, those of Namyslowski (1955, 1956), Brunner (1941), Matthes (1941), Wiebel (1939), Early and Carlson (1969), Sidlava and Kroupa (1968), Prokop (1961), and Yakovlev (1941, 1961) deserve particular mention. In several of the early studies no dietary controls or assessment of entry saturation levels were included. However, these controls were present in at least six of the studies. In essence they showed that with the increased training, whether the activity was skiing, aerobic endurance running, or training for power events, the need for vitamin C was increased. Under heavy endurance activity the average supplement needed for serum level maintenance was 200 to 250 mg. With less ascorbic acid, the serum level decreased; with more, it increased. In no study was the amount or intensity of the work quantified. Also, some investigators suggest that the serum level of ascorbic acid may not be the best indicator, but white blood cell concentrations may be better.

The recommended requirements for sportsmen derived by Yakovlev (1961) and Prokop (1961) are shown in Table 32.2. Only the Yakovlev and Prokop data are presented as they were the pioneers in this work. The more recent recommendations of Kvartovkina and Minkh (1968), Schlussel (1967), Williams (1968), and Parizkova and Rogozkin (Ryan, 1977) support the earlier findings.

When considering the vitamin C requirement, the phenomenon of "overtraining" deserves some comment. Carlile (1963) reported training data from the Australian Olympic swimmers of 1960 that showed electrocardiographic observations in athletes unable to complete designed workouts. Similar reversible ECG aberrations have been observed in vitamin C deficiencies. More careful study of the alterations in vitamin C requirements and related changes is needed. Letunov (1964) and Yakovlev (1961) take the position that in overtrained skeletal muscle there are disturbances in the electron transport system and in glycolysis. For the elimination of these effects Yakovlev (1961) recommends increased vitamin C and B complex, but he did not quantitatively support his position.

Table 32.2
Vitamin C Daily Requirements for Sportsmen

Phase	Speed and Strength Events (mg)		Prolonged Effort (mg)	
	Yakovlev (1961)	Prokop (1961)	Yakovlev (1961)	Prokop (1961)
Off Season	75	—	100	—
Preseason	100	—	150	—
Training	200	100-140	250	140-200
Competition	250	140-200	300	200-400

ABOVE-THRESHOLD FEEDING

Above-threshold feeding studies can be divided into two types: (1) those in which the vitamin C feeding has been administered daily for some five to seven days prior to performance measurement, and (2) those in which a given dosage has been administered on the same day as the performance measurement.

Hoitink (1946) worked subjects to exhaustion on a bicycle ergometer before and after taking 300 mg vitamin C daily for a week. The results of the vitamin C feeding was to increase the amount of work done. Vitamin C concentration in the blood was increased, and the pulse rate, respiration rate, and systolic blood pressure at comparable stages in work were decreased. This work was criticized for lack of controls (Hawthorne effect) and the fact that the subjects may have been subclinically deficient in the vitamin. In further study, Hoogerwerf and

Hoitink (1963) used experimental and control groups (N = 15 untrained subjects in each) in which the experimental group received 1000 mg of vitamin C per day for five days and the controls received a similar placebo. Both groups were measured before and following the vitamin administration period. In this experiment they measured the vitamin C content of the blood, excess metabolism of work, and mechanical efficiency of riding a bicycle ergometer at a 120-watt load for ten minutes. The experimental or vitamin group performed the standard work more economically. The mean vitamin C content of the blood before the experiment was in the high normal level for both groups. In this experiment the double-blind protocol was followed. There are some statistical problems in the study but the results appear to reflect beneficial effects of the additional vitamin C.

Recently Howald and his associates (1975) alternated 14-day placebo and experimental periods in 13 subjects. During the experimental period the subjects were fed one gram of ascorbic acid daily. Performance was evaluated by a progressive test on the bicycle ergometer until the subjects were exhausted. Maximum performance was unaffected; but during the tests with vitamin C ingestion, the pulse rates and blood glucose levels were significantly lower and the free fatty acid levels in the plasma were significantly higher. The researchers concluded that the vitamin C ingestion led to greater utilization of free fatty acids as an energy source in working skeletal muscle.

Bailey and others (1970) and Kirchoff (1969) both essentially repeated the Hoogerwerf-Hoitink design with negative results. In the Bailey study a larger dosage of 2000 mg of ascorbic acid was given for five days prior to standard work tasks of three minutes at each of three intensities of three, six and nine miles per hour at zero grade. The subjects included 20 trained athletes and 20 untrained young males. The trained and untrained groups were split into experimental and control groups, and the double-blind protocol was followed. Oxygen uptake, pulse rate, ventilation, and oxygen pulse results did not reflect any significant differences between treatments.

Prokop (1960) studies the effects of above-threshold feeding on a single day in well nutritioned subjects. Used on different days were orange juice containing 100 mg of vitamin C, a placebo solution containing 100 mg synthetic vitamin C, a placebo solution containing no additional vitamin C, and a further control in which no feeding was used. The experiment was arranged in nonbiasing order with each subject serving as his own control. The standard work test involved three minutes of stepping on a 40-centimeter high step at a rate of 30 steps per minute. The energy expenditure, pulse rate, and recovery blood pressures were measured under the four conditions. Prokop found significant improvements in the recovery oxygen, pulse rate, and systolic blood pressure levels. The differences were greatest for the orange juice condition and next highest for the placebo with synthetic C. The results for the placebo as contrasted with no placebo were significant. No relationship was observed between the serum ascorbic acid levels and the other variables. He concluded that orange juice is superior as a source of vitamin C due to the synergistic effects of the bioflavonoids present in orange juice.

Van Huss (1966) replicated the study of Prokop. Before initiating any data collection, the time peak serum ascorbic acid levels in well-nutritioned individuals was determined following ingestion of 250 to 300 mg. The data showed that peak serum ascorbic acid levels were reached two hours following ingestion and decreased progressively thereafter until it leveled off at about 1.35 milligrams percent. Therefore, the study was designed so that performance testing would take place at the time of peak serum ascorbic acid levels. Nine subjects were used with all subjects tested on a maximal treadmill run under four different conditions arranged in a nonbiasing order. The double-blind protocol was followed. The conditions were: (1) 15 ounces of orange juice, with all but 15 mg of the vitamin C destroyed by heat; (2) 15 ounces of orange juice containing 2.98 mg vitamin C per kilogram of body weight of the subject; (3) 15 ounces of synthetic orange drink containing 2.98 mg synthetic ascorbic acid per kilogram of body weight; and (4) 15 ounces of synthetic orange drink containing no ascorbic acid. Variables measured included time to exhaustion, maximum oxygen intake, gross oxygen debt, work pulse rate, reaction time, and static knee extension strength. Performance times, maximum oxygen intake, and oxygen debt were not significantly altered by the supplements. However, faster recovery and altered exercise and recovery pulse rates were observed. The rate of recovery was enhanced by the ascorbic acid-bioflavonoid supplement. Reaction time was significantly faster and surprisingly the static knee extension strength was significantly lower following the orange juice supplement. The results of the 1966 study were surprising so the design was repeated using an ascorbic acid supplement of 2 mg per kilogram of body weight. The results replicated. Later, the same study was repeated at a supplement level of 3 mg per kilogram of body weight. In that study, the results did *not* replicate.

As the brief review of the literature above clearly demonstrates, the results are controversial and inconsistent. It is quite evident that there is a need for more carefully controlled studies during intensive training regimens as well as supplementations prior to performance to further clarify the role of ascorbic acid in performance. However, although there is a need for further research, there appears to be sufficient evidence to warrant some recommendations.

RECOMMENDATIONS

It would seem prudent to include 3 to 5 mg of vitamin C per kilogram of body weight in the diet during training and competition involving prolonged work, primarily to prevent the development of deficiencies. This is of particular importance during the growth period since ascorbic acid deficiency is well known to be associated with growth impairment. Whether the vitamin C is derived from either or both, it appears likely that if at least a portion of the supplement is in combination with bioflavonoids of citrus origin it might be more effective. There is no evidence to indicate that a supplement of 3 to 5 mg per kilogram of body weight has any negative effects.

Recommendations regarding above threshold feeding in well-nutritioned individuals is less difficult to resolve. There appears to be no sound experimental evidence to support the viewpoint that massive doses of vitamin C will enhance physical performance.

REFERENCES

Bailey, D. A., A. V. Carrow, R. G. Teece, and H. Wehner. 1970. Effect of vitamin C supplementation upon the physiological responses to exercise in trained and untrained runners. *Int Z Vitaminforch*, 40, 435.

Bensley, E. H. 1961. The feeding of athletes. *Can Med Assoc J*, 64, 503.

Brunner, H. 1941. Vitamin C experiences with Redoxan in the Swiss army in Frauenfeldt. *Schweiz Med Wochschr*, 71, 715.

Carlile, F. 1963. *On Swimming*. London: Pelham Books, Pp. 202.

Crandon, J. H., C. C. Lund, and D. B. Dill. 1940. Experimental human scurvy. *N Eng J Med*, 223, 353.

Cureton, T. K. 1962. New training methods and dietary supplements are responsible for many of new records. *Ath J*, Jan., 1.

De Felice, F. 1950. Vitamin C and swimming training. *Boll Soc Ital Biol Spec*, 26, 1184.

Early, R. G. and B. R. Carlson. 1969. Water soluble vitamin therapy in the delay of fatigue from physical activity in hot climatic position. *Arbeitsphysiologie*, 27, 43.

Efremove, V. V. 1960. Study of human vitamin requirements. *Vopr pitanija Moskva*, 19, 80.

Farmer, C. J. 1944. Some aspects of vitamin C metabolism. *Fed Proc*, 3, 1979.

Gey, G. O., K. H. Cooper, and R. A. Bottenberg. 1970. Effect of ascorbic acid on endurance performance and athletic injury. *JAMA*, 211, 105.

Henschel, A., H. L. Taylor, J. Brozek, O. Mickelsen, and A. Keys. 1944. Vitamin C and ability to work in hot environments. *Am J Trop Med*, 24, 259.

Hoitink, A. W. 1946. Vitamin C and work. Studies on the influence of work and of vitamin C intake on the human organism. *Verhand Nederlands Inst Praevent Geneesk*, 4, 176.

Hoogerwerf, A. and A. W. Hoitink. 1963. The influence of vitamin C administration on the mechanical efficiency of the human organism. *Arbeitsphysiologie*, 20, 164.

Horwood, W. A. 1964. *A national study of the current practices of secondary coaches in recommending diets for athletes*. Doctoral dissertation, Michigan State University.

Howald, H., B. Segesser, and W. K. Korner. 1975. Ascorbic acid and athletic performance. *Ann N Y Acad Sci*, 258, 458.

Huse, D. M. and R. A. Nelson. 1977. Basic, balanced diets meets requirements of athletes. *Physician and Sp Med*, 5, 1 & 52.

Kirchoff, H. W. 1969. Uber den einfluss von vitamin C auf energieverbrauch, kreislauf und ventilationensgrossen im belastungversuch. *Nutr Dieta* (Basel), II, 184.

Kvartovkina, L. K. and A. A. Minkh. 1968. Nutrition in athletes. *Gigiena Sanit*, 3, 75.

Letunov, S. P. 1964. Effect of many years of sport activities on the cardiovascular system. In *Proc Int Cong Sp Sci (Tokyo)*. K. Kato (ed.). 66.

Matthes, S. 1941. Athletic performance and vitamin C. *Untersuch Lebensm*, 81, 81.

Mayer, J. and B. Bullen. 1960. Nutrition and athletic performance. *Physiol Rev*, 40, 369.

Medical Research Council. 1953. *Vitamin C requirements of young adults*. Special Report No. 280, London: Her Majesty's Stationery Office, pp. 179.

Namyslowski, L. 1956. Investigations of the vitamin C requirement of athletes during physical exertion. *Roxzniki Panstwowego Zakladu Hig*, 7, 97.

Namyslowski, L. 1955. The vitamin C content of the blood in a selected group of students. *Roczniki Panstwowego Zakladu Hig*, 6, 289.

Prokop, L. 1961. Vitamins and athletic performance. *Med u Ernahrung*, 2, 174, 199.

Prokop, L. 1960. The effect of natural vitamin C on oxygen utilization and metabolic efficiency. *N Z f Arztliche Fortbildung*, 49, 6.

Ryan, A. (ed.). Nutritional practices in athletics abroad. 1977. *Physician and Sp Med*, 5, 1 and 32.

Schlussel, H. 1967. Athletic performance as influenced by suitable nutrition. *Ernahrungs-Umschan*, 14, 408.

Sidlava, A. and O. Kroupa. 1968. Biological supplements to the diet of athletes. *Ces Hygiena*, 13, 403.

Upjohn, H. L., J. A. Shea, F. J. Stare, and L. Little. 1953. Nutrition of athletes: Council on Foods and Nutrition. *JAMA*, 151, 818.

Van Huss, W. What makes the Russians run. 1966. *Nutr Today*, 1, 20.

Wiebel, H. 1939. Vitamin C dosage in female athletic students. *Deut Med Wochschr*, 65, 60.

Williams, J. G. P. 1968. Nutrition in sport. *Practitioner*, 201, 324.

Yakovlev, N. N. 1961. *The Nutrition of the Athlete*. Moscow: Physical Culture and Sport.

Yakovlev, N. N. 1958. Vitamin C requirements. *Ernahrungsforschung*, 3, 446.

Yakovlev, N. N. 1941. Significances of high vitamin C content in the food for good muscle training. *J Physiol USSR*, 30, 390.

33

Electrolyte Solutions

Robert W. Patton

The use of glucose-electrolyte solutions (GES) for rehydration and electrolyte replacement has evolved during the past decade as the result of an increased awareness of nutritive needs in maximizing physical performance. For many years it was considered harmful for an athlete to consume fluids during periods of strenuous exertion. However, it was later recognized that large sweat losses evidenced in hyperthermic conditions resulted in decreased performances (Adolph 1947). Eventually, researchers realized that salts were also lost in the copious volumes of sweat, and such losses were associated with muscle cramps and fatigue (Johnson et al. 1942). There then followed a period of large scale salt tablet administration, sometimes with catastrophic effects. Salt tablet administration alone without adequate hydration and/or electrolyte replacement frequently precipitated nausea and possible potassium deficiencies (Knochel and Vertel 1967). The complete formulation of glucose (energy restoration), water (rehydration), and electrolytes (replacement) in an isotonic solution was the ultimate outcome of many investigations.

The nutritional aspects of glucose and water have been discussed in Chapters 15 and 26 of this volume. The focus of this presentation is on the role of electrolytes in human performance and how the collective effect of glucose, electrolytes, and water is evidenced in commercially available GES.

ELECTROLYTES

Electrolytes are substances that, when placed in water, dissociate into charged particles called ions. Those with a positive charge are referred to as cations while those negatively charged are anions. In each fluid compartment of the body the solutions must be isotonic, or equally distributed with anions and cations. Any hypo- or hypertonic condition results in fluid transfer via osmosis to or from the body compartments, thereby causing localized ion or water imbalance.

Although equal quantities of cations and anions are normally maintained in body fluid, the various compartmental fluids are qualitatively different with regard to positively and negatively charged electrolytes. The intracellular fluid (ICF) has a predominance of magnesium and potassium while the extracellular fluid (ECF) has sodium and chloride as the major electrolyte constituents (see

Fig. 33.1). Sodium represents 90 percent of the total cationic influence in the ECF and plays a decisive role in controlling water balance. The concentration of sodium in the serum is carefully regulated by nerve receptors in the hypothalamus that are sensitive to changes in ion concentrations (tonicity) of the blood.

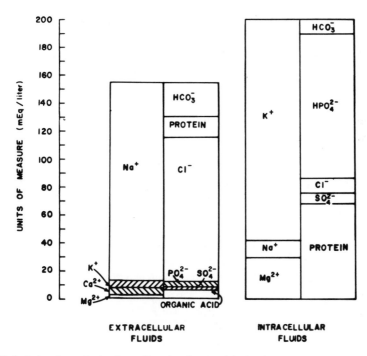

Fig. 33.1 Anion (negatively charged) and cation (positively charged) materials in extracellular and intracellular fluids. (From Morgan and Costill 1972, p. 298. Used by permission.)

Under various conditions, including those regularly seen during sports, the body fluids may become disturbed, and both fluid volume and osmolarity of the body compartments may be affected. Should water be retained, as in water intoxication, both fluid compartments (ECF and ICF) are increased in size (see Fig. 33.2A). Specifically, the osmotic pressure of the blood is reduced favoring the outflow of water into cells and tissue spaces. The extra blood volume passes into limited areas of storage as in the sinusoids of the liver, spleen, and other organs. Ingestion of isotonic saline solutions increases the ECF volume, but has no effect on the ICF volume (see Fig. 33.2B). Isotonic GES could, therefore, be effective in providing a ready reserve for fluid losses associated with exercise. An ECF compartment surplus would logically be the first source of fluid loss, leaving the ICF compartment relatively undisturbed (Dill et al. 1967; Kleeman et al. 1953; Pitts 1965). These circumstances would intuitively support the use of an isotonic GES as a fluid replacement drink.

The ingestion of hypertonic saline solution causes water to leave the cells and flow into the hypertonic ECF compartment (see Fig. 33.2C). Hypertonic GES would then be an undesirable replacement solution in the presence of large sweat losses in hyperthermic environments.

As is shown in Fig. 33.2D, during exercise and/or thermal dehydration, water is drawn from both fluid compartments causing decreased volumes and increased osmolarities in each (Costill 1976). Thus, water would then be the preferred replacement fluid in the absence of electrolyte losses. It has been demonstrated that electrolyte losses do occur, however, during dehydration (Dill et al. 1967). Extracellular sodium and chloride appear to be the major ionic losses, but intracellular potassium and magnesium are lost in significant amounts as well. It should be noted that since the osmolarities rise, the loss of water during dehydration exceeds the electrolyte loss. This loss appears to occur first in the ECF compartment and later in the ICF compartment (Costill 1976).

During the initial stages of dehydration when ECF electrolyte and water loss is most prevalent, a hypotonic condition in the ECF may cause passage of water into the ICF, diluting the ICF compartment (see Fig. 33.2E) (Schottelius and Schottelius 1973). The use of a hypotonic GES could be supportable, therefore, during the initial stages of dehydration to offset ICF and ECF water imbalance. Indeed, most commercially available GES are currently isotonic or hypotonic to provide for the most effective fluid replacement compositions.

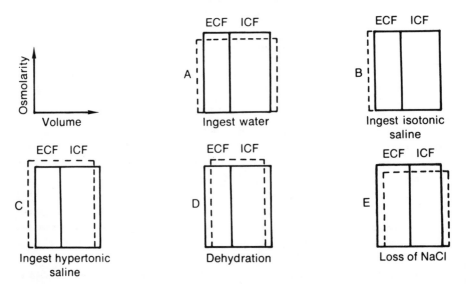

Fig. 33.2 Effects of various conditions on ECF and ICF volume and osmolarity. (From Schottelius, Byron A., and Schottelius, Dorothy D., *Textbook of Physiology*, ed. 18, St. Louis, 1978, The C. V. Mosby Co. Used by permission.)

GLUCOSE-ELECTROLYTE SOLUTIONS

While a variety of domestic and foreign GES are available to the consumer, comparisons of these products are quite difficult. The package labels of commercially available products usually give mixing instructions with a qualitative list of the ingredients, but rarely provide exact quantitative information. Table 33.1 compares the contents of the commercially available GES qualitatively and, where possible, quantitatively.

The nutritive value of the solutions are very similar in that all are protein and fat-free, and each derives carbohydrates from easily assimilated sugars such as glucose or sucrose. The electrolyte composition of the various products do not differ with regard to ECF compartment components. All products contain sodium and chloride, the two ions that represent the major electrolyte losses associated with exercise or thermal dehydration. Only one domestic (Body Punch) and one foreign product (Champ) contain both potassium and magnesium, the ICF compartment electrolytes. Recent evidence suggests that magnesium losses may be sizeable (Costill 1976), yet commercially available GES fails to include magnesium in the solutions.

Sodium bicarbonate is included in three of the GES products. The addition of sodium bicarbonate may have been prompted by early reports of nausea associated with unbuffered concentrated electrolyte doses. Bork (1977) indicated that the manufacturers of Body Punch, a buffered product, exercised further caution by reducing the tonicity of the solution by a factor of two. Body Punch then is a buffered, hypotonic GES.

RELATED LITERATURE

GES use by many is based on the idea that excessive sweat losses containing electrolytes should be replaced to permit sustained exertion in heated environments. Sweat contains large quantities of ECF electrolytes and smaller quantities of ICF electrolytes (Costill 1976). During heavy sweating the total body electrolyte content is decreased significantly, but the concentration of ICF and ECF tends to increase (Costill 1976). These electrolyte losses are linearly related to the work intensity when expressed as percentages of maximal oxygen consumption (Wilkerson et al. 1976).

When subjects were exposed to repeated sessions of heat and/or prolonged exercise, Adolph (1947) found that with a sweat rate of 1 liter per hour, the salt loss was about 1 gm per hour. Although normal sweat contains 3 gm of salt per liter, heat acclimatized subjects may excrete a decreased sweat concentration of 1 gm salt per liter (Nahum 1963). Interestingly, Costill and his coworkers (1975) recently observed that when comparing the effects of water and electrolyte replacement during repeated days of work in the heat, there was little value in adding electrolytes to drinking water. This appears to be true even for subjects who dehydrate (−3 percent) on repeated days and are permitted to ingest food

Table 33.1
Glucose—Electrolyte Solution Contents
(per fluid oz.)

	Calories	Glucose (gm)	Sucrose	Carbohydrate (gm)	Fat (gm)	Protein (gm)	Sodium (mg)	Chloride	Potassium (mg)	Magnesium (mg)	Calcium (mg)	Phosphorus	Citric Acid	Sodium Citrate	Ascorbic Acid (mg)	Sodium or Calcium Saccharin (mg)	Sodium Bicarbonate	Hypotonic	Isotonic	Hypertonic	Artificial Color	Artificial Flavors
Domestic																						
Body Punch	3.1	X	X	.75			X	X	X	X	X	X	X	X	X		X	X			X	X
Brake Time	1.0	X	X	0.30			14.00	X	11.00			X	X	X	1.70	6.00		X			X	X
E.R.G.	6.0	X	X	X			X	X	X		X	X	X	X	1.50		X		X		X	
Gatorade	7.0	X		1.77			16.00	X	3.00		.271	X	X			2.10	X		X		X	X
Quickick	5.5			1.37			17.25	X	0.69				X			5.75			X			X
Foreign																						
Champ	13.5	3.55	X	X			0.08	X	0.07	0.01		X	X							X		
Game	X			X			X	X	X			X	X	X					X			

X = contains at least trace amounts. Exact quantity could not be determined from information.

and drink ad libitum. Thus, electrolyte losses appear to be secondary in importance to water loss during human performance.

Rose et al. (1970) and Costill and his associates (1976) have observed significant magnesium losses following dehydrative exercise. This gives rise to concern when one observes the absence of magnesium in commercial GES, especially in view of magnesium's involvement in muscular contraction.

Costill, Coté, and Fink (1976) recently observed muscle electrolyte changes associated with varying degrees (−2.2, −4.1, and −5.8 percent) of dehydration and confirmed previous studies by finding that ECF compartment body losses are relatively greater than ICF losses. However, in terms of absolute losses both ICF and ECF volumes contribute similar quantities of water to account for total fluid losses. Moreover, significant electrolyte losses were evidenced during the dehydration, yet there was little evidence to suggest that dehydration alters muscle cell membrane permeability.

The only reported investigation in which comparisons of commercially available GES was a double-blind study by Patton and Randolph (1971). Gatorade, Take Five, a dextrose solution, and a placebo solution formulated to taste and appear the same, were compared in their relative effectiveness during maximal treadmill walk for one hour in a hyperthermic environment. No significant differences were found on any performance measure of cardiovascular response or sweat loss. Researchers concluded that no differences in ergogenic value were found between the solutions and a placebo made from colored water and saccharine.

SUMMARY

During sports participation in heated and humid environments it is possible to disturb the water and ion balance in the ECF and ICF compartments. The electrolyte and water loss associated with profuse sweating can eventually result in diminished performances or heat stress injuries.

Dehydration clearly results in performance decrements, and significant electrolyte losses are evidenced during such dehydration. Electrolytes are lost first from the ECF and later from the ICF compartment. However, the addition of electrolytes to drinking water appears to be of minimal value either during or after work bouts. This appears to be true for single day and repeated day conditions as well. The complete research findings would suggest that electrolyte replacement is clearly of secondary importance to the replacement of water during rehydration.

The combined effects of glucose, electrolytes, and water are equivocal. Several commercially available GES have been developed and all appear to contain simple sugars and electrolytes in generally isotonic or hypertonic solutions. Although several studies have investigated the independent effects of glucose, electrolytes, or water, few studies have evaluated the interaction effects of these components via direct comparisons of GES currently available to the consumer. Further research on this subject seems warranted.

Should GES be administered to an athlete, it would appear that environmental conditions should be the determinant in the choice of selection. During hyperthermic conditions where sweat loss is great, a diluted hypotonic GES would be the preferred solution because of large fluid intake requirements. Although this recommendation is advanced, it should be emphasized that the major ergogenic influence derived from the ingestion of GES is the fluid intake requirements. Further discussion of fluid balance during exercise in hyperthermic conditions may be found in Chapter 13, Section II, dealing with environmental aspects of exercise.

REFERENCES

Adolph, E. F. 1947. *Physiology of Man in the Desert*. New York: Wiley.

Bork, J. 1977. Personal Communication, Nov. 7. *Rummer's World Office*, Mountain View, Cal.

Costill, D. L., R. Coté, E. Miller, T. Miller, and S. Wynder. 1975. Water and electrolyte replacement during repeated days of work in the heat. *Med Sci Spts*, 7, 79.

Costill, D. L., R. Coté and W. Fink. 1976. Muscle, water and electrolytes following varied levels of dehydration in man. *J Appl Physiol*, 40, 6-11.

Dill, D. B., S. M. Horvath, W. van Beaumont, G. Gehlsen, and K. Burris. 1967. Sweat electrolytes in desert walks. *J App. Physiol*, 23, 746-751.

Johnson, R. E., H. S. Belding, F. C. Consolazio, and G. C. Pitts. 1942. Harvard Fatigue Laboratory 13, Cambridge, Mass.

Kleeman, C. R., D. E. Bass, and M. Quinn. 1953. The effect of an impermeable vapor barrier on the electrolyte and nitrogen concentrations in sweat. *J Clin Invest*, 32, 736-741.

Knochel, J. P. and R. M. Vertel. 1967. Salt loading as a possible factor in the production of potassium depletion, rhabdomyolysis and heat injuries. *Lancet*, 659-661.

Nahum, L. J. 1963. Acclimation to heat: An exercise in the scientific method. *Conn Med J*, 27, 495-497.

Patton, R. W. and J. Randolph. 1972. A comparison of dextrose, Gatorade, and Take-Five as ergogenic aids for endurance performance. Paper presented at AAHPER Convention, Houston.

Pitts, R. F. 1965. *Physiology of the Kidney and Body Fluids*. Chicago: Yearbook Publications.

Rose, L. I., D. R. Carroll, S. L. Lowe, E. W. Peterson, and K. H. Cooper. 1970. Serum electrolyte changes after marathon running. *J Appl Physiol*, 29, 449-451.

Schottelius, B. A. and D. D. Schottelius. 1973. *Textbook of Physiology*. St. Louis: C. V. Mosby.

Wilkerson, J. E., B. Gutin, S. Molnar, and S. M. Horvath. 1976. Exercise-induced changes in plasma electrolyte levels. *Med Sci Spts*, 8, 70.

34

Iron Supplementation

Emily M. Haymes

The human body contains 35 mg of iron per kg of body weight as hemoglobin, myoglobin, cytochromes, and certain enzymes, and may contain an additional 20 mg/kg stored as ferritin and hemosiderin (Finch 1976). Adult males lose approximately 1 mg iron daily. Most of the iron is excreted in the feces with smaller quantities lost in the urine and sweat. Loss of blood during the menses results in an additional iron loss averaging 0.5 mg per day for the female.

About ten percent of the dietary iron is absorbed, but there is considerable variation depending on the source of the iron and the combination of foods eaten at the same meal. Heme iron is more readily absorbed than nonheme sources. Absorption of iron supplements also varies depending upon the form of the supplement. Ferrous sulfate is one of the most highly absorbable forms. Iron depleted individuals may absorb up to 30 percent of the iron contained in food.

The requirements for iron are 10 mg for males 19 years and over and 18 mg for females 11 years and older and males 11 to 18 years. Average iron intake is 6 mg per 1000 kcal. Since the male has an average caloric intake of 3000 kcal, few men have difficulty meeting the requirement for iron. Females have an average iron intake of 10 to 12 mg per day, well below the recommended dietary intake (White 1968).

IRON DEFICIENCY

At the time of the menarche, the increased iron loss due to the menses results in an average iron loss of 1.5 mg per day. Since only 1.2 mg is replaced in the diet (10 percent of 12 mg = 1.2 mg), the result will be a 0.3 mg iron deficit per day that must be replaced from the iron stores. If we assume that a female has an iron storage of 20 mg per kg of body weight at the age of 12 and weighs 45 kg, her total iron storage of 900 mg will supply this increased need for about eight years. By the age of 20, the female may have completely depleted her iron stores in the bone marrow, liver, and spleen. Females with heavy menstrual flows will lose iron at a faster rate and reach the iron depletion state earlier, while females with light menstrual flows will lose iron more slowly (Beaton et al. 1970; Hallberg at al. 1966). Scott and Pritchard (1967) reported that two-thirds of a sample of young college women had little or no iron stored in their bone marrow.

Once the iron stores have been depleted, the plasma iron bound to transferrin begins to decrease and the rate of iron absorption through the intestinal musosa increases. Iron for the formation of hemoglobin, myoglobin, cytochromes, and certain enzymes must be supplied by the daily dietary intake. If insufficient iron is supplied, less hemoglobin will be formed, which can eventually result in a microcytic, hypochromic anemia.

It is possible through clinical tests to detect iron depletion and iron deficiency before anemia develops. Bone marrow biopsies of the iliac crest were used by Scott and Pritchard (1967). Serum ferritin levels decrease and the iron-binding capacity of transferrin, the plasma protein responsible for transferring iron, increases as iron stores are depleted (Finch 1976). Low plasma iron levels indicate exhaustion of iron stores. As hemoglobin formation is impaired, red blood cell protoporphyrin levels increase. All of these symptoms precede the development of iron deficiency anemia.

Iron Deficiency among Athletes

DeWijn et al. (1971) reported that five to six percent of the male and female members of the 1968 Netherlands Olympic team were anemic. Only two to three percent of both sexes were suffering from iron deficiency anemia. Some 9 percent of the male athletes and 22.5 percent of the female athletes had low plasma iron levels, suggesting iron deficiency.

Haymes et al. (1972) examined a group of women participating in a U.S. Field Hockey Association tournament and found none of the subjects were anemic. However, 25 percent of the women had low plasma iron levels. Four percent of the women from moderately active and sedentary groups were found to be anemic. Low plasma iron levels were found in 33 and 8 percent of the moderately active and sedentary women, respectively.

The 22 to 25 percent of women athletes with low plasma iron levels agrees closely with data from a survey of American women (Ten State Nutrition Survey 1972). Low plasma iron levels indicative of iron deficiency were found in 22 percent of the adult women with hemoglobin levels above 10 gm per 100 ml blood. About 60 percent of the anemic women had iron deficiency anemia. Quite possibly, the very small percentage of sedentary women with low plasma iron levels observed by Haymes et al. (1972) could be attributed to the large percentage of women in that group using oral contraceptives or iron supplements.

Iron Depletion during Training

Changes in iron status have been observed during training. Kilbom (1971) found a 25 percent decrease in serum iron levels among three different groups of women following six weeks of training. No increase in blood volume was observed in any of the groups. A similar, but smaller, decrease was observed following training in a group of middle-aged men (Kilbom et al. 1969). However, Wirth et al. (1975) were unable to detect a significant drop in serum iron levels of college women after ten weeks of training. Ericsson (1970) found that a decrease in bone marrow stainable iron correlated with an increase in physical work capacity among older adults. In each of the studies, the subjects had been sedentary prior to training. The results suggest that a mobilization of iron stores takes place during training. Increases in concentration of hemoglobin, myoglobin, and cytochromes would necessitate increased iron mobilization.

Iron Mobilization during Training

Training does increase the myoglobin (Pattengale and Holloszy 1967) and cytochrome content of the muscle (Holloszy 1967). Athletes in training have greater concentrations of transferrin in the plasma than nonathletes (DeWijn 1972; Haralambie 1969, 1970). DeWijn (1972) suggested that athletes have higher rates of erythropoiesis, which result in a greater need for iron. It has been reported that total hemoglobin increases with training (Holmgren et al. 1960; Kjellberg et al. 1950) and is greater among athletes than nonathletes (Astrand et al. 1963; Dill et al. 1974). However, low hemoglobin concentrations (gm Hb per 100 ml blood) have been observed among endurance trained athletes (Astrand et al. 1963; Dill et al. 1974; Stewart et al. 1972). Expansion of plasma volume is the most likely reason for the dilution of the hemoglobin content.

CAUSES OF IRON DEFICIENCY

Inadequate Iron Intake

The most common cause of iron deficiency is inadequate dietary intake (Finch 1976). DeWijn and others (1971), however, have suggested that the iron intakes of their athletes were satisfactory. They proposed that the high levels of fat in the athletes' diets may have interfered with iron absorption. Concerning the two teams for which iron intakes were reported—14.5 mg for the hockey team and 17 mg for crew—the mean intakes were adequate for males but inadequate for females.

Stewart and his associates (1972) examined the iron intakes of Australian Olympic athletes who had suboptimal hemoglobin levels (defined as less than 15.0 g per 100 ml for males and 14.1 g per 100 ml for females). Mean iron intakes ranged from 21.7 to 26.8 mg for the males and 18.1 to 30.3 mg for females. It is unlikely that inadequate intake of iron was the cause of the lower hemoglobin levels in these athletes.

Red Blood Cell Destruction

Increased red blood cell destruction reportedly occurs during the first week of training (Usami et al. 1966; Yoshimura 1966, 1970) in previously sedentary animals and humans but not in well-conditioned athletes. Red blood cell destruction is accompanied by an increase in reticulocytes. Fragility of the erythrocyte increases during the first week of training but is gradually restored as training proceeds (Usami et al. 1966). Gollnick et al. (1965) found that the red cell of the trained rat was more fragile after six weeks of training than that of the untrained rat.

Yoshimura (1966) proposed that the purpose of the increased red cell destruction during training was to utilize the iron in hemoglobin for the formation of myoglobin and new red blood cells. Increased uptake of radioactive iron by skeletal muscle, heart muscle, bone marrow, liver, and spleen was found after one week of training. Hemoglobin iron was used preferentially by skeletal muscle, heart muscle, and bone marrow.

In Fig. 34.1, the pathways of iron utilization within the body are shown. Following erythrocyte destruction a small amount of iron will be excreted in the urine but most of the iron will re-enter the labile iron pool for use again.

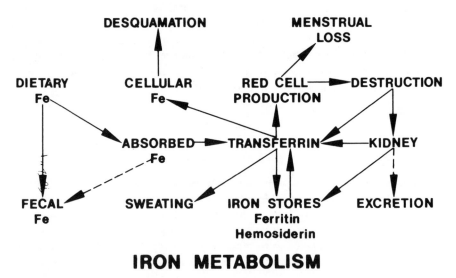

IRON METABOLISM

Fig. 34.1 Pathways of iron utilization by the body. (Reprinted with permission from Buskirk and Haymes 1972, p. 367.)

Both plasma iron and transferrin levels increase 10 to 20 percent following exercise (Haralambie 1972). Haralambie (1972) proposed that the increased plasma iron was due to the mobilization of storage iron rather than intravascular hemolysis. Ceruloplasmin, a copper containing plasma protein, also increases during exercise in both trained and untrained persons. One of the functions of ceruloplasmin is to oxidize iron in the ferrous form (Fe++) to the ferric form (Fe+++), the form in which it is bound to transferrin. However, the ferrous form of iron is found in both ferritin, a storage form of iron, and hemoglobin.

Iron in Sweat

The amount of iron lost in sweat has generally been thought to be minimal. However, Vellar (1968) found that the iron content of sweat amounted to 0.5 mg per hour in young men sweating profusely. Most of the iron was found in the cell-free sweat. Consolazio et al. (1963) observed that young men remained in iron balance even though exposure to heat resulted in a daily loss of 1 mg iron in the sweat. Average iron intake for the men was 23.4 mg per day.

If an athlete training two hours a day loses 1 mg of iron in sweat, an intake of at least 20 mg of iron is necessary to stay in positive iron balance. Female athletes need an iron intake of 25 mg to maintain balance unless they have amenorrhea. Women with iron deficiency anemia lose very little iron in sweat (Hussian and Patwardhan 1959).

IRON DEFICIENCY AND PHYSICAL PERFORMANCE

Anemic Subjects

The major portion of iron in the human body is found in hemoglobin. Since the function of hemoglobin is to carry oxygen to the tissues, a reduction in hemoglobin concentration should reduce the oxygen content of the blood. Lowering the hemoglobin content will also decrease the ability to transport carbon dioxide from the tissues. In order to adequately supply the tissues with oxygen, several physiological adjustments can occur. These include a greater extraction of oxygen from the erythrocyte, which increases the arterial venous difference (a-$\bar{v}O_2$ difference), and an increase in cardiac output due to increases in heat rate and/or stroke volume. When an anemic individual is at rest, normal oxygen uptakes are maintained by one or more of these adjustments (Sproule et al. 1960).

During exercise, heart rate, stroke volume, and a-$\bar{v}O_2$ difference increased as the demand for oxygen increases. Anemic individuals can maintain the same oxygen uptake as normal persons by elevating their heart rates more than the normals during submaximal exercise (Davies et al. 1973; Gardner et al. 1977). Longer recovery periods following submaximal exercise are necessary for the anemic person to restore resting respiratory functions (Andersen and Barkve 1970).

At maximal oxygen uptake, heart rate and stroke volume should also be maximal. Anemic persons have lower maximal oxygen uptakes than persons with normal hemoglobin concentrations even though heart rate and stroke volume are the same in both groups (Sproule et al. 1960). Maximal work capacity is achieved at lower work loads by the anemic individual (Gardner et al. 1977). Dogs made anemic by phlebotomy have the same maximal oxygen uptake as dogs with normal hemoglobin levels because the anemic dogs increased their cardiac outputs more than the normal dogs (Horstman et al. 1974). Most of the increase in cardiac output was due to an increase in stroke volume, which the authors attributed to lower resistance to blood flow. Reducing the hemoglobin concentration reduces viscosity of the blood, which directly affects the resistance. Since the dogs' spleens had been removed, it is unlikely that additional blood entered the circulation during exercise.

Normal Subjects

Total hemoglobin has been found to be significantly related to maximal oxygen uptake (Kjellberg et al. 1950; Vellar and Hermansen 1971). However, both total hemoglobin and maximal oxygen uptake increase with body size. When subjects were subdivided into more homogenous subgroups, Vellar and Hermansen (1971) found that the relationships were reduced. Significant correlations between hemoglobin concentration and maximal oxygen uptake were reduced to nonsignificance in all subgroups except one.

Hemoglobin concentration was significantly related to maximal oxygen uptake among groups of field hockey players and moderately active women but not among sedentary women (Haymes et al. 1972). Plasma iron concentration was also significantly related to maximal oxygen uptake in the field hockey group and to maximal oxygen uptake per kilogram weight in the moderately active group. Since quite a few women in both groups were iron deficient, it is possible that depletion of iron containing substances in the muscle may also have affected maximal performance.

Edgerton and others (1972) examined the interrelationships between hemoglobin, myoglobin, various cytochromes, and running time in rats. The highest correlation was found between hemoglobin concentration and running time. Both cytochrome c and myoglobin correlated fairly well with both running time and hemoglobin concentration.

Deficiency of iron-containing substances in the muscle may be more important than hemoglobin concentration in determining performance. Iron deficient rats whose hemoglobin levels were adjusted to match a normal group by transfusion had lower running times than normal rats or iron deficient rats who received iron (Finch et al. 1976). Running times of the group receiving iron increased over the first three to four days. Myoglobin and cytochrome content of the skeletal muscle and heart were still depressed after four days. Phosphorylation of mitochondrial preparations were still depressed with pyruvate-malate and succinate substrates, but had returned to near normal values with alpha-glycerophosphate. Finch et al. (1976) suggested alpha glycero-phosphate dehydrogenase may be the critical iron containing enzyme in skeletal muscle.

IRON SUPPLEMENTATION AND PHYSICAL ACTIVITY

Since iron deficiency anemia reduces performance levels, restoration of the hemoglobin concentration to a normal level should improve performance. Use of iron supplements lowered heart rates during exercise in a group of anemic persons, while no change of heart rate occurred in a group receiving a placebo (Gardner et al. 1975). However, no change was observed in muscle strength following iron supplementation. Davies and Van Haaren (1973) also observed a decrease in heart rate during exercise after three months of iron supplementation among anemic persons, but no change in heart rate among persons with normal hemoglobin levels who received iron supplements. Andersen and Staven (1972) observed a smaller shift in the acid-base balance following exercise after anemic subjects received iron therapy.

Cotes and others (1969) found lower heart rates during exercise in both iron supplemented and placebo groups, although hemoglobin concentration increased only in the iron supplemented group. No increase in hemoglobin concentration was observed following iron supplementation in a group of older adults, but the iron content of the bone marrow increased (Ericsson, 1970). Physical work capacity improved more in the iron treatment group than in a placebo group.

There is little evidence that supplementing the diet with iron when hemoglobin levels are normal improves performance. Although iron therapy improved performance of anemic rats, no improvement in performance was observed when normal rats received iron (Finch et al. 1976). Vellar and Hermansen (1971) found little difference in maximal oxygen uptake, hemoglobin concentration, or iron levels between groups receiving iron and a placebo. Iron supplementation also had little effect on the hemoglobin and plasma iron levels of male swimmers (Westwig and Winkler 1974).

Because iron deficiency seldom occurs among males, use of iron supplements by male athletes is likely to be of little value. Female athletes have a much greater chance of being iron deficient. Routine use of iron supplements by female athletes may be beneficial.

SUMMARY

Iron deficiency is a problem for approximately 25 percent of the adult female population in the United States, although iron deficiency anemia is less prevalent. Frequency of iron deficiency among female athletes appears to be about the same as that for adult females. Iron deficiency among male athletes occurs less frequently. There is some evidence that iron stores may be depleted during training. Lack of sufficient iron in the diet and excessive loss of iron through either sweat or the menses may be responsible for this iron depletion. Iron depletion leads to lower hemoglobin and tissue iron levels. Low hemoglobin decreases the oxygen-carrying capacity of the blood and puts ore strain on the cardiovascular system during exercise. Iron therapy improves performance among anemic persons but has little effect on persons with normal hemoglobin levels. Since about one out of every four female athletes may be iron deficient, efforts should be made to ensure that females receive adequate iron in the diet. This may necessitate the use of iron supplements.

REFERENCES

Andersen, H. T. and H. Barkve. 1970. Iron deficiency and muscular work performance. *Scand J Clin Lab Invest,* 25, Supplement 114.

Andersen, H. T. and P. Staven. 1972. Iron deficiency anemia and the acid-base variations of exercise. *Nutr Metabol,* 14, 129-135.

Astrand, P. O., B. O. Eriksson, I. Nylander, L. Engstrom, P. Karlberg, B. Saltin, and C. Thoren. 1963. Girl swimmers with special reference to respiratory and circulatory adaptation and gynaecological and phychiatric aspects. *Acta Pediat Scand,* Supplement 147.

Beaton, G. H., M. Thein, H. Milne, and M. J. Veen. 1970. Iron requirements of menstruating women. *Amer J Clin Nutr,* 23, 275-283.

Buskirk, E. R. and E. M. Haymes. 1972. Nutritional requirements for women in sport. In *Women and Sport: A National Research Conference.* D. V. Harris (ed.). University Park: The Pennsylvania State University.

Consolazio, C. F., L. O. Matoush, R. A. Nelson, R. S. Harding, and J. E. Canham. 1963. Excretion of sodium, potassium, magnesium and iron in human sweat and the relation of each to balance and requirements. *J Nutr,* 79, 407-415.

Cotes, J. E., J. M. Dabbs, P. C. Elwood, A. M. Hall, A. McDonald, and M. J. Saunders. 1969. The response to submaximal exercise in adult females; relation to hemoglobin concentration. *J Physiol,* 203, 79P.

Davies, C. T. M. and J. P. M. Van Haaren. 1973. Effect of treatment on physiological responses to exercise in East African industrial workers with iron deficiency anemia. *Brit J Ind Med,* 30, 335-340.

Davies, C. T. M., A. C. Chukweumeka, and J. P. M. Van Haaren. 1973. Iron deficiency anemia: its effect on maximum aerobic power and responses to exercise in African males aged 17-40 years. *Clin Sci,* 44, 555-562.

DeWijn, J. F. 1972. Haemoglobin, packed cell volume, serum iron and iron binding capacity of selected athletes during training. In *Nutritional Aspects of Physical Performance.* J. F. DeWijn and R. A. Binkhorst (eds.). The Hague: Mouton and Company.

DeWijn, J. F., J. L. DeJongste, W. Mosterd, and D. Willebrand. 1971. Hemoglobin, packed cell volume, serum iron and iron binding capacity of selected athletes during training. *J Spts Med,* 11, 42-51.

Dill, D. B., K. Braithwaite, W. C. Adams, and E. M. Bernauer. 1974. Blood volume of middle-distance runners: Effect of 2300-m altitude and comparison with non-athletes. *Med Sci Spts,* 6, 1-7.

Edgerton, V. R., S. L. Bryant, C. A. Gillespie, and G. W. Gardner. 1972. Iron deficiency anemia and physical performance and activity of rats. *J Nutr,* 102, 381-400.

Ericsson, P. 1970. The effect of iron supplementation on the physical work capacity in the elderly. *Acta Med Scand,* 188, 361-374.

Finch, C. A. 1976. Iron metabolism. In *Nutrition Reviews' Present Knowledge in Nutrition.* 4th ed. New York: The Nutrition Foundation.

Finch, C. A., L. R. Miller, A. R. Inamdar, R. Person, K. Seiler, and B. Mackler. 1976. Iron deficiency in the rat: Physiological and biochemical studies of muscle dysfunction. *J Clin Invest,* 58, 447-453.

Gardner, G. W., V. R. Edgerton, R. J. Barnard, and E. M. Bernauer. 1975. Cardiorespiratory, hematological and physical performance responses of anemic subjects to iron treatment. *Amer J Clin Nutr,* 28, 982-988.

Gardner, G. W., V. R. Edgerton, B. Senewiratne, R. J. Barnard, and Y. Ohira. 1977. Physical work capacity and metabolic stress in subjects with iron deficiency anemia. *Amer J Clin Nutr,* 30, 910-917.

Gollnick, P. D., P. J. Struck, R. G. Soule, and J. R. Heinrick. 1965. Effect of exercise and training on the blood of normal and splenectomized rats. *Int Z angew Physiol,* 21, 169-178.

Hallberg, L., A. M. Hogdahl, L. Nisson, and G. Rybo. 1966. Menstrual blood loss and iron deficiency. *Acta Med Scand,* 180, 639-650.

Haralambie, G. 1969. Serum glycoproteins and physical exercise. *Clin Chim Acta,* 26, 287-291.

Haralambie, G. 1970. Serum glycoprotein levels in athletes in training. *Experientia,* 26, 959-960.

Haralambie, G. 1972. Some aspects of iron and copper metabolism during physical exercise. In *Nutritional Aspects of Physical Performance.* J. F. DeWijn and R. A. Binkhorst (eds.). The Hague: Mouton and Company.

Haymes, E. M., D. V. Harris, M. D. Beldon, J. L. Loomis, and W. C. Nicholas. 1972. The effect of physical activity level on selected hematological variables in adult women. Presented at the annual AAHPER convention. Houston.

Holloszy, J. O. 1967. Biochemical adaptations in muscle. *J Biol Chem,* 242, 2278-2282.

Holmgren, A., F. Mossfeldt, T. Sjostrand, and G. Strom. 1960. Effect of training on work capacity, total hemoglobin, blood volume, heart volume and pulse rate in recumbent and upright positions. *Acta Physiol Scand,* 50, 72-83.

Horstman, D. J., M. Gleser, D. Wolfe, T. Tryon, and J. Delehunt. 1974. Effects of hemoglobin reduction on VO_2 max and related hemodynamics in exercising dogs. *J Appl Physiol,* 37, 97-102.

Hussian, R. and V. N. Patwardhan. 1959. Iron content of thermal sweat in iron deficiency anemia. *Lancet,* I, 1073-1074.

Kilbom, A. 1971. Physical training with submaximal intensities in women. I. Reaction to exercise and orthostatis. *Scand J Clin Lab Invest,* 28, 141-161.

Kilbom, A., L. H. Hartley, B. Saltin, J. Bjure, G. Grimby, and I. Astrand. 1969. Physical training in sedentary middle-aged and older men. I. Medical evaluation. *Scan J Clin Lab Invest,* 24, 315-322.

Kjellberg, S. R., U. Rudhe, and T. Sjostrand. 1950. The amount of hemoglobin (blood volume) in relation to the pulse rate and heart volume during work. *Acta Physiol Scand,* 19, 152-169.

Pattengale, P. K. and J. O. Holloszy. 1967. Augmentation of skeletal muscle myoglobin by a program of treadmill running. *Amer J Physiol,* 213, 783-785.

Scott, D. E. and J. A. Pritchard. 1967. Iron deficiency in healthy young college women. *JAMA,* 199, 897-900.

Sproule, B. J., J. H. Mitchell, and W. F. Miller. 1960. Cardiopulmonary physiological responses to heavy exercise in patients with anemia. *J Clin Invest,* 39, 378-388.

Stewart, G. A., J. E. Steel, A. H. Toyne, and M. J. Stewart. 1972. Observations on the hematology and the iron and protein intake of Australian Olympic athletes. *Med J Australia*, 2, 1339-1343.

Ten State Nutrition Survey 1968-1970: IV. Bioechemical. 1972. DHEW Pubs. No. (HMS) 72-8133.

Usami, S., H. Yoshimura, T. Yamada, T. Yoshioka, A. Otsuka, S. Kimura, and J. Momota. 1966. Studies on sports anemia by training in strenuous sports. In *Proceedings of International Congress of Sports Sciences, 1964*. K. Kato (ed.). Tokyo: The Japanese Union of Sport Sciences.

Vellar, O. E. 1968. Studies on sweat losses of nutrients. I. Iron content of whole body sweat. *Scand J Clin Lab Invest*, 21, 157-167.

Vellar, O. D. and L. Hermansen. 1971. Physical performance and hematological parameters. *Acta Med Scand*, Supplement 522.

Westwig, P. H. and W. Winkler. 1974. Iron supplementation and hematological data of competitive swimmers. *J Spts Med*, 14, 112-119.

White, H. S. 1968. Iron nutriture of girls and women—A review. *J Amer Diet Assoc*, 53, 563-569.

Wirth, J. C., T. Hildebrandt and T. G. Lohman. 1975. Effect of physical training on serum iron levels of college age women. *Med Sci Spts*, 7, 84-85.

Yoshimura, H. 1970. Anemia during physical training (sports anemia). *Nutr Rev*, 28, 251-253.

Yoshimura, H. 1966. Sports anemia. In *Physical Activity in Health and Disease*. K. Evang and K. L. Anderson (eds.) Baltimore: Williams and Wilkins.

35

Body Composition*

Frank I. Katch and William D. McArdle

In the early 1940s Albert Behnke, a Navy physician and renowned authority on body composition, made detailed measurements of the size, shape, and structure of 25 professional football players, many of whom had achieved All-American status while in college. According to the military standards at that time, a person

---

* From *Nutrition, Weight Control and Exercise* by F. I. Katch and W. D. McArdle. Boston: Houghton-Mifflin, 1977.

whose body weight was 15 percent above the "average weight for height," as determined from insurance company statistics, was designated as overweight and rejected by the military. When these overweight standards were applied to the football players who ranged in weight from 170 to 260 pounds, 17 players were classified as too fat and unfit for military service. However, a more careful evaluation of each player's body composition revealed that 11 of the 17 overweight players actually had a relatively small percentage of body fat. The players' excess weight was due primarily to their large muscular development.

These data were among the first to illustrate clearly that the popular height-weight tables provide little information with regard to the composition or quality of an individual's body weight. A football player may indeed weigh much more than some "average," "ideal," or "desirable" body weight based on height-weight tables, but these athletes are neither excessively fat nor in need of reducing their body size. Such a player's extra weight is likely to consist of a considerable amount of muscle mass. Thus, the term "overweight" refers only to body weight in excess of some standard, usually the average weight for a specific height, and that's all. Consequently the use of height-weight tables can be quite misleading for the person who wants to know, "How fat am I?"

During the past 50 years many laboratory procedures have been developed to analyze the body in relation to its three major structural components—fat, muscle, and bone. Some of the procedures are time-consuming and require the use of sophisticated, expensive laboratory equipment, while other procedures are fairly simple and inexpensive. Therefore, this chapter will contain a brief analysis of the gross composition of the body as well as a presentation of the rationale underlying the various direct and indirect methods for quantitatively partitioning the body into two basic compartments, body fat and lean body weight.

BODY COMPOSITION

Figure 35.1 illustrates the gross composition of an average or "reference" man and woman in terms of fat, muscle, and bone. This concept of the reference body was developed by Behnke and is based on the physical dimensions obtained from thousands of people who varied greatly in body size.

The reference man and woman differ considerably in their relative proportions of fat, muscle, and bone. Not only is the reference man taller by four inches and heavier by 29 pounds than the reference woman, but his skeleton weighs more (23 versus 15 pounds), he has a larger muscle mass (69 versus 45 pounds), yet his total content of fat is considerably less (23.1 versus 33.8 pounds). These sex differences in body composition exist even when the amount of fat, muscle, and bone are expressed as a percentage of body weight. This is especially true in terms of body fat.

Total body fat exists in two basic depots or storage sites. The first depot, termed *essential* fat, is the fat stored in the marrow of bones and in organs like

345

Reference Man

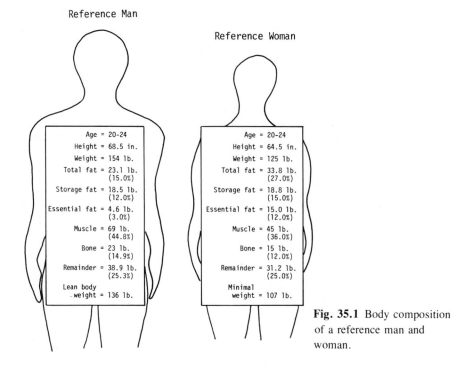

Reference Woman

Fig. 35.1 Body composition of a reference man and woman.

the heart, lungs, liver, spleen, kidneys, intestines, and lipid-rich tissues in the spinal cord and brain. The other major fat depot, *storage fat*, consists of fat that accumulates in adipose tissue. This consists of fatty tissues that protect the various internal organs from trauma, and sub-cutaneous fat deposited beneath the skin.

The percentage values for storage fat are quite similar between the sexes, representing about 12 and 15 percent of the total body weight of men and women, respectively. However, essential fat represents only about 3 percent of the 154-pound reference man, whereas this fat depot is approximately 12 percent of the 125-pound reference woman. This larger quantity of essential fat in the female is present predominantly in the mammary glands and other organ tissues of the body, including the marrow of bones. It is assumed that the additional essential fat possessed by women serves a different function than storage fat. More than likely, it is related to child-bearing and hormonal functions.

LEAN BODY WEIGHT AND MINIMAL WEIGHT

Each person seems to have a biological limit below which he or she cannot reduce body weight and still maintain good health. In men this lower limit is referred to as *lean body weight*. For the 154-pound reference man, lean body weight is equivalent to the body weight minus the 12 percent of body weight (18 pounds) that is storage fat. Of the remaining 136 pounds of lean body weight, approximately 3 percent is essential fat (4.1 pounds), 50 percent muscle (68 pounds), 17 percent bone (23.1 pounds), and 4.5 percent fat-free adipose tissue (6.1 pounds); the remainder accounts for 25.5 percent, or 34.7 pounds. The size of the storage depot of fat can vary considerably depending on a person's nutritional status, yet it is amenable to change through exercise and/or diet.

Experiments have confirmed that about three percent of the body weight of the leanest males during adolescence and early maturity is fat. Presumably this quantity represents the body's store of essential fat and appears to be a lower limit below which a man cannot reduce his body weight significantly without impairing physiological function or capacity for exercise. Studies conducted during prolonged periods of starvation have confirmed that the lower limit of fatness in the leanest men is, in fact, usually about three to four percent of body weight. Similar low values of body fat have also been obtained for champion male athletes in various sports, although values lower than three percent have also been observed. The body fat content of world-class, male marathon runners ranges from about three to eight percent, which is about the quantity of essential fat that apparently cannot be reduced. The low fat content and body weight for these exceptional athletes reflect, to some degree, a positive adaptation to the prolonged, severe requirements of distance training. A minimal quantity of body fat permits a more effective transfer of metabolic heat during exercise and reduces the quantity of excess weight that the athlete must transport while running. Similar low values for body fat have been obtained for other athletes. In our own body composition studies of the New York Jets and Dallas Cowboys football teams, seven players were measured with body fat values below three percent. One former three-time All-American linebacker had only 3.1 percent body fat, while a defensive secondary player and All-Pro offensive back were both one percent fat!

In contrast to the lean body weight of the reference male with three percent essential fat, the lower limit of body weight for the 125-pound reference female includes approximately 12 percent essential fat. This theoretical lower limit is termed *minimal weight*, which is 107 pounds for the reference woman. Behnke concluded that the leanest women cannot reduce their essential fat below about 10 to 12 percent, which probably represents the lower limit of fatness for women in good health. This concept of minimal weight in females, with about 12 percent essential fat, is equivalent to lean body weight in males with about three percent essential fat. There are, however, exceptions to this lower limit of fatness for women. In our own studies of highly trained distance runners and gymnasts, body fat values in the range of 8 to 12 percent have been recorded. More research is needed in this area for a clearer understanding of the theoretical basis of the role of essential fat in women.

LABORATORY METHODS OF ASSESSING BODY COMPOSITION

The fat and lean components of the human body have been determined by two general procedures. One procedure measures body composition directly by chemical analysis. The second approach assesses body composition indirectly with hydrostatic weighing and/or simple circumference of skinfold measurements. While direct methods form the basis for indirect techniques and are useful in animal research and for human cadaver analysis, the use of indirect procedures enables the exercise scientiest to assess with considerable accuracy the body composition of living people.

Indirect Assessment

This section presents two indirect procedures to assess body composition. The first procedure describes Archimedes' principle as applied to hydrostatic weighing. With this method the percentage of body fat is computed from body density, that is, the ratio of body weight to body volume. The second procedure involves the *prediction* of body fat from circumference or girth measurements. This method is of practical significance because body fat can be predicted both simply and accurately.

Body Volume Determination

About 2000 years ago the Greek mathematician Archimedes discovered a basic principle that is currently applied in the evaluation of body composition. Through experimentation, he developed the concept of specific gravity—that is, ratio of the weight of an object to the weight of an equal volume of water. Thus:

$$\text{specific gravity} = \frac{\text{weight of an object}}{\text{weight of an equal volume of water}}$$

Applying the procedure outlined above, it is possible to determine the specific gravity of any object merely by weighing the object and then weighing an equal volume of water. Weighing an object on a scale is an easy matter; however, determining the weight of an equal volume of water presents more difficulty. This problem was solved when Archimedes, to his delight, realized that the volume of water that overflowed his bath was equal to the volume of his submerged body. Archimedes probably also reasoned that an object submerged in water must by buoyed up by a counterforce that equals the weight of the water it displaces. This buoyancy force helps to support an object in water against the downward pull of gravity. Thus, the object is said to lose weight in water. Because the object's loss of weight in water equals the weight of the volume of water it displaces, we can redefine specific gravity as the ratio of the weight of an object in air divided by its loss of weight in water. Thus:

$$\text{specific gravity} = \frac{\text{weight of an object in air}}{\text{loss of weight in water or}}$$

$$= \frac{\text{weight of object in air}}{\text{weight in air} - \text{weight in water}}$$

Very carefully conducted experiments with different species of animals have used Archimedes' principle to determine an animal's composition in terms of its proportion of fat and lean tissue. Figure 35.2 illustrates the nearly perfect inverse relationship between the specific gravity of an animal and its percentage of fat. In this particular experiment with guinea pigs, the animals were killed and the weight of the carcass was determined in air and then while submerged underwater. This procedure, shown in the insert graph of Fig. 35.2, allowed the researchers to compute the specific gravity of each animal. The next phase of the experiment involved the determination of the total fat content of the carcass by direct chemical methods. Once they had done this, the scientists were able to plot the points in Fig. 35.2, with each point representing a particular animal's value for carcass specific gravity and its corresponding value for body fat. The results were unequivocal: animals with a high specific gravity had a low fat percentage, while animals that tended to be buoyed up easily in the water had a low specific gravity and a considerable quantity of fat. Both animal and human experiments have established that the specific gravity of fat extracted from adipose tissue has a value of 0.90, whereas fat-free tissue has a specific gravity of approximately 1.10. Since the body composition can be thought of as consisting of two components, one fat and the other fat-free, specific gravity of an animal must be somewhere between 0.90 and 1.10.

Density of the Human Body

Let us now determine the density of the human body. For illustrative purposes, suppose our subject weighs 50 kilograms as measured on a conventional scale, and 2 kilograms when submerged completely under water. According to Archimedes' principle, the buoyancy of counterforce of the water must equal 48 kilograms. The loss of weight in water of 48 kilograms is exactly equal to the weight of the displaced water. Because we know the density of water at any temperature, we can easily compute the volume of water displaced by this person. In the present example, 48 kilograms (48,000 grams) of water would equal a volume of 48 liters or 48,000 cubic centimeters (1 gm water $= 1$ cm^3 in volume). If volume were measured at the cold water temperature of 39.2°F, no density correction would be necessary. In practice, however, researchers use warmer water and apply the appropriate density value for water. The density of the subject, computed as weight volume, would be 50,000 gm (50 kg) : 48,000 gm/cm^3 or 1.0417 gm/cm^3. The specific gravity would also be 1.0417. This

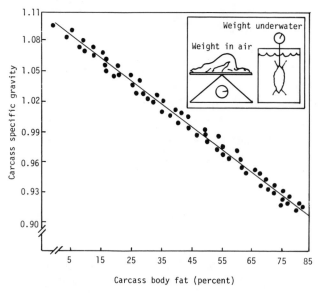

Fig. 35.2 Relationship between carcass specific gravity and percentage fat. The same relationship has been determined in guinea pigs, cattle, sheep, and rats.

particular value for body density is approximately midway between the value of 0.90 gm/cm³ for pure fat and 1.10 gm/cm³ for fat-free tissue. Once body density has been determined, the next step is to determine the amount of fat that corresponds to that value.

Computing Percent Body Fat from Body Density

It is possible to determine the relative percentages of fat in the human body with a simple equation that incorporates density. This equation was derived from the theoretical premise that the densities of fat and fat-free tissues remain relatively constant (density of fat = 0.90 gm/cm³; density of fat-free tissue = 1.10 gm/cm³) even with large variations in total body fat. Thus, the proportions of the fat and lean components can be determined from an algebraic expression that relates these proportions to the density of the whole body. The following equation is used to compute percent body fat by incorporating the determined value of body density:

$$\text{percent body fat} = \frac{495}{\text{body density}} - 450$$

The value for body density of 1.0417 gm/cm³ determined for the 50-kg subject in the previous example can now be substituted in the equation for percent body fat as follows:

$$\text{percent body fat} = \frac{495}{1.0417} - 450 = 25.2 \text{ percent fat}$$

Thus, 25.2 percent, or 12.6 kg, of the 50-kg body weight is fat. The remaining 37.4 kg is lean body weight.

The weight of fat is calculated by multiplying body weight by percent fat:

$$\text{fat weight (kg)} = \frac{\text{body weight (kg)} \times \text{percent fat}}{100}$$
$$= 50 \text{ kg} \times 0.252$$
$$= 12.6 \text{ kg}$$

Lean body weight is calculated by subtracting the weight of fat from body weight:

$$\text{lean body weight (kg)} = \text{body weight (kg)} - \text{fat weight (kg)}$$
$$= 50 \text{ kg} - 12.6 \text{ kg}$$
$$= 37.4 \text{ kg}$$

The determination of body weight and the calculations for body density, percent body fat, and lean body weight are quite simple. The more difficult task is the accurate assessment of body volume and thus body density. By application of the principle discovered by Archimedes, this can be done in one of two ways: water displacement and underwater or hydrostatic weighing. The latter method is discussed briefly.

Underwater weighing computes body volume as the difference between body weight measured in air and weight measured during water submersion. In other words, body volume is equal to the loss of weight in water with the appropriate temperature correction for the water's density. This is the technique used by scientists measuring the specific gravity of animals. Figure 35.3 illustrates the procedure in our laboratory for measuring body volume by underwater weighing. The technique has been explained fully by Katch and McArdle (1977).

Prediction of Body Fat from Circumference Measurements

Hydrostatic weighing is one of the most accurate indirect methods currently available to assess the body's fat content. However, proper measurement with these techniques requires equipment and facilities not normally available in a physician's office, hospital, physical education department, or physical conditioning center. Thus, alternative but simple procedures to predict body fatness have been developed. One of these procedures is to measure the girth or circumferences at selected sites on the body. It is easy to take circumferences

Fig. 35.3 Underwater weighing apparatus.

with a cloth measuring tape and reasonable levels of accuracy can be attained with a minimum of practice. For added precision, measurements should be recorded in centimeters.

Usefulness of Circumference Scores

In recent experiments we have determined the best combination of circumference measures for predicting body fatness in a sample of young adults and older men and women. The younger group ranged in age from 17 to 26 years and consisted of students enrolled at Queens College in New York. The age range of the older subjects was 27 to 50 years. These subjects were volunteers in a study conducted by Pollock at Wake Forest University in Winston-Salem, North Carolina. The criterion values for body density and percent body fat were determined in the laboratory by hydrostatic weighing or water displacement methods. The data were analyzed to determine the combination of circumference measures that came closest to predicting actual body fatness as determined by the more sophisticated laboratory techniques. A combination of three circumferences resulted in a very accurate prediction of fatness for all subjects. These predicted values for body fat were within 2.5 to 4.0 percent of values determined in the laboratory. The practical significance of this finding was obvious, that is percent body fat can be predicted easily from a few simple circumference measurements. The equations are described in detail elsewhere (Katch and McArdle 1977).

Measurement of Subcutaneous Fat by the Skinfold Technique

Approximately one-half of the body's total fat content is located in the tissues directly beneath the skin. The feasibility of measuring this subcutaneous fat was suggested by anthropologists at the end of World War I, and by 1930 researchers had developed a special pincer-type caliper that enabled them to measure this fat at representative sites on the body with relative accuracy. The caliper works on the same principle as the micrometer used to measure the distance between two points. The procedure for measuring skinfold thickness is to grasp firmly with the thumb and forefinger a fold of skin and subcutaneous fat and to separate it from the underlying muscular tissue following the natural contour of the skinfold. The pincer arms of the caliper exert constant tension at their point of contact with the skin. The thickness of the double layer of skin and subcutaneous tissues can then be read directly from the caliper dial. The procedure for taking the skinfold measurements, as well as the precise location of the skinfold sites, must be standardized if the results are to be reliable and used for comparative purposes. A variety of body fat equations have been developed based on skinfold measures. However, it should be remembered that the equations are probably *population specific*, in that they accurately predict fatness in samples of subjects similar to those from which the equations were derived.

Average Values for Body Composition

Values for body fat for a sample of men and women throughout the United States are presented in Table 35.1. In comparing values for body fat with these results, one should bear in mind that these data represent average values. The table includes values that are plus and minus one standard deviation in order to give some indication of the amount of variation of spread from the average. The column headed "68 percent variation limits" indicated the range of values for percent body fat, which include about 68 of every 100 people measured. As an example, the average value for percent body fat for young men from the New York sample is 15.0 percent, and the 68 percent variation limits are from 8.9 to 21.1 percent body fat. Thus, for 68 of every 100 people measured, expected values for percent fat would range between 8.9 and 21.1 percent. Of the remaining 32 young men, 16 would possess more than 21 percent of body fat, while for the other 16 people, body fat would be less than 8.9 percent. Certainly a value within the 68 percent variation limit for body fat could be considered "normal."

Although considerable data are available concerning the average body composition of many groups of men and women of different ages and fitness levels, there has been no systematic evaluation of the body composition of representative samples from the general population that would warrant setting up precise norms or desirable values for body composition. At present, the best we can do is to present the average values from various studies of different age groups. In addition to the data presented in Table 35.1, the data in Table 35.2 include the average values for circumferences based on the 1972 North Carolina data and the 1973 New York data.

A general conclusion based on these data is that with increasing age the percentage of body fat tends to increase in both men and women. This increase in fat could be due in part to the fact that the aging skeleton becomes

Table 35.1

Average Values of Percent Body Fat for Younger
and Older Women and Men from Selected Studies

Location, Year	Age Range	Average Percent Fat*	68% Variation Limits
Younger women			
Minnesota, 1953	18-30	23.3	21.0-30.1
North Carolina, 1962	17-25	22.9	17.5-28.5
New York, 1962	16-30	28.7	24.6-32.9
Colorado, 1967	17-24	25.3	16.5-34.3
California, 1968	19-23	21.9	17.0-26.9
California, 1969	17-29	25.5	21.0-30.1
New York, 1973	17-26	26.2	23.4-33.3
Older women			
Minnesota, 1953	31-45	31.2	25.4-37.3
New York, 1963	30-40	28.6	22.1-35.3
	40-50	34.4	29.5-39.5
Texas, 1968	30-40	32.0	26.4-37.7
North Carolina, 1972	33-50	29.7	23.1-36.5
Younger men			
Minnesota, 1951	17-26	11.8	5.9-18.1
Colorado, 1956	17-25	13.5	8.3-18.8
Indiana, 1966	18-23	12.6	8.7-16.5
California, 1968	16-31	15.3	6.3-24.2
New York, 1973	17-26	15.0	8.9-21.1
Older men			
Maryland, 1963	30-39	32.0	22.8-41.2
	40-49	32.9	25.0-41.1
Indiana, 1966	24-38	17.8	11.3-24.3
	40-48	22.3	16.3-28.3
North Carolina, 1972	27-50	23.7	17.9-30.1

* Percent body fat was computed from body density measured by hydrostatic weighing or water displacement with the formula, percent fat = 495 density − 450.

demineralized and porous. Such a process reduces body density because of the decrease in bone density. Another reason for the relative increase in body fat with age is the reduction in the level of daily physical activity. The adaptation of a more sedentary life style tends to increase the deposition of storage fat and reduce the quantity of muscle mass. This occurs even if the daily caloric consumption remains unchanged. The exact interaction of the aging process per se and the numerous ramifications of the sociology and psychology of aging on fitness and body composition have not as yet been adequately evaluated.

Table 35.2

Average Values for Circumferences of Younger and Older Age Subjects

Circumferences, cm	Young Women, 17-26 Years		Older Women, 27-55 Years		Young Men 17-26 Years		Older Men 27-55 Years	
	Average Value	68% Variation Limits	Average Value	68% Variation Limits	Average value	68% Variation limits	Average value	68% Variation limits
Mid-abdomen	72.3	65.6-79.0	82.7	77.5-91.9	78.8	72.0-85.6	91.1	82.2-100.0
Right forearm	22.6	21.3-23.9	24.4	23.1-25.7	26.0	24.7-27.3	29.2	27.4- 31.0
Right thigh	55.5	51.4-59.6	57.6	52.8-62.4	55.4	51.3-59.5	59.0	54.8- 63.2
Right calf	34.7	32.5-36.9	34.4	32.1-36.7	37.1	32.8-41.4	36.9	34.3- 39.5
Right upper arm	25.2	23.1-27:3	28.6	26.0-31.2	27.7	25.4-30.0	34.0	31.7- 36.3

REFERENCES

Behnke, A. R. 1968. Physique and Exercise. In *Exercise Physiology*. H. B. Falls (ed.). New York: Academic Press.

Behnke, A. R. 1969. New concepts in height-weight relationships. In *Obesity*. N. Wilson (ed.). Philadelphia: F. A. Davis.

Behnke, A. R., B. G. Geen, and W. C. Welham. 1942. The specific gravity of healthy men. *JAMA*, 118, 495-498.

Behnke, A. R. and J. H. Wilmore. 1974. *Evaluation and Regulation of Body Build and Composition*. Englewood Cliffs, N.J.: Prentice-Hall.

Garrett, W. N. 1968. Experiences in the Use of Body Density as an Estimator of Body Composition of Animals. In *Body Composition in Animals and Man*. Washington, D.C.: National Academy of Sciences, Publication 1598.

Katch, F. I. 1969. Practice curves and errors of measurements in estimating underwater weight by hydrostatic weighing. *Med Sci Spts*, 1, 212-216.

Katch, F. I. and W. D. McArdle. 1973. Prediction of body density from simple anthropometric measurements in college-age men and women. *Hum Biol*, 45, 445-454.

Katch, F. I. and W. D. McArdle. 1977. *Nutrition, Weight Control and Exercise*. Boston: Houghton-Mifflin.

Katch, F. I. and W. D. McArdle. 1975. Validity of body composition prediction equations for college men and women. *Am J Clin Nutrit*, 28, 105-109.

Katch, F. I., E. D. Michael, and S. M. Horvath. 1967. Estimation of body volume by underwater weighing: Description of a simple method. *J Appl Physiol*, 23, 811-813.

Katch, F. I. and V. L. Katch. 1978. Body Composition Evaluation of the New York Jets and Dallas Cowboys Football Teams, 1974-1978. Unpublished Manuscript.

Pitts, G. C. 1963. Studies of body composition by direct dissection. *Ann NY Acad Sci*, 110, 11-22.

Rathbun, E. N. and N. Pace. 1945. Studies on body composition. *J. Biol Chem*, 158, 667-676.

Siri, W. E. 1956. Gross composition of the body. In *Advances in Biological and Medical Physics*. J. H. Lawrence and C. A. Tobias (eds.). Vol IV. New York: Academic Press.

36

Obesity*

Lawrence B. Oscai

Obesity is a metabolic abnormality caused by excessive caloric intake. It is characterized by an excessive accumulation of triacyglycerols in adipose depots distributed throughout the body. For experimental purposes, Buskirk (1974) has arbitrarily established 25 percent or more in adult men and 30 percent or more in adult women as the fatness levels [(stored lipid/body weight) × 100] to denote obesity. But from the viewpoint of current health attitudes, a label of obesity has been given to those men who exceed 20 percent fat and those women who exceed 25 percent. Thus, depending on the definition used, between approximately 15 and 40 percent of our adult population would be called obese.

A variety of methods are available to estimate fat content in humans. The reader is referred to the previous chapter by Katch and McArdle for a thorough discussion.

ADIPOSE TISSUE CELLULARITY

Under normal conditions (i.e., in the absence of obesity), fat cells accumulate at a vary rapid rate in early life in humans. Knittle et al. (1977) have shown that about one-half of the adult number is reached between ages two and four. The data show that this period of rapid proliferation is followed by a much slower but continuous increase in adipocyte number that extends into early adulthood. It appears that adipocyte proliferation ceases between about 14 and 16 years. Evidence in support of this notion comes from a study of individuals 20 years and older (Salans et al. 1971). Adipocyte number remained stable even though the subjects under observation gained an average of 16.2 kg body weight, of which 10.4 kg was determined to be fat, as a result of prolonged high caloric intake. In this study, then, an increase in the size of the adipocytes was responsible for the expansion of adipose mass. Similar to that seen with hyperplasia, fat cell enlargement occurs at a very rapid rate in early life. In the nonobese individual, the average adult adipocyte contains about 0.6 mg of lipid (Stern and Greenwood 1974). From the work of Knittle et al. (1977), it appears that more than one-half of the adult size, 0.35 mg of lipid per cell, is reached between ages two and four.

* This work was supported by U.S. Public Health Service Research Grants Am-17357 and KO4 AM-00216.

It is clear now that, once formed, adipocytes are not easily destroyed. To date, no known clinical procedure, outside of surgical removal, is effective in reducing the total number of cells in an adipose depot. Even in the face of substantial weight loss produced by means of caloric restriction, adipocytes of rats were greatly reduced in size but cell number remained unaffected (Hirsch and Han 1969; Salans et al. 1971).

TYPES OF OBESITY

Evidence is available to show that obesity can exist in one of two forms (Hirsch et al. 1966; Hirsch and Knittle 1970; Salans et al. 1971; Salans et al. 1974). The first type of obesity is that of early onset. This condition is characterized by excessive weight gain during the early stages of life, which can persist into adulthood as evidenced by studies showing that approximately 80 percent of all overweight children remain so as adults (Knittle 1972; Wolff and Lloyd 1973). Obesity of early onset manifests itself in a marked increase in adipocyte number; adult humans plagued with this abnormality can have as many as 100 to 125 billion fat cells as opposed to the normal number of some 25 billion (Stern and Greenwood 1974). In contrast to cell number, cell size in the severely obese is increased only about 40 percent. The second type of obesity is that of adult onset. This condition is characterized by mild to moderate weight gain, but only in adult life. Adipose tissue expansion, then, occurs solely in response to fat cell enlargement with no increase in adipocyte number. A lack of physical activity is commonly implicated as an important factor leading to the development of adult onset obesity. Greene (1939) reported that in 236 out of 350 cases of the mild form of obesity, the beginning of this condition could be traced directly to a sudden decrease in physical activity. With sufficient determination, adult onset obesity can be corrected.

OBESITY AND HEALTH

Hypertension, clinical coronary heart disease, insulin resistance, and diabetes are the cardiovascular abnormalities commonly associated with obesity (Albrink 1975). Apparently high blood pressure accelerates the rate of development of atherosclerosis in the presence of elevated serum lipid levels (Robbins 1974). With sufficient weight loss, it is possible to reduce or actually normalize high blood pressure (Pfeiffer and Laube 1974) and elevated serum lipid levels (Lees and Wilson 1971). As adipocytes enlarge in the development of obesity, they become progressively less responsive to insulin resulting in elevated levels of insulin in the blood even under basal conditions (Rabinowitz 1970). Weight reduction, resulting in a significantly smaller adipocyte, causes circulating insulin levels to return to normal and corrects the decreased insulin binding associated with obesity (Rabinowitz 1970; Olefsky and Reaven 1975). Diabetes is four times more common in obese than in nonobese individuals (Albrink 1975). Many believe that the hyperinsulinemia that so often accompanies obesity may be a contributing factor leading to the increased susceptibility of the obese individual to diabetes. Over many years, increased insulin production may lead to pancreatic exhaustion and diabetes, accounting for the association between the two metabolic abnormalities (Albrink 1975).

TREATMENT

Numerous approaches have been advanced in the treatment of obesity, including starvation, surgery, and drugs. Total fasting was introduced by Bloom in 1959, and since then this approach has been used fairly extensively but restricted to cases of severe obesity. Treatment is usually carried out under close medical supervision because total fasting places considerable strain on the body and metabolic complications can result. The advantage of total fasting over other approaches is psychological in nature in that grossly overweight individuals lose weight at a very rapid rate. Reports indicate that obese individuals subjected to total fasting can lose between 500 to 1000 gm per day (Ball et al. 1967; Bloom 1959).

The intestinal bypass surgery technique for treatment of severe obesity has become widely practiced over recent years. Apparently, weight loss after surgery is due mainly to a reduction in voluntary food intake and to some degree to malabsorption (Bray et al 1976). At the present time, however, caution in the use of this experimental technique is warranted since bypass surgery has been followed in some cases by massive fatty changes in the liver, cholestasis, fibrosis, and interstitial and fatal hepatic necrosis (Williams 1974).

Drugs in the therapy of obesity have received considerable attention in past years. Amphetamine has been used widely in the treatment of obesity (Innes and Nickerson 1975). With the use of amphetamine, weight reduction appears to be due almost entirely to a reduction in food intake and only in small measure to increased metabolism. Presumably the site of action is the lateral hypothalamic feeding center. Rivlin (1975) discussed the use of human chorionic gonadotropin, thyroxine, triiodothyronine, human growth hormone, and progesterone in the treatment of obesity. After consideration of rationale, effectiveness, and the hazards resulting from the use of drugs, it was concluded that the pharmacologic approach to the treatment of obesity is largely unsatisfactory. As a matter of fact, the growing opinion of many in clinical and scientific circles is that there is no satisfactory long-term treatment for severe obesity (Albrink 1975). Once established, it is remarkably self-sustaining.

Even if weight is temporarily lost, the former weight is regained with astonishing regularity. In one study, 106 obese patients were weight-reduced to varying degrees by means of food restriction (Feinstein et al. 1958). Follow-up data on these subjects indicate that a vast majority gained back all of the lost weight within a few years after treatment (Oscai 1973). One difficulty confronting obese individuals who have experienced a substantial weight loss is that if body weight is to be maintained at the reduced level, it is necessary for them to exist on a diet lower in total calories than their habitual, voluntary intake of food. Thus, if success is to be maintained, a lifetime of vigilance is a necessity.

Animal experimentation serves as a suitable model for obtaining clues regarding biological function. When feasible, attempts are made to apply results obtained on animals to human research. Recently, information was obtained on laboratory rats that, if applicable to humans, could have interesting implications with respect to prevention of obesity. As mentioned earlier, obesity results from excessive caloric intake. It seems logical, therefore, that some attention should be directed toward factors responsible for regulation of voluntary food intake. Manipulation of litter size to alter caloric intake of the newborn rat was first described by Parkes (1926, 1929). In the intervening years, this technique was developed by Kennedy (1950, 1957) and used by others (Dickerson and Widdowson 1960; Knittle and Hirsch 1968; McCance and Widdowson 1962; Penney et al. 1976; Widdowson and McCance 1960) to study certain aspects of growth and development in the rat. The most striking feature associated with early nutritional manipulation is that rats raised in large litters (undernutrition) gain weight more slowly and have lower final body weights than those raised in small litters (overnutrition), even though all animals are provided unrestricted access to food after weaning. For example, we were able to show that rats from large litters were about 140 gm lighter than those from small litters at 62 weeks of age (Oscai and McGarr 1977). One factor responsible for the smaller body size was a markedly lower voluntary food intake. These results provide evidence that the amount of food consumed during suckling plays an important role in determining the habitual food intake of rats in later life. More recently we demonstrated that by controlling the food intake of the newborn rat it is actually possible to "program" the animal for a desired voluntary food intake in later life. These observations could have interesting implications with respect to the prevention of obesity since this condition is the result of excessive caloric intake. In this context, it is of interest that the difference in the total body content of fat between the smaller and larger rats was enough to account for 63 percent of the difference in body weight (Oscai and McGarr 1977).

REFERENCES

Albrink, M. J. 1975. Obesity in *Textbook of Medicine*. P. B. Beeson and W. McDermott (eds.). Philadelphia: W. B. Saunders.

Ball, M. F., J. J. Canary, and L. H. Kyle. 1967. Comparative effects of caloric restriction and total starvation on body composition in obesity. *Ann Intern Med,* 67, 60-67.

Bloom, W. L. 1959. Fasting as an introduction to the treatment of obesity. *Metabolism,* 8, 214-220.

Bray, G. A., R. E. Barry, J. R. Benfield, P. Castelnuovo-Tedesco, and J. Rodin. 1976. Intestinal bypass surgery for obesity decreases food intake and taste preferences. *Am J Clin Nutr,* 29, 779-783.

Buskirk, E. R. 1974. Obesity: A brief overview with emphasis on exercise, *Fed Proc,* 33, 1948-1950.

Dickerson, J. W. T. and E. M. Widdowson. 1960. Some effects of accelerating growth. II. Skeletal development. *Proc Royal Soc London B,* 152, 207-217.

Feinstein, A. R., V. P. Dole, and I. L. Schwartz. 1958. The use of a formula diet for weight reduction of obese out-patients. *Ann Intern Med,* 48, 330-343.

Greene, J. A. 1939. Clinical study of the etiology of obesity. *Ann Intern Med,* 12, 1797-1803.

Hirsch, J. and P. W. Han. 1969. Cellularity of rat adipose tissue: Effects of growth, starvation, and obesity. *J Lipid Res,* 10, 77-82.

Hirsch, J. and J. L. Knittle. 1970. Cellularity of obese and nonobese human adipose tissue. *Fed Proc,* 29, 1516-1521.

Hirsch, J., J. L. Knittle, and L. B. Salans. 1966. Cell lipid content and cell number in obese and nonobese human adipose tissue. *J Clin Invest,* 45, 1023.

Innes, I. R. and M. Nickerson. 1975. Norepinephrine, epinephrine, and the sympathomimetic amines. In *The Pharmacological Basis of Therapeutics.* L. S. Goodman and A. Gilman (eds.). pp. 477-513. New York: MacMillan.

Kennedy, G. C. 1950. The hypothalamic control of food intake in rats. *Proc Royal Soc London B,* 137, 535-549.

Kennedy, G. C. 1957. The development with age of hypothalamic restraint upon the appetite of the rat. *J Endocrinol,* 16, 9-17.

Knittle, J. L. 1972. Obesity in childhood: A problem in adipose tissue cellular development. *J Pediatrics,* 81, 1048-1059.

Knittle, J. L., F. Ginsberg-Fellner, and R. E. Brown. 1977. Adipose tissue development in man. *Am J Clin Nutr,* 30, 762-766.

Knittle, J. L. and J. Hirsch. 1968. Effect of early nutrition on the development of rat epididymal fat pads: Cellularity and metabolism. *J Clin Invest,* 47, 2091-2098.

Lees, R. S. and D. E. Wilson. 1971. The treatment of hyperlipidemia. *New Engl J Med,* 284, 186-195.

McCance, R. A. and E. M. Widdowson. 1962. Nutrition and growth. *Proc Royal Soc London B,* 156, 326-337.

Olefsky, J. M. and G. M. Reaven. 1975. Effects of age and obesity on insulin to isolated adipocytes. *Endocrinol,* 96, 1486-1498.

Oscai, L. B. 1973. The role of exercise in weight control. In *Exercise and Sport Sciences Reviews.* J. H. Wilmore (ed.). pp. 103-123. New York: Academic Press.

Oscai, L. B. and J. A. McGarr. 1977. Insights into the regulation of appetite in the rat. *Fed Proc,* 36, 1132.

Parkes, A. S. 1926. The growth of young mice according to size of litter. *Ann Appl Biol,* 13, 374-394.

Parkes, A. S. 1929. Note on the growth of young mice suckled by rats. *Ann Appl Biol,* 16, 171-173.

Pfeiffer, E. F. and H. Laube. 1974. Obesity and diabetes mellitus. In *Advances in Metabolis Disorders.* R. Levine and R. Luft (eds.). pp. 243-255. New York: Academic Press.

Penney, D., D. Anderson, and J. Dongas. 1976. Effects of early severe malnutrition on heart and skeletal muscle lactate dehydrogenase. *J Nutr,* 106, 1235-1240.

Rabinowitz, D. 1970. Some endocrine and metabolic aspects of obesity. *Ann Rev Med,* 21, 241-258.

Rivlin, R. S. 1975. Therapy of obesity with hormones. *New Engl J Med,* 292, 26-29.

Robbins, S. L. 1974. *Pathologic Basis of Disease.* Philadelphia: W. B. Saunders.

Salans, L. B., G. A. Bray, S. W. Cushman, E. Danforth, Jr., J. A. Glennon, E. S. Horton, and E. A. H. Sims. 1974. Glucose metabolism and the response to insulin by human adipose tissue in spontaneous and experimental obesity: Effect of dietary composition and adipose cell size. *J Clin Invest,* 53, 848-856.

Salans, L. B., E. S. Horton, and E. A. H. Sims. 1971. Experimental obesity in man: Cellular character of the adipose tissue. *J Clin Invest,* 50, 1005-1011.

Stern, J. S. and M. R. C. Greenwood. 1974. A review of development of adipose cellularity in man and animals. *Fed Proc,* 33, 1952-1955.

Widdowson, E. M. and R. A. McCance. 1960. Some effects of accelerating growth. I. General somatic development. *Proc Royal Soc London B,* 152, 188-206.

Williams, R. H. 1974. *Textbook of Endocrinology.* Philadelphia: W. B. Saunders.

Wolff, O. H. and J. K. Lloyd. 1973. Childhood obesity. *Proc Nutr Soc,* 32, 195-198.

37

Weight Control: Diet and Physical Activity

William D. McArdle and Frank I. Katch

An excess accumulation of body fat is undesirable for a variety of reasons. From a health standpoint, medical problems exist for which obesity or "over fatness" is considered a risk factor and for which a reduction in excess fat is desirable.

These problems include certain types of heart disease; high blood pressure; impaired carbohydrate and fat metabolism; joint, bone, and gallbladder diseases; diabetes; asthma; and various lung disorders (Mayer 1967). Being obese is also often accompanied by changes in personality and behavior that can be manifested as depression, withdrawal, self-pity, irritability, and aggression. Unfortunately, being too fat is a condition shared by 60 to 70 million adults and 10 million teenagers. Until recently it was a common belief that the major cause of obesity was simply a problem of overeating. However, considerable scientific evidence now exists to indicate that the underlying causes for excess caloric storage are numerous and complex.

BALANCING ENERGY INPUT WITH ENERGY OUTPUT: THE ENERGY BALANCE EQUATION

For most adults body weight remains relatively stable throughout the year, despite the fact that the annual food intake averages between 1600 and 1800 pounds. Accumulation of excess fat is the end result of an imbalance in the energy balance equation. This equation states that for body weight to remain constant the number of calories consumed as food in the diet must balance the calories expended to sustain one's daily activities. An accumulation of 3500 extra kilocalories (Kcal) due to an imbalance on either side of the equation is equal to about one pound of stored fat. For example, eating an extra apple (70 Kcal) each day and keeping energy output constant increases the yearly caloric intake by an amount equivalent to about seven pounds of body fat, while an additional slice of cherry, apple, or mince pie daily will cause the accumulation of about 35 pounds of excess fat in a year. Conversely, for weight loss of one pound to occur an energy deficit of 3500 Kcal must be established either by decreasing the energy intake (dieting), increasing the energy output (exercise), or a combination of the two. If daily food intake is reduced by just 100 Kcal and energy expenditure increased by 100 Kcal by jogging 1½ miles each day, then the monthly caloric deficit will amount to a weight loss of 1.75 pounds of fat or 21 pounds in one year.

UNBALANCING THE ENERGY BALANCE EQUATION

Three approaches can be taken to create a caloric imbalance and cause weight loss. These are dieting, exercise, and dieting plus exercise.

Dieting

This approach to weight loss creates a disequilibrium in the energy balance equation by reducing energy intake. Suppose an obese woman who consumes 2800 Kcal daily and maintains her body weight at 175 pounds wishes to lose weight. She maintains her regular level of activity but reduces her daily food intake to 1800 Kcal to create a caloric deficit of 1000 Kcal. In seven days the caloric deficit created would equal 7000 Kcal, the caloric equivalent to two pounds of body fat. Actually, considerably more than two pounds would be lost during the first week of caloric restriction because some of the glycogen stores would be metabolized. This stored nutrient contains fewer calories and much more water (three grams of water per gram of glycogen) compared to fat. This is why short periods of caloric restriction often prove encouraging to the dieter, but results in a large percentage of water and carbohydrate loss per unit weight reduction with only minimal decrease in body fat (Grande 1961). Then as weight loss continues, a larger proportion of body fat is metabolized for energy to supply the caloric deficit created by food restriction. To reduce fat by another three pounds, the reduced caloric intake of 1800 Kcal would have to be maintained for another 10.5 days. If she held to this diet, body fat would theoretically become reduced at a rate of one pound every 3.5 days. While the mathematics of weight loss through caloric restriction are straight-forward, they depend upon several basic assumptions that, if violated, reduce the effectiveness of weight loss through dieting.

The first assumption is that energy expenditure remains relatively unchanged throughout the period of caloric restriction. Frequently, dieting causes lethargy and thus reduces the daily activity level. In addition, as body weight decreases, the energy cost of moving the body is reduced proportionately. Consequently, the energy output side of the energy balance equation becomes smaller. Also, physiological changes may occur during caloric restriction that can affect the rate at which weight loss occurs. One such change is in the resting metabolic rate. With semistarvation, both body weight and resting metabolic rate decline (Bray 1969). Interestingly, the percentage decrease in resting metabolism is greater than the decrease in body weight. This actually conserves energy and causes the diet to be less effective. This retarding effect on the theoretical weight loss curve often leaves the dieter frustrated and discouraged.

Providing the diet is nutritionally sound, what one eats matters less than how many calories are consumed. Weight loss will occur with a reduced caloric intake regardless of the diet's percentage composition of carbohydrate, protein, and fat. With obese patients who consumed either an 800 Kcal high-fat diet or an 800 Kcal high-carbohydrate diet, weight loss on each diet was nearly identical as was the percentage of fat tissue lost during a ten-day period (Kinsell 1964). These findings illustrate an important principle of dieting and weight control: no "magic metabolic mixture" assures a more effective weight loss, even though a low-calorie diet high in fat content may seem more filling and perhaps produce less hunger. Anyone contemplating a diet that deviates from a low-calorie but well-balanced diet should consult a physician with particular expertise in nutrition and the energetics of weight control.

Adequate hydration should be maintained at all times during a dietary period. While restricting water intake will result in a relatively large initial weight loss, this is substantially due to a loss in body water. The total quantity of fat lost is essentially independent of the water intake (Grande 1961).

A review of the scientific literature dealing with weight loss through diet in obese subjects indicates that individuals who succeed at first in weight loss are usually unsuccessful in permanently maintaining their desired body size and shape (Stunkard and McLaren-Hume 1959). In one survey, the drop-out rate from obesity clinics varied from 20 to 80 percent. Of those who remained in the program, no more than 25 percent lost as much as 20 pounds and only 5 percent lost 40 pounds or more. Such statistics are discouraging and indicate that long-term maintenance of a particular low-calorie diet is extremely difficult. Equally discouraging are the observations that weight loss through dieting alone results in a considerable loss of lean tissue in addition to the desired loss in body fat. (Benoit 1965; Oscai 1973).

Exercise

The importance of exercise in weight control has not always been well understood. It is often promulgated that exercise always causes an increase in appetite and food intake, thereby negating the caloric burning effect of the exercise. It is also argued that the amount of energy expended during physical activity is too low to justify the effort required. Finally, because it is generally (though incorrectly) believed that weight gain is the result of overeating, many conclude that reducing food intake is the most effective means to alleviate the overweight condition. These misconceptions have down-played the fact that exercise can serve an important role in disturbing the energy balance equation and, therefore, produce a caloric deficit.

Exercise effects on appetite. People who regularly perform hard physical labor, such as lumberjacks, farm laborers, and certain athletes, consume about twice the daily calories ingested by average sedentary people. Woodcutters who spend four to six hours a day in heavy labor consume between 4000 and 7000 Kcal daily, the average intake being about 5500 Kcal. Because these workers are usually quite lean, high caloric intakes are necessary to balance the extremely high caloric expenditure required during lumberjacking and logging (Karvonen et al. 1954). The same is true for athletes whose physical training is particularly strenuous and time-consuming. Table 37.1 lists the estimated caloric intake of international caliber athletes who devote as much as eight hours a day to training. Endurance athletes such as marathon runners, cross-country skiers, and cyclists consume about 6000 Kcal each day. Yet some of these athletes are the leanest in the world! Clearly, this extreme caloric intake is required just to meet the energy requirements of the training and is not at all related to an accumulation of body fat.

Among individuals who train for relatively short periods of time, the appetite-stimulating effect of exercise is not readily apparent (Dempsey 1964;

Table 37.1

Estimated Daily Caloric Intake for Athletes in Various Sports Activities

Sport	Average Body Weight (kilograms)	Estimated Daily Kcal Intake
Cross-country skiing	67.5	6105
Bicycle racing	68.0	5995
Canoe racing	75.0	5995
Marathon racing	68.0	5940
Soccer	74.0	5885
Field hockey (men)	75.0	5720
Handball (European)	75.0	5610
Basketball	75.0	5610
Ice hockey	68.0	5390
Gymnastics (men)	67.0	5000
Sailing	74.0	5170
Fencing	73.0	5000
Sprinting (track)	69.0	4675
Boxing (middle and welter weight)	63.5	4675
Diving	61.0	4620
Pole vault	73.0	4620

Jankowski and Foss 1972; Katch et al. 1969). Women engaged in swim training averaged about 15 percent greater caloric intake than collegiate tennis players during the training and competitive seasons (Katch et al. 1969). Neither group, however, consumed many more calories during the season than before and after the experiment. In another study (Bray 1969), obese young men participated in a three-phase, physical conditioning program consisting of five weeks of exercise, five weeks of sedentary living, and another five weeks of exercise. Despite variations in energy output, daily caloric intake was essentially unchanged throughout the experiment and significant reductions in body weight and body fat were observed. These modifications in body size can be attributed to calorigenic effects of exercise per se, since exercise did not increase caloric intake.

Data have been reported suggesting that a moderate increase in physical activity above the sedentary range may actually depress the appetite and reduce food intake in both animals and humans (Mayer 1967). In one study (Mayer 1956), the food intake was evaluated for an industrial population in West Bengal, India. For these people, the dietary composition was quite uniform but the physical activity level ranged from sedentary to very heavy. As shown in Table 37.2, for persons in occupations classified as moderately heavy and heavy in terms of physical activity, the daily food intake increased proportionately with the intensity of work. For these workers, however, body weight was well below the people in the sedentary range and remained stable throughout the heavy work categories. Of considerable importance is the observation that for workers in occupations requiring relatively light physical activity, the daily food intake (and body weight) was actually lower than for sedentary people. These results are nearly identical to findings with animals and clearly indicate that light exercise does not necessarily stimulate the appetite and may even depress food intake compared to the sedentary range.

How exercise effects energy expenditure. An argument frequently raised against exercise as a means for weight control concerns the number of calories that can be expended through regular exercise. For example, one must chop wood for 14 hours, golf for 20 hours, or perform mild calisthenics for 22 hours just to reduce body fat by one pound. Small wonder such a commitment seems overwhelming and discourages the overweight individual planning to lose 20 to 30 pounds or more. While facts form the basis for this attack against exercise as a means for weight control, the same facts support a strong counterattack in favor of exercise. Consider this: if golf is played only two hours (about 350 Kcal/day), two days a week (700 Kcal), then five weeks or ten golfing days would be needed to lose one pound of fat. The point is that the caloric expending effects of exercise are cumulative; a caloric deficit of 3500 Kcal is equivalent to a one pound loss of fat whether or not the deficit occurs rapidly or systematically over a long period. Combine this with the fact that a moderate increase in activity may even depress food intake in previously sedentary people and exercise becomes a very effective tool for weight control.

Tabled values for energy expenditure are available from which one can estimate the caloric cost of a variety of occupational, recreational, and sports activities (Katch and McArdle 1977; Passmore and Durnin 1955). These values are "averages," applicable under "average" conditions when applied to the "average" person of a given body weight. While they provide a good approximation of energy output, some variation is to be expected due to individual differences in style and technique of performance, environmental factors such as terrain, temperature, and wind resistance, as well as the intensity of participation. In addition, for the overweight person, exercise can provide a significant caloric stress as the energy expended in moving one's body weight is directly related to the body weight (McArdle and Magel 1970).

Is overeating the cause of weight gain? From the available evidence it appears that the genesis of weight gain and resulting obesity is often related to a reduced level of daily activity rather than to an increased food intake. For example, the caloric intake of obese high school girls was *below* that of nonobese peers. The distinguishing differences was the low daily energy expenditure on the part of the fat girls (Bullen et al. 1864; Huenemann 1972; Johnson et al. 1956). Identical findings have been reported for adolescent boys (Huenemann 1972; Stefanik et al. 1959).

Table 37.2
Effect of Exercise on Caloric Intake
and Body Weight

Job Classification	Daily Caloric Intake (kcal)	Body Weight (lbs)
Sedentary	3300	148
Light work	2600	118
Medium work	2800	114
Heavy work	3400	113
Very heavy work	3600	113

Modified from J. Mayer et al. 1956. Relation between caloric intake, body weight, and physical work; studies in an industrial male population in West Bengal. *Am J Clin Nutr* 4:169.

Diet Plus Exercise

For men and women, combinations of exercise and diet offer considerably more flexibility in achieving a negative caloric balance and accompanying fat loss than either exercise or diet alone (Boileau et al. 1971; Moody et al. 1972). In fact, the addition of exercise to the program of weight control may facilitate a more permanent weight loss compared to total reliance on caloric restriction (Mayer and Bullen 1960).

Consider an obese person who desires to reduce body weight by 20 pounds. How can this best be done utilizing exercise *and* diet? Most nutrition experts agree that a loss in body fat of up to two pounds each week is within acceptable medical limits (Mayer 1968). This guideline is partially based on the fact that individuals who have successfully achieved and maintained a desirable body weight lost no more than one and one-half pounds per week during the period of caloric deficit. Some more conservative nutritionists suggest a target loss of only one pound per week (Gregg 1970). Then even under the best circumstances, 20 weeks would be required to achieve a 20-pound fat loss. With this goal, the average weekly deficit would have to be 3500 Kcal while the daily deficit must be 500 Kcal.

One-half hour of moderate exercise (about 350 extra Kcal) performed three days a week adds 1050 Kcal to the weekly caloric deficit. Consequently, the weekly caloric intake would have to be reduced by only 2400 Kcal instead of 3500 Kcal in order to lose the desired one pound of fat each week. If the number of exercise days is increased from three to five, food intake need only be reduced by 250 Kcal each day. If the duration of the five-day-per-week workouts prolonged from 30 minutes to one hour, then no reduction in food intake would be necessary for weight loss to occur because the required 3500 Kcal deficit would have been created entirely through exercise. For middle-aged men, if 300 Kcal are expended in each session of moderate exercise four times each week, fat loss will occur without attention to food intake (Pollock et al. 1971).

Clearly, physical activity can be used effectively by itself or in combination with mild dietary restriction to bring about an effective loss of body fat. This approach is likely to produce fewer of the feelings of intense hunger and other psychological stress that occur with a program of weight loss that relies exclusively on caloric restriction. In fact, the use of exercise in a program of weight control provides protection against a loss in lean tissue; for both children and adults exercise enhances the mobilization and breakdown of fat (Parizkova 1973). When weight is reduced by diet alone, more lean tissue is lost and less fat compared to a similar weight loss brought about with an appropriate exercise program (Jokl 1963; Oscai 1973).

REFERENCES

Benoit, F. L. 1965. Prolonged fasting: Physiologic undesirability studied. *Med Tribune,* May 16.

Boileau, R. et al. 1971. Body composition changes in obese and lean men during prolonged physical conditioning. *Med Sci Spts,* 3, 183-189.

Bray, G. 1969. Effect of caloric restriction on energy expenditure in obese subjects. *Lancet,* 2, 397-398.

Bullen, B. A. et al. 1964. Physical activity of obese and non-obese adolescent girls appraised by motion picture sampling. *Am J Clin Nutr,* 14, 211-223.

Dempsey, J. A. 1964. Anthropometrical observations on obese and nonobese young men undergoing a program of vigorous physical exercise. *Res Quart,* 35, 275-287.

Grande, F. 1961. Nutrition and energy balance in body composition studies. In *Techniques for Measuring Body Compositions.* Washington, D.C.: National Academy of Sciences, National Research Council.

Gregg, W. 1970. *A Boy and his Physique.* Chicago: National Dairy Council.

Huenemann, R. 1972. Food habits of obese and non-obese adolescents. *Postgrad Med,* 51, 99-105.

Jankowski, L. and M. Foss. 1972. The energy intake of sedentary men after moderate exercise. *Med Sci Spts,* 4, 11-13.

Jokl, E. 1963. Physical activity and body composition: Fitness and fatness. *Ann NY Acad Med,* 110, 778-794.

Karvonen, M. et al. 1954. Consumption and selection of food in competitive lumber work. *J Appl Physiol,* 6, 603-612.

Katch, F. I. and W. D. McArdle. 1977. *Nutrition, Weight Control, and Exercise.* Boston: Houghton Mifflin.

Katch, F. I. et al. 1969. Effects of physical training on the body composition and diet of females. *Res Quart,* 40, 99-104.

Kinsell, L. W. et al. 1964. Calories do count. *Metabolism,* 3, 195-204.

Mayer, J. 1956. Relation between caloric intake, body weight and physical work; studies in an industrial male population in West Bengal. *AM J Clin Nutr, 4, 169-175.*

Mayer, J. 1967. Inactivity, an etiological factor in obesity and heart disease. In *Nutrition and Physical Activity*. G. Glix (ed.). Uppsala: Almqvist and Wiksells.

Mayer, J. 1968. *Overweight: Causes, Cost and Control*. Englewood Cliffs: Prentice-Hall.

Mayer, J. and B. Bullen. 1960. Nutrition and athletic performance. In *Exercise and Fitness*. Chicago: The Athletic Institute.

Mayer, J. et al. 1954. Exercise, food intake and body weight in normal rats and genetically obese adult mice. *Am J Physiol*, 177, 544-548.

McArdle, W. D. and J. R. Magel. 1970. Physical work capacity and maximum oxygen uptake in treadmill and bicycle exercise. *Med Sci Spts*, 2, 118-123.

Moody, D. L. et al. 1972. The effect of a jogging program on the body composition of normal and obese high school girls. *Med Sci Spts*, 4, 210-213.

Oscai, L. B. 1973. The role of exercise in weight control. In *Exercise and Sports Sciences Reviews*. J. H. Wilmore (ed.). New York: Academic Press.

Parizkova, J. 1973. Body composition and exercise during growth and development. In *Physical Activity: Human Growth and Development*. G. Rarick (ed.). New York: Academic Press.

Passmore, R. and J. V. G. A. Durnin. 1955. Human energy expenditure. *Physiol Rev*, 35, 801-840.

Pollock, M. C. et al. 1971. Effects of walking on body composition and cardiovascular function of middle aged men. *J Appl Physiol*, 30, 126-130.

Stefanik, P. A. et al. 1959. Caloric intake in relation to energy output of obese and non-obese adolescent boys. *Am J Clin Nutr*, 7, 55-62.

Stunkard, A. J. and M. McLaren-Hume. 1959. The results of treatment for obesity. *Arch Int Med*, 103, 79-85.

38

Weight Loss for Sports Competition

Edward J. Zambraski

Many individuals involved in competitive athletics are confronted with the problem of weight loss. People in this situation may be placed in one of three categories. The first category is comprised of individuals who lose weight for sports competition for the sole purpose of decreasing body fat, increasing their relative muscle mass, and thereby improving their ability to perform. The second category involves individuals who participate in sports, such as wrestling, where weight restrictions or weight classes exist. These athletes often attempt to attain a body weight that will enable them to compete in a weight division or class that either they or their coaches deem desirable. Often weight loss is encouraged by the belief that participating in a lower weight class will give them the advantage of being able to compete against a smaller individual. Unlike the first category, the motivation for weight loss by this group is not necessarily derived from the desire for better performance. They are simply losing weight to enable entrance into competition, and this may be done by compromising their ability to perform. The third category consists of individuals who are not voluntarily losing weight but are unintentionally experiencing weight loss during training and/or competition.

The purpose of this chapter is to expand upon some of the problems associated with weight loss and sports competition. Even though information presented is pertinent to all three types of individuals or reasons for weight loss, an attempt will be made to focus on the second group of individuals who are losing weight for sports with inherent weight restrictions. In this segment of the athletic population the extent of the weight loss is the greatest and the resultant problems the most severe.

Many different methods of weight loss are currently being used by athletes. The most commonly employed are simply decreasing or elimination of one's food intake (fasting) or liquid consumption (hypohydration). Since approximately 70 percent of our body weight is water, many individuals are reinforced by rapid changes seen on the scale when they either knowingly or unintentionally decrease their body fluids. Dehydration, elicited by profuse sweating during heavy exercise or exposure to hot environments, is often used. This procedure, frequently used by wrestlers, is often facilitated by utilizing rubber suits, saunas, and steam baths (Tipton and Tcheng 1970). In an attempt to decrease weight by reducing body fluids some athletes have even resorted to the use of laxatives, diuretics, and the induction of vomiting (AMA Committee on Medical Aspects of Sports 1967).

The unfortunate fact about weight loss, which many athletes and nonathletes fail to realize, is that the reduction of body fat cannot always be accurately assessed by changes in total body weight seen when one steps on a scale. This is because one must consider the source of the weight reduction and not simply how much total weight is being lost. The equation below illustrates that total body weight may be divided into two components: fat-free weight (muscle, bone, connective tissue, and fluids) and fat weight (adipose).

$$\text{total body weight} = \text{fat-free weight} + \text{fat weight}$$
$$100\% = (60 \text{ to } 95\%) + (5 \text{ to } 40\%)$$

Ideally the procedures utilized to achieve weight loss should be designed and conducted to decrease fat weight and non fat-free weight. In most athletic situations one would like to increase the fat-free component by increasing muscle mass. The simplified equation also illustrates that the percentages of the two components may vary. An obese individual may have a 60 percent fat-free and 40 percent fat distribution, whereas a highly trained wrestler may only have 5 percent fat and 95 percent fat-free weight. All individuals, even though they may be at their minimal body weights, will still have at least 3 to 5 percent fat. This adipose tissue is essential lipid found throughout the body. An important point to understand is that when rapid weight loss is achieved by fasting and/or fluid deprivation, it is the fat-free component—that is, muscle mass and body fluids—that is reduced and not solely the fat component.

As previously indicated, almost all athletes attempt to attain the minimal body weight that they consider to be most desirable for their particular sport. The amount of weight lost in these cases is usually minimal, and the changes that occur in body weight take place over a long time period. In sports such as wrestling, however, the amount of weight lost is much greater and the time period over which this weight loss is achieved is much shorter, that is, several hours or one to two days (Tipton and Tcheng 1970). A study by Zambraski and others (1975) on Iowa high school wrestlers found that these athletes lost, on the average, 9 to 13 percent of their preseason body weight. From other studies by Tcheng and Tipton (1973) it is known that these wrestlers have only 8 percent body fat before the season starts and 5 percent body fat when they are at the height of competition. These facts demonstrate the key point that weight losses amounting to 9 to 13 percent of body weight can only mean that these individuals were decreasing muscle mass and/or body fluids to attain these minimal weights. More recent studies by Zambraski and his colleagues (1976) have documented that similar patterns of weight loss are characteristic of collegiate wrestlers.

As indicated earlier, a major problem associated with weight loss is in ascertaining the source of the weight reduction—whether fat or fat-free component. Another problem is knowing what an athlete's ideal or minimal weight should be in terms of percent body fat. The latter questions would depend on the sport in which one is participating. Several studies have been conducted to determine the most prevalent body compositions of athletes in specific sports. It has been reported that untrained college males have 13.2 percent body fat (Wilmore 1974), untrained college females 24.5 percent (Wilmore 1974), male college weight lifters 15.0 percent (Fahey and Brown 1973), female world class marathon runners 15.2 percent (Wilmore and Brown 1974), ice hockey players 9 percent (Green and Houston 1975), male marathon runners 3.7 percent (Novak, Hyatt, and Alexander 1968), and high school wrestlers 5 percent (Tcheng and Tipton 1973).

It is a sound procedure to quantify an athlete's body fat at the start of the season so that he or she can determine how much weight should be lost in order to compete at what is considered to be an "ideal" body weight for a given sport. There are numerous methods available for determining body composition. In Chapter 35, Katch and McArdle have provided a thorough discussion on methods employed in assessing body fat and density. In 1973 Tcheng and Tipton developed such a regression equation for use with high school wrestlers based on the measurement of various skinfolds and bone diameters. Using the Tcheng-Tipton formula it is possible to determine a wrestler's "ideal" body weight, which will represent that weight at which he will have approximately five percent body fat. It is in the sport of wrestling that perhaps the problems of sudden, deliberate weight reduction are most prevalent. Since the weight loss is accomplished at the expense of body fluids and/or muscle mass, two important problems must be considered. The first concerns a method of assessing the amount of weight loss in terms of body fluids, and second, ascertaining the influence of rapid weight loss on the ability to perform.

It is well known that the composition of the urine will be drastically altered if body fluid content is decreased by liquid deprivation or dehydration. In an effort to correct this abnormal situation, the kidneys will attempt to conserve water by excreting less urine. The composition of the urine will be altered so as to minimize the water content of urine that is excreted. The examination of the urinary prolife has been utilized to assess body fluid deficit in high school and college wrestlers. Zambraski and others (1974) reported that the urinary profile of high school wrestlers, obtained immediately prior to a prematch weigh-in, was significantly different from the urinary profile of nonwrestlers of similar body size and age. The results, Fig. 38.1 and 38.2, demonstrate that the wrestlers' urine was higher in terms of specific gravity, acidity, osmolarity, creatine content, and potassium concentration, while lower in sodium content. The wrestlers' urinary profile was characteristic of individuals who were severely dehydrated. Bosco and others (1974) found similar changes in the urine of individuals who abstained from food or liquid for three days.

Many coaches and wrestlers believe that it is possible to consume enough fluid and rehydrate during the time interval between the weigh-in and the match. This time interval may be several or more hours in duration. To answer this question Zambraski and his associates (1975) compared the weigh-in urinary profile with the urinary profile from the same individuals obtained immediately before competition about five hours later. The results were similar to those seen in Fig. 38.1 and 38.2. The weight-in urinary profile demonstrated dehydration. The precompetition urinary profile was for the most part unchanged and still characteristic of a dehydrated state even though these individuals attempted to rehydrate by fluid ingestion. This key finding demonstrated that under competitive conditions, appreciable rehydration will not occur over a five-hour time span despite attempts to regain body fluids. The implication is that if dehydration is utilized to make weight, several hours of fluid ingestion will not be effective in causing rehydration, consequently the individual will be competing while in a dehydrated state.

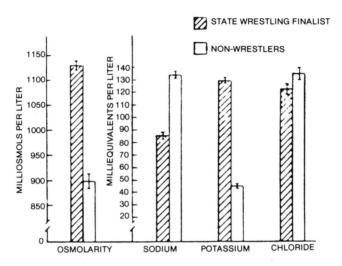

Fig. 38.1 Urinary osmolarities and electrolyte levels in state wrestling finalists and nonwrestlers. Means and SE listed. With the exception of the chloride data, all group differences were statistically significant at .05 level (Reproduced with permission of the publisher, the American College of Sports Medicine, from *Med and Sci in Sports*, 6, 129-132, 1974.)

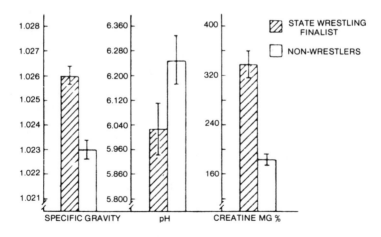

Fig. 38.2 Urinary profiles of state wrestling finalists and nonwrestlers. Means and SE listed. All group differences were statistically significant at .05 level. (Reproduced with permission of the publisher, the American College of Sports Medicine, from *Med and Sci in Sports*, 6, 129-132, 1974.)

It has been repeatedly documented that short-term weight loss, in amounts exceeding four to five percent of one's initial body weight, will adversely affect physical performance. Physiologically, rapid weight loss results in a decrease in maximal oxygen consumption (Taylor et al. 1957), increased stress on the cardiovascular system (Saltin 1964), and an increased difficulty in the dissipation of body heat (Grande et al. 1959). Performance tends to be characterized by a decrease in muscle strength, endurance, and speed of movement (Bosco et al. 1974; Taylor et al. 1957).

There may also be medical implications of rapid weight loss. No long-term study has ever been conducted to evaluate what effects several years of repeated drastic weight reduction has on adolescent growth and development. Many athletes begin competitive wrestling in junior high school. Even though these individuals are at a critical age insofar as nutritional demands are concerned, the importance of "making weight" often far outweighs considerations of a balanced diet, adequate fluid consumption, and minimum daily caloric requirements.

In their attempt to conserve body fluids, the kidneys alter the composition of the urine. This fluid conservation, however, places a stress on the kidneys, cardiovascular system and the body's acid-base buffer system. Questions have been raised as to whether these stresses do harm to the kidneys or cardiovascular system (Zambraski et al. 1975; Zambraski et al. 1974). Fortunately, most of the changes observed in the urinary profiles of wrestlers, as a consequence of dehydration and extreme weight loss, appear transitory in nature (Sergurson 1977; Vacaaro, Zauner, and Cade 1974). Urinary profiles return to more normal values when body weight is restored and rehydration occurs. It must be remembered, however, that body weight deviations of 3 to 20 percent, often seen in wrestlers, and excessive dehydration are abnormal states. At this point in time, the cumulative or long-term effects on renal or cardiovascular function of these practices are not definitely known.

Problems in athletics because of rapid or excessive weight loss will be difficult to eliminate. The first step must be the education of coaches, athletes, and parents with regard to the effects of weight loss on performance and possible medical implications. A problem, however, is that in some sports, such as wrestling, the weight classification system encourages excessive weight loss. A study was recently conducted by Tipton, Tcheng, and Zambraski (1976) on 8900 Iowa high school wrestlers. They reported that over half of these individuals were certified for weight classes in the 112- to 145-pound range. This means that the majority of these wrestling candidates were competing in only four to five of the 12 available weight classes. This situation encourages wrestlers to lose large amounts of weight so that they may attempt to compete in a weight class where there is less competition.

Concerns regarding weight loss in athletics have prompted several responsible and knowledgeable organizations to take a stand on this issue. In 1967 the American Medical Association denounced practices used to "make weight" in interscholastic wrestling (AMA Committee on Medical Aspects of Sports 1967). More recently the American College of Sports Medicine, an organization of physicians, physiologists, coaches, trainers, and physical educators, published a *Position Stand on Weight Loss in Wrestling* (American College of Sports Medicine 1976). In that paper it was stated that potential health hazards existed as a consequence of procedures used to "make weight."

Based on information previously discussed and suggestions contained in the American College of Sports Medicine's position stand, the following recommendations are made:

1. Body composition should be assessed on wrestling candidates prior to each wrestling season. This will provide wrestlers and coaches with an indication of what an individual's minimal weight should be.

2. Weight loss should be accomplished gradually through a nutritionally sound dietary plan and that minimal caloric requirements of 1200 to 2400 Kcal per day for high school and college athletes, respectively, should be met.

3. Weight loss achieved by fluid deprivation and/or dehydration should be discouraged. The use of rubber suits, hot rooms, saunas, steam baths, diuretics, or laxatives should be prohibited. Weight losses in excess of three to four pounds per day are indicative of fluid loss and therefore not beneficial to the athlete.

4. In interscholastic wrestling rapid weight loss should be discouraged by having weigh-ins immediately prior to matches and scheduling more weigh-ins during the week between matches. More than one participant per team should be allowed to compete in weight classes in the 119- to 145-pound range.

REFERENCES

AMA Committee on Medical Aspects of Sports. 1967. Wrestling and weight control. *JAMA*, 201, 541-543.

American College of Sports Medicine. 1976. Position stand on weight loss in wrestling. *Med Sci Spts*, 8, XI-XIV.

Bosco, J. S., J. E. Greenleaf, E. M. Bernauer, and D. H. Card. 1974. Effects of acute dehydration and starvation on muscular strength and endurance. *Acta Physiol Pol*, 25, 411-421.

Fahey, T. D. and C. H. Brown. 1973. The effect of an anabolic steroid on the strength, body composition, and endurance of college males when accompanied by a weight training program. *Med Sci Spts*, 5, 272-276.

Grande, F., J. E. Monagle, E. R. Buskirk, and H. L. Taylor. 1959. Body temperature responses to exercise in man on restricted food and water intake. *J Appl Physiol*, 14, 194-198.

Green, H. J. and M. E. Houston. 1975. Effect of a season of ice hockey on energy capacities and associated functions. *Med Sci Spts,* 7, 299-303.

Novak, L. P., R. E. Hyatt, and J. F. Alexander. 1968. Body composition and physiologic function of athletes, *JAMA,* 205, 764-770.

Saltin, B. 1964. Circulatory response to submaximal and maximal exercise after thermal dehydration. *J Appl Physiol,* 19, 1125-1132.

Sergurson, J. 1977. Effect of rapid weight reduction of college wrestlers on selected tests of the blood and urine which are used to diagnose kidney and liver problems. *Med Sci Spts,* 9, 56.

Taylor, H. L., E. R. Buskirk, J. Brozek, J. T. Anderson, and F. Grande. 1957. Performance capacity and effects of caloric restriction with hard physical work on young men. *J Appl Physiol,* 10, 421-429.

Tcheng, T. K. and C. M. Tipton. 1973. Iowa wrestling study: Anthropometric measurements and the prediction of a "minimal" body weight for high school wrestlers. *Med Sci Spts,* 5, 1-10.

Tipton, C. M. and T. K. Tcheng. 1970. Iowa wrestling study: Weight loss in high school students. *JAMA,* 2114, 1269-1274.

Tipton, C. M., T. K. Tcheng, and E. J. Zambraski. 1976. Iowa wrestling study: Weight classification system. *Med Sci Spts,* 8, 101-104.

Vacaaro, P., C. W. Zauner, and J. R. Cade. 1975. Changes in body weight, hematocrit and plasma protein concentration due to dehydration and rehydration in wrestlers. *Med Sci Spts,* 7, 76.

Wilmore, J. H. 1974. Alterations in strength, body composition and anthropometric measurements consequent to a 10-week weight training program. *Med Sci Spts,* 6, 133-136.

Wilmore, J. H. and C. H. Brown. 1974. Physiological profiles of women distance runners. *Med Sci Spts,* 6, 178-181.

Zambraski, E. J., D. T. Foster, P. M. Gross, and C. M. Tipton. 1976. Iowa wrestling study: Weight loss and urinary profiles of collegiate wrestlers. *Med Sci Spts,* 8, 105-108.

Zambraski, E. J., C. M. Tipton, T. K. Tcheng, H. R. Jordan, A. C. Vailas, and A. K. Callahan. 1975. Iowa Wrestling Study: Changes in the urinary profiles of wrestlers prior to and after competition. *Med Sci Spts,* 7, 217-220.

Zambraski, E. J., C. M. Tipton, H. R. Jordan, W. K. Palmer, and T. K. Tcheng. 1974. Iowa Wrestling Study: Urinary profiles of state finalists prior to competition. *Med Sci Spts,* 6, 129-132.

39

Alcohol

Melvin H. Williams

Beverages containing ethyl alcohol, or ethanol, are consumed by the majority of the adult population throughout the world, and although the vast majority are social drinkers, a considerable number of individuals abuse the use of alcohol. Indeed, alcohol is the number one drug problem in the United States both in the adult and teenage population (Anonymous 1973). Although the chronic ingestion of alcohol leading to addiction and alcoholism is an important problem, with implications for physical fitness, it falls outside the scope of this article. Thus, this section deals only with the acute effects of alcohol ingestion upon physical performance.

Ethyl alcohol is not a foreign substance to the body, as it can be isolated in small amounts from any animal tissue or organ (Palarea 1963). Although exogenous sources of alcohol may be taken into the body in a variety of ways, the oral route is the most common. It is absorbed directly from the stomach and small intestine into the blood stream, with maximum concentration occurring in less than one hour. Alcohol is distributed in the water of the body, and its concentration in each tissue depends upon the water content of that tissue. Thus, the distribution of alcohol in the body is essentially a process of dilution. The elimination of alcohol proceeds at a constant rate, approximately three quarters of an ounce per hour. It is oxidized in three stages, with the first rate-limiting stage occurring primarily in the liver; alcohol dehydrogenase converts alcohol to acetaldehyde. The acetaldehyde is transformed to acetic acid, which is subsequently oxidized to carbon dioxide and water. In the process, one gram of alcohol yields seven calories.

Blood alcohol levels (BAL) are expressed in milligrams (mg) per 100 milliliters (ml) of blood. Thus, a BAL of 40 mg per 100 ml blood would be expressed as .04 percent or 40 mg percent. BALs up to .05 percent are not usually intoxicating, and the effect above the .05 level is dependent upon the individual. Many states interpret the .10 level as being legally intoxicated, whereas at the .15 to .20 level, most individuals are definitely drunk.

*   From M. H. Williams. *Drugs and Athletic Performance*. Springfield, Illinois: C. C. Thomas, 1974.

USE IN ATHLETICS

Alcohol affects all cells of the body, the most dramatic results of ingestion being the effects on the brain. Gould (1970) indicated that in spite of the long use of alcohol as a stimulant, it is actually a central nervous system depressant. The apparent stimulation is evinced because of the depressive action of ethanol on the reticular activating system. The inhibitory control mecahnisms are decreased, and this results in unrestrained activity of many areas of the brain with loss of the integrating control of the cerebral cortex. Several investigators (Doctor and Perkins 1961; Perman 1958) have noted a stimulating effect of alcohol in some individuals, but attributed the cause to increased secretions from the adrenal medulla and increased sympathetic nervous activity. A biphasic hypothesis regarding the effect of alcohol has been advanced, indicating that it may produce a transitory sensation of excitement followed by depressive effects. Hence, the application of alcohol may be based upon two paradoxical effects. In some cases, it may be used for the apparent stimulating effect, while in others for the depressive or tranquilizing effect on reducing excessive tension.

Boje (1939) and Wolf (1963) indicated that in cases of extreme athletic exertion, or in events of brief maximal effort, alcohol has been given to athletes to serve as a stimulant by releasing inhibitions and lessening the sense of fatigue. This viewpoint relative to mental stimulation, which has been reiterated by others (Chenowith and Selkirk 1953; Hickman 1958; Ikai and Steinhaus 1961; Jellinck 1954), would suggest alcohol exerts its influence through its effects on the subject's state of mind. On the other hand, Shephard (1972) noted that in some events, anxiety may disrupt performance by inducing excessive arousal of the cerebral cortex. In this case, the sedative action of alcohol may be beneficial.

Prior to 1972, alcohol was proscribed as a doping agent by the International Olympic Committee, and Shephard (1972) noted that two pistol shooters were disqualified during the 1968 Olympics due to the alleged use of alcohol in an attempt to increase their competitive ability. Fischbach (1972), however, noted that alcohol, although called goldwater by athletes involved in shooting competition, was not listed as a specific doping agent for the 1972 Munich Olympics.

Since alcohol is a popular beverage with potent pharmacological effects on behavior, it has received considerable research attention in relationship to physical performance. The majority of the research has centered about psychomotor ability, primarily in skills involving automobile operation, but a considerable number of studies also have been conducted regarding its influence upon intense muscular effort.

EXPERIMENTATION WITH HUMANS

Subjective Effects

Coopersmith (1964) succinctly summarized current knowledge regarding the effect of small amounts of alcohol upon behavior in normal subjects. He noted that both popular impressions and clinical evidence suggest that alcohol reduces feelings of insecurity, tension, and discomfort, thereby permitting a freer and less constrained behavioral expression. Thus, as Shephard (1972) has noted, alcohol may elicit greater self-confidence in the athlete. These statements reinforce the concept, advanced in the preceding section, that the acute ingestion of small amounts of alcohol may be ergogenic in nature due to inhibition of psychological factors that may limit performance.

Effects on Psychomotor Performance

In a critical review of studies from 1940 to 1961 concerning the effects of alcohol on some psychological processes including reaction time, Carpenter (1962) noted that in general motor performance is impaired at low and moderate blood alcohol levels. In a series of tests during the same time period, Hebbelinck (1961) also reported that in tests of physical performance, neuromuscular performance was adversely affected at BALs lower than .05; he later concluded that neuromuscular incoordination and poorer reflexive control appeared to be responsible mainly for the deleterious effects of alcohol on the basic components of physical performance (Hebbelinck 1963). Nelson (1959) reiterated these viewpoints, indicating that highly coordinated skills seemed to decrease most in efficiency following alcohol injection.

More recent investigations substantiate the fact that psychomotor performance is retarded at low blood alcohol levels. Significant decrements in hand-eye coordination (Sidell and Pless 1971), balance (Begbie 1966), complex coordination (Tang and Rosenstein 1967), and visual tracking (Forney et al. 1964) have been reported at BALs between .04 and .06.

Summarizing a number of laboratory reports, Shephard (1972) noted a variety of measures such as arm steadiness, body sway, dynamic balance, and more complicated psychomotor tests are all adversely affected by alcohol, even as low as 30 mg percent; all subjects show a loss of motor performance at 100 mg percent.

In summary, the evidence overwhelmingly supports the conclusion that alcohol does adversely affect fine psychomotor performance. However, Shephard (1972) interjects the intriguing thought that the greater self-confidence produced by alcohol may override the loss of skill and slowing of body reactions.

Effect on Physiological Adjustments to Exercise

The effect of alcohol upon cardiovascular, respiratory, and metabolic adjustments to submaximal and maximal exercise has been investigated recently. Heart rate response has received considerable attention. Hebbelinck (1959) evaluated the effect of a moderate dose (0.6 ml per kg of body weight) of absolute alcohol on the cardiac response before, during, and after a five-minute work load at 1500 kilopond-meters (kpm). He noted an increase of four systoles per minute during rest and recovery, and a marked average increase of 23 beats per minute during the early stages of the work load. In a subsequent report (Hebbelinck 1962), using a small dose of ethanol and a work load of 1000 kpm, identical results were obtained. Although his data are indicative of a significant cardiac response, no statistical analyses were performed. Adolph (1969) found that the ingestion of 1 ml of pure ethanol per kg of body weight produced a statistically significant tachycardia during the first five minutes of the Balke treadmill test. However, of the six subjects, two had resting heart rates during the alcohol phase that averaged 30 beats higher than the control phase, a finding that may influence the results as previous research (Williams 1970) has indicated a high relationship between the resting heart rate and the initial stages of a submaximal work task. Blomqvist and colleagues (1970) reported that 150 ml of 86 proof alcohol elevated the heart rate 12 to 14 beats per minute during submaximal exercise. The rate during maximal exercise was unchanged. However, they did not counterbalance the order of treatments in this repeated-measure design.

Contrary to the above, other studies indicate alcohol exerts no effect on cardiac response to exercise. Mazess and others (1968), using 0.6 gm ethanol per kg of body weight and a work load of 1000 kpm, found no significant differences in heart rate before, during, and after work at sea level; but, they did note a detrimental effect at altitude. Using three different types of work (step-wise increases, continuous, and intermittent), Garlind and associates (1960) found that the average heart rate response to submaximal work tests was not influenced significantly by ethanol. Using four different dosages of pure ethanol (0.0, 0.2, 0.4, and 0.6 ml per pound), Bobo (1972) revealed no change in exercise heart rate at submaximal or near maximal runs on a treadmill. Williams (1972a) concluded that three variant dosages (0.0, 0.2, 0.4 ml per pound) had no significant effect on heart rate responses to exercise at 500, 1000, or 1500 kpm on a bicycle ergometer. In a subsequent study (Williams 1972b), a moderate dose (0.4 ml per pound) had no effect on either submaximal heart rate (400 to 1200 kpm) or maximal heart rate determined just prior to exhaustion on an all-out bicycle ride.

Gould (1970) postulated that alcohol may serve as a myocardial depressant in humans, decreasing cardiac output without a change in heart rate. Summarizing other investigations with animals, he indicated that alcohol reduced cardiac contractility. However, it is not known whether these results may be extrapolated to the human organism during exercise. The findings of Blomqvist and his colleagues (1970) indicated no influence of ethanol on cardiac contractility during exercise since maximal cardiac output and stroke volume did not change.

One of the physiological effects of ethanol during rest is a cutaneous vasodilation, with a concomitant vasoconstriction in resting musculature (Fewings et al. 1966; Graf and Strom 1960). If this condition persisted during exercise, it could prove detrimental if the cardiac output did not compensate. However, Graf and Strom (1960), using venous occlusion plethysmography to study skin and muscle blood flow, reported that ethanol did not measurably influence the central circulatory response to leg work and did not decrease physical work capacity.

Garlind and his associates (1960) reported that neither a small (0.3 gm per kg) nor a moderate dose (0.6 gm per kg) of absolute alcohol had any effect upon the respiratory rate, respiratory quotient, ventilatory quotient, or oxygen uptake in nine subjects before, during, or after exercise. In other reports concerning oxygen consumption, Blomqvist and others (1970) found that oxygen uptake during submaximal work was 0.05 to 0.15 liters per minute higher after administration of alcohol. Adolph (1969) also reported small, but not significant, increases in oxygen uptake during the early stages of the Balke treadmill test following alcohol ingestion. Conversely, Mazess (1968) found no significant effect during submaximal work, while Bobo (1972) reported similar findings for both submaximal and near maximal exercise with four dosage levels of alcohol. Williams (1972b) also failed to observe any significant effect of a small or moderate dose upon oxygen consumption during submaximal and near maximal exercise on a bicycle ergometer; also, no changes were noted in oxygen uptake during a five-minute recovery period. In general, these studies indicate that alcohol has no effect on oxygen consumption capacity.

In summary, it would appear that the acute ingestion of ethanol elicits neither favorable nor unfavorable physiological modifications in the cardiovascular, respiratory, or metabolic responses to exercise, particularly if it is maximal exercise. Apparently the various physiological changes produced by alcohol during a resting state are abrogated by the various neural and hormonal adjustments associated with the onset of exercise.

Effect on Strength and Endurance

Since alcohol has been a common beverage for thousands of years, and its behavioral effects well known by medical personnel, it was one of the first substances investigated regarding its ergogenic effect. Most of the early research dealt with its effect upon local muscular strength and fatigue, while later studies included tests of general endurance capacity.

For the interested reader, a comprehensive review of the literature published prior to 1908, including his own research, was presented by Rivers (1908). However, in interpreting these studies, one should be aware of methodological irregularities. For example, only one or two subjects were used, with general conclusions based on their performances. Also, in the majority of studies, no mention was made of such factors as control doses, assignment of dose by body weight, presence of food in the digestive tract, or the type of alcohol administered, all of which are considered today to bear upon the acceptability of the results. Nevertheless, Rivers' general conclusion was that a small dose of alcohol neither increased nor decreased the capacity for muscular work on an ergograph.

In more recent years, several reports have substantiated the conclusions of Rivers. Hebbelinck (1959) reported no significant effect of 0.6 ml per kg absolute alcohol upon muscular strength; however, he did report a slight decrease in power. In a subsequent study (Hebbelinck 1963), although several individuals did better on strength and power tests under the influence of alcohol, he concluded that static strength as measured by a manuometer and back dynamometer was not changed after consumption of a small dose of alcohol. On the other hand, dynamic strength showed a decrease of 5.8 percent.

Contrary to Hebbelinck's findings, Nelson (1959) indicated that two and three ounces of pure alcohol elicited a decrease in isometric grip strength. Of the various gross motor tests involved in his study, he concluded strength was one of the most adversely affected.

In an experiment to measure the effect of alcohol on several parameters, Simonson and Ballard (1944) reported that the effects of alcohol on muscle strength were inconclusive. Testing subjects at five time intervals, ranging from 15 minutes to three hours after ingestion of alcohol, they noted no constant effects upon the strength of the hand and arm extensor muscles. In a well-controlled study, Ikai and Steinhaus (1961) evaluated the effect of 15 to 20 ml of 95 percent ethanol on measured tension in the right forearm flexors, using one maximal contraction per minute for 30 minutes. An increase of 3.7 pounds, or 5.6 percent, was attributable to alcohol. However, this increase was not statistically significant.

Williams (1969) studied the interaction effects of a control (0.0 ml per pound), small (0.2 ml per pound), moderate (0.4 ml per pound), and large (0.6 ml per pound) dose of alcohol with variant elapsed time periods following ingestion; allowing 30 minutes for complete absorption, elapsed time periods were 0, 15, 30, and 60 minutes. Thirty-five university males were exposed to the control, small, and moderate dose, while an experimental subgroup of nine also took the criterion test following the large dose. The standardized work load consisted of intermittent maximal contractions of the forearm flexors at the rate of 30 per minute for six minutes. Parameters studied included initial strength, maximal strength, steady state or final strength, total work, fatigable work, and the mathematical rate of fatigue. The results of the statistical analysis revealed no significant main or interaction effects, and Williams concluded that the alcohol doses utilized in his study had no effect upon the strength or endurance variables under investigation. In summary, the general results of contemporary research indicate that the acute ingestion of alcohol has little or no effect on subsequent tests of local muscular strength or endurance.

Effect on General Endurance

The research regarding the effect of alcohol upon general endurance capacity is more limited. In one of the earliest studies, Asmussen and Boje (1948) investigated the influence of alcohol on the ability to perform maximal muscular work and concluded the effect was not significant. Two tasks on the bicycle ergometer were utilized, simulating a 100-meter dash and a 1500-meter run. They found that alcohol in small doses (25 gm pure ethanol) had no effect, and alcohol in larger doses (75 gm pure ethanol) had only a diminishing effect on the ability to perform maximal muscular work. Two other independent Scandinavian investigations (Garlind 1960; Graf and Strom 1960) also noted that small or moderate doses of alcohol did not affect physical working capacity. Although Nelson (1959) noted a decrease in performance on seven gross motor tests following the intake of two and three ounces of pure ethanol, bicycle ergometer work time was one of the tests to show least change in efficiency when compared with control.

In more recent investigations, Williams (1972b) studied the effect of a moderate dose (0.4 ml per pound) or pure ethanol upon time to exhaustion on a progressive bicycle ergometer work task. Ten conditioned males underwent four test trials, two with a control dose and two with alcohol. He concluded that a moderate dose of alcohol failed to affect maximal endurance performance. Therefore, the results of these studies suggest that alcohol is not a very effective ergogenic aid in athletic events characterized by all-out general muscular endurance.

SUMMARY

When interpreting the results of experimentation involving the acute effects of alcohol on human performance, such as in single or double dose administration studies, one must be cautious not to generalize the findings to include the effect of chronic ingestion on performance. In experimentation regarding the acute effects, it appears that the possible limiting physiological manifestations mediated by alcohol during rest are abrogated during an exercise situation. However, the chronic ingestion of alcohol may produce certain physiological changes in the liver and heart that may result in decreased performance capacity.

REFERENCES

Adolph, J. 1969. The effects of ethyl alcohol on physical performance. Unpublished doctoral dissertation. The Ohio State University.

Anonymous. 1973. Alcohol-the latest teen drug. *Newsweek,* March 5, 1973.

Asmussen, E. and O. Boje. 1948. The effects of alcohol and some drugs on the capacity for work. *Acta Physiol Scand,* 15, 109-18.

Begbie, G. 1966. The effects of alcohol and of varying amounts of visual information on a balancing test. *Ergonomics,* 9, 325-33.

Blomqvist, G., et al. 1970. Acute effects of ethanol ingestion on the response to submaximal and maximal exercise in man. *Circulation,* 42, 463-70.

Bobo, W. 1973. Effects of alcohol upon maximum oxygen uptake, lung ventilation, and heart rate. *Res Quart,* 43, 1-6.

Boje, O. 1939. Doping. *Bull Hlth Org League of Nations,* 8, 439-69.

Carpenter, J. 1963. Effects of alcohol on some psychological processes. *Q J Stud Alcohol*, 23, 274-314.

Chenowith, L. and T. Selkirk. 1953. *School Health Problems*. Des Moines: Appleton.

Coopersmith, S. 1964. The effects of alcohol on reaction to affective stimuli. *Q J Stud Alcohol*, 25, 459-75.

Doctor, R. and R. Perkins. 1961. The effects of ethyl alcohol on autonomic and muscular responses in humans. *Q J Stud Alcohol*, 22, 374-86.

Fewings, J., et al. 1966. The effects of ethyl alcohol on the blood vessels of the hand and forearm in man. *Br J Pharmacol Chemother*, 27, 93-106.

Fischbach, E. 1972. Problems of doping. *Med Monatsschr*, 26, 377-81.

Forney, R., et al. 1964. Measurement of attentive motor performance after alcohol. *Percept Mot Skills*, 19, 151-54.

Garlind, T., et al. 1960. Effect of ethanol on circulatory, metabolic, and neurohumoral function during muscular work in man. *Acta Pharmacol et Toxicol*, 17, 106-14.

Gould, L. 1970. Cardiac effects of alcohol. *Am Heart J*, 79, 422-25.

Graf, K. and G. Strom. 1960. Effect of ethanol ingestion on arm blood flow in healthy young men at rest and during work. *Acta Pharmacol et Toxicol*, 17, 115-20.

Hebbelinck, M. 1959. The effects of a moderate dose of alcohol on a series of functions of physical performance in man. *Arch Internat Pharmacod*, 120, 402-5.

Hebbelinck, M. 1960. The effect of a moderate dose of ethyl alcohol on human respiratory gas exchange during rest and muscular exercise. *Arch Internat Pharmacod*, 126, 214-18.

Hebbelinck, M. 1961. *Spierarbeid en Ethylalkohol*. Brussel: Arsica Uitgaven.

Hebbelinck, M. 1962. The effects of a small dose of ethyl alcohol on certain basic components of human physical performance. The effect of cardiac rate during muscular work. *Arch Internat Pharmacod*, 140, 61-67.

Hebbelinck, M. 1963. The effects of a small dose of ethyl alcohol on certain basic components of human physical performance. *Arch Internat Pharmacod*, 143, 247-57.

Hickman, C. 1958. *Health for College Students*. Englewood Cliffs: Prentice-Hall.

Ikai, M. and A. Steinhaus. 1961. Some factors modifying the expression of human strength. *J Appl Physiol*, 16, 157-61.

Jellinek, E. 1954. Effect of small amounts of alcohol on psychological functions. In *Alcohol, Science and Society*. New Haven: *Q J Stud Alcohol*.

Mazess, R., et al. 1968. Effects of alcohol and altitude on man during rest and work. *Aerospace Med*, 39, 403-6.

Nelson, D. 1959. Effects of ethyl alcohol on the performance of selected gross motor tests. *Res Quart*, 30, 312-20.

Palarea, E. 1963. Some physiological effects of alcohol and their application in modern therapeutics. *J Am Geriatr Soc*, 11, 933-44.

Perman, E. 1958. The effect of ethyl alcohol on the secretions from the adrenal medulla in man. *Acta Physiol Scand*, 44, 241-47.

Rivers, W. 1908. *The Influence of Alcohol and Other Drugs on Fatigue*. London: Edward Arnold.

Shephard, R. 1972. *Alive Man: The Physiology of Physical Activity.* Springfield: Thomas.

Sidell, F. and J. Pless. 1971. Ethyl alcohol: blood levels and performance decrements after oral administration to man. *Psychopharmacologia,* 19, 246-61.

Simonson, E. and G. Ballard. 1944. The effect of small doses of alcohol on the central nervous system. *Am J Clin Pathol,* 14, 333-41.

Tang, P. and R. Rosenstein. 1967. Influence of alcohol and dramamine, alone and in combination, on psychomotor performance. *Aerospace Med,* 38, 818-21.

Williams, M. H. 1969. Effect of selected doses of alcohol on fatigue parameters of the forearm flexor muscles. *Res Quart,* 40, 832-40.

Williams, M. H. 1970. Comparison of the submaximal cardiovascular step test response to a maximal aerobic performance task. *Am Correct Ther J,* 24, 127-29.

Williams, M. H. 1972a. Effect of small and moderate doses of alcohol on exercise heart rate and oxygen consumption. *Res Quart,* 43, 94-104.

Williams, M. H. 1972b. The effect of a moderate dose of alcohol on maximal heart rate and maximal endurance capacity. Unpublished data. Old Dominion University.

Wolf, S. 1963. Psychosomatic aspects of competitive sports. *J Spts Med,* 3, 157-63.

40

Caffeine

Peter J. Van Handel and David Essig

Small improvements in athletic performance often require major increases in intensity and/or duration of training. The fact that more work is done or more time is spent in training, however, is no guarantee in itself that performance will be enhanced. Moreover, participation in some sports (distance running for example) already involves a tremendous expenditure of time for many athletes. Based on these considerations, it is easy to understand why the surreptitious use of work-enhancing or "ergogenic" aids to improve performance is on the increase. The purpose of this paper is to discuss the effects of caffeine and related compounds, especially as related to endurance performance.

CAFFEINE AS A DOPING AGENT

As a zanthrine derivative, caffeine is known to act as a stimulant on the central nervous system, both cardiac and skeletal muscle, the kidneys, respiratory rate and depth, and possibly the adrenal glands. Its proposed use as an ergogenic aid has traditionally been based on the notion that it produces the same general type of central stimulation and reduction of fatigue as do amphetamines. If these effects supplement the natural sympathetic responses to exercise stress, then caffeine would act as a powerful ergogenic aid. Recent studies, however, suggest that this traditional view is no longer tenable (Costill et al. 1978; Essig 1979; Ivy et al. 1979; Perkins and Williams 1975).

Based on early reports of enhanced work capacity following the administration of coffee or other beverages containing caffeine and the basic metabolic and physiological effects described above, caffeine was at one time regarded as a doping agent (Kourounakis 1972). In 1939, Boje (1939) suggested that the use of pure caffeine or caffeine preparations should be prohibited in conjunction with athletic competition. In the 1960s, a study by the Federation Internationale de Medicine Sportive reported that caffeine was a common doping agent among Italian athletes. As a result, its use was banned (Vererando 1963). Mustala (1967) reported that caffeine was one of the few drugs able to enhance athletic performance. About the same time, the Medical Commission of the British Commonwealth Games (1971) reported that the caffeine present in a normal cup of coffee was not regarded as a doping agent. The International Olympic Committee removed caffeine from its list of doping agents in 1972.

The observations cited in the preceding paragraph illustrate a problem common to many studies involving so-called ergogenic aids; that is, the actual ergogenic effects are unclear and often equivocal. Pertaining to caffeine this is in part due to the fact that the body's response(s) to a physiological dose may be masked by similar responses to the work stress itself. These may include, for example, changes in various cardiovascular measures, alterations in blood hormone levels, and increased concentration or delivery of fuels needed for muscular work. The type of work task, fitness and nutritional status of the individual, and environmental factors may also interact to influence these responses. The isolation of caffeine effects in *in vivo* performance studies is, therefore, extremely difficult. For this reason, one must consider *in vitro* studies of caffeine to gain insight into the mechanisms suggested to be responsible for its ergogenic effects.

BIOCHEMICAL AND PHYSIOLOGICAL EFFECTS

Gastric Emptying, Absorption and Distribution

Caffeine solutions are rapidly emptied from the stomach and absorbed from the gastrointestinal tract (Axelrod and Reichenthal 1953). They reach peak concentrations in the blood approximately one hour after ingestion (Bellet et al. 1968; Axelrod and Reichenthal 1953) with a half-life of 3.5 hours. The latter authors have also shown that caffeine rapidly distributes into the tissues roughly in proportion to their water content and the subsequent physiological response is proportional to the concentration. As a result, both dosage and body water (and fat) content may be important factors in experimental studies, especially when attempts are made to relate *in vitro* data to observations *in vivo*. For example, as little as 50 mg produces typical actions on the central nervous system (Syed 1976), while doses above 250 mg may be associated with tremor, nervousness, and irritability (Stephenson 1977). It may be that this "overdose" effect is responsible for the adverse reactions reported in recent exercise studies (Costill et al. 1978; Essig 1979) and Little's (1966) observations that caffeine may act only in "susceptible persons."

Once distributed by the blood, caffeine acts on the central nervous and cardiovascular systems. In addition, there are effects on the mobilization and utilization of substrates by the tissues and on the contractility of heart and skeletal muscle.

Actions on the Central Nervous System

Oldendorf (1971) showed that caffeine readily passes the blood-brain barrier and Syed (1976) indicated that caffeine may act directly on the medullary, vasomotor, and vagal centers. In addition to the peripheral results of this stimulation, there is increased alertness, decreased drowsiness, and a reduced sensation of fatigue. This action may account for the reduced perception of fatigue during work tasks (Costill et al. 1978; Essig 1979). These effects have been suggested to be due to an enhanced tissue turnover of catacholamines (Berkowitz, Tarver, and Spector 1970). While several mechanisms for this action have been suggested (Berkowitz and Spector 1971; Waldek 1973), there is no doubt that caffeine has adrenergic effects. The blood concentration of catecholamines also increases as does urinary excretion (Atuk et al. 1967; Van Handel et al. 1977) and urine volume (Bellet et al. 1969; Van Handel et al. 1977) following caffeine ingestion.

Actions on the Heart and Cardiovascular System

Various cardiovascular parameters also respond to xanthine administration mediated both by stimulation of the central nervous system and/or direct actions on the heart. These include altered cardiac and stroke indexes, brachial artery pressure (Gould et al. 1973), blood flow (Goodman and Gilman 1965), and cardiac contractility (Pickering 1893; Grass 1972). The latter directly affects the former and may be due to alterations in the activity or concentration of cAMP (Crass 1972; Waldek 1973) or to increased mobilization of calcium (Berkowitz et al. 1970). Kukovetz et al. (1960) have suggested that a caffeine mediated inhibition of phosphodiesterase with concomitant alterations in cAMP activity may alter sarcolemmal permeability to calcium. Caffeine may also antagonize the cellular uptake of adenosine; the latter compound is known to inhibit formation of cAMP (Fain 1977) and calcium exchange (Guthrie and Nayler 1967). Whatever the mechanisms, there is a positive inotropic effect of methylxanthines on cardiac output (Grollman 1930; Guthrie and Nayler 1967; Hess and Haugaard 1958). Ivy et al. (1979) have also shown that ingestion of caffeine prior to endurance exercise of moderate to heavy intensity results in a greater oxygen pulse. The significance of these cardiovascular changes for exercise performance are unclear since oxygen availability would not be a factor during submaximal exercise and enhanced cardiac contractility with a demand for greater oxygen uptake may actually be detrimental for some subjects at high work loads.

Substrate Mobilization and Utilization

The effect of caffeine on adipose and muscle tissue metabolism are not fully understood, but may provide the most dramatic ergogenic effects on work performance. As cited above, cAMP seems to be the focus for metabolic control and, in turn, its activity appears to be regulated by several different mechanisms.

Caffeine acts to increase the blood catecholamine levels (Bellet et al. 1969; Berkowitz and Spector 1971). They and other lipolytic hormones are thought to act at the adipose cell membrane (see Fig. 40.1). By activating adenyl cyclase, they increase the intracellular concentration of 3'-5' (cyclic) AMP. Cyclic AMP, in turn, activates a protein kinase, which accelerates phosphorylation of inactive triglyceride lipase. The activated form of the lipase increases hydrolysis of stored triglyceride, thus increasing the release of FFA and glycerol into the blood.

Caffeine effects on FFA mobilization are thought to be related not only to catecholamine mediated increases in cAMP, but also to xanthine inhibition of phosphodiesterase (Butcher et al. 1965; Davis 1968). The latter response prolongs and/or increases the activity of cAMP as phosphodiesterase controls the degradation of cAMP to 5'-AMP. *In vitro,* the concentration of caffeine needed to inhibit phosphodiesterase, such that cAMP levels increase, is 10 to 20 mM (Cheung 1966; Butcher and Sutherland 1962). In light of the gastric emptying, absorption and distribution characteristics of ingested caffeine solutions (Axelrod and Reichenthal 1953; Bellet et al. 1968), it is unlikely that the forecited concentrations are achieved *in vivo.* Butcher and Baird (1969) have noted, however, that one mM caffeine in combination with epinephrine, stimulates adipose tissue lipolysis to a significantly greater degree than does caffeine alone. *In vivo,* plasma levels of FFA have been found to be elevated two to three hours following caffeine ingestion at rest (Bellet et al. 1965; 1968) and only during the latter stages of endurance exercise (Ivy et al. 1979). More recently, Essig (1979) found that ingestion of 5 mg per kg body weight resulted in a significant increase (22 percent) in FFA one hour after ingestion. The reason for this discrepancy is unclear, but may be related to subtle interactions between concentrations of the ingested caffeine solution, training status of the subjects and/or susceptibility to effects of the caffeine, and concomitant sympathetic effects of exercise on catecholamine levels.

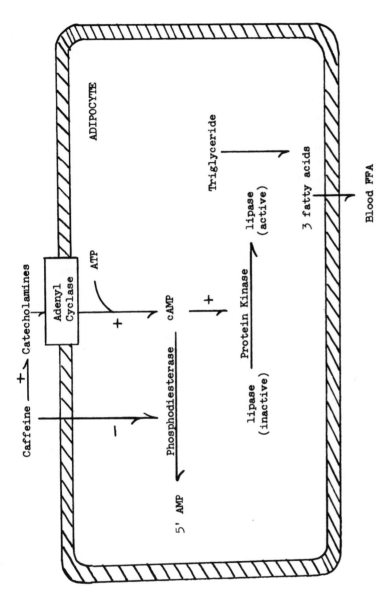

Fig. 40.1 Mechanism for FFA release from the fat cell. Various lipolytic hormones including epinephrine act to increase adenyl cyclase activity at the fat cell membrane. As a result, cyclic cAMP levels are increased; cAMP, in turn, modulates lipase activity resulting in an increased release of free fatty acids. Increased levels of plasma FFA are associated with altered rates of muscular FFA uptake and oxidation as well as esterification into triglyceride. Caffeine inhibits phosphodiesterase, thereby prolonging or increasing the activity of cAMP and/or altering the uptake of adenosine, which may have similar effects.

Of some concern is the fact that caffeine administration has been linked to circulatory and hormonal factors associated with coronary risk. Little et al. (1966) found, however, that coffee elevates serum lipids only in susceptible persons, and Avogaro et al. (1973) suggested that as long as caffeine was ingested in moderate amounts, the related lipid mobilization and atherogenic influence were of minor importance. Studlar (1973) showed no relationship between the amount of caffeine consumed and the level of serum lipids. He found that high caffeine doses were required to induce significant increases in lipolysis concomitant with elevated serum triglyceride levels, and that the caffeine induced lipolysis was inhibited by simultaneous food intake.

In addition to its lipolytic effects, caffeine also alters glucose homeostatis; reportedly having a hyperglycemic action (Cheraskin et al. 1967; MacCornack 1977; Syed 1976), though the mechanism for this response is unclear in light of the previously cited effects on FFA. On the one hand, enhanced cAMP activity stimulated hepatic glycogenolysis (Strubelt 1969; Syed 1976) and, in turn, insulin secretion (Studlar 1973). The adipokinetic effects of caffeine, however, would likely curtail peripheral glucose catabolism via the glucose-FFA cycle (Randle, Newsholme, and Garland 1964) so that the hyperglycemia may be due to a reduced peripheral glucose uptake rather than an increased hepatic glucose output (Van Handel et al. 1977). In addition, even small amounts of insulin would inhibit FFA mobilization, and norepinephrine is a potent inhibitor of insulin release (Porte et al. 1966). Wachman and coworkers (1970) found that the increased lipolysis observed following caffeine ingestion was related to retarded insulin secretion. Low plasma insulin levels act as a barrier to glucose uptake by muscle, helping to preserve hepatic glycogen stores during prolonged work stress (Pruett 1970).

Effects on Muscle Substrate Use

As cited above, caffeine distributes in the body water and as such the greatest amount is concentrated in skeletal muscle (Burg 1975). Axelrod and Reichenthal (1953) have shown that tissue response to caffeine is proportional to its concentration. It may be suggested, therefore, that potentially the greatest effects of caffeine ingestion occur in skeletal muscle. *In vitro* studies do, in fact, indicate mechanisms exist whereby caffeine may act directly to enhance muscle function (see Fig. 40.2).

Contractility, for example, is enhanced due to increased intracellular calcium content (Novotony and Bianchi 1967) and appears to be due to a reduced ability of the sarcoplasmic reteculum to store or release calcium (Brust 1976). It is important to note that caffeine and other methylxanthines are known to increase glycogenolysis (MacCornack 1977; Strubelt 1969; Syed 1976) due to alterations in cAMP activity. Therefore, in addition to calcium effects, there may be a potentiating action with epinephrine to increase glucose-6-phosphate levels, which are also known to enhance contractility (Bowman and Raper 1964). As a

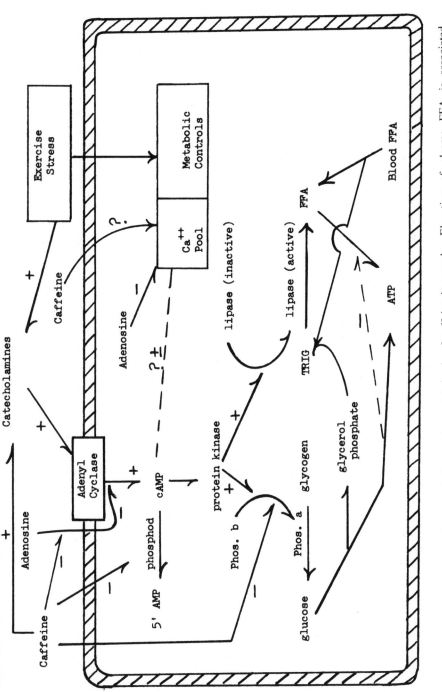

Fig. 40.2 Summary of intermediate metabolism and suggested role of caffeine in muscle. Elevation of plasma FFA is associated with increased uptake by muscle. The use of blood-borne or triglyceride-derived FFA is known to feedback and slow the rate of carbohydrate utilization by inhibition of various steps of glycolysis. Caffeine may block glycogen breakdown and increase triglyceride use. The sum of these effects appears to "spare" carbohydrates during endurance work, thus enhancing performance.

consequence of these inotropic effects, there is an increase in tissue oxygen consumption (Hoffman 1976; Manchester et al. 1973; Novotony and Bianchi 1967) and an increased a-$\bar{v}O_2$ difference (Grollman 1930).

Interestingly, caffeine may also act directly to inhibit glycogenolysis in muscle. Kavinsky et al. (1978) noted in a series of kinetic and x-ray crystallographic studies that one mM caffeine inhibits the binding of glucose-1-phosphate to muscle phosphorylase a. They suggest that caffeine acts in synergy with intracellular glucose to inhibit the enzyme at sites on the enzymes' surface. This occurs at physiological concentrations of glucose and appears to be dependent upon the binding of caffeine or other methylated oxy-purines so that glucose can exert maximal inhibitory effects. Caffeine may also have direct effects on the phosphofructokinase reaction (Mansour 1972b).

While the lipolytic effect of methylxanthines on adipose tissue are well defined, there is little information on their role in metabolism of muscle triglyceride. It is unclear, for example, whether or not cAMP mediates lipolysis (Mayer et al. 1967; Keely et al. 1975; Sobel and Mayer 1973). Crass, however, has recently shown that in isolated, perfused rat hearts, theophylline reduces endogenous triglyceride content (1973). Whether these effects occur in skeletal muscle is unknown. Bellet et al. (1965) observed that caffeine administered intramuscularly increases plasma FFA levels. Based on these known effects of caffeine and other xanthines *in vitro* on catecholamine release, cAMP and phosphodiesterase activity, and phosphorylase, a model of the possible actions in skeletal muscle can be illustrated (Fig. 40.2). These biochemical effects provide some insight into the recent *in vivo* studies on caffeine and glycogen sparing (Costill et al. 1978; Essig 1979; Ivy et al. 1979).

ERGOGENIC EFFECTS

Many early studies on the ergogenic effects of caffeine had methodological problems. These include (1) a wide variation in individual response to caffeine, (2) too few subjects, (3) use of different caffeine doses and compounds containing caffeine, (4) work tasks utilizing small muscle mass, (5) questionable test protocols, and (6) uncontrolled extraneous variables that might affect performance. These factors may be responsible for the fact that overall the question of whether or not caffeine is an "ergogenic" aid for sports performance remains unanswered. This is in spite of nearly 80 years of research on the problem.

Short-term Work Tasks

When work capacity is expressed as the ability to perform large muscle, short-term, intense exercise, caffeine appears to have no effect. Perkins and Williams (1975), for example, found that there were no differences between trials for maximal heart rate, perceived exertion, or ride times to exhaustion when females were randomly given either a placebo or 4, 7, or 10 milligrams caffeine per kilogram of body weight 30 minutes prior to ergometer exercise. Other investigators have reported similar results. Haldi and Wynn (1946) observed that caffeine has no effect on a 100-yard swim for speed; Margaria, Aghemo, and Rovelli (1964) found that neither 100 nor 250 milligrams of caffeine has any effect on maximal oxygen consumption or performance time during a treadmill run to exhaustion. Ganslen and his associates (1964) were unable to show that caffeine (200 milligrams) has any effect on work capacity using the Balke Treadmill Test. From these observations one should not conclude that the sympathetic response is unaffected by caffeine during intense work. It appears, however, that *work performance* under these conditions is not improved. It is possible that the response to the work stress is of such magnitude and variability that it masks any caffeine-induced alterations that may be observed under resting conditions.

Endurance Exercise

In contrast to those observations that caffeine does not enhance maximal work capacity, numerous investigators have indicated that the drug may be of benefit during work of longer duration. For example, it was reported as early as the 1890s that caffeine can increase voluntary work capacity (Alles and Feigen 1942). Rivers and Webber (1907) noted that the caffeine increases the capacity for muscular work as measured by "ergographic" techniques. Asmussen and Boje (1948) found that 300 mg of caffeine could overcome the effects of fatigue when cycling to exhaustion on the ergometer if the task was of "longer" rather than of "short" duration. Both Schirlitz (1930) and Herxheimer (1960) noted that caffeine increases *work output* on a cycle ergometer. Ivy et al. (1979) found similar results during isokinetic cycling. Based on a review of many studies, Weiss and Laties (1962) suggested that caffeine could prolong work time to exhaustion.

The mechanism for this enhanced endurance performance appears to be related to shifts in substrate mobilization and utilization. Costill and his coworkers have recently investigated these effects (Costill et al. 1978; Essig 1979; Ivy et al. 1979) and have suggested that increased FFA mobilization and use "spares" carbohydrate and allows for a greater work output or time to exhaustion. This seems to be only partially true.

Lack of carbohydrate as a fuel source in recruited muscle fibers is acknowledged to be a cause for exhaustion during endurance exercise (Costill et al. 1974; Gollnick et al. 1973). Thus, despite a progressive increase in both FFA mobilization and lipid utilization, carbohydrate remains a necessary carbon source for continued muscle metabolism. High rates of fat oxidation, however, are known to inhibit carbohydrate use (Paul et al. 1966) apparently by slowing glucose transport and phosphorylation and inhibition of both the phosphofructokinase and pyruvate dehydrogenase reactions (Bremer 1965; Neely et al. 1968; Randle 1963). Increased blood FFA levels results in an increased uptake by muscle (Hagenfeldt and Wahren 1971; Spitzer and Gold 1964) such that citrate accumulates. This metabolite is known to act on both pyruvate dehydrogenase (Taylor and Halperin 1973) and phosphofructokinase (Mansour 1972a), thus slowing glycolysis and "sparing" carbohydrate use. It is on this basis that recent studies have attempted to enhance endurance performance by inducing shifts in substrate utilization (Costill et al. 1978; Essig 1979; Hickson et al. 1977; Ivy et al. 1979; Rennie et al. 1976).

Rennie et al. (1976) showed that rodents subjected to a fatty meal in combination with a heparin treatment achieved plasma FFA levels 200 percent above controls at rest and 100 percent greater during prolonged exhaustive exercise. This shift in carbon source was reflected in a "sparing" or red muscle (approximately 50 percent depletion versus 75 percent in controls) and liver (25 percent versus 83 percent) glycogen and higher blood glucose levels following exhaustive work. There was no effect in fast-twitch white muscle, possibly due to inherent differences between the fiber types for fatty acid oxidation (Baldwin et al. 1972). Endurance performance using this technique was enhanced (Hickson et al. 1977).

Costill et al. (1977) made similar observations on human subjects. Compared to control conditions, plasma FFA were elevated 32 percent by the diet plus heparin treatment, and there was a 40 percent decrease in muscle glycogen utilization during 30 minutes of work (approximately 70 percent max VO_2).

As indicated previously, caffeine is known to have lipolytic effects resulting in increased blood FFA levels (Bellet et al. 1965). Van Handel et al. (1977) have shown, for example, that 150 mg caffeine in a cola-flavored drink resulted in a 22 percent increase in FFA within 15 minutes after ingestion. It is the potential shift to fat oxidation due to caffeine ingestion that has been suggested to enhance endurance performance (Costill et al. 1978; Ivy et al. 1979). These studies, while demonstrating a significantly greater use of lipid in caffeine versus control trials, found that plasma FFA were not significantly elevated prior to or during the time when glycogen depletion was suggested to occur. Two important observations should be made. The first is that the plasma FFA levels in the caffeine experiments are considerably lower than those in the diet/heparin studies (approximately 0.35 mM vs 1.01 mM) at the start of exercise. If FFA uptake and oxidation are roughly proportional to their rate of delivery to the muscle (Hagenfeldt and Wahren 1971), it is unclear how estimated lipid utilization (based on R and VO_2) averaged 1.30 gm per minute in the caffeine versus only 0.72 gm in the heparin study. The exercise intensities were 80 percent (≈ 3.3 liter O_2 per minute) and 70 percent (3.0 liters O_2 per minute), respectively. Moreover, the estimated reduction in rate of carbohydrate use relative control was similar in these studies, 15 percent less per minute in the caffeine study and

17 percent in the diet/heparin task. This suggests some potential differences between these studies in the mechanism of "carbohydrate sparing."

Secondly, blood lactic acid levels were slightly, though nonsignificantly, higher in the caffeine versus the placebo trials (Costill et al. 1978; Essig 1979)—this in spite of significantly lower respiratory exchange and estimated carbohydrate utilization data. In order to provide further insight into the ergogenic effects of caffeine, Essig (1979) studied subjects during 30 minutes of ergometer cycling at 70 percent max VO_2. Caffeine ingested (5 mg per kg body weight) one hour prior to exercise resulted in an 18 percent increase in plasma FFA, decreased the use of muscle glycogen by 42 percent, and increased muscle triglyceride use by 60 percent as compared to a control trial. Estimates of substrate oxidation based on respiratory exchange indicated that during the caffeine trial the subjects used 22 percent less carbohydrate. In spite of direct and indirect evidence of significant carbohydrate "sparing," however, blood lactates were slighly higher following caffeine ingestion. Evidence of increased carbohydrate use with caffeine was noted in several subjects who appeared to be negatively influenced by the drug.

These *in vivo* observations concur with the previously cited *in vitro* biochemical and physiological effects of caffeine on adipose and muscle tissue and suggest that any carbohydrate "sparing" may be due to mechanisms other than increased use of plasma borne FFA as has occurred in diet/heparin studies. Support for this conclusion is provided by the data of Crass (1972) who found that theophyline produced a concentration dependent stimulation of lipolysis and triglyceride fatty acid oxidation in working hearts. These effects were due to the inhibition of phosphodiesterase, which was secondary to the release of tissue catecholamines. There was also a coincidental stimulation of contractile performance and glycogenolysis. Addition of oxegenous FFA inhibited theophyline stimulated lipolysis of endogenous triglyceride. It is apparent, therefore, that the "sparing" of carbohydrate and enhanced endurance performance following caffeine administration is more likely due to altered intracellular events shifting substrate use as opposed to increased uptake of mobilized FFA, though the latter may contribute to modulation of the muscle triglyceride pools (Dagenais et al. 1976; Froberg et al. 1978; Stankiewicz-Choroszucka and Gorski 1978; Zierler 1976).

A final note concerning a basic discrepancy should be made. In spite of significant reductions in carbohydrate use following caffeine administration (Costill et al. 1978; Essig 1979), blood lactate levels were elevated relative to control trials. This seems to be contradictory to the known effects of shifts in substrate use but may be explained if the recent *in vitro* studies of Cheema-Dhadli (1976) and Lee (1979) apply to the *in vivo* metabolic state that existed following caffeine ingestion. They have shown that increased levels of long-chain fatty actyl-CoA and/or increased β-oxidation of fatty acids results in a higher Km for the mitochondrial citrate transporter (Cheema-Dhadli and Halperin

1976). As a consequence, mitochondrial citrate levels rise decreasing the proportion of active pyruvate dehydrogenase (Taylor and Halperin 1973). A similar effect is caused by inhibition of the adenine nucleotide transporter such that the ATP-ADP ratio increases (Pande and Blancher 1971). The net effect of this inhibition of pyruvate dehydrogenase is to reduce the influx of pyruvate carbon into the mitrochondria allowing it to be channeled to other metabolic pathways including alanine and lactic acid production. Simultaneously, cytosolic citrate levels fall, potentially increasing glycolytic flux (Cheema-Dhadli and Halperin 1976). Increased tissue levels of citrate have been suggested as inhibiting the PFK reaction following caffeine ingestion (Costill et al. 1978), thus slowing glycolysis. As indicated by Williamson et al. (1976), total tissue content of a metabolite provides a poor estimate of its concentration in a particular compartment. As a consequence, there can be errors in interpretation of data especially if there are large concentration gradients across the mitochondrial membrane. Another possible mechanism for increased lactic acid levels could be described from the data of Lee and Davis (1979). They suggest that as mitochondrial acetyl CoA levels increase and a new steady state for citric acid cycle intermediates is achieved, there is also an increased and simultaneous removal of these intermediates; the flux going directly to the three carbon acids pyruvate, alanine, and lactic acid.

While extrapolation of the forecited *in vitro* data to *in vivo* conditions is tenuous, the suggestion can be made that while there may be enhanced lipid utilization and depressed glycogen use with caffeine, glycolysis may not be slowed (normal glucose use) such that lactate and/or alanine levels increase.

There is evidence that not all individuals respond to caffeine in the same manner. Our studies, for example, showed that even though caffeine enhanced either work time to exhaustion or total work output for most subjects, several did not respond as expected. Others have observed that caffeine may affect lipid mobilization only in susceptible persons (Little et al. 1966). Fischbach (1970, 1972) concluded that normal doses will not affect athletes who are accustomed to coffee, but that high doses may actually cause a decrease in performance. In the latter studies it was also observed that even normal doses may have a deleterious effect on individuals not accustomed to coffee. These effects may be related to differences in the distribution of caffeine to various tissues, the water (or fat) content of the body, training status, or dose given.

SUMMARY

Caffeine has historically been considered an ergogenic aid. Attempts to demonstrate this effect have had mixed results, in part due to methodological problems. The biochemical and physiological effects of caffeine or related substances *in vitro* or in the resting organism are well defined and include increased mobilization of free fatty acids from adipose tissue, enhanced catecholamine concentrations in the blood and urine, increased diuresis, and a general sympathetic response of the cardiovascular system.

The sympathetic response to exercise, however, appears to mask many of the changes seen at rest or under *in vitro* conditions. This is especially true during large muscle activity of an intense nature. Studies on the ergogenic effects of the methylxanthines under these conditions are somewhat equivocal but generally show that there is no effect on work performance.

In contrast, endurance performance may be enhanced by caffeine administration though some subjects have a negative response. A physiological basis for the former effect appears to be due to altered substrate utilization by the exercising muscle. This may include a modest increase in the rate of mobilization and delivery of fatty acids to the muscle combined with enhanced use of endogenous lipid and suppression of glycogen catabolism. As a result, a greater percentage of the fuel for work comes from fat oxidation, thereby producing a glycogen sparing effect. Since exhaustion in endurance work tasks has been related to depleted carbohydrate stores, the sparing may possibly result in an increased work time to exhaustion or increased total work output.

REFERENCES

Alles, G. and G. Feigen. 1942. The influence of benzedrine on work decrement and patellar reflex. *Am J Physiol,* 136, 392-400.

Asmussen, E. and O. Boje. 1948. The effects of alcohol and some drugs on the capacity to work. *Acta Physiol Scand,* 15, 109-118.

Atuk, N. O., M. C. Blaydes, P. O. Westerveldt, and J. E. Wood. 1967. Effect of aminophylline on urinary excretion of epinephrine and norepinephrine in man. *Circulation,* 35, 745-753.

Avogaro, P., C. Capri, M. Pais, and G. Cazzolato. 1973. Plasma and urine cortisol behavior and fat mobilization in man after coffee ingestion. *Isr J Med Sci,* 9, 114-119.

Axelrod, J., and J. Reichenthal. 1953. The fate of caffeine in man and a method for its estimation in biological material. *J Pharm Exper Ther,* 107, 519-523.

Baldwin, K. M., G. H. Klinkerfuss, R. L. Terjung, P. A. Mole, and J. O. Holloszy. 1972. Respiratory capacity of red, white and intermediate muscle: Adaptive response to exercise. *Am J Physiol,* 222, 373-378.

Bellet, S., A. Kershbaum, and E. Finch. 1968. Response of free fatty acids to coffee and caffeine. *Metabolism,* 17, 702-707.

Bellet, S., A. Kershbaum, and J. Aspe. 1965. The effect of caffeine on free fatty acids. *Arch Intern Med,* 116, 750-752.

Bellet, S., L. Roman., O. DeCastro, K. E. Kim, and A. Kershbaum. 1969. Effect of coffee ingestion on catecholamine release. *Metabolism,* 18, 288-291.

Berkowitz, B. and S. Spector. 1971. Effect of caffeine and theophylline on peripheral catecholamines. *Europ J Pharm,* 13, 193-196.

Berkowitz, B., J. H. Tarver, and S. Spector. 1970. Release of norepinephrine in the central nervous system by theophylline and caffeine. *Europ J Pharm,* 10, 64-71.

Bojo, O. 1939. Doping. *Bull Health Org League of Nations,* 8, 439-469.

Bowman, W. C. and C. Raper. 1964. The effects of adrenalin and other drugs affecting carbohydrate metabolism on contractions of the rat diaphragm. *Brit J Pharmacol,* 23, 184-200.

Bremer, J. 1965. The effect of acylcarnitines on the metabolism of pyruvate in rat heart mitochondria. *Biochem Biophys Acta,* 104, 581-590.

Brust, M. 1976. Fatigue and caffeine effects in fast-twitch and slow-twitch muscles of the mouse. *Pflügers Arch,* 367, 189-200.

Burg, A. W. 1975. Physiological disposition of caffeine. *Drug Metab Rev,* 4(2), 199-228.

Butcher, R. W. and C. E. Baird. 1969. The regulation of cAMP and lipolysis in adipose tissue by hormones and other agents. In: *Drugs Affecting Lipid Metabolism.* Holmes, W. L., L. A. Carlson, and R. Paoletti (eds.). Plenum Press, New York.

Butcher, R. W., R. J. Ho, H. C. Meng, and E. W. Sutherland. 1965. Adenosine 3', 5'-monophosphate in biological materials. II. The measurement of adenosine 3', 5'-monophosphate in tissues and the role of the cyclic nucleotide in the lipolytic response of fat to epinephrine. *J Biol Chem,* 240, 4515-4523.

Butcher, R. W. and E. W. Sutherland. 1962. Adenosine 3', 5' phosphate in biological materials. *J Biol Chem,* 237, 1244-1255.

Carlson, L. A., S. O. Liljedahl, and C. Wirsen. 1965. Blood and tissue changes in the dog during and after excessive free fatty acid mobilization: A biochemical and morphological study. *Acta Med Scand,* 178, 81-107.

Carlson, L. A. and E. R. Nye. 1966. Acute effects of nicotinic acid in the rat. I. Plasma and liver lipids and blood glucose. *Acta Med Scand,* 179, 453-461.

Cheema-Dhadli, S. and M. L. Halperin. 1976. Effect of palmitoyl-CoA and β oxidation of fatty acids on the kinetics of mitochondrial citrate transporter. *Canad J Biochem,* 54, 171-177.

Cheraskin, E., W. H. Ringsdorf, A. Setyaadmadja, and R. Barrett. 1967. Effect of caffeine versus placebo supplementation on blood glucose concentration. *Lancet,* i, 1299-1300.

Cheung, W. Y. 1967. Properties of cyclic 3', 5' nucleotide phosphediesterase from rat brain. *Biochemistry,* 6, 1079-1087.

Costill, D. L., E. Coyle, G. Dalsky, W. Evans, W. Fink, and D. Hoopes. 1977. Effects of elevated plasma FFA and insulin on muscle glycogen usage during exercise. *J Appl Physiol,* 43, 695-699.

Costill, D. L., G. P. Dalsky, and W. Fink. 1978. Effects of caffeine ingestion on metabolism and exercise performance. *Med Sci Spts,* 10(3) 155-158.

Costill, D. L., E. Jansson, P. D. Gollnick, and B. Saltin. 1974. Glycogen utilization in leg muscles of men during level and uphill running. *Acta Physiol Scand,* 91, 475-481.

Crass, M. F. 1972. Exogenous substrate effects on endogenous lipid metabolism in the working rat heart. *Biochem Biophys Acta,* 280, 71-81.

Crass, M. F., III. 1973. Heart triglyceride and glycogen metabolism: Effects of catecholamines, dibutyrl cAMP, theophylline and fatty acids. *Recent Adv Stud Cardiac Struc Metab,* 3, 275-290.

Dagenais, G. R., R. G. Tancredi, and K. L. Zierler. 1976. Free fatty oxidation by forearm muscle at rest, and evidence for an intramuscular lipid pool in the human forearm. *J Clin Invest,* 58, 421-431.

Davis, I. 1968. *In Vitro* regulation of the lipolysis of adipose tissue. *Nature,* 218, 349-352.

Essig, D. 1979. The influence of caffeine on the utilization of skeletal muscle glycogen during exercise. Master's thesis. Ball State University, Muncie, Indiana. 47306.

Fain, J. N. 1977. Cyclic nucleotides in adipose tissue. In *Cyclic 3' 5' Nucleotides: Mechanisms of Action.* H. Cramer and J. Schultz (eds.). J. Wiley and Sons, London.

Fischbach, E. 1970. Coffee and sports, *Minerva Med,* 61, 4367-4369.

Fischbach, E. 1972. Problems of doping. *Med Monatsschr,* 26, 377-381.

Fröberg, S. O., S. Rossner, and M. Ericsson. 1978. Relation between triglycerides in human skeletal muscle and serum and the fractional elimination rate of exogenous plasma triglycerides. *Eur J Clin Invest,* 8, 93-97.

Ganslen, R. V., B. Balke, F. Nagle, and E. Phillips. 1964. Effects of some tranquilizing, analeptic and vasodilating drugs on physical work capacity and orthostatic tolerance. *Aerospace Med,* 35, 630-633.

Gollnick, P. D., R. B. Armstrong, C. W. Saubert, W. L. Sembrowich, R. E. Shephard, and B. Saltin. 1973. Glycogen depletion patterns in human skeletal muscle fibers during prolonged work. *Pflügers Arch,* 344, 1-12.

Goodman, L. S. and A. Gilman. 1965. *The Pharmacological Basis of Therapeutics.* New York: Macmillan.

Gould, L., C. V. Manoj Duman Goswami, R. Ramana, and R. Gomprecht. 1973. The cardiac effects of tea. *J Clin Pharmacol,* 13, 469-474.

Grollman, A. 1930. The action of alcohol, caffeine and tobacco on the cardiac output (and its related functions) of normal man. *J Pharm Exper Therap,* 39, 313-327.

Guthrie, J. R. and W. G. Nayler. 1967. Interaction between caffeine and adenosine on calcium exchangeability in mammalian atria. *Arch Int Pharmacol Ther,* 170(1), 249-255.

Hagenfeldt, L. and Wahren, J. 1971. Metabolism of free fatty acids and ketone bodies in skeletal muscle. In *Muscle Metabolism During Exercise.* B. Pernow and B. Saltin (eds.). Plenum Press, New York, 153-163.

Haldi, J. and W. Wynn. 1946. Action of drugs on the efficiency of swimmers. *Res Quart,* 17, 96-101.

Hess, M. E., and N. Haugaard. 1958. The effects of epinephrine and aminophylline on phosphorylase activity of perfused, contracting heart muscle. *J Pharm Exp Ther,* 122, 169-175.

Herxheimer, H. 1960. Zur Wirkung des Koffeins auf die Sportliche Leistung. *Moenchen Med Wochenschr,* 21 140-149.

Hickson, R. C., M. J. Rennie, R. K. Conlee, W. W. Winder, and J. O. Holloszy. 1977.

Effects of increased plasma free fatty acids on glycogen utilization and endurance. *J Appl Physiol: Respirat Environ Exercise Physiol,* 43(5), 829-833.

Hoffman, W. W. 1976. Oxygen consumption by human and rodent striated muscle in vitro. *Am J Physiol,* 230, 34-40.

Ivy, J. L., D. L. Costill, W. J. Fink, and R. W. Lower. 1979. Influence of caffeine and carbohydrate feedings on endurance performance. *Med Sci Spts,* 11, 6-11.

Kavinsky, P. J., S. Shechosky, and R. J. Fletterick. 1978. Synergistic regulation of phosphorylase a by glucose and caffeine. *J Biol Chem,* 253(24), 9102-9106.

Keely, S., J. D. Corgin, and C. R. Park. 1975. Regulation of adenosine 3', 5' monophosphate dependent protein kinase. Regulation of the heart enzyme by epinephrine, glucagon, insulin and 1-methyl-3-isobutylxanthine. *J Biol Chem,* 250, 4832-4840.

Kourounakis, P. 1972. Pharmacological conditioning for sporting events. *Am J Pharm,* 144, 151-158.

Kubovetz, W. R., N. Havgaard, M. E. Hess, and J. Shanfeld. 1960. Zur frage der bezrehung zwischen kontraktion und phosphorylase-aktivitat des rattenherzens. *Arch Exp Path Pharmak,* 238, 119-120.

Kukovetz, W. R. and G. Poch. 1967. The action of imidazole on the effects of methylxanthines and catecholamines on cardiac contraction and phosphorylase activity. *J Pharm Exp Ther,* 156(3), 514-521.

Lee, S. H. and E. J. Davis. 1979. Carboxylation and decarboxylation reactions. Anaplerotic flux and removal of citric cycle intermediates in skeletal muscle. *J Biol Chem,* 254, 420-430.

Little, J. A., H. M. Shanoff, A. Csima, and R. Yano. 1966. Coffee and serum-lipids in coronary heart disease. *Lancet,* i, 732-734.

MacCornack, R. A. 1977. The effects of coffee drinking on the cardiovascular system: Experimental and epidemiological research. *Prev Med,* 6, 104-119.

Mansour, T. E. 1972a. Phosphofructokinase. *Curr Top Cell Regul,* 5, 1-46.

Mansour, T. E. 1972b. Phosphofructokinase activity in skeletal muscle extracts following administration of epinephrine. *J Biol Chem,* 247, 6059-6066.

Manchester, K. L., G. Bullock, and U. M. Roetzscher. 1973. Influence of methylxanthines and local anesthetics on the metabolism of muscle and associated changes in mitochondrial morphology. *Chem Biol Interactions,* 6, 273-296.

Margaria, R., P. Aghemo, and E. Rovelli. 1964. The effect of some drugs on the maximal capacity of athletic performance in men. *Int Z Angew Physiol,* 20, 281-287.

Mayer, S. E., M. V. Cotton, and N. C. Moran. 1963. Dissociation of the augmentation of cardiac contractile force from the activation of myocardial phosphorylase by catecholamines. *J Pharm Exp Ther,* 139, 275-282.

Medical Commission of the British Commonwealth Games. 1971. Prevention and detection of drug taking (doping) at the IX British Commonwealth Games. *Scot Med J,* 16, 364-368.

Mustala, O. 1967. Improvement of athletic performance by drugs. *Suomen Laakarilehti,* 22, 690-695.

Neely, J. R., R. H. Bowman, and H. E. Morgan. 1968. Conservation of glycogen in the perfused rat heart developing intraventricular pressure. In *Control of Glycogen Metabolism*. W. J. Whelan (ed.). Academic Press: New York. 49-64.

Novotony, I., and C. P. Bianchi. 1967. The effect of xylocaine on oxygen consumption in the frog sartorius. *J Pharm Exp Ther*, 155, 450-462.

Oldendorf, W. H. 1971. Brain uptake of metabolites and drugs following carotid arterial injections. *Trans Am Neurol Assoc*, 96, 46-50.

Pande, S. V. and M. C. Blanchaer. 1971. Reversible inhibition of mitochondrial adenosine diphosphate phorphorylation by long chain acylcoenzyme A esters. *J Biol Chem*, 246, 402-411.

Paul, P., B. Issekutz, and H. I. Miller. 1966. Interrelationship of free fatty acids and glucose metabolism in dogs. *Am J Physiol*, 211, 1313-1320.

Perkins, R. and M. H. Williams. 1975. Effect of caffeine upon maximum muscular endurance of females. *Med Sci Spts*, 7, 221-224.

Pickering, J. W. 1893. Observations on the physiology of the embryonic heart. *J Physiol (Lond.)*, 14, 383-466.

Porte, D., A. Graber, T. Kuzuya, and R. Williams. 1966. The effect of epinephrine on immunoreactive insulin levels in man. *J Clin Invest*, 45, 228-236.

Pruett, E. D. R. 1970. Glucose and insulin during prolonged work stress in men living on different diets. *J Appl Physiol*, 28, 199-208.

Randle, P. J. 1963. Endocrine control of metabolism. *Ann Rev Physiol*, 25, 291-324.

Randle, P. J., E. A. Newsholme, and P. B. Garland. 1964. Regulation of glucose uptake by muscle. Effects of fatty acids, ketone bodies and pyruvate and of alloxan diabetes and starvation on the uptake and metabolic rate of glucose in rat heart and diaphragm muscles. *Biochem J*, 93, 652-665.

Rennie, M., W. W. Winder, and J. O. Holloszy, 1976. A sparing effect of increased free fatty acids on muscle glycogen content in exercising rat. *Biochem J*, 156, 647-655.

Rivers, W. and H. Webber. 1907. The action of caffeine on the capacity for muscular work. *J Physiol*, 36, 33-47.

Schirlitz, K. 1930. Über Coffein bei ermoedender Muskerlarbeit. *Arbeitsphysiol*, 2, 273.

Sobel, B. E. and S. E. Mayer. 1973. Cyclic adenosine monophosphate and cardiac contractility. *Circ Res*, 32, 407-414.

Spitzer, J. J. and M. Gold. 1964. Free fatty acid metabolism by skeletal muscle. *Am J Physiol*, 206, 159-163.

Stankiewicz-Choroszucha, B. and J. Gorski. 1978. Effect of decreased availability of substrates on intramuscular triglyceride utilization during exercise. *Eur J Appl Physiol*, 40, 27-35.

Stephenson, P. E. 1977. Physiologic and psychotropic effects of caffeine on man. *J Amer Dietetic Assoc*, 71, 240-247.

Strubelt, O. 1969. The influence of respirine, propanolol, and adrenal medullectomy on the hyperglycemic actions of theophylline and caffeine. *Arch Int Pharmacol Ther*, 179, 215-224.

Studlar, M. 1973. Über den Einfluss von Caffein auf den Fett-und Kohlen-hydratestoffwechsel des Menschen. *Z Ernaehrungswiss,* 12, 109-120.

Syed, I. B. 1976. The effects of caffeine. *J Amer Pharm Assoc,* 16(10), 568-572.

Taylor, W. A. and M. L. Halperin. 1973. Regulation of pyruvate dehydrogenase in muscle: Inhibition by citrate. *J Biol Chem,* 248(17), 6080-6083.

Van Handel, P. J., E. Burke, D. L. Costill, and R. Cote. 1977. Physiological responses to cola ingestion. *Res Quart,* 48, 436-444.

Venerando, A. 1963. Doping: Pathology and ways to control it. *Medicine dello Sport,* 3, 972-993.

Wachman, A., R. S. Hattner, B. George, and D. S. Bernstein. 1970. Effects of decaffinated and nondecaffinated coffee ingestion on blood glucose and plasma radioim-munoreactive insulin responses to rapid intravenous infusion of glucose in normal men. *Metabolism,* 19, 539-546.

Waldeck, B. 1973. Sensitization by caffeine of central catecholamine receptors. *J Neurolog Trans,* 34, 61-72.

Weiss, B. and V. Laties. 1962. Enhancement of human performance by caffeine and the amphetamines. *Pharm Rev,* 14, 1-36.

Williamson, J. R., C. Ford, J. Illingworth, and B. Safer. 1976. Coordination of citric acid cycle activity with electron transport flux. *Circ Res,* 38, Suppl 1, 139-151.

Zierler, K. L. 1976. Fatty acids as substrates for heart and skeletal muscle. *Circ Res,* 38, 459-463.

Introduction

The promotion of physical fitness in youth is an objective of many agencies and organizations. Most current programs emphasize the individual's fitness status relative to certain standards or norms and the prescription of various forms of exercise for improvement. The importance of a continued future commitment toward the maintenance of one's physical health and an understanding of the various factors that describe fitness are generally given less serious attention. Nevertheless, current evidence clearly indicates the specific and nonpermanent nature of the adaptations occurring as a result of exercise stress. The purpose of this section is to provide a contemporary look at knowledge and practices significant to the promotion of physical fitness in youth.

In the first paper of the section, McAdam presents a review of modern youth fitness testing and generalized findings from recent research efforts. The next paper by Cureton explores the historical development of and evaluates the physical fitness test currently attracting the widest use, the AAHPER Youth Fitness Test. The results of the national fitness surveys of 1958, 1965, and 1975 are compared and provide an interesting glimpse of changes in the norms over the 1960s and 1970s. The evolution of the AAHPER test is also examined.

The next two entries, "Growth, Strength, and Physical Performance," by Malina, and "Individual Differences and the Assessment of Youth Fitness," by Krahenbuhl, focus on factors influencing one's physical performance during youth and consider the significance of individual differences in the youth fitness evolution process. The discussion of age and sex-associated variation in growth is of interest because it reveals concrete evidence about the multiple aspects of growth. This knowledge is then related to performance. A discussion of the nature and extent of interindividual differences in maturity and genetic potential and their significance to fitness testing is then presented.

The paper by Cunningham consists of a contemporary review of the physical working capacity of youth. The reader will find the treatment thorough and well documented. The entry contains a good deal of useful information for anyone interested in the scientific foundations of fitness testing. Next, Gilliam and Katch provide evidence that significant numbers of children exhibit cardiovascular disease risk profiles at an early age. The relationship of the incidence of these risk factors to obesity and physical activity levels is discussed. The concluding chapter by Pangrazi provides a practical approach to the implementation of fitness programs for the overweight child. Topics range from the selection of low-fit individuals to the elements of a realistic program.

The section was formulated to provide insight about current practices and problems in the assessment and improvement of youth fitness. General aspects of training and conditioning have been discussed in Section 1 of this volume. While most of the same principles apply for young children, adjustments must be made for such factors as maturity, sex, strength, and a variety of additional factors. The information provided should be informative and thought provoking. It is hoped that by bringing this section to the attention of those interested in human physical well-being, inquiry and criticism will be stimulated and, ultimately, improved fitness programs and practices for youth will result.

GSK
RPP

Section Editors

Dr. Gary S. Krahenbuhl is professor and chairman of the Department of Health and Physical Education at Arizona State University. He earned both a B.S.Ed. and M.S.Ed. from Northern Illinois University and the Ed.D. from the University of Northern Colorado. Prior to taking his current position, Dr. Krahenbuhl taught intermediate school physical education and later was a member of the faculty at the University of Hawaii.

Dr. Krahenbuhl has served on the Southwest District Board of Directors, AAHPERD, and is a Fellow in the American College of Sports Medicine. He has published widely and is currently the coeditor of the *Arizona Journal for Health, Physical Education, and Recreation*. Dr. Krahenbuhl's primary interests are in sports sciences and physical fitness, and he has received research support from the United States Air Force, the American Heart Association, and the National Science Foundation. His consulting work includes such groups as Sport Canada and the United States Olympic Committee.

Dr. Robert P. Pangrazi is associate professor of physical education at Arizona State University. His primary field of interest is elementary school physical education, and he has coauthored the text, *Dynamic Physical Education for Elementary School Children* and contributed to *Lesson Plans for Dynamic Physical Education* and *Essential Movement Experiences for Primary and Preschool Children*. In cooperation with Dr. Victor P. Dauer, Washington State University, Dr. Pangrazi has developed a series of films illustrating and describing physical education programs and activities.

Dr. Pangrazi has been involved in research dealing with cardiorespiratory fitness levels of children. He is coeditor of the *Arizona Journal for Health, Physical Education, and Recreation*, and was a coeditor of the AAHPER publication, *Echoes of Influence*. Dr. Pangrazi has served as chairperson of the

Elementary Physical Education Division, Southwest District AAHPERD, chair-person of the Elementary Physical Education Section, Southwest AAHPERD, and president of the Arizona Association for Health, Physical Education, and Recreation.

41

Milestones in Youth Fitness Testing

Robert E. McAdam

With a full appreciation for the concept of the "totality of the individual," physical educators and closely allied researchers have in the last five decades heightened their efforts to learn more about that part of the person's totality called "physical fitness." In their searches they have attended to the dynamics of health—including the ability to tax one's physical capabilities to perservere and recover from exertion—more than to a simple absence of disease.

In keeping with the theme that fitness is something more than the absence of disease, efforts to appraise physical performance and the capacity to perform have evolved in several discernible steps. At first, perhaps of necessity, appraisal of fitness tended to be subjective, or at best only crudely objective. Judgments of body physique and measures of gross body strength characterized early efforts. There followed a period of refinement in the testing and interpreting of strength measures, and tests were developed to measure qualities of performance such as agility, endurance, and balance. As techniques for measuring human performance improved, particularly in the 1950s, and new opportunities for researching circulatory-respiratory and other organic performance increased the understanding of physical fitness.

Several factors contributed to a special interest in youth fitness in the second and third quarters of the 20th century. The rejection rate of youth for military service in times of national crisis, an increase in the percentage of the population made up of youth and children, and comparative studies of fitness in American and European children led ultimately to the formation of a President's Council on Physical Fitness and Sport.

In a limited sense, youth is defined as that period between adolescence and adulthood (ages 15 to 21). In studies of youth fitness, however, it is common to include the formative periods of childhood and adolescence inasmuch as they are so important to the development of youth. For example, the best known and perhaps most universally used fitness test—the American Alliance of Health, Physical Education, and Recreation Youth Fitness Test—is designed for boys and girls ages 10 through 17.

Relatively few tests have been constructed to measure youth fitness exclusively. However, many tests have application to childhood and adulthood as well. The quality or level of performance on those tests may be expected to vary, however, from population to population. Tests of pulse rate, strength, and speed are applicable to a wide range of ages, but the expectation for performance tends to differ as a function of age. For this reason, *norms* of performance are often constructed based upon the individual's age. In general, therefore, youth fitness tests are often the same tests used in appraising fitness for other ages except that usually there are separate norms for youth.

THE EMERGENCE OF FITNESS TESTS

Body Build

Early efforts to appraise fitness often included subjective judgments of physique. E. Kretschmer identified basic body builds as they could be distinguished by proportions of fat, muscle, and bone tissue (Willgoose 1961). W. H. Sheldon (1940) followed Kretschmer's cues in setting up scales for rating each individual from one to seven in fat (endormophy), muscle (mesomorphy), and bone (ectomorphy). A person high in proportion of fat was, therefore, classified as an endomorph; high in muscle, a mesomorph; and one light or fragile (i.e., high in bone), an ectomorph. Generally those classified as mesomorphs were thought to be more athletic and more fit.

Early objective efforts to appraise fitness through attributes of physique were crude but useful. Height and weight are still rough indicators of fitness, though the *change* in weight is likely to be a more useful indicator of relative fitness. In this regard the Wetzel Grid (Wetzel 1948) provides a plan through which children can be classified by age, height, and weight during their period of growth. Deviation from an established channel for growth can be detected with periodic recordings of height and weight. Deviations too far from the expected growth channels signal the need for analysis of possible deteriorating fitness.

More objective measures of body mass, height, girths, and widths led to the development of several indexes of fitness. Among these, the Arm, Chest, Hip Index (ACH Index) (Franzen and Palmer 1934) represented an effort to screen children age 7 through 12 who should be referred to a doctor for medical examination. Another, the McCloy Classification Index III (McCloy 1532), used a simple formula:

$$(10 \times \text{age in years}) + \text{weight in pounds}$$

to provide a plan for grouping elementary children for activity competition. Modifications of this index for high school and college students were also produced.

Still more complex indexes were developed from other body measures. The ponderal index (the height divided by the cube root of the weight) yields information on the individual's degree of ectomorphy. The ratio of shoulder width to hip width has been purported to be an index of masculinity of physique.

The extent to which such derived indexes are valid for children and youth in varying stages of growth is somewhat speculative. There appears to be more credibility in those indexes that are normed for combinations of age, sex, weight, and height than for those normed in a singular way. It is fair to say, however, that most measures of body build are easy to obtain and that they often yield crude data, somewhat useful in making generalizations about fitness. When supplemented with other information regarding physical performance, measures of body composition, girths, and linear dimensions can be employed to enhance the appraisal of physical fitness.

Strength

In the earlier days of human existence strength was undoubtedly recognized as an important factor in the "survival of the fittest." Strength was also one of the primary targets of early formalized testing of fitness. While it may be less important for physical survival in an increasingly automated society, strength is still highly associated with skill in physical performance, dynamic living, and health appearance.

A strength test battery was developed by Dudley Sargent just before the turn of the century and refined by Frederick Rand Rogers in 1925 (Rogers 1926). The test consisted of seven items including left and right grip strengths, back lift, leg lift, pull-ups, parallel bar dips, and lung capacity. The combined scores yielded two kinds of indexes, the Strength Index (SI) and the Physical Fitness Index (PFI). The SI is a reflection of gross strength, whereas the PFI is the gross strength normed for age, weight, and sex—important factors in appraising strength. This test, used for both males and females ages 8 to 38, became the foundation of strength testing for many years and, although sometimes modified in form, is prevalent as a strength test today.

In the early 1950s the Kraus-Weber Test (Kraus and Hirschland 1954)—a test of minimum muscular fitness developed originally as a test for lower back pain in adults—was used in a study comparing the fitness of American and European children. The test consisted of six items, one trunk-hip flexion and five minimal strength challenges such as the single sit-up. The items were scored on a simple pass-fail basis. European children scored better on those tests than the American children, and the results caused much concern in the United States and spirited new interest in youth fitness and the construction of fitness tests.

An approach yielding more refined measures of strength was developed by Clarke and his associates at the University of Oregon (Clarke and Monroe 1970). This method, in which the subjects produce tension that is recorded on a cable tensionmeter, has yielded several strength test batteries. One battery for boys at all grade levels consists of items testing shoulder extension, knee extension, and ankle flexion. Several batteries exist for girls at varying grade levels. For example, the elementary tests for girls consist of items testing shoulder extension, hip extension, and trunk flexion. As in the case of the Rogers Strength Test, the batteries can be scored as a gross "strength composite" or as a relative "strength quotient." There are many other tests by which strength as a part of fitness may be appraised. Some of these tests are included in broader batteries of fitness tests described later in this section. Let it suffice here to say that in the history of fitness testing, strength has been one of the central targets because it is so intricately related to muscular endurance, balance, power, and many other qualities of performance comprising the whole of physical fitness.

Motor Performance Testing

As the interest in fitness and fitness testing expanded beyond the appraisal of physique and strength, many tests of general body movement emerged. Some were designed to measure the *skill* or *ability* to perform. Others were designed to ascertain the capacity or *fitness* to perform. In practice, however, it was often difficult to separate skill from fitness. For example, a test of high jump "ability" is more likely to be viewed as a skill test. Yet it is obvious that certain components of fitness (strength and power), particularly of the take-off leg muscles, play an important role in the performance.

Motor performance tests measure a functional quality of movement rather than a learned skill. Many of the accepted tests today measure conglomerates of several identifiable functional qualities of movement. Among the qualities most often included are: (1) *agility*, the ability to change direction quickly; (2) *flexibility*, the ability to move body segments through a wide range of movement; (3) *balance*, the ability to maintain postural stability or to recover efficiently from a state of instability; (4) *endurance*, the ability to continue repetitive movement; (5) *speed*, the ability to move rapidly with successive movements; and (6) *strength*, the ability to exert muscular force. Almost all body movement involves interdependence of these qualities of movement. For example, one cannot change the direction of a body part quickly (agility) without exerting sufficient muscular force (strength). Furthermore, combinations of some of these qualities provide new identifiable qualities of performance. Thus, the ability to exert force (strength) rapidly (speed) produces a secondary quality of performance—that is, *power*.

A number of limitations make accurate appraisal of general motor performance difficult. Among these are that motor performance is affected by one's level of organic fitness, body build, and learned experiences (skill). In addition, not all motor qualities or all muscle groups can be selected for measurement in a single motor performance test. The better general motor tests, therefore, are likely to be those which sample both the qualities (such as agility and balance) and the regions of the body (muscle groups) in an appropriate and representative way. When individual qualities of performance are adequately represented in a single test, it is not only possible to derive a measure of composite motor performance, but also to construct a profile of relative contribution of each quality to the composite measure.

A thorough review of the multiplicity of motor performance tests described in the physical education literature is beyond the scope of this chapter. However, a brief overview of some of the tests and a more detailed discussion of one of the most widely used tests would seem to be of value.

Following World War II, the military services recognized the need to update or select new tests that would appraise the physical fitness of their personnel. The Marine Corps and Army have since adopted physical fitness tests consisting of some motor performance items (Clarke 1975). The Marine Corps test for women includes such items as the shuttle run, bent-knee sit-ups, and a three-mile run. The Army has several test batteries that are selected based upon the nature of the duty to which the individual is assigned. Sit-ups, dodge run, jumps, push-ups, and half-mile runs are typical of the motor performance items in the batteries.

The Air Force and Navy have taken a somewhat different approach in testing the physical fitness of their personnel (Clarke 1975). Following the work of Kenneth Cooper, an Air Force Research officer whose work in "aerobics" brought a new perspective to appraising fitness, these services classify the fitness of their personnel on a distance run (Cooper 1970). Air Force personnel are classified on the basis of the time for running 1.5 miles. Navy personnel are classified on the basis of the distance they can run in 12 minutes. Both of these tests are directed at endurance rather than at a wider range of physical fitness qualities.

A number of states have found it useful to construct their own motor fitness tests (with norms) for school age children. The examples following serve to illustrate only the commonality of the items, since each test is unique and is normed for its own population (Clarke 1975).

A major change in physical fitness testing in the schools occurred with the creation of the AAHPER Youth Fitness Test in the late 1950s. The Kraus-Weber study and follow-up studies comparing the fitness of American children to the children of other countries had alarmed some of our country's leaders. The concern caused President Dwight D. Eisenhower to form the President's Council of Physical Fitness and Sport in 1956 (Hunsicker and Reiff 1976).

In 1956 the then American Association for Health, Physical Education, and Recreation conducted a nationwide testing program in the schools under the leadership of the late Paul Hunsicker in an attempt to establish national norms for the AAHPER Youth Fitness Test. That successful effort and the periodic evaluative studies that followed in 1965 and 1975 have given increased popularity and utility to the test. As a result of those studies, the test has been modified and new norms for performance have been constructed. The softball throw has been deleted from the original group of items, the sit-up test has been changed from the straight leg to the bent-knee sit-up, and options have been given for the 600-yard run-walk.* Figure 41.1, reprinted from the *AAHPER Youth Fitness Test*

---

* Copies of the test can be purchased from the American Alliance for Health, Physical Education, Recreation, and Dance, 1201 Sixteenth Street, N.W., Washington D.C., 20036.

Manual, revised 1976 edition, illustrates the six categories of the test. At the present time the test is again undergoing revision (see Chapter 42).

A comparison of the most recent norms with those developed previously reveals a pronounced improvement between 1957 and 1965 in youth fitness among school children tested on all items of the test at all age levels (10 through 17). In the 1965-1975 decade, however, there was little, if any, improvement in fitness at any age level (Hunsicker and Reiff 1975).

In summary, it should be said that there are many tests proclaimed to measure physical fitness. Some possess items that test in a large part skill and/or physical fitness. Tests that appropriately sample agility, balance, flexibility, endurance, strength, and speed of body parts or the total body form the core of the large group of motor performance tests. The AAHPER Youth Fitness Test is perhaps the most widely employed because of its appropriateness for the school setting, the availability of national norms, and its use in periodic evaluation of national youth fitness trends. The President's Council on Youth Fitness and Sport has endorsed its use for fitness testing across the nation.

Circulatory-Respiratory Fitness

The presence of oxygen in the cells is essential for sustaining prolonged muscular activity. Atmospheric oxygen is made available to the cells by the cooperative action of the respiratory and circulatory systems. The respiratory system is responsible for transporting air to and from the lungs. It is comprised mainly of a tubular system, through which the air moves, and the lungs, where oxygen is picked up and carbon dioxide released by the blood. The circulatory system is comprised of the blood, which is the vehicle for carrying oxygen and carbon dioxide, the blood vessels, through which the blood flows to and from the heart, and the heart itself, which pumps the blood through the system. The degree to which these systems function efficiently during muscular work has often been used in appraising physical fitness. There are both indirect and direct ways that the efficiency of the systems can be measured.

Earlier, endurance was defined as the ability to continue repetitive movement. Repetitive movement requires a continuous supply of oxygen to the active muscles. Therefore, endurance events requiring gross muscular activity that place stress upon the circulatory-respiratory systems have been used as a means for assessing circulatory-respiratory fitness. Any activity such as swimming, cycling, or jumping up and down that can be repeated over a reasonably long period of time might be used to evaluate one's circulatory-respiratory fitness. Running, however, is most often used in endurance testing. Two measures can be used as fitness scores in running: (1) the time it takes to travel a specified distance, and(2) the distance traveled in a specified time. In the 600-yard run-walk, for example, an item of the AAHPER Youth Fitness Test mentioned earlier, the distance is set and the time to cover the distance is recorded as the score. Conversely, in the 12-minute run popularized by Cooper, the time is specified and the distance traversed in that time constitutes the score. This test in

pull-up

BOYS

FIGURE 1
Improvised equipment for pull-up—
doorway gym bar in background,
ladder in foreground.

FIGURE 2
Starting position for pull-up.

EQUIPMENT

A metal or wooden bar approximately 1½ inches in diameter is preferred. A doorway gym bar can be used, and, if no regular equipment is available, a piece of pipe or even the rungs of a ladder can serve the purpose (FIGURE 1).

DESCRIPTION

The bar should be high enough so that the pupil can hang with his arms and legs fully extended and his feet free of the floor. He should use the overhand grasp (FIGURE 2). After assuming the hanging position, the pupil raises his body by his arms until his chin can be placed over the bar and then lowers his body to a full hang as in the starting position. The exercise is repeated as many times as possible.

RULES

1. Allow one trial unless it is obvious that the pupil has not had a fair chance.
2. The body must not swing during the execution of the movement. The pull must in no way be a snap movement. If the pupil starts swinging, check this by holding your extended arm across the front of the thighs.
3. The knees must not be raised and kicking of the legs is not permitted.

SCORING

Record the number of completed pull-ups to the nearest whole number.

Fig. 41.1 AAPHER Youth Fitness Test. (Reprinted with permission from Paul Hunsicker and Guy G. Reiff, *AAHPER Youth Fitness Test Manual*, Washington, D.C.: AAHPER, 1976 rev. ed., pp. 29-35.)

flexed-arm hang

GIRLS

EQUIPMENT

A horizontal bar approximately 1½ inches in diameter is preferred. A doorway gym bar can be used; if no regular equipment is available, a piece of pipe can serve the purpose. A stopwatch is needed.

DESCRIPTION

The height of the bar should be adjusted so it is approximately equal to the pupil's standing height. The pupil should use an overhand grasp (FIGURE 3). With the assistance of two spotters, one in front and one in back of pupil, the pupil raises her body off the floor to a position where the chin is above the bar, the elbows are flexed, and the chest is close to the bar (FIGURE 4). The pupil holds this position as long as possible.

RULES

1. The stopwatch is started as soon as the subject takes the hanging position.
2. The watch is stopped when (a) pupil's chin touches the bar, (b) pupil's head tilts backwards to keep chin above the bar, (c) pupil's chin falls below the level of the bar.

SCORING

Record in seconds to the nearest second the length of time the subject holds the hanging position.

FIGURE 3
Starting position for flexed-arm hang.

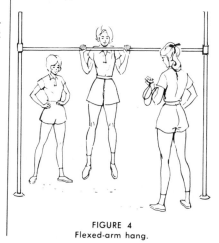

FIGURE 4
Flexed-arm hang.

Fig. 41.1 (cont.)

sit-up (flexed leg)
BOYS AND GIRLS

EQUIPMENT
Clean floor, mat or dry turf and stopwatch.

DESCRIPTION
The pupil lies on his back with his knees bent, feet on the floor and heels not more than 12 inches from the buttocks. The angle at the knees should be less than 90 degrees. The pupil puts his hands on the back of his neck with fingers clasped and places his elbows squarely on the mat, floor or turf. His feet are held by his partner to keep them in touch with the surface. The pupil tightens his abdominal muscles and brings his head and elbows forward as he curls up, finally touching elbows to knees. This action constitutes one sit-up. The pupil returns to the starting position with his elbows on the surface before he sits up again. The timer gives the signal "ready-go," and the sit-up performance is started on the word "go." Performance is stopped on the word "stop." The number of correctly executed sit-ups performed in 60 seconds shall be the score.

FIGURE 5
Starting position for flexed leg sit-up

RULES
1. Only one trial shall be allowed unless the teacher believes the pupil has not had a fair opportunity to perform.
2. No resting is permitted between sit-ups.
3. No sit-ups shall be counted in which the pupil *does not* (a) keep the fingers clasped behind the neck; (b) bring both elbows forward in starting to sit up without pushing off the floor with an elbow; or (c) return to starting position, with *elbows flat on the surface,* before sitting up again.

SCORING
Record the number of correctly executed sit-ups the pupil is able to do in 60 seconds. A foul nullifies the count for that sit-up. The watch is started on the word "go" and stopped on the word "stop."

FIGURE 6
Flexed leg sit-up

Fig. 41.1 (cont.)

shuttle run
BOYS AND GIRLS

3

EQUIPMENT
Two blocks of wood, 2 inches x 2 inches x 4 inches, and stopwatch. Pupils should wear sneakers or run barefooted.

DESCRIPTION
Two parallel lines are marked on the floor 30 feet apart. The width of a regulation volleyball court serves as a suitable area. Place the blocks of wood behind one of the lines as indicated in FIGURE 7. The pupil starts from behind the other line. On the signal "Ready? Go!" the pupil runs to the blocks, picks one up, runs back to the starting line, and *places* the block behind the line; he then runs back and picks up the second block, which he carries back across the starting line. If the scorer has two stopwatches or one with a split-second timer, it is preferable to have two pupils running at the same time. To eliminate the necessity of returning the blocks after each race, start the races alternately, first from behind one line and then from behind the other.

RULES
Allow two trials with some rest between.

SCORING
Record the time of the better of the two trials to the nearest tenth of a second.

────30ft────▶

FIGURE 7
Starting the shuttle run.

Fig. 41.1 (cont.)

standing long jump

BOYS AND GIRLS

EQUIPMENT

Mat, floor, or outdoor jumping pit, and tape measure.

DESCRIPTION

Pupil stands as indicated in FIGURE 8, with the feet several inches apart and the toes just behind the takeoff line. Preparatory to jumping, the pupil swings the arms backward and bends the knees. The jump is accomplished by simultaneously extending the knees and swinging forward the arms.

RULES

1. Allow three trials.
2. Measure from the takeoff line to the heel or other part of the body that touches the floor nearest the takeoff line (FIGURE 8).
3. When the test is given indoors, it is convenient to tape the tape measure to the floor at right angles to the takeoff line and have the pupils jump along the tape. The scorer stands to the side and observes the mark to the nearest inch.

SCORING

Record the best of the three trials in feet and inches to the nearest inch.

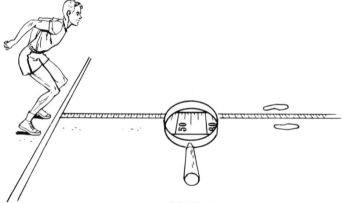

FIGURE 8
Measuring the standing long jump.

Fig. 41.1 (cont.)

50-yard dash
BOYS AND GIRLS

EQUIPMENT
Two stopwatches or one with a split-second timer.

DESCRIPTION
It is preferable to administer this test to two pupils at a time. Have both take positions behind the starting line. The starter will use the commands "Are you ready?" and "Go!" The latter will be accompanied by a downward sweep of the starter's arm to give a visual signal to the timer, who stands at the finish line.

RULES
The score is the amount of time between the starter's signal and the instant the pupil crosses the finish line.

SCORING
Record in seconds to the nearest tenth of a second.

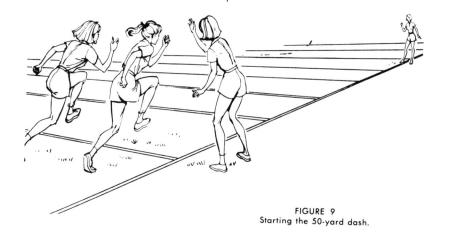

FIGURE 9
Starting the 50-yard dash.

Fig. 41.1 (cont.)

EQUIPMENT
Track or area marked according to FIGURES 11-13, and stopwatch.

DESCRIPTION
Pupil uses a standing start. At the signal "Ready? Go!" the pupil starts running the 600-yard distance. The running may be interspersed with walking. It is possible to have a dozen pupils run at one time by having the pupils pair off before the start of the event. Then each pupil listens for and remembers his partner's time as the latter crosses the finish. The timer merely calls out the times as the pupils cross the finish.

RULES
Walking is permitted, but the object is to cover the distance in the shortest possible time.

SCORING
Record in minutes and seconds.

600-yard run
BOYS AND GIRLS

Options:
Ages 10-12, 1-mile or 9-minute run

Ages 13 or older, 1½-mile or 12-minute run

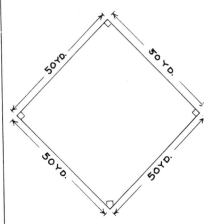

FIGURE 12
Using any open area for 600-yard run

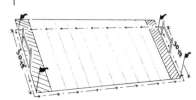

FIGURE 11
Using football field for 600-yard run

FIGURE 13
Using inside track for 600-yard run

Fig. 41.1 (cont.)

particular has been demonstrated to have moderate to high correlation with maximum oxygen uptake (max $\dot{V}O_2$), for many years a standard laboratory test of circulatory-respiratory fitness. In the 1975 revision of the AAHPER Youth Fitness Tests, options (with norms) were given for the 600-yard run-walk. The options, a nine-minute or one-mile run, were designed to provide a better measure of circulatory-respiratory response than does the 600-yard run-walk.

More direct measures of circulatory-respiratory fitness are also available. Of these, the recording of heart rate has been the most universally used measure in nonlaboratory settings. For any given person, resting heart rate might well be an indicator of relative fitness. It is well known that the fit person's resting heart rate tends to be lower than that of the unfit. Perhaps even more important is that during submaximal exercise the fit person's heart rate does not rise as rapidly and following exercise returns to the resting rate sooner than the unfit's.

One classic test using the direct measure of heart rate as an indicator of circulatory-respiratory fitness was the Harvard Step Test (Brouha 1943). The basic principle of the test was to impose work on the subject, after which periodic recovery pulse rates were taken. The work consisted of five minutes of stepping (when possible) on a 20-inch bench at the rate of 30 executions per minute. Heart rate was recorded 60 to 90, 120 to 150, and 180 to 210 seconds after exercise and then totaled. A Physical Efficiency Index was computed in the following way:

$$\text{Physical Efficiency Index} = \frac{\text{Duration of exercise in seconds} \times 100}{2 \times \text{sum of pulse counts in recovery}}$$

There was later a shortened version of this test that permitted the pulse-taking time to be reduced.

The Harvard Step Test, developed originally for college students, was modified by Brouha and others for use in testing elementary and secondary school boys and girls. The test for high school girls requires four minutes of stepping on a 16-inch step (Brouha and Gallagher 1943). The test for high school boys separated boys first on the basis of body size. The larger boys were tested on a 20-inch bench, the smaller boys on an 18-inch step. The testing time for both groups was four minutes (Rogers 1946). The test for elementary age children stepping on a 14-inch bench was for two minutes if seven years old and for three minutes if older (Brouha and Ball 1952).

The President's Council on Physical Fitness and Sport has suggested another modification of the Harvard Step Test (Clarke 1975). The council's version varies the bench height at 14, 16, or 20 inches depending on the height of the subject. The testing time is four minutes. A child failing to complete the test or who falls below a given score in the norms (by virtue of high recovery heart rates) is considered to be unfit for strenuous exercise, and medical referral is indicated.

A variation in the use of the pulse rate as an indicator of physical fitness is the Tuttle Pulse Ratio Test (Tuttle 1931). In this test the ratio is ascertained between the resting pulse rate and the pulse rate for two minutes following a specified exercise. After the pulse has returned to its resting rate (or a steady rate), a more intense exercise is given with the same procedure of counting the pulse after exercise. This is continued with exercises of progressive intensity until the postexercise ratio reaches 2.5 times the resting rate. Presumably the physically fit person can endure more increments of progressively intense exercise before reaching a ratio of 2.5. While this test is applicable to several age groups including youth, it is not a practical test for school use because of the length of time involved in giving the test.

A number of indexes have been derived from measures of pulse rate and blood pressure. The Barach Index (Barach 1914) and the Crampton Blood Ptosic test (Crampton 1905) are among the better known. These tests are beset with the same limitations as the tests of pulse rate, namely the influence of temperature, humidity, fatigue, body position, anxiety, and other emotional states. These derived indexes are more suited to special study and laboratory use and so will not be elaborated here.

Electrical measures of the energy of the heart in its beating cycle and the waves set up by changing pressures of the blood within the vessels also reflect something of the character of the heart and the vessels, which adds new dimensions of information on fitness. The strength of the heart beat, the ratio of rest time to work time of the heart, and the rhythm or arhythm of the beat can be important indicators of fitness. In addition, chemical analysis may reveal fluctuations in the oxygen-carrying capacity of the blood or the acid-base balance as a consequence of exercise. These rather sophisticated measures, while capable of reflecting one's fitness level, are usually restricted to the laboratory.

GENERALIZED FINDINGS

In many areas of exploration of fitness in youth, the variation in findings is great enough that the results of individual studies can often be misleading. In some areas of investigation, the trends are strong enough, nevertheless, to permit useful generalizations.

Exercise and Body Structure

Body silhouette can be changed through exercise as a consequence of fat loss and muscle growth. In children of the same age, the degree of muscular change resulting from a program of physical training is likely to vary greatly because of individual differences in genetic make-up and the extent of maturation. Muscle bulk is closely associated with muscle strength. Programs that strenuously tax the muscles promote growth of individual fibers, thereby increasing total muscle bulk.

Fat, as measured by skinfold tests, is diminished through vigorous exercise. Change of fat in children with exercise programs of eight to ten weeks duration tends to be small and varied in direction, however. There is an indication that the obese or overweight child will lose adipose tissue, while the thin child may increase slightly the adipose when diet is unrestricted during an exercise program. Programs in the schools that encourage running, jogging, swimming, bicycling, or rhythmical light calisthenics as a part of each day's activity are likely to aid the reduction of fat.

Skeletal changes in children due to exercise are not pronounced, if present at all. Both the normal and the expanded chest circumference increase following exercise training programs. The question has been raised by some researchers as to the possible retardation of length of bone growth in prepubescent children when they engage in intensive endurance exercise programs such as running. A preponderance of exercise studies of body changes in children, however, indicate that exercise creates no unusual characteristic changes in the normal growth of the skeletal system.

Exercise and Motor Performance

Research in the area of motor performance supports the concept that appropriate exercise programs can improve, even in young children, the elements of agility, balance, endurance, flexibility, speed, and strength. Agility appears to be positively correlated with growth in both boys and girls up to about 15 years, after which boys appear to gain in agility at a fairly rapid rate, while the girls have a slight tendency to become less agile. Endomorphs tend to be less agile than people of other body types. Exercise programs providing many opportunities for quick change in direction of body movement will generally improve agility. Dodge-type games, squat-thrust exercises, and obstacle running are examples of activities that should be included in an agility-building program.

Research on balance yields many interesting findings. For example, there appears to be little correlation between static and dynamic balance, and further "balance fitness" tends to be rather specific to the particular balance posture being practiced. Age and ability to balance are not highly correlated in youth. Since one's balance is dependent upon reactions of the vestibular apparatus of the ear, the eyes, and the proprioceptors of the muscle, physical activity can play an important role in developing balance. Programs requiring frequent changing of body postures and a varying base of support are most likely to improve dynamic balancing abilities.

Muscular endurance has been the object of much fitness research because of its obvious role in conditioning for sports performance. Muscular endurance is highly dependent upon the circulatory system because of the great demand of oxygen in the muscle cells during repeated contractions of the muscles. In active children, even when the circulatory system is functioning efficiently, the inadequacy of muscle relative to bony structure at certain ages impedes endurance.

Nevertheless, it has been demonstrated that muscular endurance of most children can be improved through such repetitive activities as push-ups, pull-ups, sit-ups, and hops. Programs that encourage light to moderate work loads with many repetitions of the contracting muscle groups offer the best means of developing muscular endurances. Examples of these can be found in calisthenics, including pull-ups and push-ups, and the use of light weights in repeated movements.

Because the skeletal and joint structures have not been firmly fixed in childhood, children generally possess good flexibility. Throughout childhood girls appear to have greater flexibility than boys. Much controversy has arisen over testing techniques in the measurement of flexibility, since such simple tasks as toe touching or raising the trunk a given distance from the floor when in a prone position may be more a function of the relative body segment lengths than of the ability to "flex" or "extend" through a *range* of motion. Diving, swimming, and gymnastics, all of which require large range of motion in the joints, have been found to be extremely good activities for improving flexibility in children.

Speed of muscular movement improves with age until early adulthood. Males appear to retain their ability to respond with speed longer than do females. Muscle temperature and vicosity play important roles in speed of muscular movement. The ultimate manifestation of quick muscular response in young children is determined, in part, by the relative mass of bone, muscle, and fat that is to be moved by the muscle. Speed can be improved by practice of a given response, heightening motivation, concentration on the act, and perhaps by warm-up; but the optimal speed will not be reached until the maturation of the muscle is adequate for the skeletal, muscle, and fat mass that it is required to move.

Of all the elements of fitness, strength has been studied more extensively than any other. In both boys and girls strength appears to improve with age. However, individual differences in muscular strength in children are very pronounced. For example, in a given classroom the strongest boy may be four times as strong as the weakest boy of the same age. There is high correlation between muscular strength and muscle endurance. Programs providing activities in which muscles act against relatively heavy loads and resistances are most apt to contribute to improvement in this important aspect of fitness.

Circulatory-Respiratory Fitness

The evidence that exercise greatly improves the circulatory-respiratory function in youth is not as dramatic as is the evidence that exercise improves motor fitness. Several investigators have found that groups of children in eight- to ten-week training programs experience reductions in heart rate, but the within-group variations may show nearly as many individuals with increased as with decreased rates. Similarly confusing results are obtained in the children's blood pressure studies. Cardiovascular data collected on children and youth in the active state are more likely to be accepted with confidence than data collected in the resting states.

The capacity to increase work in rather specific ways (which may indirectly reflect the change in circulatory-respiratory function) has, however, been demonstrated in many studies. Running, swimming, and rope skipping programs of just a few weeks duration can improve the vital capacity, breath-holding capacity following exercise, and the efficient utilization of oxygen in both the resting and the exercise states. The circulatory-respiratory changes that occur as a consequence of training during childhood and youth are consistent with those experienced by adults — that is, lower resting pulse rate, lower oxygen consumption at a given work load, faster heart rate recovery following exercise, and the ability to perform greater loads of work.

School programs, which include ample opportunity for activities employing large segments of the body in a light to moderately intensive repetitive action for long periods of time, are conducive to building circulatory-respiratory fitness. Examples of such activities are jogging-running, swimming, rhythmical calisthenics, rope skipping, and games such as soccer, speedball, and hockey.

REFERENCES

Barach, J. H. Feb. 1914. The energy index. *JAMA*, 62, 525-530.

Brouha, L. 1943. The step test: A simple method of measuring physical fitness for muscular work in young men. *Res Quart*, 14, 31-36.

Brouha, L. and M. V. Ball. 1952. *Canadian Red Cross Society's School Meal Study*. Toronto: University of Toronto Press.

Brouha, L. and J. R. Gallagher. 1943. A functional fitness test for high school girls. *J Hlth Phys Ed*, 15, 517.

Clarke, H. H. and R. A. Munroe. 1970. *Test Manual: Oregon Cable-Tension Strength Batteries for Boys and Girls from Fourth Grade Through College*. Eugene: Microform Publications in Health, Physical Education, and Recreation. University of Oregon.

Coooer, K. H. 1970. *The New Aerobics*. New York: M. Evans.

Crampton, C. W. 1905. A test of condition: Preliminary report. *Medical News*, 87, 529-530.

Franzen, R. and G. Palmer. 1934. *The AOH Index of Nutritional Status*. New York: American Child Health Association.

Gallagher, J. R. and L. Brouha. 1943. A simple method of testing the physical fitness of boys. *Res Quart*, 14, 23-30.

Hunsicker, P. and G. G. Reiff. 1976. *AAHPER Youth Fitness Test Manual*. Rev. Ed. Washington, D.C.: AAHPER.

Kraus, H. and R. P. Hirschland. 1954. Minimum muscular fitness tests in school children. *Res Quart*, 25, 178-188.

McCloy, C. H. 1932. *The Measurement of Athletic Power*. New York: A. S. Barnes.

Rogers, F. R. 1926. *Physical Capacity Tests in the Administration of Physical Education.* New York: Bureau of Publications, Teacher's College, Columbia University.

Sheldon, W. H., S. S. Stevens, and W. S. Tucker. 1940. *The Varieties of Human Physique.* New York: Harper.

Tuttle, W. W. 1931. The use of the pulse-ratio test for rating physical efficiency. *Res Quart,* 2, 5-17.

Wetzel, N. C. 1948. *The Treatment of Growth Failure in Children.* Cleveland: NEA Service.

Willgoose, C. E. 1961. *Evaluation in Health Education and Physical Education.* New York: McGraw-Hill.

42

The AAHPER Youth Fitness Test

Kirk J. Cureton

The AAHPER Youth Fitness Test is a battery of physical performance tests designed to assess the level of physical fitness of children and adolescents. The test is unique in that it is the only physical fitness test for which there are national norms. Since its development in 1957, the test has been administered to millions of children in the United States and foreign countries (AAHPER 1976). By serving as the instrument for assessing and documenting the level of physical fitness of the nation's youth, and by providing impetus for improvement of youth physical fitness, the test has been of remarkable value to the physical education profession, to other organizations concerned with youth physical fitness, and to the nation. Current information on the test may be found in the *AAHPER Youth Fitness Test Manual* (1976).

HISTORICAL DEVELOPMENT

The AAHPER Youth Fitness Test was developed in 1957 by a committee of the Research Council of the then American Association for Health, Physical Education, and Recreation (AAHPER). The development of the test was part of the

AAHPER Youth Fitness Project, an attempt to both evaluate and improve the level of youth physical fitness in the United States. Impetus for the project came from a national conference called by President Eisenhower in 1956 to consider the fitness of American children. The conference considered, in particular, reports that the physical fitness of American youth, as measured by the Kraus-Weber Test of minimum muscular fitness, was poorer than that of children in several European countries (Kraus and Hirschland 1953, 1954). The AAHPER Test was developed to provide a more comprehensive and valid test of physical fitness than the Kraus-Weber Test, one with which a national survey of youth physical fitness levels could be conducted.

THE TEST AND REVISIONS

The original AAHPER Youth Fitness Test consisted of seven items selected by a group of experts according to the following criteria: (1) the tests should require little or no equipment, (2) students should be reasonably familiar with the items, (3) the tests should be easily administered by classroom teachers with little or no background in physical education, (4) the tests should be applicable to both boys and girls, (5) the tests could be easily administered to the entire range of grades 5 through 12, and (6) the tests should indicate different components of physical fitness. The seven items were pull-ups (modified for girls), sit-ups, shuttle run, 50-yard dash, softball throw, standing long jump, and the 600-yard run. The items were assumed to reflect the physical fitness components of strength, muscular endurance, agility, speed, coordination, power, and cardiovascular efficiency as well as proficiency in running, jumping, and throwing. Each item was viewed as indicating a strength or weakness and interpreted independently. When taken together, the entire battery was designed to provide an overall picture of a young person's physical fitness.

In 1965 a minor modification in the test battery was made when the flexed-arm hang was substituted for the modified pull-ups for girls. The flexed-arm hang was considered a more efficient and reliable measure of girls' arm and shoulder girdle strength. This change was incorporated into the national survey that utilized the test conducted during the 1963-64 school year.

In 1975, the test was revised again. The softball throw for distance was eliminated, bent-knee sit-ups for one minute replaced the unlimited number of straight-knee sit-ups, and two optional runs were added as an alternative to the 600-yard run: a 1-mile run or 9-minute run for children 10 to 12 years, or a 1.5-mile or 12-minute run for children 13 years or older. These changes made the test more efficient in terms of time, potentially less injurious to students by not requiring the straight-leg sit-up, and more valid by including running tests more representative of distance running ability. These changes were incorporated into the test prior to the national survey conducted in 1974-75.

NATIONAL SURVEYS AND NORMS

The first national youth fitness survey was conducted during the 1975-58 school year under the direction of Paul A. Hunsicker from the University of Michigan. The AAHPER Test was administered to a representative nationwide sample of 8500 boys and girls in grades 5 through 12. Two sets of percentile-rank norms were developed and published in 1958 in the *AAHPER Youth Fitness Test Manual*. One set of norms was based on age and the second set on the Neilson-Cozens Classification Index, a means of grouping individuals according to age, height, and weight.

Results of the first national survey revealed that on the average American boys and girls did not demonstrate high levels of performance on the fitness tests. Studies reported soon after the American norms were published indicated that European children scored considerably higher on almost all items than mean scores for the Americans on the 1957-58 survey (Campbell and Pohndorf 1961; Knuttgen 1961). Differences in the level of habitual physical activity, school physical education programs, and participation in sports were hypothesized to account for the difference.

The comparatively poor levels of youth physical fitness indicated by the 1957-58 survey provided incentive to improve American physical education programs. Practicing for the test itself became a technique for improving performance capabilities. The survey results provided stimulation for increasing physical activity offerings in the public schools, and as a result programs of physical education and recreation across the country were strengthened.

Two conferences, the National Conference on Secondary School Youth in 1958 (AAHPER 1959) and the National Conference on the Fitness of Children of Elementary School Age in 1959 (AAHPER 1960), were sponsored in an attempt to improve the physical education offerings to elementary and secondary school children. The effort was supported by the establishment of the President's Council on Physical Fitness and Sports. The council officially adopted and endorsed the use of the AAHPER Youth Fitness Test and recommended testing as the first step toward improvement of physical fitness.

In 1960, the fitness testing program was expanded to include college men and women. Data were collected on college students enrolled in required basic physical education classes at selected representative universities under the direction of Paul Hunsicker from the University of Michigan and Dorothy Mohr at the University of Maryland. Percentile norms were developed based on data from some 2200 college men and 4800 college women and published in the 1965 edition of the *AAHPER Youth Fitness Test Manual*.

A second national survey was carried out during the 1963-64 and 1964-65 school years in order to revise the norms and to determine whether the increased emphasis on fitness testing and improvement in physical education programs since the initial survey had increased the level of youth physical fitness. A report of this survey was published in 1965 (Hunsicker and Reiff 1965). Revised norms based on test results from about 9200 boys and girls were published in a revised edition of the *AAHPER Youth Fitness Test Manual* (1965).

A third national survey was conducted during the 1974-75 school year, incorporating changes in the test described earlier. Percentile norms based on age were computed utilizing data from about 7600 children and published in another revised edition of the *AAHPER Youth Fitness Test Manual* (1976). Norms based on the Neilson-Cozens Classification Index were omitted, and a set of norms based on the combined boys and girls data was added. Reports comparing the mean scores on the six items obtained in 1975 with results of the two earlier surveys were widely circulated (Reiff 1977).

COMPARISON OF SURVEY RESULTS

Hunsicker and Reiff (1965) compared the average performances achieved by boys and girls in the 1958 and 1965 surveys. In general, youth physical fitness as measured by the AAHPER Test had improved greatly during the seven-year period. When mean performances obtained in the 1965 survey were compared with those obtained in 1958, all but one of the means obtained in 1965 were higher; better performances were recorded for every test at every year of age except for the 17-year-old girls softball throw (see Fig. 42.1). For boys, all but two gains were statistically significant. For girls, 39 of 48 comparisons revealed significant differences. The improvement in performance over the seven-year period was partly attributed to increased efforts by school physical educators throughout the nation to enhance the physical fitness of boys and girls in their classes (Clarke 1975).

In contrast to the improvement in physical fitness found between 1958 and 1965, little if any increase in the level of physical fitness of school children was found for the ten years between 1965 and 1975 (Reiff 1977). Although girls improved somewhat in endurance running and muscular power, the average fitness scores for the 1974-75 school years were almost identical to those recorded ten years earlier. Among the 40 comparisons made between the 1965 and 1975 mean scores, the only significant difference was a decline in the standing long jump for the 14-year-old boys. The girls data revealed significant gains in seven of the 40 comparisons: 600-yard run by 13-, 14-, and 15-, and 17-year-olds; standing long jump by 13- and 14-year olds; and flexed arm hang by 14-year-olds. The 10-year-old girls scored significantly poorer on the 600-yard run than ten years earlier. No simple explanation could be given for the lack of improvement from 1965 to 1975, but it was hypothesized that plateauing interest in physical fitness in the schools, drop-off in school physical education programs due to economic conditions and other causes, and continued sedentary life-style practiced by Americans may have been contributing factors (Reiff 1977). The suggestion that boys and girls may have reached their potential in 1965 was discounted as an explanation (PCPFS April 1976).

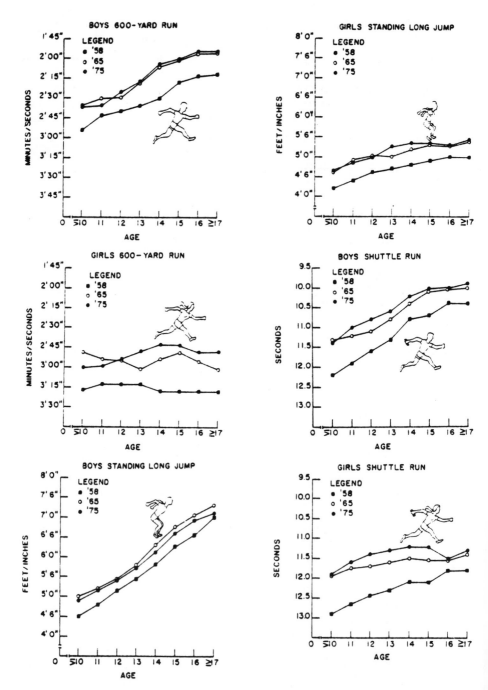

Fig. 42.1 Comparative mean scores for AAHPER Youth Fitness Test, Coterminous USA 1958-1965-1975. (Reprinted with permission from *JOHPER,* January 1977, pp. 32-33.)

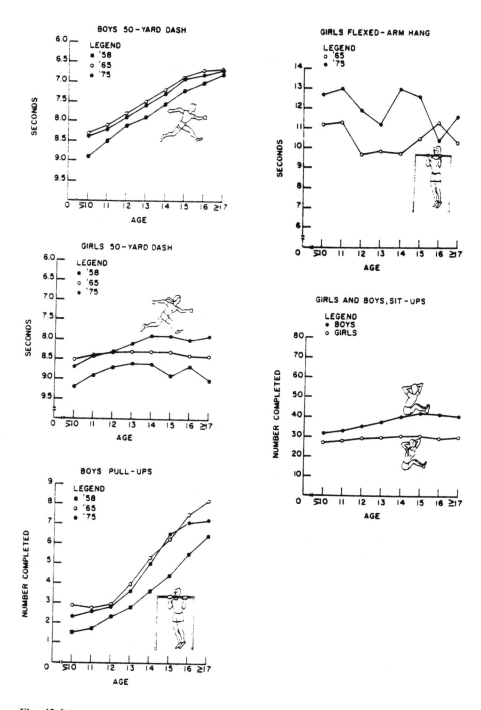

Fig. 42.1 (cont.)

PRESIDENTIAL PHYSICAL FITNESS AWARD PROGRAM

The AAHPER Test is utilized as the basis for the Presidential Fitness Award Program. Children who score above the 85th percentile on all six items of the AAHPER Test according to the most recent national norms qualify for the award. Winners receive a certificate suitable for framing, a decal, and an emblem.

The program was conceived by the President's Council on Physical Fitness and Sports and is administered jointly with the American Alliance for Health, Physical Education, Recreation, and Dance. The program was established in 1966 to honor boys and girls who demonstrate exceptional physical achievement. It was designed to: (1) motivate boys and girls to develop and maintain a high level of physical fitness, (2) encourage good testing programs in schools and communities, (3) stimulate improvement of health and physical education programs, and (4) provide additional information on the physical condition of America's youth. All schools and youth groups in the United States that have qualified physical education and/or physical fitness personnel are encouraged to participate in the program. The number of winners of the award has increased progressively from slightly more than 9000 in the 1965-66 school year to 406,448 during the 1975-76 school year (PCPFS March 1977).

AAHPER TEST FOR MENTALLY RETARDED CHILDREN

In 1968 a modification of the AAHPER Youth Fitness Test for use with educable mentally retarded (EMR) children was published with norms by age and sex. The norms were developed from data collected on a random nationwide sample of 4200 children, 8 through 18 years of age, under the direction of G. L. Rarick from the University of California at Berkeley. The test battery designed for use with mildly mentally retarded children is composed of the following items: flexed-arm hang, sit-up, shuttle run, standing long jump, 50-yard dash, softball throw for distance, and 300-yard run. Current information on this test may be found in the *Special Fitness Manual for Mildly Mentally Retarded Children* (AAHPER 1976).

The Special Fitness Test was based on the premise that mentally retarded children have the same needs for physical development and recognition as children of normal intelligence, and that programs of physical activity for these children need to be as similar as possible to those for nonretarded children. Thus, the test was made as close as possible to the regular Youth Fitness Test, but with norms appropriate so these children could experience success. An award system with four levels was developed to recognize mildly mentally retarded children who attain certain levels of physical fitness as indicated by their test scores.

RESEARCH EVALUATING THE AAHPER TEST

Because of its widespread use, considerable research has been conducted to evaluate various aspects of the AAHPER Youth Fitness Test. A review and discussion of some of this research follows.

Reliability

The items of the AAHPER Test have generally been found to have acceptable reliability. The range of test-retest reliability coefficients reported for two studies involving young boys (Rothermel, Pollock, and Cureton 1968; Cureton, Boileau, and Lohman 1975) and two studies on high school boys and girls (Stein 1964; Klesius 1968) in which the items were administered according to instructions in the test manual were as follows: pull-ups, .80 to .98; sit-ups, .57 to .96; shuttle run, .68 to .86; standing long jump, .90 to .95; 50-yard dash, .83 to .94; softball throw, .90 to .97; and 600-yard run, .74 to .92. Reliability coefficients for the AAHPER Test items reported in other studies have been summarized by Safrit (1973). Marmis et al. (1969) studied the between-trial reliability and reproducibility of the multitrial items on the AAHPER Test to determine the number of trials required for a stable performance measure. They concluded that two trials, instead of the recommended three, would be sufficient for the standing long jump and softball throw; two trials, as prescribed, would be sufficient for the 50-yard dash; and at least three trials should be required for the shuttle run.

Validity

The items originally selected to make up the AAHPER Test were assumed to be valid reflections of proficiency in running, jumping, and throwing as well as the physical fitness components of strength, muscular endurance, power, agility, speed, coordination, and cardiovascular efficiency. Although the face validity of the items in assessing the capability to perform selected common motor performance tasks has been generally accepted, the validity of some of the items in measuring more basic components of physical fitness has been questioned. In addition, the test has been criticized for not adequately taking into account biomechanical or structural factors in interpretation of the test scores (Ricci 1970). Moreover, certain of the test items have been considered more tests of motor "skill" or "ability" than physical fitness (Jackson et al. 1976). Other recent reviews of the validity of the items in the AAHPER Youth Fitness Test may be found in the position paper by Jackson et al. (1976) and in measurement texts by Safrit (1973) and Baumgartner and Jackson (1975). Selected aspects of the validity and interpretation of each of the test items are discussed below.

433

Pull-ups and flexed-arm hang. Pull-ups or the flexed-arm hang measure the ability of a person to repeatedly lift or continuously support the body weight against the force of gravity. The task reflects the ability to repeatedly or continuously exert sufficient force to lift or support the body weight. In the *AAHPER Youth Fitness Test Manual* (1976), the test is interpreted as measuring arm and shoulder girdle strength. Since strength is usually defined as the maximum force that can be exerted against a resistance, the test does not appear to be a valid measure of absolute strength in the strict sense of the term. The test is more clearly a measure of muscular endurance, that is, a measure of the ability to maintain or persist at a given rate of work and to resist fatigue. However, even this interpretation is not strictly correct since the rate of work is not standardized and varies with body weight. Furthermore, the rate of performing the pull-ups is not controlled.

The interpretation of the pull-ups as a measure of absolute arm and shoulder-girdle strength has been repeatedly questioned (Ricci 1970) because the test also reflects the influence of the total body weight and its composition. Persons with very high body weight and particularly a high percentage of body fat are handicapped in performing pull-ups. Norms for the AAHPER Test based on age do not account for the difference in work performed nor mention body fatness as a factor that may influence the outcome of the test.

Use of the pull-up test with young children or older individuals with poor fitness is also a problem since many zero scores may be obtained. In this situation, the test is a poor discriminator and the data become difficult to analyze because of the skewed distribution. Use of the flexed-arm hang in place of the pull-up has proved a successful solution to the problem for females, although this test no longer evaluates the ability to actually lift the body weight. The relationship between the flexed-arm hang and pull-ups, however, is relatively good (Cotten and Marwitz 1969).

Sit-ups. The one-minute bent-knee sit-up test measures the ability of a person to repeatedly lift the upper portion of the body against the force of gravity. This movement is known to require the contraction of the abdominal and hip flexor muscles. In the *AAHPER Youth Fitness Test Manual* (1976), the test is interpreted as a measure of the "efficiency of the abdominal and hip flexor muscles." Use of the term efficiency is unfortunate and not really correct since efficiency has a precise mechanical definition. This test, like the pull-up, is probably best interpreted as a measure of the muscular endurance of the abdominal and hip flexor muscles. However, since the test is timed and the rate of work is not standardized, endurance is not actually being measured.

The bent-knee sit-up is preferred over the straight-leg sit-up because flexion of the knee and hip joints reduces the involvement of the illiopsoas and quadriceps muscles in producing the movement, while maximizing the involvement of the abdominal muscles (Flint 1965). The bent-knee style minimizes the hyperextension of the lumbar spine, a possible cause of lower back pain (Kendall 1965).

Performance of the sit-up rapidly as in the timed test is more strenuous and requires involvement of greater muscle mass (Godfrey, Kindig, and Windell 1977). The timed test is also much more efficient in terms of the time required for administration. Supporting the feet is necessary to enable individuals with a heavy trunk to perform the sit-up movement.

Standing long jump. The standing long jump measures the ability to jump or to project the body weight through space. This item reflects skill in performing the jump as well as the ability to accelerate the body mass. Its interpretation in the *AAHPER Youth Fitness Test Manual* (1976) as a test of "explosive muscle power" has been questioned. Several biomechanical studies have found low correlations between performance on jumping tests and actual measurements of power (Considine 1970; Barlow 1970). Therefore, it appears that interpretation of the standing long jump as a test of power may not be valid.

Shuttle run. The shuttle run requires the subject to run back and forth between two lines 30 feet apart. The item measures the ability to run fast and to accelerate, decelerate, and change direction quickly. In the *AAHPER Youth Fitness Test Manual* (1976), it is interpreted as measuring "speed and change of direction," which appears to be a valid interpretation as it applies to running. The ability to change direction quickly is often called agility. Running agility improves with practice and, therefore, familiarization with the test prior to administration is essential. Agility in running should not also be generalized to indicate agility in performing other tasks as it appears to be task specific (Baumgartner and Jackson 1975).

50-yard dash. The 50-yard dash measures the time required to run a short distance. It reflects both the ability to start running and to accelerate the body weight as well as the maximum running speed. In the *AAHPER Youth Fitness Test Manual* (1976), the test is interpreted as measuring "speed." A more specific interpretation might be that of a test of acceleration and speed in running. Baumgartner and Jackson (1965) have shown that most of the unreliability in the 50-yard dash is associated with the first 20 yards or with the start. A more valid test of running speed would be to measure the time required to run the last 30 yards of the 50-yard dash.

600-yard run or longer optional distance run tests. Distance run tests measure the maximal average speed that can be maintained over a given distance or time. Because the tests require relatively prolonged exertion, they also reflect the level of energy expenditure that can be maintained over an extended period of time or what is commonly called the physical work capacity. Performance on these tests has implications for performance of other weight-bearing tasks requiring similar high levels of energy expenditure.

In the revised (1976) edition of the *AAHPER Youth Fitness Test Manual,* the 600-yard run and longer optional distance runs are interpreted as measures of endurance. They are not strictly measures of endurance since the ability to maintain a given rate of work or the decrement in work (fatigue) is not measured. Rather, the maximal rate of work that can be maintained over a given distance or time is assessed. Interpretation of these tests as measures of distance running ability is probably more appropriate.

In earlier editions of the *AAHPER Youth Fitness Test Manual* (1958, 1965), the 600-yard run has been interpreted as a measure of cardiovascular efficiency. Others have also interpreted distance running performance tests as indicators of cardiovascular fitness (Cooper 1968) or cardiorespiratory endurance (Texas Governor's Commission on Physical Fitness 1973). These interpretations imply that individual differences in distance running performance are determined predominantly by cardiovascular function. Support for the validity of this type of interpretation in recent years has been based on the moderately high correlations between distance running performance and maximal oxygen uptake (aerobic capacity) expressed relative to body weight (max $\dot{V}O_2$ in ml/min per kg of body weight). A summary of correlation coefficients obtained in a large number of research studies has been compiled by Baumgartner and Jackson (1975). In general, correlation coefficients obtained on various groups of individuals have ranged from moderate ($r \simeq .50$) to high ($r \simeq .90$). There is a tendency for correlations to be higher for longer distance runs.

Although a moderately high relationship between distance running performance and max $\dot{V}O_2$ (ml/min/kg BW) exists, interpretation of distance run test scores solely in terms of cardiovascular function has been questioned, in that max $\dot{V}O_2$ (ml/min/kg BW) is not a pure measure of cardiorespiratory capacity, but may also reflect variation in body fatness (Buskirk and Taylor 1957). In addition, a number of other factors including body size, body composition, and running speed have been shown to be important determinants of distance running performance in children (Cureton et al. 1977). Thus, interpretation of the 600-yard or optional distance runs solely in terms of cardiovascular function is an oversimplification and omits consideration of other important factors that influence the outcome of these tests.

A factor analytic study of the construct validity of running tests (Disch, Jackson, and Frankiewicz 1975) in college students revealed that the "purest" measures of distance running ability were those of one mile in length or longer. This study supports the validity of using distance runs longer than 600 yards to assess distance running ability.

Relationships Among the AAHPER Test Items

Items comprising the AAHPER Test were selected to measure different aspects of physical fitness and were assumed not to be highly intercorrelated. Ponthieux and Barker (1963) reported intercorrelations between the seven original test items ranging from .17 to .54 using data on 1335 college freshmen. Hunsicker and Reiff (1965), utilizing data collected in the second national survey, computed intercorrelations between the seven original items for each year of age between 10 and 17 years and for both sexes. The 336 correlations reported ranged from zero to about .60. The highest relationships were between the standing long jump and the shuttle run and between the standing long jump and the 50-yard dash. Mohr (1967) found similar intercorrelations ranging from .03 to .42 among the test scores using data on 4391 college women.

Ponthieux and Barker (1963) analyzed scores on the AAHPER Test obtained from 1335 college males. They obtained three factors they labeled ''cardiorespiratory endurance'' (high factor loadings on pull-ups, sit-ups, and 600-yard run), ''gross body coordination'' (high loading on the softball throw for distance), and ''muscular explosiveness'' (high factor loadings on the long jump, shuttle run, and 50-yard dash). Fleishman (1964) also found that the AAHPER Youth Fitness Test represented less than seven factors. In a factor analysis of a large number of physical fitness and motor ability tests, he found that four of the same AAHPER Test items, namely, the shuttle run, the 50-yard dash, the softball throw for distance, and the standing long jump, loaded on a factor labeled ''explosive strength.'' It would appear that the AAHPER Test items do not indicate completely different aspects of physical fitness and that there is some overlap in terms of the basic factors being measured. This is not surprising, however, since the AAHPER Test was originally developed logically, not using factor analysis techniques. Jackson (1975) has criticized the development of the AAHPER Test for this reason. Eckert (1974) has pointed out, however, that use of the items is perhaps best justified not in terms of components as identified by factor analysis, but on the basis of the activities of running, jumping, and throwing represented, which are basic to most physical activities.

Relationships of AAHPER Test Items to Age, Height, Weight, and Body Composition

Mean scores for the AAHPER Youth Fitness Test items obtained on the three national youth fitness surveys plotted against age (see Fig. 42.1) clearly reveals that most performances are related to age for children between 10 and 17 years. In general, mean scores for boys tend to improve regularly on all items throughout this age range. The one exception is the bent-knee sit-up test in which the mean scores peak at age 15. Girls, on the other hand, improve on most items between the ages of 10 and 14, but show little change from age 14 to 17. The exception to this is the flexed-arm hang, in which mean scores decrease somewhat between 10 and 17 years of age. These trends agree with other similar published data (Espenschade 1960; Cureton 1964). Montoye, Frantz, and Kozar (1972) reported correlation coefficients between age and performance on the AAHPER Test for 1147 boys and 948 girls in grades 4 through 12, tested as part of the Tecumseh Community Health Study. Correlation coefficients for boys ranged from .49 to .74 and for girls from .02 to .51. The items most highly related to age for both sexes were the softball throw, 50-yard dash, standing broad jump, and shuttle run.

Substantial differences in performance exist between the sexes on each of the items on the AAHPER Test, with boys on the average scoring better at all ages. These differences become considerably larger after age 14, suggesting that sex differences in performance reflect the biological differences between the sexes that become increasingly evident after puberty, such as differences in height, muscular development, and accumulation of body fat. However, cultural performance expectations and physical activity patterns may also partly explain these differences.

The relationships of age and sex to the items on the AAHPER Youth Fitness Test indicate norms based on age and sex are justified and desirable. The norms based on data with boys and girls considered together, presented for the first time in the 1976 edition of the *AAHPER Youth Fitness Test Manual,* appear to offer little advantage since there is good reason to believe the sex differences in performance largely reflect real biological differences between the sexes. These "average" norms do not represent realistic standards for either sex.

Several research studies have been conducted to determine whether height and weight in addition to age should be taken into account in construction of norms for the AAHPER Test. Gross and Casciani (1962) studied the relationship between age, height, and weight and the seven original items on the AAHPER Test using data on some 13,600 boys and girls in Pennsylvania. Within the groupings of junior high school boys, junior high school girls, high school boys, and high school girls, multiple correlations between age, height, and weight and performances on the AAHPER Test were low, generally below .30. The authors concluded that within these groups, age, height, and weight singly, or in combination, were of little value in classifying children into homogeneous groups. These results imply that within the relatively restricted age groupings, height and weight are of little additional value in predicting physical performance scores. Epenscade (1963) also found low correlations between height and weight and scores on physical performance tests involving running, jumping, and throwing for children of any given age between 10 and 18 years, using data on 7600 boys and girls in California. She recommended the use of age alone in constructing motor performance norms in this age range. Montoye, Frantz, and Kozar (1972) reached a similar conclusion in analyzing data on 2095 boys and girls tested on the AAHPER Test items as part of the Tecumseh Community Health Study. This research supports the omission in the 1976 edition of the *AAHPER Youth Fitness Test Manual* of norms based on the Neilsen-Cozens Classification Index.

Although total body weight has not been found to be an important determinant of performances on the AAHPER Test for children of any given age, significant relationships have been found between relative body fatness or leanness and physical performance scores on items included in the AAHPER Test. Ismail, Christian, and Kessler (1963) found substantial positive correlations between percent lean body mass and performances on the 50-yard dash (.55), pull-ups (.47), and the standing long jump (.44) in 81 boys 10 to 12 years. Each of these correlations was higher than the correlation of the performance scores with total body weight. In a factor analysis of a large number of motor performance and physical development variables, the researchers found that percent lean body mass (or percent fat) was the most important item in a factor labeled "body fitness." The motor performance variables that loaded heavily on this factor were the 50-yard dash, pull-ups, and vertical jump. Cureton, Boileau, and Lohman (1975) also found moderate correlations in children between body fatness or leanness and scores on the items of the AAHPER Test in which the body weight must be moved. Based upon data on 54 boys, 8 to 11 years, significant moderate negative correlations were found between percent body fat and each of the AAHPER Test items with the exception of the softball throw and sit-ups, tasks which do not require movement of the total body weight. When multiple regression analysis was used, it was found percent body fat contributed significantly to prediction of each of the performance tests except sit-ups when age, height, and weight were held constant. This research suggests that body composition should be included in interpretation of the AAHPER Test items in which the body weight must be lifted against gravity (pull-ups and standing long jump), accelerated horizontally (50-yard dash), or carried for some distance (600-yard run or optional distance runs).

Relationship of the AAHPER Test Items to Aerobic Capacity

During the 1950s and 1960s a number of exercise physiologists and physicians suggested that the aerobic capacity or maximal oxygen uptake capacity was the best single measure of physical fitness, when physical fitness was defined as the ability to perform prolonged, exhaustive work (Astrand 1956). Therefore, a number of research studies were conducted to determine the extent to which the items on the AAHPER Youth Fitness Test could be used to predict maximal oxygen uptake. In retrospect, this research appears to be somewhat limited in meaning since the purpose of the AAHPER Test is to assess a number of components of physical fitness, most of which are unrelated to the capacity to perform prolonged, exhaustive work.

Studies by Olree et al. (1965), Fall, Ismail, and MacLeod (1966), Carroll (1969), and Metz and Alexander (1970), using various groups of children and adults, found that in general aerobic capacity could not be accurately predicted from the seven AAHPER Test items. Multiple R's predicting aerobic capacity expressed relative to body weight ranged from .68 to .78 in each of these studies. The single item found to relate strongest to max $\dot{V}O_2$ (ml/min/kg BW) was the 600-yard run, as would be expected.

FUTURE REVISION AND EMPHASIS ON HEALTH-RELATED FITNESS

In 1975 a joint committee on physical fitness representing the Measurement and Evaluation, Physical Fitness, and Research Councils of AAHPER began a study of the AAHPER Youth Fitness Test designed to determine the need for revision. Work of this joint committee resulted in a position paper (Jackson et al. 1976) calling for: (1) alteration of the traditional concept of physical fitness to distinguish between health-related and performance-related components and tests of physical fitness; (2) revision of the AAHPER Test to place increased emphasis on evaluation of health-related physical fitness; and (3) the use of both norm-referenced and criterion-referenced standards for interpretation of test scores. The Board of Governors of AAHPER supported the position paper and a task force was appointed to implement its proposals.

At the time of this writing, the task force is drafting a new test manual that will include sections on evaluation of both health-related and performance-related aspects of physical fitness. Proposed tests of health-related physical fitness include: (1) a distance run (1600 m or nine minutes) for evaluation of physical work capacity; (2) a sum of skinfolds for evaluation of body composition; (3) a sit-up test for assessing abdominal muscle strength and endurance; and (4) a sit-and-reach test for evaluation of flexibility in the posterior thigh and low back areas. Tests of performance-related fitness will include some of the items in the current version of the test as well as suggestions for alternative tests. Plans are for both criterion-referenced and norm-referenced standards to be presented. In addition to a section on the test-item instructions and norms, the manual will probably also include a section on rationale and technical aspects of the test items and a section on methods for improving components of physical fitness evaluated by the test. It is hoped the new test will provide an important mechanism through which the concept of health-related physical fitness, and the importance of its development and maintenance throughout life, will be conveyed to youth of this country.

REFERENCES

AAHPER. 1958, Revised ed. 1965, 1975, 1976. *AAHPER Youth Fitness Test Manual.* Washington, D.C.: AAHPER.

AAHPER. 1959. *Youth and Fitness, A Program for Secondary Schools.* Report of the AAHPER National Conference on Secondary School Youth, 1958. Washington, D.C.: AAHPER.

AAHPER. 1960. *Children and Fitness, A Program for Elementary Schools.* Report of the AAHPER National Conference on Fitness of Chidlren of Elementary School Age, 1959. Washington, D.C.: AAHPER.

AAHPER. 1976. *Special Fitness Test for Mildly Mentally Retarded Persons.* Washington, D.C.: AAHPER.

Astrand, P. O. 1956. Human physical fitness with special reference to sex and age. *Physio Rev,* 36, 307.

Barlow, D. A. 1970. Relation between power and selected variables in the vertical jump. In *Selected Topics on Biomechanics,* J. M. Cooper (ed.). Chicago: Athletic Institute.

Baumgartner, T. A. and A. S. Jackson. 1967. Measurement schedules for tests of motor performances. *Res Quart,* 36, 368-370.

Baumgartner, T. A. and A. S. Jackson. 1975. *Measurement for Evaluation in Physical Education.* Boston: Houghton Mifflin.

Buskirk, E. R. and H. L. Taylor. 1957. Maximal oxygen intake and its relation to body composition, with special reference to chronic physical and obesity. *J Appl Physiol,* 11, 72-78.

Campbell, W. and R. Pohndorf. 1961. Physical fitness of British and United States Children. In *Health and Fitness in the Modern World.* Chicago: The Athletic Institute.

Clarke, H. H. (ed.). 1975. *Phys Fit Res Digest.* Series 5, No. 1, 15-16.

Considine, W. J. 1970. A validity analysis of selected leg power tests utilizing a force platform. In *Selected Topics in Biomechanics,* J. M. Cooper (ed.). Chicago: Athletic Institute.

Cooper, K. H. 1968. A means of assessing maximal oxygen intake. *JAMA,* 203, 201-204.

Carroll, V. 1969. Relationship of the AAHPER Youth Fitness Test items and maximal oxygen intake. Doctoral Dissertation, University of Illinois, Urbana, Illinois.

Cotten, D. M. and B. Marwitz. 1969. Relationship between two flexed-arm hangs and pull-ups for college women. *Res Quart,* 40, 415-416.

Cureton, K. J., R. A. Boileau, and T. G. Lohman. 1975. Relationship between body composition measures and AAHPER Test performances in young boys. *Res Quart,* 46, 218-229.

Cureton, K. J., R. A. Boileau, T. G. Lohman, and J. E. Misner. 1977. Determinants of distance running performance in children: Analysis of a path model. *Res Quart,* 48, 271-279.

Cureton, T. K. 1964. Improving the physical fitness of youth. *Monog Res Child Development.* 29, No. 4, Serial No. 95.

Disch, J., A. S. Jackson, and R. Frankiewicz. 1975. Construct validation of distance run tests. *Res Quart,* 46, 169-176.

Eckert, H. M. 1974. *Practical Measurement of Physical Performance.* Philadelphia: Lea and Febiger.

Espenschade, A. S. 1960. Motor development. In *Science and Medicine of Exercise and Sports,* W. R. Johnson (ed.). New York: Harper.

Espenschade, A. S. 1963. Restudy of relationships between physical performance of school children and age, height, and weight. *Res Quart,* 34, 144-153.

Falls, H. B., A. H. Ismail, and D. F. MacLeod. 1966. Estimation of maximum oxygen uptake in adults from AAHPER Youth Fitness Test items. *Res Quart,* 37, 192-201.

441

Fitness of American Youth (A Report to the President of the United States on the West Point Conference). 1956. Washington, D.C.: U.S. Government Printing Office.

Fleishman, E. A. 1964. *The Structure and Measurement of Physical Fitness.* Englewood Cliffs, N. J.: Prentice-Hall.

Flint, M. M. 1965. Abdominal muscle involvement during the performance of various forms of sit-up exercise. *Am Journal Phys Med,* 44, 224-234.

Godfrey, K. E., L. E. Kindig, and E. J. Windell. 1977. Electromyographic study of duration of muscle activity in sit-up variations. *Arch Phys Med Rehab,* 58, 132-135.

Gross, E. and J. A. Casciani. 1962. Value of age, height, and weight as a classification device for secondary school students in the seven AAHPER Youth Fitness Tests. *Res Quart,* 33, 51-58.

Hunsicker, P. and G. Reiff. 1965. A survey and comparison of youth fitness 1958-1965. U.S. Office of Education, Report of Cooperative Research Project No. 2418. Ann Arbor: University of Michigan.

Ismail, A. H., J. E. Christian, and W. V. Kessler. 1963. Body composition relative to motor aptitude for preadolescent boys. *Res Quart,* 34, 462-470.

Jackson, A. S. 1975. An evaluation of the AAHPER Youth Fitness Test. Paper presented at the AAHPER National Convention, Atlantic City, N. J.

Jackson, A. S. and others. 1976. A Position Paper on Physical Fitness. A position paper from a joint committee representing the Measurement and Evaluation, Physical Fitness and Research Councils of the Association for Research, Administration, Professional Councils and Societies, AAHPER.

Kendall, F. P. 1965. A criticism of current tests and exercises for physical fitness. *J Am Phys Therapy Assoc,* 45, 187-197.

Klesius, S. E. 1968. Reliability of the AAHPER youth fitness test items and relative efficiency of the performance measures. *Res Quart,* 39, 809-811.

Knuttgen, H. 1961. Comparison of fitness of Danish and American school children. *Res Quart,* 30, 190-196.

Kraus, H. and R. P. Hirschland. 1953. Muscular fitness and health. *JOHPER,* 24, 17-19.

Kraus, H. and R. P. Hirschland. 1954. Minimum muscular fitness test in school children. *Res Quart,* 25, 178-187.

Marmis, C., H. J. Montoye, D. A. Cunningham, and A. J. Kozar. 1969. Reliability of the multi-trial items of the AAHPER youth fitness test. *Res Quart,* 40, 240-245.

Metz, K. F. and J. F. Alexander. 1970. An investigation of the relationship between maximum aerobic work capacity and physical fitness in twelve- to fifteen-year old boys. *Res Quart,* 41, 75-81.

Mohr, D. 1967. Interrelationships between physical fitness scores. *Res Quart,* 38, 725-726.

Montoye, H. J., M. E. Frantz, and A. J. Kozar. 1972. The value of age, height, and weight in establishing standards of fitness for children. *J Spts Med Phys Fit,* 12, 174-179.

Olree, H., C. Steven, T. Nelson, G. Agnevik, and R. Clark. 1965. Validity of the AAHPER youth fitness test. *J Spts Med Phys Fit,* 5, 67-71.

Ponthieux, N. and D. Barker. 1963. An analysis of the AAHPER youth fitness test. *Res Quart,* 34, 525-526.

President's Council on Physical Fitness and Sports. April, 1976. *Newsletter.*

President's Council on Physical Fitness and Sports. March, 1977. *Newsletter.*

President's Council on Physical Fitness and Sports. April, 1977. *Newsletter.*

Reiff, G. 1977. Youth fitness report: 1958-1965-1975. *JOPER,* 48, 31-33.

Ricci, B. 1970. For a moratorium on "physical fitness" testing. *JOPHER,* 41, 28-29.

Rothermel, B. L., M. L. Pollock, and T. K. Cureton, Jr. 1968. AAHPER physical fitness score changes resulting from an eight-week sports and physical fitness program. *Res Quart,* 39, 1127-1129.

Safrit, M. 1973. *Evaluation in physical education.* Englewood Cliffs, N. J.: Prentice Hall.

Stein, J. 1964. The reliability of the youth fitness test. *Res Quart,* 35, 330-334.

Texas Governor's Commission on Physical Fitness. 1973. *Physical Fitness-Motor Ability Test.* Austin: The Commission.

43

Growth, Strength, and Physical Performance

Robert M. Malina

Growth is a dynamic process, implying movement toward adulthood or maturity. It involves a series of changes from conception to adulthood during which time the individual increases in size as a whole and of component parts, changes in body proportions, changes in physique and body composition, and eventually matures. Maturity is a variably used term, and in growth studies is most commonly used to indicate sexual maturity or the attainment of adult stature. Human growth, however, does not cease when maturity is attained.

There are basically two kinds of growth studies—cross-sectional and longitudinal. In a cross-sectional study, a large sample of children is seen on only one occasion. Thus, each child is represented only once in a sample. Such data are generally averaged by age and sex and provide information on growth status or size-attained in a particular dimension at a given point in time. The data, however, provide no information on individual growth rates from one age to the next since each subject is represented only once in the sample. To obtain growth rates, longitudinal studies are essential. In such a study a child or group of children is seen at one age and subsequently at regular intervals until sufficient information is obtained. The focus of longitudinal studies is on growth change in individuals. Thus, the same child or children are repeatedly measured throughout the whole period of growth or part of the growth period. Data derived from longitudinal studies provide information not only on growth attained but also on the rate or velocity of growth.

Growth curves based largely on cross-sectional data will be used in the subsequent discussion to illustrate the pattern of growth in physical characteristics, strength, and performance from childhood through adolescence. The limitations of using curves of average values, especially during adolescence, are obvious. Such curves are ordinarily smooth and thus mask individual variation in growth. Curves of average values, nevertheless, indicate the general pattern of age-, sex- and maturity-associated variations in growth, strength, and motor performance.

AGE- AND SEX-ASSOCIATED VARIATION IN GROWTH

Body Size

Standing height (stature) and body weight are the most commonly used measures of body size. Age trends in height and weight are shown in Fig. 43.1. From infancy to early adulthood height and weight generally follow a double sigmoid or four-phased growth pattern: rapid gain in infancy and early childhood (birth to 5 years); steady gain in middle childhood (6 years to the onset of adolescence, about the elementary school years); rapid gain during the adolescent spurt (about 10 to 14 years in girls and 12 to 16 years in boys); and finally slow increase and eventual cessation of growth at the attainment of adult size or maturity. Both sexes follow the same general course of growth. Sex differences before the adolescent spurt are minor, although boys tend to be, on the average, slightly taller and heavier. During the early part of adolescence, girls are taller and heavier than boys, due to the earlier maturation of girls. Girls, however, soon lose this size advantage as the male adolescent spurt starts. Males catch up and eventually surpass females in height and weight. The type of growth curve illustrated in Fig. 43.1 is called a *distance curve* in that it indicates the distance a child has traversed on his or her path of growth. Such a curve shows the size attained at a given age and indicates growth status.

Rates of growth—that is, centimeters or kilograms in height and weight— differ prior to adolescence. Height growth occurs at a constantly decelerating rate. The child is getting taller but at a slower rate. Weight growth occurs at a slightly but constantly accelerating rate. During the adolescent spurt, growth in both height and weight accelerates sharply. The adolescent height and weight

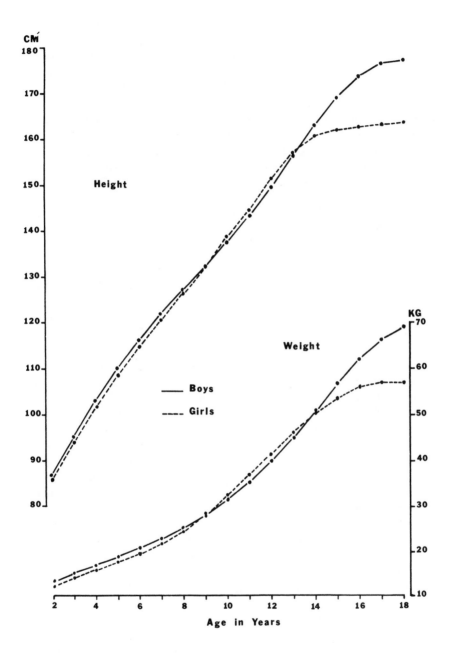

Fig. 43.1 Size-attained curves for height and weight for boys and girls. (Drawn from the data of the National Center for Health Statistics, in press.)

spurts occur earlier and are only slightly less in magnitude in girls than in boys. Sex differences in adult height are due primarily to the fact that boys on the average are growing over a longer period of time than are girls. Girls on the average nearly stop growing in height by 16 years of age, while boys continue to gain for another two years or so.

Most external dimensions of the body—such as sitting height, leg length, shoulder breadth, hip breadth, limb circumferences, etc.—follow the same general growth pattern for size attained and growth rate as height and weight. In general, prior to adolescence, sex differences are minor; in the early adolescent years, females have a temporary size advantage, but males eventually surpass females in size attained in most dimensions.

Body Proportions

Sex differences in proportions, though apparent, are relatively minor during preadolescent years. Sex differences in the adolescent growth spurt produce the characteristic sexual dimorphism (morphological differences between males and females) seen in young adulthood. For example, the obvious broadening of the shoulders relative to the hips is characteristic of male adolescence, while the broadening of the hips relative to the shoulders and waist is characteristic of female adolescence.

Proportional differences reflecting physique changes are apparent in the ratio of sitting height to standing height during growth. This ratio is an index of the contributions of the trunk and legs to stature. Note that standing height minus sitting height provides an estimate of the length of the lower extremities. Age changes in the ratio of sitting height to stature are shown in Fig. 43.2. The ratio is highest in infancy and early childhood, and declines throughout childhood into adolescence. Thus, young children have relatively short legs for their statures, that is, the sitting height comprises a greater percentage of standing height. The legs, however, grow at a faster rate than the trunk, neck, and head, which constitute sitting height, so that the ratio gradually declines during childhood. The ratio is lowest during the adolescent spurt, about 12 to 13 years in girls, and 13 to 15 years in boys. It then rises gradually. This slight increase in the ratio in late adolescence is due to growth in trunk length, after growth in the lower extremities has already decelerated or stopped.

The sitting height/standing height ratio is identical for boys and girls until about 11 years of age, when it is slightly higher in girls and remains so through adolescence into adulthood. Thus, prior to the adolescent spurt, both boys and girls are proportionally similar in terms of the contributions of the lower extremities and the trunk to total height. However, during adolescence and in adulthood, females have, for equal stature, shorter legs than males. Thus, females are, on the average, relatively short-legged compared to males, who are relatively long-legged.

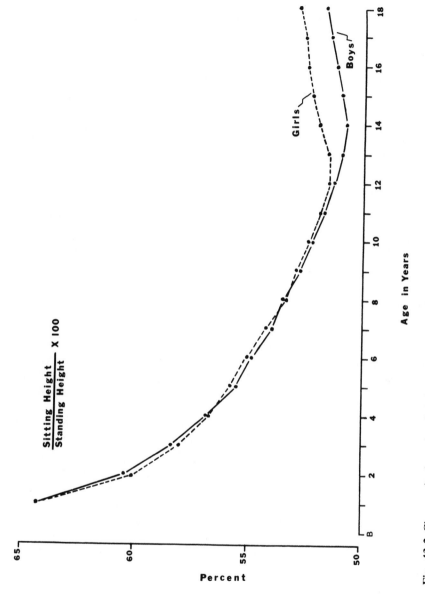

Fig. 43.2 Changes in the ratio of sitting height to standing height during growth. (Drawn from the data of Hansman 1970.)

Physique

Physique refers to the general configuration of the individual's body. Sheldon's approach (Sheldon et al. 1954) to physique assessment is perhaps the most widely used, although a modification of this method is currently receiving extensive use (Carter 1975). Sheldon's method is founded on the premise that there is continuous variation in physique based upon the contribution of varying components to the conformation of the entire body. These components are termed *endomorphy*, referring to a relative preponderance of the digestive organs and of softness and roundness of contour throughout the body, as in an individual who tends toward fatness; *mesomorphy*, referring to a predominance of muscle and bone, so that muscles are prominent with sharp contours, as in a muscular individual; and *ectomorphy*, referring to a general linearity of build, poor muscular development, and a preponderance of surface area over body mass, as in an extremely thin individual. A clear-cut dominance of one of these three components defines the individual's physique, which is called a *somatotype*.

Somatotype studies during early childhood indicate that girls tend to have higher ratings* for endomorphy and boys have higher ratings for mesomorphy. Differences of lesser magnitude are apparent for ectomorphy. The distribution of ratings for each somatotype component shows a marked sex difference in physique during early childhood. There are more endomorphic girls and more mesomorphic boys. In one study, for example, only 25 percent of the boys' ratings reached or exceeded a value of 4 for endomorphy, while more than half of the girls' ratings reached or exceeded this value for endomorphy. Conversely, in mesomorphy over half the boys reached or exceeded a rating of 4 whereas only 16 percent of the girls' ratings reached or exceeded this value (Walker 1962).

Although the preceding suggests a clear-cur sex difference in physique during early childhood, it should be emphasized that the physiques of male and female endomorphs (or of male and female mesomorphs) are much alike. The important point is that there are more endomorphic girls and more mesomorphic boys, which represents a sex difference in physique that is probably of genetic origin.

Somatotype ratings during early and middle childhood are reasonably similar. Comparisons of somatotypes in early and late adolescence illustrate the effects of the adolescent spurt on physique development. Male adolescence is characterized by major development in the mesomorphic component, a reduction in the endomorphic component, and an increase in the ectomorphic component. Female adolescence, on the other hand, involves primary development in endomorphy, slight increase in mesomorphy, and a reduction in ectomorphy.

---

* Somatotype ratings generally vary between 1 and 7 units. A rating of 1 indicates the least expression or development of a component, while a rating of 7 indicates the fullest expression of the component.

The effects of adolescence on physique are such that in young adulthood, as in childhood, there are more endomorphic females than males and more mesomorphic males than females. Females are more concentrated in the high endomorphic sector of a somatotype distribution while males tend toward the mesomorphic sector. However, males are more extensively distributed throughout the somatotype spectrum than are females.

Body Composition

Body weight is a heterogeneous mass composed of different tissues. There are a variety of methods available to partition this mass and thus provide estimates of the body's composition. Estimates of body composition can be broadly grouped into two categories—those that are whole-body oriented and those that are regional (Malina 1969). The former indicates the gross competition of the body as a whole, most commonly within the framework of a two-component model: Body Weight = Lean Body Mass + Fat. Measurements of body density, body water, and potassium concentration in the body are used most frequently as estimates of leanness/fatness in the two-component framework. Urinary creatinine excretion, though affected by diet and physical activity, is also used as an index of muscle mass in the body as a whole. Observations derived from these varied approaches to body composition show generally similar patterns of age-related changes and sex differences during childhood and adolescence.

Body density is inversely related to body fat content, though not linearly. A measure of density can thus provide an estimate of body fatness. Males have greater body densities than females at all ages during childhood and adolescence and, therefore, a lower percentage of body weight as fat (Fig. 43.3). Sex differences in density and relative fatness are consistent during childhood. During adolescence, sex differences are magnified. Males increase considerably in density, while females decrease somewhat. These changes reflect the male increase in lean tissue, especially muscle mass, and/or a decrease in fat, and the female accumulation of fat during adolescence.

Water comprises about 72 percent of the fat-free mass of the body in normally hydrated individuals. Thus, a measure of the total amount of water in the body can provide an estimate of lean tissue or lean body mass. Males have slightly higher percentages of body weight as water during childhood, and thus larger lean body masses. Estimates of total body water as a percentage of body weight vary between 60 and 63 percent over childhood in both sexes. During the adolescent years, sex differences in percentage of total body water become considerable. Between ages 12 and 18, the relative contribution of total body water to body weight increases from 60 to 65 percent in males and decreases from 61 to 54 percent in females (Friss-Hansen 1965).

Total body water is generally subdivided into water in the cells (intracellular water) and water outside the cells (extracellular water). When the body's composition is viewed in terms of the contributions of the extracellular and intracellular water components to the genesis of sex differences in adolescence,

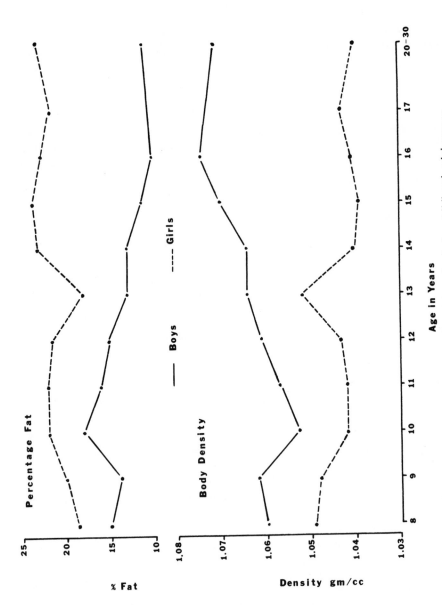

Fig. 43.3 Body density and percentage of body weight as fat during childhood, adolescence, and young childhood. (Drawn from the data of Parizkova 1973.)

changes in the intracellular component are even more significant. Water in cells increases in males from 36 to 39 percent and decreases in females from 36 to 29 percent between 12 and 18 years. The extracellular component of total body water, however, remains stable in both sexes between ages 12 and 18 (25 to 26 percent). The changing proportions of water in cells and outside of cells are the result of disproportionate growth of tissues with different composition; for example, changes in the amount of fat or muscle or changes in the mineralization of the skeleton (Friis-Hansen 1965).

Another estimate of body composition is derived from measures of potassium in the body. Potassium occurs primarily in the intracellular component of the body, and most of it is concentrated in muscle tissue (about 5 to 70 percent of body's stores). Age-related changes in estimates of lean body mass derived from potassium measures, closely parallel growth curves for height and weight during childhood and adolescence (Fig. 43.4). Boys have consistently larger lean body mass estimates than girls throughout childhood. Males also have a rather abrupt increase in lean body mass during adolescence, while in females it is more gradual. The increase in lean body mass in male adolescents in relatively greater than the increase in body weight, since body fat content decreases at this time (lower part of Fig. 43.4). Mature lean body mass values are reached earlier in females than in males.

The preceding observations derived from whole-body estimates of body composition indicate consistent sex differences in body composition prior to the adolescent spurt and marked differences during and after the spurt. Thus, average lean body mass values for postadolescent girls are only about two-thirds of the male values. On the other hand, young adult females have almost twice the amount of body fat as males. A part of the sex difference in fatness during adolescence and into adulthood is related to the development of "essential" fat in females. Essential fat is found primarily in the breasts and probably in other tissues (Behnke 1967). The growth pattern for lean body mass parallels closely the pattern for height and weight. Body fatness changes are more variable than those for lean body mass. Absolute amounts of total body fat generally increase during childhood but show a decrease in accumulation or a reduced rate of accumulation during adolescence, especially in males.

Muscle tissue is a major component of lean body mass. Estimates of muscle mass in the body during childhood and adolescence are shown in Fig. 43.5. Boys generally have a larger muscle mass than girls, and the sex difference becomes most apparent during adolescence. At five years of age, muscle mass accounts for about 40 percent of body weight in girls and 42 percent in boys, a minor sex difference. In late adolescence (17 years) muscle mass accounts for only 42 percent of body weight in girls, but 53 percent in boys. The slight change in the relative contribution of muscle tissue to body weight in females during adolescence probably reflects the accumulation of body fat.

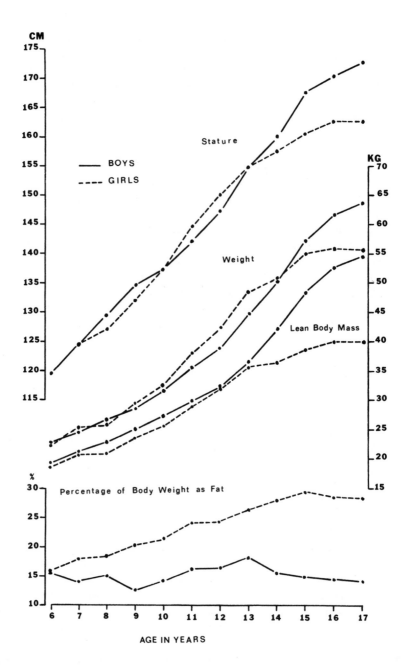

Fig. 43.4 Size-attained curves for stature, body weight, and lean body mass, and percentage of body weight as fat during childhood and adolescence. Lean body mass is estimated from potassium-40. (Drawn from the data of Burmeister 1965.)

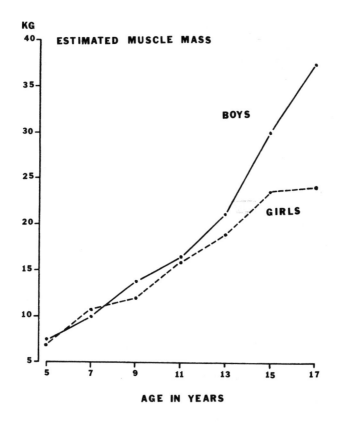

Fig. 43.5 Estimated muscle mass during childhood and adolescence. Muscle mass is estimated from creatinine excretion. (Drawn from the data of Clark et al. 1951.)

Skinfold measurements of subcutaneous fat at selected extremity and trunk sites and radiographic studies of fat, muscle, and bone development in the extremities also provide estimates of body composition similar to those derived from density, water, and potassium measurements. Age-related changes and sex differences in two of the more commonly used skinfold measurements, the triceps and subscapular skinfolds, are shown in Fig. 43.6. Fat increases during childhood in both sexes. Girls continue to increase in both skinfolds through adolescence, whereas boys increase in subscapular skinfold thickness and decrease in triceps skinfold thickness. As for other measures of body composition, sex differences in the thickness of skinfolds are apparent in childhood and become especially marked during adolescence. Adolescent sex differences are more apparent for the triceps (an extremity site) than for the subscapular (a trunk site) skinfold thickness, which suggest differential patterning of subcutaneous fat on the extremities and torso.

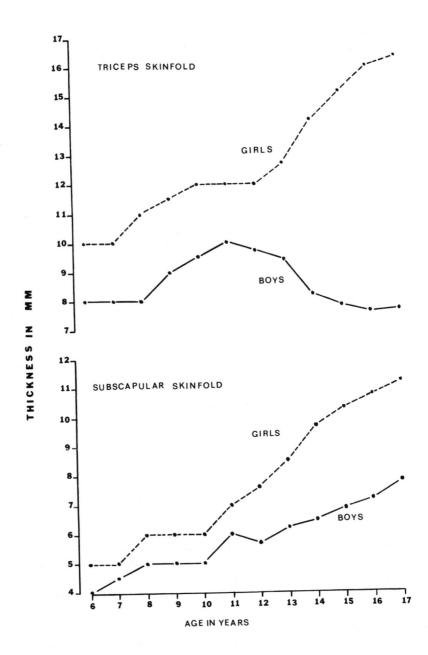

Fig. 43.6 Changes in the triceps and subscapular skinfolds in boys and girls during childhood and adolescence. (Drawn from the data of the National Center for Health Statistics 1972, 1974.)

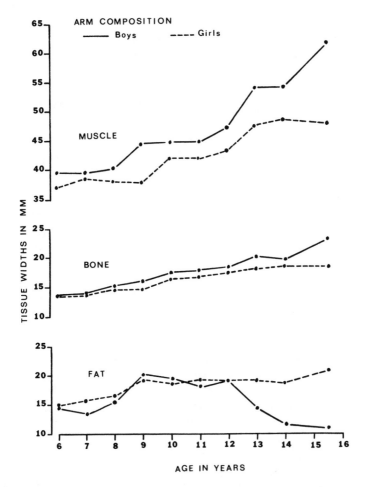

Fig. 43.7 Changes in the muscle, bone and fat composition of the arm during childhood and adolescence. (Drawn for the data of Johnson and Malina 1966.)

Age-related changes in fat, muscle, and bone thicknesses studied from radiographs of the arm are shown in Fig. 43.7. Changes in arm fatness are similar to those noted for the triceps skinfold, especially in the reduction of fat widths during male adolescence. Muscle and bone measurements of the arm increase with age, as expected. Sex differences in muscle tissue are small prior to adolescence but become considerable during the adolescent spurt. Conversely, sex differences in bone widths appear in childhood and persist through adolescence. Thus, muscle and bone widths show considerable increase in size during adolescence, the increase being greater in males. Males show a reduction in fat widths, while the rate at which females accumulate fat on the arm slows down during adolescence.

In summary, generally similar age-related changes in body composition are provided by several different methods of estimating the body's composition on whole-body, regional, and specific tissue bases. Sex differences, though present, are usually minor prior to the adolescent spurt, at which time adult sexual dimorphism in body composition becomes established. The range of variation within and between sexes, however, is considerable and should be carefully noted.

MATURITY-ASSOCIATED VARIATION IN SIZE, SHAPE, AND COMPOSITION

The preceding discussion has been concerned with progress with age or over time. The measure of age used is the child's chronological age. Size, build, and composition, however, vary considerably with the child's biological age or maturity status as indicated by skeletal age, age at menarche, development of secondary sex characteristics, or the timing of most rapid growth during adolescence (peak height velocity).

Maturity-associated variation, though apparent prior to adolescence, is most pronounced during this period of accelerated growth and sexual maturation. In girls the first sign of impending puberty is enlargement of the breasts, which is generally followed in sequence by the appearance of pubic hair, the height spurt, the final stages of pubic hair development, and menarche. In boys the first sign of impending puberty is the beginning growth of the testes and scrotum, followed in sequence by the appearance of pubic hair, the height spurt and rapid growth of the penis, and the final stages of pubic hair development (Tanner 1962). Although the sequence of maturational events is relatively uniform, children pass through adolescence at widely different chronological ages. Furthermore, the rate at which the events of the accelerated growth phase are passed through varies considerably.

Children are commonly grouped into maturity categories as "early," "average," and "late" maturing for growth studies. Early-maturing children are those in whom the maturity indicators are in advance of chronological age. For example, a child having a chronological age of 10 and a skeletal age of 12 would be early maturing, as would a girl experiencing menarche at 11 years of age. In contrast, late-maturing children are those in whom the maturity indicators lag relative to chronological age. For example, a child having a chronological age of 10 and a skeletal age of 8 would be late maturing, as would a girl experiencing menarche at 15 years of age. Average-maturing children make up the broad middle range of normal variation, with the normal range in growth studies usually being defined as plus or minus one year of an individual's chronological age. For example, in a group of 10-year-old children, those with skeletal ages of between 9 and 11 years are in the average-maturing group.

Early-maturing children of both sexes are generally heavier and taller for their age from early childhood through adolescence than their average- and late-maturing peers (Fig. 43.8). The differences between the maturity groups are most apparent during adolescence. In late adolescence, late-maturing children generally catch up to the early maturers in stature but not in body weight. Early maturers thus have more weight for their height, that is, they have stockier builds than late maturers. Viewed in somatotype terms, extreme mesomorphy is related to early maturation in boys, whereas endomorphy and early maturation are related to girls. On the other hand, extreme ectomorphy or linearity of physique is associated with lateness of maturity in both boys and girls. Many of the physique features that characterize early- and late-maturing children are apparent before adolescence and, thus, are not entirely dependent upon the adolescent spurt. The differential timing and magnitude of the spurt, however, tends to magnify the apparent differences.

Maturity-associated variation in physique implies similar variation in body composition. Early-maturing children, as compared to late-maturing children, generally have larger amounts of muscle and bone tissue and larger lean body masses, reflecting to a great extent their larger body size. On a relative basis, however, early-maturing children are fatter and not as lean as late maturers; that is, fat comprises a greater percentage of body weight in the early maturer. Maturity-related differences in fatness are shown in Fig. 43.9. Differences between late-maturing children and those in the average, or middle, range of the maturity continuum are generally not as marked as the differences between these two maturity groupings and early-maturing children.

The specific effects of the adolescent spurt on body composition are well illustrated when longitudinal data for tissue measurements are related to the peak height velocity (PHV). Such an analysis, of course, requires longitudinal data over adolescence. An absolute fat loss (negative velocity) is coincident with PHV in males, while females show a deceleration in the rate of fat accumulation at PHV. Thus, girls continue to put on fat during adolescence, but at a slower rate. When curves for the arm, calf, and thigh are compared, in all three areas boys show a negative velocity for the arm fat, but not for the fat on the thigh and calf (Tanner 1965).

Aligning muscle measurements on PHV indicates a peak in muscle tissue growth coincident with PHV for males. Girls show a less intense spurt in muscle just after the PHV. The peak velocity for muscle tissue development in males is about one and one-half times the peak velocity for females. Aligning the two components of total bone width, cortical bone and marrow cavity widths, on PHV shows that the adolescent spurt in humerus width is due primarily to an increase in cortical thickness, with little widening of the marrow cavity during adolescence (Tanner 1965, 1968).

MUSCULAR STRENGTH

The composition and size of muscle is functionally manifest in muscular strength, the capacity to develop tension. Strength of a muscle is related to its cross-sectional area.

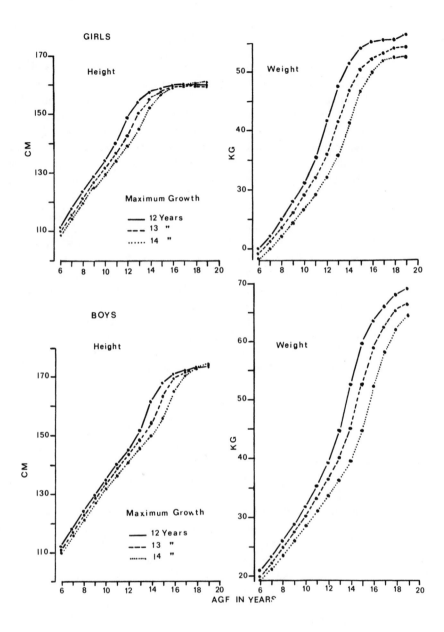

Fig. 43.8 Height and weight of children grouped according to the age at maximum growth (peak height velocity). (Drawn from the data of Shuttleworth 1939.)

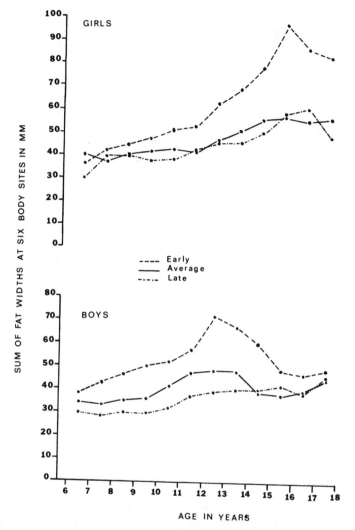

Fig. 43.9 Fatness in children grouped according to maturity status, based on the age of first appearance of pubic hair. (Drawn from the data of Reynolds 1950.)

As has been thoroughly discussed by Clarke in Chapter 2, studies of strength development during growth have generally used measures of static strength. These include measurements of strength in a variety of muscle groups singly and in combination, using dynamometers, cable tensiometers, strain gauges, and spring scales. Interrelationships among various strength tests range from moderate to high, although considerable variation is apparent within and between individuals, with age, and between sexes.

Muscular strength increases linearly with chronological age from early childhood to 13 or 14 years in males, then there is a marked acceleration in strength development through 17 years (Fig. 43.10). Strength, however, continues to increase into the third decade of life. In girls, strength improves linearly with age through 17 years of age with no clear evidence of an adolescent spurt. Boys tend to have greater strength than girls at all ages; sex differences throughout childhood are consistent, though generally small. The marked acceleration of strength development during male adolescence magnified the preadolescent sex difference. With increasing age during adolescence, the percentage of girls whose performance on strength tests equals or exceeds that of boys drops considerably, so that after 16 years old few girls perform as high as the boys' average and, conversely, few boys perform as low as the girls' average (Jones 1949).

The relationship between strength development and general growth and maturation during male adolescence is such that the strength spurt is frequently considered as a maturity indicator. Maximum strength development occurs after peak velocity of growth in height and weight, the relationship being better with body weight (Stolz and Stolz 1951; Carron and Bailey 1974). The adolescent peak in strength development occurs about nine months to one year after peak weight gain.

The pattern of maximum strength development in girls is not so clear. The apex of strength development occurs more often after peak height velocity in girls, but there is considerable variation. In more than one-half of the girls studied, the peak dynamometric strength gain precedes the peak weight gain (Faust 1977). Thus, the timing of peak strength development in adolescent girls is not as meaningful an indicator of maturity as in adolescent boys.

Strength is related to body size and lean body mass so that sex differences in strength after adjusting for height differences are not apparent in lower extremity strength from 7 to 17 years. However, from 7 years on, boys are significantly stronger in upper extremity and trunk strength even after adjusting for sex differences in height alone. In boys, strength improves disproportionately to gains in height or age especially after 14 years (or during adolescence). For example, in boys followed longitudinally from 10 to 16 years, the predicted average yearly increase in strength was approximately 12 percent, while the actual average yearly strength increase was about 23 percent or about twice the predicted value (Carron and Bailey 1974). The disproportionate strength increase in male adolescence is more apparent in strength of the upper extremities than in the trunk or lower extremities.

PERFORMANCE

Performance in motor tasks is an important item in the behavior of children and youth. Performance in motor tasks can be viewed in terms of the process and the

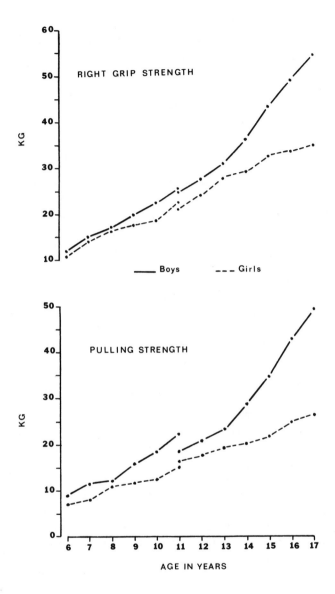

Fig. 43.10 Changes in muscular strength during childhood and adolescence. (Data from 6 to 11 years are drawn from Malina, unpublished data, while those from 11 to 17 years are drawn from the data of Jones 1949.)

product of the particular task under observation. The process of performing a motor skill may involve such component movements or specific mechanical elements as hip rotation, angle of take-off, lengths of lever arms, angles of inclination at specific joints, etc. The product of a motor act, however, concerns the result of the movement process, that is, the distance jumped, the time elapsed, or other measures of performance.

Studies of motor performance during growth have generally used measures of the product of performance often incorporating track and field tests. These tests generally involve the basic motor skills of running, jumping, and throwing or their variations.

Performance results in three commonly used motor tests are shown in Fig. 43.11. Running, jumping, and throwing performances improve with age during childhood and adolescence in boys. Performance in jumping, an explosive event, shows somewhat of an acceleration during male adolescence. Performance of girls on the three items, on the other hand, improves over childhood and early adolescence, and reaches a plateau at about 13 to 14 years of age, with little improvement thereafter.

Sex differences in running and jumping tend to be slight but consistent throughout childhood. Differences between boys and girls are more apparent in throwing and increase with age. During adolescence, sex differences in average performance are considerable and become greater with increasing age.

FACTORS INFLUENCING STRENGTH AND PERFORMANCE

Size, physique, body composition, and maturity status are factors that can influence strength and performance during childhood and adolescence. Moreover, the influence of other factors such as motivation, peer status, and other nonphysical variables must also be recognized. These factors, however, are beyond the scope of this discussion. It should also be noted that strength and performance in many gross motor skills are related and that the factors influencing strength and performance are themselves interrelated. As indicated earlier, the early maturing male is usually taller and heavier and more mesomorphic than his late maturing peers. Early maturing boys also differ behaviorally from late maturers. Much of the subsequent discussion is based on a more comprehensive overview of anthropometric correlates of strength and performance by Malina (1975).

Height and Weight

Correlations* between height, weight, and various strength measurements during childhood and adolescence are moderate, suggesting that the bigger youngster

---

* The following arbitrary ranges are offered as guidelines indicating poor, moderate, or close relations:<0.45, poor or low relationship; 0.46 ot 0.79, moderate;>0.80, close.

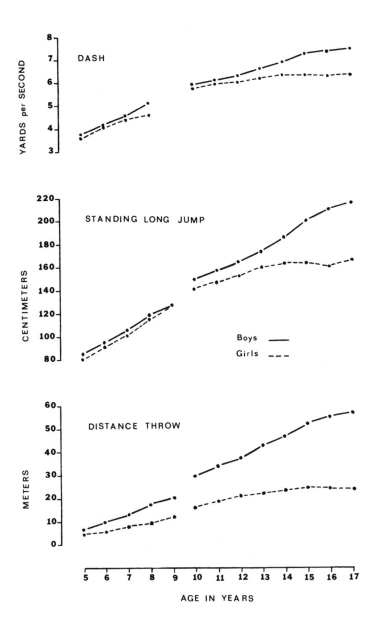

Fig. 43.11 Changes in running, jumping, and throwing performance during childhood and adolescence. (Data from 5 to 9 years are drawn from data collected by Espenschade and Eckert 1974; data from 10 to 17 years are drawn form the data of AAHPER 1965, for throwing, and from AAHPER 1976, for running and jumping.)

tends to also be stronger. Correlations are highest during male adolescence. Similar data for age-associated relationships of size and strength in adolescent girls are not extensive. Correlations between grip strength and height and weight in young college females are lower than those for adolescent boys and young adult college males.

Correlations between height and weight and performance in a variety of motor tasks during childhood and adolescence are generally low. The relationships vary, however, as a function of the kind of performance tested. The direction of the correlations point to negative effects of excess body weight on running and jumping items—items in which the body is propelled or projected. Espenschade (1963), for example, estimated that the multiple relationship of age, height, and weight accounts for only 25 percent of the variance in running, jumping, and throwing performance of boys 12 to 15 years of age, and accounts for only 15 percent of the variance in jumping and 10 percent of the variance in throwing performance of boys 15 to 19 years of age. A similar pattern of age, height, and weight relationships was not apparent in girls. This finding suggests the significance of other factors in performance especially during adolescence.

Studies looking at relationships between specific body segments or proportions and strength and performance are not extensive. The available data indicate lower relationships.

Physique

Somatotype components vary in their relationship with strength during childhood and adolescence. The data, however, are more available for boys than for girls, and correlations are generally low to moderate. Among preadolescents, both endomorphy and mesomorphy are positively related to muscular strength, while ectomorphy is negatively related to strength. The fact that endomorphy correlates with strength to the same extent as mesomorphy during childhood indicates the significant contribution of muscularity to endomorphy ratings and the importance of overall body size in strength tests.

During male adolescence, correlations between endomorphy and mesomorphy and strength are also positive. However, the relationships between mesomorphy and strength are slightly higher than those between ectomorphy and strength. As expected, correlations between ectomorphy and strength are consistently negative. Thus, ectomorphy is associated with strength deficiency, while mesomorphy is related to strength proficiency during male adolescence.

Studies of strength and physique in female adolescents are lacking. Some observations indicate consistently greater scores for adolescent girls with lateral physiques compared to those with linear builds as derived from the ratio of hip width to stature. Strength differences between girls of lateral and linear physiques are generally most marked during early adolescence (11 to 13 years) but tend to persist into late adolescence (at least to 17 years).

Relationships between somatotype and motor performance during childhood and adolescence indicate consistently negative correlations (low to moderate in magnitude) between endomorphy and performance, especially in those items in which the body is projected or those requiring agility. Correlations between mesomorphy and performance are generally positive but low. Those between ectomorphy and performance vary considerably but are generally low. These general observations are derived primarily from studies of males. Data relating physique and motor performance of girls are lacking. Girls who excell in performance during adolescence have generally more slender physiques than those who perform poorly. The latter tend to be overweight with broad physiques.

Physique-associated variation in strength and performance persists into young adulthood. In marked endomorphy excess fat is a handicapping factor whereas marked ectomorphy deficient strength is a handicap in some tasks. Mesomorphic males generally perform better than ectomorphs on motor tasks, while ectomorphs perform better than endomorphs on the same items. Among young adult females, mesomorphy is related to strength and performance, and endomorphy is negatively related to performance on items requiring power and agility. Ectomorphy does not appear to be a significant factor in the strength and performance of young adult women, probably because endomorphy is the dominant somatotype component in young adult females.

Correlations between physique and strength and performance during childhood and adolescence considered in the preceding discussion are generally low and at best moderate. Thus, they are not sufficiently high for predictive purposes. The directions of the correlations suggest negative effects for endomorphy and motor performance, negative effects for ectomorphy and strength, and positive effects for mesomorphy and strength and performance. Since the relationships are generally low, this would suggest that physique does not markedly influence performance, except at the extremes of the physique distribution. Espenschade (1940) has summarized the relationship between physique and extremes of performance as follows:

> . . . the superior performer in each sex in gross motor activities is less different from the total group in physical characteristics than is the inferior performer. A certain constellation of physical traits may prevent performance within the normal range but no combination of measures studied appears adequate to determine superiority (Espenschade 1940, p. 88).

It should be noted that studies of champion athletes indicate that physique plays an important role in specialized skills. Outstanding performers tend to have similar body builds that are more or less compatible with requirements of the specific activity in which they participate (Tanner 1964).

Body Composition

Relationships of body composition, strength, and performance during childhood and adolescence can be inferred from the preceding discussion of physique. Nevertheless, data relating body composition measures to strength and performance are limited, especially for females.

As might be anticipated, strength is significantly related to lean body and muscle mass. The correlation between estimated lean body mass and grip strength, for example, reaches 0.90 in boys 9 to 18 years old. Correlations between measurements of muscle breadth in the arm and leg and strength of the respective muscle groups are lower, but generally moderate in both sexes during childhood, adolescence, and young adulthood. This suggests that there is more to the expression of muscular strength than the absolute size of the muscle mass.

Correlations between skinfold thicknesses (fatness) and performance on a variety of motor tasks are consistently negative and low to moderate in magnitude during childhood, adolescence, and even into young adulthood. The direction of the relationship emphasizes the negative effects of fatness on performance. Interestingly, the correlations between skinfold thicknesses and performance are reasonably similar in magnitude and direction as those between endomorphy and performance.

Data on the contribution of absolute and relative lean body mass to motor performance are not extensive. However, among boys 10 to 12 years old, both absolute and relative lean body mass are similarly related to the performance of items in which the body is projected or moved. In contrast, in tasks involving the projection of an object rather than the body (e.g., throwing or kicking a ball) absolute lean body mass is more significant than relative lean body mass. Thus, activities in which the body or an object other than the body is projected are related differently to absolute and relative lean body mass in preadolescent boys. Further, the observations emphasize the importance of absolute body size and mass in the performance of growing youngsters in events requiring dynamic expressions of power. On the other hand, excessive amounts of body fat can function as a handicapping factor in that the fat represents dead weight that must be moved. The relationship between absolute and relative lean body mass and performance, however, differs in adult males. Relative lean body mass is more important to performance of tests involving movement of the entire body. This would emphasize the negative effects of relative fatness on performance. Those who are relatively lean generally perform better than those who tend to be more fat.

Maturity Status

As indicated earlier, size, physique, and body composition vary considerably with the maturity status of the developing individual. Although maturity-associated variation is most apparent during adolescence, effects are also evident during childhood.

Correlations between strength and skeletal maturity are moderate in primary-grade boys, thus suggesting that the more mature boys are generally stronger. However, when the effects of body size are controlled, correlations between skeletal maturity and strength are considerably reduced. When boys are divided into the skeletally mature and immature, the former are stronger, taller, and heavier (Rarick and Oyster 1964). Thus, strength differences among young boys reflect primarily size differences.

During adolescence, maturity relationships with strength are more apparent for boys than girls. Early-maturing boys are stronger than their average- and late-maturing peers from preadolescence into adolescence (Jones 1949; Clarke 1971; Carron and Bailey 1974). Strength differences between early and late maturers are especially apparent between 13 and 16 years and the strength advantage for the early-maturing boys reflects their larger body size and muscle mass. When the effects of body weight are removed in comparing early- and late-maturing boys, strength differences between the maturity groups are eliminated (Carron and Bailey 1974).

Early-maturing girls are stronger than their late-maturing peers during early adolescence. They do not, however, maintain this advantage as adolescence progresses (Jones 1949). Early- and late-maturing girls attain comparable strength levels in later adolescence by apparently different routes. The early maturer shows rapid strength development through 13 years of age and then improves only slightly thereafter. The later maturer, however, improves in strength gradually between 11 and 16 years of age.

The relationship between skeletal maturity and motor performance of primary grade children are in the same direction, but of lesser magnitude than those for muscular strength. In general, the maturationally advanced children perform slightly better on a variety of motor tasks. This probably reflects their larger size and greater muscular strength.

Motor performance of adolescent boys is positively related to indices of skeletal and physiological maturity (Espenschade 1940; Clarke 1971). Between 12 and 17 years, boys advanced in maturity status perform more proficiently in a variety of motor tasks than less mature boys. This is, in part, related to the greater muscularity and strength of the more mature boy. In girls, motor performance during adolescence is not related to measures of skeletal and physiological maturity (Espenschade 1940). Correlations between skeletal maturity and age deviation from menarche and motor performance are low and in many tasks negative. In fact, late maturation is commonly associated with outstanding motor performance of adolescent girls (Malina 1978a).

In summary, contrasting maturity-performance relationships during adolescence are apparent for boys and girls. The advent of male adolescence brings about marked improvements and consequently considerable differences in strength and performance of boys of contrasting maturity status. Conversely, the advent of female adolescence brings about slight improvements in strength but no marked changes in motor performance.

Overview of Interrelationships

It should be emphasized that the correlations between (1) size, physique, composition, and maturity status, and (2) strength and performance are generally low to moderate. Thus, the correlations are not meaningful for predictive purposes. Size, physique, composition, and maturity status seem to influence the strength and performance of children and adolescents more at the extremes of these parameters than within the broad, middle range considered average. The observations emphasize the complex relationship among physical characteristics, biological maturity, strength, and performance in the growing individual. There is obviously more to strength and motor performance than the biological characteristics of the youngster, although these characteristics do enter into the complex matrix of factors influencing strength and performance.

REFERENCES

AAHPER. 1965. *Youth Fitness Test Manual*. Rev. ed. Washington, D.C.: AAHPER.

Asmussen, E. 1962. Muscular performance. In *Muscle as a Tissue,* K. Rodahl and S. M. Horvath (eds.). New York: McGraw-Hill.

Behnke, A. R. 1969. New concepts in height-weight relationships. In *Obesity,* N. Wilson (ed.). Philadelphia: F. A. Davis, pp. 25-53.

Burmeister, W. 1965. Body cell mass as the basis of allometric growth functions. *Ann Paediat,* 204, 65-72.

Carter, J. E. L. 1975. *The Heath-Carter Somatotype Method*. Rev. ed. San Diego: San Diego State University.

Carron, A. V. and D. A. Bailey. 1974. Strength development in boys from 10 through 16 years. *Mon Soc Res Child Develop,* 39, 1-37.

Clark, L. C., H. L. Thompson, E. L. Beck, and W. Jacobson. 1951. Excretion of creatine and creatinine by children. *Amer J Dis Child,* 81, 774-783.

Clarke, H. H. 1971. *Physical and Motor Tests in the Medford Boys' Growth Study*. Englewood Cliffs, N.J.: Prentice-Hall.

Espenschade, A. 1940. Motor performance in adolescence. *Mon Soc Res Child Develop,* 5, 1-126.

Espenschade, A. S. 1963. Restudy of relationships between physical performances of school children and age, height, and weight. *Res Quart,* 34, 144-153.

Espenschade, A. S. and H. M. Eckert. 1967. *Motor Development*. Columbus, Ohio: C. E. Merrill.

Espenschade, A. and H. Eckert. 1974. Motor development. In *Science and Medicine of Exercise and Sport,* W. R. Johnson and E. R. Buskirk (eds.). 2nd ed. New York: Harper and Row.

Faust, M. S. 1977. Somatic development of adolescent girls. *Mon Soc Res Child Develop,* 42, 1-90.

Friis-Hansen, B. 1965. Hydrometry of growth and aging. *Symp Soc Study Human Biol,* 7, 191-209.

Hansman, C. 1970. Anthropometry and related data. In *Human Growth and Development,* R. W. McCammon (ed.). Springfield, Illinois: C. C. Thomas.

Johnston, F. E. and R. M. Malina. 1966. Age changes in the composition of the upper arm in Philadelphia children. *Human Biol,* 38, 1-21.

Jones, H. E. 1949. *Motor Performance and Growth.* Berkeley: University of California Press.

Krogman, W. M. 1972. *Child Growth.* Ann Arbor: University of Michigan Press.

Malina, R. M. 1969. Quantification of fat, muscle and bone in man. *Clin Orthop Rel Res,* 65, 9-38.

Malina, R. M. 1973. Ethnic and cultural factors in the development of motor abilities and strength in American children. In *Physical Activity: Human Growth and Development,* G. L. Rarick (ed.). New York: Academic Press.

Malina, R. M. 1974. Adolescent changes in size, build, composition and performance. *Human Biol,* 46, 117-131.

Malina, R. M. 1975. Anthropometric correlates of strength and motor performance. In *Exercise and Sport Sciences Reviews,* J. H. Wilmore and J. F. Keogh (eds.). Vol. 3. New York: Academic Press.

Malina, R. M. 1978a. Physical growth and maturity characteristics of young athletes. In *Children and Youth in Sport: A Contemporary Anthology,* R. A. Magill, M. H. Ash, and F. L. Smoll (eds.). Champaign, Illinois: Human Kinetics.

Malina, R. M. 1978b. Growth of muscle tissue and muscle mass. In *Human Growth: Volume II. Postnatal Growth,* F. Falkner and J. M. Tanner (eds.). New York: Plenum.

Malina, R. M. and G. L. Rarick. 1973. Growth, physique, and motor performance. In *Physical Activity: Human Growth and Development,* G. L. Rarick (ed.). New York: Academic Press.

National Center for Health Statistics. 1972. Skinfold thickness of children 6-11 years, United States. *Vital and Health Statistics,* Series 11, Number 120.

National Center for Health Statistics. 1974. Skinfold thickness of youths 12-17 years, United States. *Vital and Health Statistics,* Series 11, Number 132.

National Center of Health Statistics. In press. NCHS Growth Curves for Children, Birth-18 years, United States.

Parizkova, J. 1973. Body composition and exercise during growth and development. In *Physical Activity: Human Growth and Development,* G. L. Rarick (ed.). New York: Academic Press.

Rarick, G. L. and N. Oyster. 1964. Physical maturity, muscular strength, and motor performance of young school-age boys. *Res Quart,* 35, 523-531.

Reynolds, E. L. 1950. The distribution of subcutaneous fat in childhood and adolescence. *Mon Soc Res Child Develop,* 15, 1-189.

Sheldon, W. H., C. W. Dupertuis, and E. McDermott. 1954. *Atlas of Men: A Guide for Somatotyping the Adult Male of All Ages.* New York: Harper.

Shuttleworth, F. K. 1939. The physical and mental growth of girls and boys age six to nineteen in relation to age at maximum growth. *Mon Soc Res Child Develop,* Volume 4.

Sinclair, D. 1973. *Human Growth after Birth.* 2nd ed. New York: Oxford University Press.

Stolz, H. R., and L. M. Stolz. 1951. *Somatic Development of Adolescent Boys.* New York: Macmillan.

Tanner, J. M. 1962. *Growth at Adolescence.* 2nd ed. Oxford: Blackwell Scientific Publications.

Tanner, J. M. 1964. *The Physique of the Olympic Athlete.* London: Allen Unwin.

Tanner, J. M. 1965. Radiographic studies of body composition in children and adults. *Symp Soc Study Human Biol,* 7, 211-236.

Tanner, J. M. 1968. Growth of bone, muscle and fat during childhood and adolescence. In *Growth and Development of Mammals,* G. A. Lodge and G. E. Lamming (eds.). New York: Plenum.

Walker, R. M. 1962. Body build and behavior in young children. I. Body building and nursery school teacher's ratings. *Mon Soc Res Child Develop,* 27, 1-94.

44

Individual Differences and the Assessment of Youth Fitness

Gary S. Krahenbuhl

Two viewpoints on physical fitness are represented by the following positions: (1) physical fitness is the body's state of adaptation to physical exertion, and (2) physical fitness is represented by the body's capability to perform physical tasks. Actually, one's performance reflects genetic potential, maturation, adaptation, skill, and motivation. Since the state of adaptation reflects only the compensatory changes resulting from habitual exercise-stresses experienced by the body, it is possible for a poorly conditioned child who is not adapted to physical work to outperform another child in a higher state of adaptation merely because of genetic and maturational differences. How then do individual differences not related to the body's state of physical adaptation affect the youth fitness evaluation process?

When a child is tested for physical fitness his or her raw scores are typically compared with other children of similar age and expressed as a percentile (the percentage of students who scored below that point). If a child scores high on fitness test items, it is taken as an indication of superior physical health and an apparent life-style that includes generous portions of vigorous physical activity. If a child performs poorly on a physical fitness test, the prescription for improvement is to increase the student's frequency, intensity, and duration of physical activity. It is commonly assumed that all can reach the upper percentiles if they work hard enough. These interpretations are based on the opinion that "physical fitness" is the body's capacity to perform physical tasks. However, this position ignores the problem of contamination by factors not related to physical fitness that influence performance on fitness test items. Such an approach may not be warranted when one considers the nature and extent of individual differences in genetic potential and maturational rate. The following sections in this chapter will identify and discuss factors influencing one's performance on tests of physical fitness and conclude with recommendations for the most appropriate uses of youth fitness test results.

GROWTH AND PHYSICAL FITNESS

When considering youth fitness, attention must be given to body size and changes in the body's composition that are influenced by physical activity. Alterations in the relative amount of muscle, bone, and fat and in the functional capabilities of the cardiovascular and nervous systems have a pronounced influence on youth fitness.

Changes in size and function occurring throughout childhood and adolescence are often considered as a single entity called growth. It may be more meaningful, however, to consider growth as consisting of two types, developmental and compensatory. Developmental growth represents the changes in body size and function that occur if minimal (but adequate) conditions of diet, exercise, and rest are met. Developmental growth is genetically determined and regulated, in part, through the growth hormone, the sex hormones, and adrenal androgens. A child's maturational age (skeletal age) would provide the best indicator of his or her developmental growth status. Compensatory growth refers to adaptations that result from an increase in the functional demands placed on certain tissues and systems. Tissues and systems grow at a certain rate and to a certain size (developmental growth), but if stressed—as in physical exertion— will compensate for the overload by increasing their mass and functional capacity (compensatory growth).

Performance on a fitness test is influenced by organic status (developmental and compensatory growth), skill, and motivation. Fitness test items are selected to control for the influence of skill and motivation so that an uncontaminated indication of organic status may be obtained. Organic status, however, is not a pure indicator of adaptation to physical work. Throughout childhood and adolescence, one's organic status is influenced by genetic and maturational factors as well as compensatory changes that have accrued as a result of habitual activity selection. Since there is little one can do to alter the genetic and maturational foundations of developmental growth, it is compensatory status that provides the best index of youth fitness. The following sections summarize what is known about genetic, maturational, and compensatory factors contributing to the structure and function of the body's tissues and systems, thereby influencing performance on youth fitness tests.

GENETIC FACTORS IN MUSCLE STRENGTH AND ENDURANCE

Muscle tissue is composed of long cylinderical tubular cells (fibers) that run longitudinally or obliquely. The number of fibers that an individual possesses is apparently genetically determined since no significant cell division is known to occur in humans after the fourth prenatal month (Sinclair 1969). Therefore, growth in muscle tissue is accomplished through hypertrophy of these independent fibers. Likewise, muscle mass at any age is determined primarily by the number of fibers with which one is born and secondarily by the size of those fibers. The growth of a fiber may also be genetically limited for the number of cellular nuclei appears to be intimately related to a muscle cell's potential for hypertrophy (Cheek 1975).

Human skeletal muscle tissue contains fibers that are fast contracting (fast twitch:FT) and others that are slow contracting (slow twitch:ST) (Saltin 1973). The FT fibers contract on an average of two to three times more rapidly than the ST fibers (Burke 1975). The muscles that influence performance on physical fitness items contain a dispersion of both types of fiber. The percentage of fast versus slow contracting fibers varies from muscle to muscle and among individuals (Edgerton et al. 1975).

The ST fibers are controlled by motoneurons with low thresholds; thus, they are recruited frequently and for sustained periods (Mommaerts 1970). The ST fiber possesses a variety of characteristics that enhance its endurance. The ST fiber possesses a richer blood supply (Gould 1973), greater concentrations of mitochondria (energy releasing organelles) (Holloszy 1973), more oxidative enzymes (Holloszy 1967), and greater triglyceride storage (Hoppeler et al. 1973). All these factors enhance the endurance of the ST fiber during submaximal work. As a result, the ST muscle cells have been referred to as SO fibers, slow contracting, oxidative (fatigue resistant) (Burke 1975).

In contrast, the FT fibers are controlled by motoneurons with high thresholds and are recruited more selectively (Burke 1975). The FT fiber possesses greater myofibril (contractile elements inside the cell) density (Gauthier 1970), more myosin ATP-ase (an enzyme affecting speed of contraction) (Engel 1974), and more enzymes that support anaerobic metabolism (Burke 1975). The FT fiber, therefore, is capable of bursts of intensive activity but tends to fatigue quite rapidly. Accordingly, the FT fibers have been called FF (fast contracting, fast fatiguing) or FG (fast contracting, glycolytic) (Burke 1975). Some FT fibers exhibit greater concentrations of oxidative enzymes than others. These fibers are referred to as FOG fibers (fast contracting, oxidative, and glycolytic) and are capable of greater endurance than the FF fiber (Burke 1975).

Differentiation of muscle fibers into FT and ST groups occurs during the first weeks of postnatal life (Dubowitz 1970). After this time the contractile speed characteristics remain unchanged regardless of the nature of physical conditioning (Ericksson et al. 1973). Most individuals probably possess about 50 percent FT and 50 percent ST fibers. A smaller percentage possess ratios approaching 60/40 in either direction, and even fewer individuals possess more extreme ratios (Saltin et al. 1977).

Youth fitness items that test muscular strength (sit-ups in 60 seconds, pull-ups, standing long jump, etc). involve the recruitment of FT units. Children born with more fibers, greater concentrations of nuclei, and greater proportions of FT fibers would possess a decided genetic advantage on tests of muscular strength (Krahenbuhl 1976). Their potential for improvement with strength training would also be greater.

GENETIC FACTORS IN PHYSIQUE AND BODY COMPOSITION

Strong genetic influence that typically reflects parental characteristics is evident in growth in the length of bone and eventual adult height (Sinclair 1969). Changes in body proportions, dimensions, and composition within somatotype are possible for growing children, but dramatic changes in physique are unlikely (Malina and Rarick 1973).

Body fat content also shows genetic influence; however, the extent of the relationship is unclear because significant fat cell hyperplasia (cell division) occurs during childhood (Garrow 1974). The respective roles of genetic predisposition and energy balance (energy intake versus energy expenditure) have not been determined (Winick 1975). Body fat reflects both the size and number of lipid cells; however, obesity is nearly always associated with excessive numbers of fat cells (Oscai 1963).

Physique and body composition exhibit strong influence on potential for physical fitness performance (Clarke 1971). Many studies have shown significant differences on youth fitness test items among groups representing the various somatotypes (Clarke 1973). Since there appear to be fairly strong genetic components for physique and body composition, children with the ''right'' parents possess a built-in advantage on certain fitness items.

GENETIC FACTORS IN CARDIORESPIRATORY FUNCTION

One's level of cardiorespiratory fitness determines the ability of the organism to perform moderate work for a sustained period of time without distress to the individual. Cardiorespiratory function involves many factors such as the oxygenation of the blood in the lungs, cardiac output, vascular transport of the blood and oxygen to the active tissues, and the ability of the muscles to extract and utilize oxygen.(The single best measure of cardiorespiratory function is believed to be maximal oxygen uptake.) Pretraining status influences the amount of improvement that will take place; however, regular endurance training can increase maximal oxygen uptake on an average of only 20 percent (Astrand and Rodahl 1970). Also, identical training regimens bring different individuals to various levels of maximal aerobic power (Lussier and Buskirk 1977). Genetic endowment is thus a very important factor in determining the individual's endurance potential.

Many field tests have been proposed for assessing cardiovascular function. Step tests and distance runs or run-walks have been most popular. Performance capacity on these youth fitness test items is influenced by efficiency and anaerobic tolerance in addition to aerobic power (Nagle et al. 1970). Efficiency and anaerobic abilities are influenced by physique, body composition, and one's proportion of FT and ST muscle fibers. Therefore, one's performance on a field test for cardiovascular fitness is influenced strongly by the genetic component.

MATURATIONAL FACTORS IN YOUTH FITNESS

Youth fitness test scores are typically interpreted relative to chronological age. While age related norms are indicated because of growth, a false sense of precision may result. Clarke (1971) has shown that differences in maturity (skeletal age) are pronounced during all ages from 7 to 18 years. Data from the Medford Growth Study showed maturity ranges that varied from 3.9 years at 18 years of age, to 7.1 years at 13 years of age. Clearly, chronological age provides no more than an estimate of maturity.

Significant positive correlations have been reported between skeletal age and a number of factors that influence performance on physical fitness tests, including body size, body proportions, gross strength, and muscular power (Clarke 1973). Growth rate variations in muscle, bone, and fat occur throughout childhood and adolescence. During early childhood (ages 2 to 6) approximately 25 percent of the weight gained is due to the growth of muscle tissue. During later childhood (ages 6 to 12), 75 percent of the weight gained is due to increases in muscle tissue (Epenschade and Eckert 1967). Nevertheless, approximately 60 to 65 percent of one's adult strength is developed during adolescence and early adulthood (Anderson, Elliot, and LaBerge 1972). Thus, it should be obvious that maturationally advanced children possess a built-in advantage on muscle strength and endurance fitness items.

Changes in body fat and the growth of bone are also related to maturity. A minor bone growth spurt occurs between 5 and 7 years of age; however, the adolescent spurt is more significant (Sinclair 1969). The adolescent spurt is directed by the sex hormones and occurs earlier in the female. Male bone growth begins later but occurs over a longer period of time; males thus become significantly taller.

Fat content in the body is about 11 percent at birth, but 25 percent at four months of age (Winnick 1975). After six months the rate of increase falls rapidly, and the fat content actually decreases until age 6 to 8. The decrease is less in girls than boys, so when children enter school girls tend to be fatter than boys. Fat content again increases prior to the adolescent spurt. During adolescence the male loses fat on his limbs; however, there is no such decrease in females (Sinclair 1969). The deposition of fat about the trunk continues in both sexes, but in girls additional fat is laid down in the secondary sex distribution.

The aforementioned changes in body fat and bone growth are related to maturity. In the case of bone growth and decreases in percent body fat, maturity related changes enhance running efficiency, which influence performance on timed distance runs and, therefore, contaminate cardiovascular fitness data.

The secondary sex distribution of body fat in the female results in more "dead weight" that could detract from performance on fitness items in which the body's weight must be supported. In this instance maturity may prove to be a handicap. The decline in mean values on fitness test items (AAHPER 1976) for females starting about 13 years of age is partially a result of changes in body composition that occur with maturity (although cultural influence may also be involved).

In summary, individual differences in genetic potential and maturity have a pronounced effect on one's organic status and, thus, performance on fitness test items at any given age. Organic status, however, is also influenced by compensatory changes that accrue for the specific tissues and systems that are utilized in habitual vigorous physical activity.

PHYSICAL ACTIVITY AND COMPENSATORY GROWTH

The process of compensatory growth is accomplished in relation to habitual physical activity. Developmental growth will occur with a minimal amount of physical activity, whereas vigorous activity is essential for compensatory growth. If physical fitness is to represent one's organic status relative to genetic potential and maturational level, then the extent of one's compensatory adaptation to exercise stress best reflects physical fitness in youth.

Compensatory changes resulting from physical training may be thought of as adaptations in tissue structure or function. The basis for most long-term bodily changes is the process of protein synthesis, since creation of new structures and enzymes depends on this process.

Physical exercise influences protein synthesis and bodily function in a variety of ways. Secretions and/or actions of growth hormones, thyroxin, insulin, and hydrocortisone are affected by physical activity. Light exercise has little effect on growth hormone; however, vigorous exercise increases plasma growth hormone levels (Shephard and Sidney 1975). Among the effects brought about by growth hormone are an increase in the rate of protein synthesis, which could enhance muscle growth (Goldberg and Goodman 1969), and an increase in fat metabolism, which may help to diminish total body fat (Sawin 1969).

Insulin, in addition to its well known role in sugar metabolism, promotes protein synthesis and, therefore, muscle development. Insulin increases the movement of amino acids into muscle cells and the rate of protein synthesis within the cell (Guyton 1976). Insulin levels tend to decrease during exercise but rise following work, probably in response to blood glucose concentrations. However, since growth hormone is elevated during and following exercise and suppresses the insulin action on carbohydrate metabolism, more insulin may be available to bind to muscle, which would augment protein synthesis and promote compensatory growth (Sawin 1969).

Thyroxin influences the body's metabolic rate by enhancing the synthesis of oxidative enzymes (Guyton 1976). Among the other effects of thyroxin are an increase in fatty acid mobilization from adipose tissue and increased metabolism of cholesterol, phospholipids, and triglycerides. Thyroxin also seems to make the body more sensitive to the actions of growth hormone and the catecholamines, which may explain the enhanced alertness experienced following a physical workout. Physical activity tends to increase the amount of free thyroxin in the blood, and it is the free thyroxin that acts on the tissues of the body (Terjung and Winder 1975). An improvement in physical condition can also result in higher chronic levels of plasma thyroxin.

Physical exertion represents a stress to the body. During stressful states the body increases its secretion of hydrocortisone (Guyton 1976). Hydrocortisone decreases glucose utilization, increases lipolysis of depot fat, and mobilizes amino acids away from muscle. If one is under persistent nonphysical stress, the body would tend to lose muscle and gain fat since little energy would be expended (Sawin 1969).

If the stress of exercise is intermittent and kept within reasonable limits, hydrocortisone facilitates the process of compensatory growth and may help explain the specificity of adaptation that results. It has been hypothesized that the action of hydrocortisone creates a greater blood supply of nutrients needed for energy and synthesis in the stressed tissues. Thus, tissue that is intermittently stressed enhances its functional capacity at the expense of tissues not being taxed, perhaps because of the actions of hydrocortisone (Goldberg and Goodman 1969).

In addition to these exercise-induced alterations that rely on hormonal mechanisms, the muscular contractions that make physical exertion possibly may enhance compensatory change in a more direct manner. New structures and enzymes are synthesized from amino acids. The amino acids enter the cells with great difficulty. The permeability of a muscle cell, however, changes prior to each contraction. The result may be an increased influx of amino acid movement into the cells of active skeletal muscle tissue.

Given this brief background, one should be able to see how physical activity can result in compensatory growth as well as the specific nature of the adaptations. The following hypothetical situation provides an example of the significance and specificity of compensatory change.

If three children possess similar genetic potential and exhibit comparable skeletal ages (levels of maturity), differences in their performances on a test of fitness would reflect the compensatory changes resulting from their habitual activity patterns (assuming factors such as diet, rest, skill, motivation, etc., are also similar). Suppose that Subject A habitually participates in activities such as tree and rope climbing. Subject B jogs two to three miles daily with his father, and Subject C prefers to remain indoors, but is under considerable emotional stress because of family problems. Let us explore the compensatory changes that would be expected to accompany their life circumstances and speculate about their performance on a youth fitness test, assuming that motivation and skill levels among the subjects are equal.

Subject A would experience normal maturational growth but would also exhibit compensatory growth in the musculature of the arms, shoulders, and trunk. The principal changes would occur in the FT fibers of the skeletal muscle being stressed. It is unlikely that A's body composition or cardiovascular system would be altered much by this activity, except for the increased muscle mass in the arms and shoulders. Subject B would also experience normal maturational growth, but would achieve compensatory changes that are specific for running training. These changes would include improvement in cardiorespiratory capacity and ST skeletal muscle function in the muscles important for jogging locomotion. The changes would probably include an increase in capillarization around the cells and an increase in sarcoplasmic mitochondria and oxidative enzymes within the cells. The cardiorespiratory system would exhibit a variety of changes such as increases in cardiac output and stroke volume, maximal work capacity, maximal aerobic power, A-V oxygen difference, exercise lactate levels, and mechanical efficiency. B's body composition would probably change in that there would be a decrease in body fat. On the other hand, Subject C might or might not experience normal maturational growth since emotional stress can retard growth. In the absence of physical activity, stress tends to cause the body to lose muscle and gain fat. This occurs because the stress hormones mobilize protein, which is then converted to glucose by the liver and eventually stored as fat. C's body composition would, therefore, be expected to experience a loss of lean tissue with a concomitant increase in body fat. Strength, muscular endurance, and cardiorespiratory endurance would suffer adversely from the absence of physical adaptations that accompny this particular condition. On the AAHPER Youth Fitness Test Subject A would be expected to excel on the pull-ups and possibly sit-ups; Subject B would be the likely winner in the distance run; and Subject C would probably perform poorly on all the items.

The point is that compensatory change reflects the body's structural and functional status relative to genetic potential and maturity. Since compensatory change reflects one's physical use or misuse of the body, it would be desirable if fitness tests measured only compensatory status. Unfortunately, they do not!

Individual differences in genetic potential and maturity combine to render almost meaningless the singular interpretation of physical fitness tests results in youth. Variations in the genetic potential and maturity of our three subjects (A,

B, and C, from the previous example) may have allowed any of them to out-perform the others on every fitness test item. Youth fitness tests provide information about the subject's ability to perform on each item; however, that performance reflects genetic, maturational, dietary, rest, and motivational as well as compensatory variables. This being the case, caution must be exercised in the use and interpretation of the test results.

RECOMMENDED USES OF YOUTH FITNESS TESTS

If one feels that "physical fitness" is defined by some universal standard that stands immutable regardless of genetic or maturational status, then valid and reliable youth fitness tests can be used for individual, group, and program evaluation and prescription. A subject's score on each item reflects his or her "physical fitness" relative to all other individuals of similar age for that particular task. If, however, one prefers a more individualized definition of physical fitness, which incorporates the idea that one's fitness status describes a state of being *relative* to genetic inheritance and maturity, then the range of uses for fitness tests is more limited and requires considerable caution.

Evaluation of groups of the physical fitness benefits of various programs would be acceptable because most reasonably sized samples would probably include a relatively representative distribution of genetic and maturational types. Thus, the group's performance when compared to normative values would reflect the compensatory status for that age and sex.

Using the latter interpretation of physical fitness leaves the practitioner with limited applications for individual evaluation. An individual's performance is influenced markedly by genetic and maturational factors that have nothing to do with fitness when defined as compensatory status. The teacher has little idea whether the student is doing well or poorly relative to what he or she is capable of doing.

Probably the best (though certainly not foolproof) method of evaluating an individual's progress in the pursuit of physical fitness is to follow the person longitudinally by comparing the percentile scores over a multiyear period. Since genetic potential will remain constant and since there are percentile scales for each age group, an improvement in a student's percentile scores would give an indication of physical fitness changes relative to potential. Even this use, however, must be made with some caution because a child may experience longitudinal percentile fluctuation that could result from advanced or retarded maturity rather than compensatory change.

Change in percentiles can also be misleading because of the peculiarities in a percentile scale constructed from a normally distributed group of scores. Since there are few scores at the extremes and many scores near the middle of the scale, the same absolute improvement on a fitness test item results in a small percentile change for someone at the end of the scale and a much larger change for someone near the center of the scale.

SUMMARY

Physical educators have developed many youth fitness test batteries. These tests assess the individual's status on a variety of test items that reflect muscular strength and endurance and cardiovascular function. Physical fitness may be thought of as either (1) a universal standard applicable to all, or (2) a flexible standard relative to one's genetic potential and level of maturity. If one accepts the prior definition of fitness, then currently available youth fitness tests can be used for individual, group, and program evaluation and prescription. One must consider, however, that many students will never appear to be physically fit because of genetic and/or maturational limitations. This may have a negative impact on a student's current feelings and future motivation for the commitment required to maintain a level of fitness throughout life. Acceptance of the latter view of physical fitness is more realistic in light of individual differences in genetic potential and maturation. This interpretation of fitness would not preclude the use of test results for the evaluation of programs or large groups; however, the evaluation of individual status would be much more hazardous. Since genetic potential and maturation strongly influence performance, longitudinal observation of a student's changing status relative to normative values provides the best use of youth fitness tests for individual prescription.

REFERENCES

AAHPER. 1976. *AAHPER Youth Fitness Test Manual*. Rev. Ed. Washington: AAHPER.

Anderson, M. H., M. E. Elliot, and J. LaBerge. 1972. *Play with a Purpose*. 2nd ed. New York: Harper & Row.

Astrand, P.-O., and K. Rodahl. 1970. *Textbook of Work Physiology*. New York: McGraw-Hill.

Burke, R. E. 1975. Motor unit properties and selective involvement in movement. In *Exercise and Sport Sciences Reviews*, J. H. Wilmore and J. F. Keogh (eds.). Vol 3. New York: Academic Press.

Cheek, D. B. (ed.). 1975. *Fetal and Postnatal Cellular Growth*. New York: John Wiley & Sons.

Clarke, H. H. (ed.). Oct., 1973. Individual differences, their nature, extent and significance. *Physical Fitness Research Digest*, 3, 1-23.

Clarke, H. H. 1971. *Physical Motor Tests in the Medford Boy's Growth Study*. Englewood Cliffs: Prentice-Hall.

Dubowitz, V. 1970. Differentiation of fiber types in skeletal muscle. In *Physiology and Biochemistry of Muscle as a Food*, E. J. Briskey, R. G. Cassens, and B. B. Marsh (eds.). Vol 2. Madison: University of Wisconsin Press.

Edgerton, V. R., J. L. Smith, and D. R. Simpson. 1975. Muscle fiber type populations of human leg muscles. *Histochem J*, 7, 981-987.

Engel, W. K. 1974. Fiber-type nomenclature of human skeletal muscle for histochemical purposes. *Neurology*, 24, 344-348.

Ericksson, B. O., P. D. Gollnick, and B. Saltin. Muscle metabolism and enzyme activities after training in boys 11-14 years old. *Acta Physiol Scand,* 87, 485-497.

Espenschade, A. S. and H. M. Eckert. 1967. *Motor Development.* Columbus, Ohio: C. E. Merrill.

Garrow, J. S. 1974. *Energy Balance and Obesity in Man.* New York: American Elsevier.

Gauthier, G. F. 1970. The ultra structure of three fiber types in mammalian skeletal muscle. In *Physiology and Biochemistry of Muscle as a Food,* E. J. Briskey, R. G. Casseus, and B. B. March (eds.). Vol 2. Madison: University of Wisconsin Press.

Goldberg, A. L. and H. M. Goodman. 1969. Relationship between growth hormone and muscular work in determining muscle size. *J Physiol,* 200, 655-666.

Gould, R. P. 1973. The microanatomy of muscle. In *The Structure and Function of Muscle,* G. H. Bourne (ed.). Vol 2. New York: Academic Press.

Goldberg, A. L. and H. M. Goodman. 1969. Relationship between cortisone and muscle work in determining muscle size. *J Physiol,* 200, 667-675.

Guyton, A. C. 1976. *Textbook of Medical Physiology.* 5th ed. Philadelphia: W. B. Saunders.

Holloszy, J. O. 1967. Biomechanical adaptations in muscle: Effects of exercise on mitochondrial oxygen uptake and respiratory enzyme activity in skeletal muscle. *J Biol Chem,* 242, 2278-2282.

Holloszy, J. O. 1973. Biomechanical adaptation to exercise: Aerobic metabolism. In *Exercise and Sport Science Reviews.* J. H. Wilmore (ed.). Vol 1. New York: Academic Press.

Hoppeler, H. P., P. Luthi, H. Claassen, E. Weibel, and H. Howald. 1973. The ultrastructure of the normal human skeletal muscle. *Pflugers Arch,* 344, 217-232.

Krahenbuhl, G. S. 1976. Muscle biopsy research: Implications for competitive athletics. *Arizona JOHPER,* 20, 8-12.

Lussier, L. and E. R. Buskirk. 1977. Effects of an endurance training regimen on assessment of work capacity in prepubertal children. *Ann N Y Acad Sci,* 301, 734-747.

Malina, R. M. and G. L. Rarick. 1973. Growth, physique, and motor performance. In *Physical Activity: Human Growth and Development,* G. L. Rarick (ed.). New York: Academic Press.

Mommaerts, W. F. 1970. The role of the innervation of the functional differentiation of muscle. In *Physiology and Biochemistry of Muscle as a Food,* E. J. Briskey, R. G. Cassens, and B. B. Marsh (eds.). Vol 2. Madison: University of Wisconsin Press.

Nagle, F., D. Robinhold, E. Howley, J. Daniels, G. Baptisa, and K. Stoedefalke. 1970. Lactic acid accumulation during running at submaximal aerobic demands. *Med Sci Spts,* 2, 182-186.

Oscai, L. B. 1973. The role of exercise in weight control. In *Medicine and Sport Sciences Reviews,* J. H. Wilmore (ed.). Vol 1. New York: Academic Press.

Saltin, B. 1973. Metabolic Fundamentals of Exercise. *Med Sci Spts,* 5, 137-146.

Saltin, B., J. Henriksson, E. Nygaard, and P. Andersen. 1977. Fiber types and metabolic potentials of skeletal muscles in sedentary men and endurance runners. *Ann N Y Acad Sci,* 301, 3-29.

Sawin, C. T. 1969. *The Hormones: Endocrine Physiology.* Boston: Little, Brown.

Shephard, R. J. and K. H. Sidney. 1975. Effects of exercise on plasma growth hormone and cortisol levels in human subjects. In *Medicine and Sport Sciences Reviews,* J. H. Wilmore and J. H. Keogh (eds.). Vol 3. New York: Academic Press.

Sinclair, D. 1969. *Human Growth after Birth.* London: Oxford University Press.

Terjung, R. L. and W. W. Winder. 1975. Exercise and thyroid function. *Med Sci Spts,* 7, 20-26.

Winick, M. (eds.). 1975. *Childhood Obesity.* New York: John Wiley.

45

Physical Working Capacity of Children and Adolescents

David A. Cunningham

Studies of the physical working capacity of children are to a great extent a recent development. Although several very good and valuable reports appeared before the 1970s, in a large part the interest in the fitness of youth, particularly as it relates to the more definitive studies of the gas transport system as a whole, is a recent occurrence. Reviews published in the early 1970s have summarized these earlier studies (Shephard 1971; Thorén 1971); therefore, the present review will not attempt to analyze these earlier investigations but will refer only to those studies prior to 1970 that are necessary for an understanding of this chapter. For work done before 1970 the reader is directed to these earlier reviews and to the proceedings of the International Pediatric Work Physiology symposia held at regular intervals since the initial meeting in Dortmund, Germany in 1968. However, few of these symposia have been published as a total report; exceptions are the reports of the Tel-Aviv meetings of 1972 (Bar-Or 1972) and the meetings at De Haan, Belgium in 1974 (Borms and Hebbelinck 1974). Other more recent reviews include: (1) the Proceedings of the National Conference Workship—The Child in Sport and Physical Activity (Albinson and Andrew 1976); (2) a text on exercise testing in children (Godfrey 1974); and (3) a review of various aspects of pediatric studies including working capacity (Davis et al. 1974).

MEASUREMENT OF PHYSICAL WORKING CAPACITY IN CHILDREN

The term "working capacity" can refer to several different physiological measurements of the human's capacity for maximal work. The measurement techniques range from the typical field test of running time (Hunsicker and Reiff 1965) to the test designed to describe the working capacity or power developed at a given set point such as a heart rate of 170 beats•min $^{-1}$ (PWC 170). In this case the working capacity is described as a rate of work or power, usually in kilogram•meters•min $^{-1}$, joules•S $^{-1}$, or watts. The utilization of this measurement depends upon the use of a bicycle ergometer as the exercise mode and its accurate calibration, as this may vary over time. This procedure lacks precision and so has become less valuable in recent years. The use of a treadmill in the measurement of the physical working capacity of children is usually preferred (Godfrey 1974), although with this mode, it is difficult to measure work load and, therefore, a direct measurement of oxygen uptake is needed.

The term "working capacity" may be a misnomer in this case, and it may be more appropriate to refer to the aerobic capacity (or power) of children. In most instances, the physical working capacity is considered to be synonomous with the measurement of maximal oxygen uptake or aerobic power and reported as liter•min $^{-1}$ or as ml•kg body wt $^{-1}$•min $^{-1}$. Maximal oxygen uptake (max VO$_2$) is considered to be the most accurate single measure of an individual's circulatory and respiratory capacities (hence, physical working capacity). While max VO$_2$ has been investigated extensively in adults, children have received less attention (Morse et al. 1949; Robinson 1938; Shephard 1971).

Measurement of Aerobic Power

The accuracy of the measurement of aerobic power in children has been questioned in several studies (Morse 1949; Shephard 1971). The usual criteria accepted as substantial evidence that max VO$_2$ has been attained in adult populations include: (1) the use of an exercise task in which large muscle groups are engaged; (2) the development of high levels of lactic acid (or blood lactate) as an indication of anaerobic metabolism; and (3) the establishment of a plateau in oxygen uptake with increased work at peak work levels.

The variability of the measurement of maximal oxygen uptake, determined by repeated evaluations over short periods of time and with no specific treatment intervention, has been studied several times in adult populations (Mitchell et al. 1958; Taylor et al. 1955; Cunningham et al. 1975; Magel and Faulkner 1967). The results of these tests have indicated that the repeated measures are reliable (r ≈ 0.90) and reproducible with an average mean difference of two to four percent. Studies on children have also indicated reproducible results (no significant difference between the mean values of repeated measures). The mean differences are about two percent (Cunningham et al. 1976), but the reliability coefficients are lower than for adults r = 0.76. If the children are tested over change in max VO$_2$ is about 3.7 percent (not significant), but the coefficient of correlation tends to decrease to 0.53 (Cunningham et al. 1977). Apparently, four to five months between tests will result in a degree of random interindividual variation with only a slight change in the mean values over that period of time.

The use of blood lactate levels, measured after exercise, to indicate that a maximal level of work has been reached is one indicator of max VO$_2$, which requires some caution in the interpretation of data from children. As indicated by earlier studies (Shephard 1971; Godfrey 1974; Blimkie and Cunningham, unpublished), the maximal postexercise lactate levels of children are much lower than for adults. The age-specific values range from 6.0 mM at age 7 to 9.6 mM at age 15 in girls and from 7.1 mM at age 7 to 10.0 mM at age 15 in boys (Table 45.1). Although boys usually reach higher values than girls, there is a tendency for young girls (under 13 years) to have higher maximal lactate values than boys (Macek et al. 1971; Davies et al. 1971).

Eriksson (1971), who also reported lactate values following exercise (as mmol·kg^{-1} wet tissue weight) in boys, observed that the muscle lactate values were related to maturation as indicated by the testicular volume index. Shephard four to five months with no intervention (training, bed rest, etc.) the mean

Table 45.1
Post-exercise Blood Lactates as
Related to Age and Sex

Author	Year	Nation	Sex	Age	Post-exercise Blood Lactate (mM)
Shephard et al.	1969	Canada	M + F	9 to 13	8.9
Macek et al.	1971	Czecho-	F	13.0	7.5
		slovakia	M	13.0	5.3
Davies et al.	1972	U. K.	F	6.9	6.0
				9.2	8.7
				11.0	8.6
				13.2	8.7
				15.3	9.6
			M	7.2	7.1
				9.0	6.4
				10.8	7.7
				12.8	9.4
				15.1	10.0
Cunningham et al.	1973	Canada	M	10.6	6.0
Cunningham et al.	1977	Canada	F	12.2	7.1
				13.9	9.2
				14.9	9.9
			M	11.8	9.0
				13.5	11.0
				14.9	12.1

(1971) hypothesized that the lower peak lactates may reflect a faster oxygen consumption at the beginning of exercise or the buffering capacity of the blood may be lower than in adults. Additionally, children may be less willing to push themselves to maximum exertion than adults.

The leveling or plateau often observed in oxygen uptake as work load is increased at the peak of oxygen uptake curve is another major criterion used to establish whether a "true" max VO_2 has been reached. This phenomenon has been studied (Cumming and Friesen 1967; Cunningham et al. 1977) in young boys. Only 35 to 38 percent of the boys studied were able to reach such a plateau. Apparently, young boys who are exercised to exhaustion may or may not demonstrate a plateau of oxygen uptake over the final minutes of exercise. Those subjects who attained a plateau demonstrated a more reliable max VO_2 over four to five months (r = 0.74). When the subject never reached a plateau, the reliability decreased drastically (r = 0.27). The boys who reached such a plateau developed a large amount of energy anaerobically as shown by high postexercise lactates and higher respiratory exchange ratios than the boys who did not reach this plateau (Cunningham et al. 1977). The maximal heart rates and max VO_2 values were similar whether a plateau was reached or not. A "true" max VO_2 can be attained regardless of whether a plateau is reached since the development of the plateau phase is probably the result of a greater utilization of anaerobic metabolism at maximal work load with no further increase in aerobic metabolism. In other words, the boys who can attain this plateau phase do so by pushing themselves into a large oxygen debt.

Prediction of Maximal Aerobic Power

Very little work has been done to develop a predictive equation of aerobic power for children. The work with adults by Astrand (1960) has not been repeated for younger age groups (under 20 years). Davies and his coworkers (1972) compared directly determined values on a bicycle ergometer with those values predicted with the 'Astrand and Rhyming nomogram (1954). They observed a large underprediction of about 18 percent in the boys and 21 percent in the girls. This is a considerable error but similar to that usually observed for young adults (Davies 1968; Hermiston and Faulkner 1971). In one other study (Cunningham and Eynon 1973), the maximal heart rates were estimated by extrapolating the Astrand curve of age against maximal heart rate so that at age ten a maximal heart rate of 213 beats$\cdot$min^{-1} was estimated. This technique resulted in an overprediction of max VO_2 (17 to 35 percent) in young athletes ages 12 to 15 years tested on a bicycle ergometer. The technique of extrapolating the maximal estimated heart rate was probably in error, since average maximal heart rates for ten-year-old boys are probably between 195 and 200 beats$\cdot$min^{-1} (Shephard 1978).

The problems of estimating or predicting the physical working capacity of children are not unlike those found in adult populations. There are, however, many good reasons for the need to develop a prediction technique with more accuracy than reported to this time, and also one that would be easily adapted to mass testing procedures.

Measurement of Field Tests of Physical Working Capacity

The use of field tests of physical working capacity is widespread in the pediatric work in physiology literature. The major thrust has been to describe the performance of large population groups such as in the studies by Hunsicker and Reiff (1965) or by Howell and MacNab (1968) who surveyed the American and Canadian school age children, respectively. Fewer reports have attempted to show the relationship between field tests of performance and the direct measurement of aerobic power. Generally, the results of such investigations (Cumming 1971; Lariviere et al. 1974) do not show strong correlations between max VO_2 and running performance. The field tests have required children to run 600 yards (Hunsicker and Reiff 1965) or less. According to Cumming (1971) one of the problems with these tests is the short distances used, and he has recommended the use of longer distances, such as one to two miles. Correlation coefficients for these running tests with max VO_2 tend to vary widely. The running tests appear to explain about 30 percent of the variability in the measurement of max VO_2 (Olree and Nelson 1965; Cumming and Keynes 1967). Klissouras (1973), on the other hand, reported a very high correlation between running speed for one kilometer and max VO_2 ($r = 0.93$) in 24 nine-year-old boys. He expressed the relationship across speed as follows:

$$Y = 0.207X + 9.6$$

where oxygen uptake (ml$\cdot$kg$^{-1}\cdot$min^{-1}) and X = running speed (m$\cdot$min^{-1}).

Silverman and Anderson (1972) have also provided an excellent analysis of the energy expenditure of young boys (6 to 11 years) running at various speeds. His equations are as follows:

Walking: $\log_{10} VO_2 = (0.0960 \times \text{speed}) + (0.021 \times \% \text{ grade}) + 0.751$
$$(r = 0.97; P < 0.001)$$

Running: $\log_{10} VO_2 = (0.0367 \times \text{speed}) + (0.0102 \times \% \text{ grade}) + 1.238$
$$(r = 0.84; P < 0.001)$$

where: VO_2 is in ml$\cdot$min^{-1}
speed is in km$\cdot$jr^{-1}
gradient is in %.

These are very useful equations for estimating energy expenditure from speed of running.

In general, the use of field tests such as running for 12 minutes or one kilometer are relatively weak predictors of max VO_2. Cummings (1971) has stated that this technique is poor and is possibly no better than could be achieved by use of height, weight, and skinfold data. Motivation to perform well—a factor prevalent in children—appears to be a major problem in demonstrating a close association between performance and max VO_2. Those studies, which have shown a strong relationship between performance and max VO_2, were also successful in the motivation of the subjects.

Measurement of Anaerobic Capacity

Anaerobic capacity has usually been determined with a very intense bout of exercise to fatigue in (1) 30 seconds in order to stress maximally the "creatine phosphate system" (Bar-Or 1977), or (2) 90 seconds in order to stress maximally the "anaerobic glycolytic system" (Cunningham and Faulkner 1969). The measurements made during such tests are varied and include performance time, postexercise blood lactates, and oxygen debt (usually for 12 to 30 minutes after exercise).

As noted previously, children appear to produce lower lactate levels than adults in short bouts of exhaustive exercise. The lower lactate levels of children are mirrored by lower levels of oxygen debt. After an 11-minute recovery period following a maximal test of aerobic capacity, Shephard (1971) reported O_2 debts that averaged 7.50 liters in adult men, but only 2.44 liters in boys and 1.76 liters in girls. Maximal O_2 debt after a test of anaerobic capacity—fatigue on treadmill at 72.1 ± 4.6 seconds (Remigis 1978)—resulted in a value of 1.71 liters in an 11-minute recovery period for 10- and 11-year-old boys.

Bar-Or and his associates (1977) reported an all-out 30-second bicycle test of anaerobic capacity and power. This test has great promise as a measurement of the so-called "creatine phosphate" capacity. The bicycle resistance is set according to body weight, and mechanical work is monitored. Reported test-retest reliability was 0.95. The test also related well with tests of performance such as running 300 meters ($r = -0.85$) and O_2 debt ($r = 0.86$). The test is easily administered and has considerable potential for widespread use. There are several possibilities for future investigation in the general area of anaerobic capacity in young children as few studies have been reported to date.

PHYSICAL WORKING CAPACITY OF CHILDREN

Physical Working Capacity of Normal Children

In the 1970s several studies were published in which the physical working capacities or aerobic capacities of children have been investigated. The most up-to-date summary at this time has been reported by Shephard (1971), which appears to be complete through 1969. Other summaries of these data appear elsewhere (Godfrey 1974; Davies and Dobbin 1974). The max VO_2 values for children under 16 years are summarized in Tables 45.2 and 45.3. The data are all cross-sectional in nature and with the exception of the data of Cunningham et al. (1973, 1976) and those of Petajokl et al. (1974) are on normal active children. The data by Cunningham et al. (1973, 1976) and Petajokl et al. (1974) were collected on young athletes. Longitudinal data on aerobic capacity are scarce (Bailey 1973); however, the longitudinal study by Bailey reports unusually high values for max VO_2 for normally active children. His values are in fact similar to the values on young athletes. The higher values may be due to the fact that all oxygen uptake values were extrapolated to 200 beat·min^{-1} in that study, if this value was not reached during the test. A value of 195 beats·min^{-1} would probably be closer to a true value for this age range. A survey of some 51 reported tests gave a mean value of 191 beats·min^{-1} across ages 8 to 16 (range 180 to 211).

Two problems of current concern are (1) the normal changes in max VO_2 across the usual school age years (6 to 16 years), and (2) the influence of the lack of or addition of physical activity on the growth patterns of children. The changes in max VO_2 across ages are equivocal. Bailey (1973), in a longitudinal study, reported a gradual decline in max VO_2 (per kg body wt) with age, while most of the cross-sectional data do not show this decline. The drop in max VO_2 with age when observed appears to be much greater in young girls (Ikai and Kitagawa 1972; Anderson et al. 1974).

It has also been hypothesized that there might be an optimal time for exposure to physical activity that will have the greatest impact on this capacity in adult years. As summarized earlier (Cunningham 1970), some evidence exists that prepubertal as compared with postpubertal activity may have a better carry-over to spontaneous activity in adult years and a greater influence upon growth.

Klissouras (1971, 1973) has studied the influence of physical activity on growth in a number of monozygotic and dizygotic twins. His experimental model is exceptional and provides an excellent vehicle to study the influence of environment and heredity on max VO_2 and physical working capacity. He has concluded that the speculation that activity will be more potent at one age is not supported by the evidence. The study by Weber and Klissouras (1976) involving 12 pairs of identical twin boys was designed to train one twin while his brother served as a control. The boys were grouped at ages 10, 13, and 16 years (four sets per age). The researchers felt that the likely explanation for the lack of change at age 13 appeared to be associated with the adolescent growth spurt occurring at about this age. Hormonal activity optimal during this age might have masked any influence of training. It still remains uncertain at which developmental period the influence of training would have its greatest impact on growth.

Table 45.2
Maximal Oxygen Uptake for Males by Age

Author	Year	Nation	N	Age	Mode*	Maximal Oxygen Uptake L.min^{-1}	ml·kg^{-1}·min^{-1}
Andersen et al.	1974	Norway	29	8.4	B	1.44+	52.7
			14	10.3	B	1.61	49.3
			12	12.4	B	1.89+	50.4
			15	14.2	B	2.26	47.2
			13	16.3	B	3.12	49.3
Nagle et al.	1977	U.S.A.	30	13.8	T	3.16	54.0
			30	14.9	T	3.74	56.3
			30	16.0	T	3.71	54.0
			30	16.9	T	3.87	57.7
Matsui	1972	Japan	18	12	T	1.93	46.4
			54	13	T	2.04	45.7
			48	14	T	2.28	47.1
			47	15	T	2.45	45.7
			50	16	T	2.75	49.2
Ikai et al.	1972	Japan	19	8-10	B	1.31	50.0
			18	10-11	B	1.50	49.1
			21	11-12	B	1.77	51.3
			14	12-13	B	1.90	44.9
			21	13-14	B	2.13	47.5
			19	14-15	B	2.35	49.5
			13	15-16	B	2.47	48.1
			19	16-17	B	2.62	47.2
Davies et al.	1972	U. K.	8	7.2	B	1.19	
			9	9.0	B	1.38	
			9	10.8	B	1.63	
			12	12.8	B	2.05	
			9	15.1	B	3.06	
Lariviere et al.	1974	Canada	20	10.0	T	1.43	46.7
Petajokl et al.	1974	South Africa	26	8-9	T	1.56	57.7
			36	10-11	T	2.01	56.1
			38	12-13	T	2.35	59.4
Yamajii et al.	1977	Japan	8	10.2	B	1.10	38.6
			8	11.2	B	1.34	39.7
			10	12.3	B	1.43	39.8
			9	13.4	B	2.05	44.5
			10	14.2	B	2.38	50.5
			8	15.0	B	2.17	47.1
			8	16.3	B	2.20	39.9
Cunningham et al.	1976	Canada	15	10.6	B	2.00	56.6
Cunningham et al.	1973	Canada	10	11.8	B	2.17	52.5
			6	13.5	B	2.65	52.9
			8	14.9	B	3.37	56.6
Bailey	1974	Canada	51	8.1	T	1.45	57.2
			51	9.1	T	1.73	61.7
			51	10.0	T	1.83	57.2
			51	14.0	T	1.98	56.9
			51	12.0	T	2.25	58.5
			51	13.0	T	2.43	55.9
			51	14.0	T	2.76	55.2
			51	15.0	T	3.00	53.7

* Mode refers to bicycle (B) or treadmill (T) exercise.

Table 45.3
Maximal Oxygen Uptake for Females by Age

Author	Year	Nation	N	Age	Mode*	Maximal Oxygen Uptake L.min⁻¹	ml·kg⁻¹·min⁻¹
Andersen et al.	1974	Norway	33	8.2	B	1.25	47.4
			18	10.5	B	1.41	41.6
			15	12.2	B	1.66	41.9
			13	14.3	B	2.02	36.9
			9	16.3	B	2.07	38.4
Nagle et al.	1977	U.S.A.	30	14.0	T	2.27	41.1
			30	14.9	T	2.30	41.2
			30	16.0	T	2.36	40.7
			30	17.0	T	2.34	40.2
Matsui et al.	1972	Japan	18	12	T	1.68	39.6
			57	13	T	1.69	37.8
			49	14	T	1.75	36.8
			54	15	T	1.72	34.1
			43	16	T	1.77	34.7
Ikai et al.	1972	Japan	20	8-10	B	1.11	43.4
			18	10-11	B	1.22	40.8
			20	11-12	B	1.41	41.5
			13	12-13	B	1.58	37.6
			19	13-14	B	1.56	35.0
			22	14-15	B	1.71	34.9
			14	15-16	B	1.82	37.1
			18	16-17	B	1.75	34.3
Davies et al.	1972	U.K.	8	6.9	B	0.98	
			8	9.2	B	1.16	
			11	11.0	B	1.46	
			11	13.2	B	1.88	
			8	15.3	B	2.11	
Lariviere et al.	1974	Canada	16	10.0	T	1.46	38.1
Cunningham et al.	1973	Canada	8	12.2	B	1.97	46.2
			6	13.2	B	2.24	43.4
			5	14.9	B	2.19	40.5

* Mode refers to bicycle (B) or treadmill (T) exercise.

On the other hand, a well-conducted study of growth and physical activity in Japan demonstrated a clear association between athletics or training in general during the rapid growth phase and the development of superior gas transport systems capacity in adults (Kobayashi et al. 1978). Maximal aerobic power was measured for five to six successive years in 50 Japanese schoolboys starting from the age of 9 or 13, and for two to three years in six superior junior runners from the age of 14. Seven boys trained (1.5 hours, four to five times per week) on a regular basis between ages 9 and 14 years whereas the other 43 attended the usual school physical education classes and some also attended sports clubs outside school, which would be responsible to some degree for the increase in aerobic power in these boys. In this study there was an increase of 133 ml O_2 for each kilogram increase in weight during the year of greatest growth in the trained boys, 68 ml for the average. This difference was significant and suggests that training increases aerobic power above the normal increases attributable to age and to the corresponding adolescent growth spurt (height, PHV). Changes in aerobic power with age at PHV in relation to relative degrees of physical training are different in the athletic and average groups. The results of this study demonstrated the relatively small effect of physical training prior to the age of PHV and the dramatic differentiation occurring thereafter. The authors concluded that training will effectively increase aerobic power above the increases normally attributable to age and the corresponding adolescent growth spurt. However, in trained boys, a large increase in aerobic power was not observed until one year before the age of PHV. The high values for aerobic power in the runners may be derived from strenuous training or may be due to superior genetic endowment. The answer to this question is not known.

The Influence of Training

Studies on training in young children, although not abundant, take several forms including those specifically designed training studies and epidemiological studies of children in school or in athletics. Some evidence indicates that the traditional school-centered programs (physical education classes) do not provide sufficient stimuli to improve or maintain physical working capacity across ages (Bailey 1973; Saunders et al. 1969; Cumming et al. 1969). Specially designed school-centered training programs have shown, however, that the physical working capacity of children can be improved within the school environment (Goode 1977).

Other studies (Ekblom 1969; Eriksson 1973; Daniels and Oldridge 1971) have demonstrated significant changes in max VO_2 with specific training programs. These studies were all done on young boys. Less is known of the possible changes in young girls with training, particularly when cross-sectional data indicate a marked drop in the max VO_2 of girls after age 12. Considerably more work is needed with young girls in order to determine whether the normal drop in max VO_2 observed with age can be reversed.

Perceived Exertion and Physical Working Capacity

Little work has been done on the perceived exertion of children during periods of activity. Bar-Or (1976) has concluded from his limited studies that there is a tendency for older people to perceive a given exercise stimulus to be higher than younger ones. This discrepancy seems greatest between adults and children. He also noted that children may be perceptually more sensitive to changes in physiological strain than adults.

Physical Working Capacity in Abnormal Groups

Several studies have been done in order to investigate the physical working capacities of special groups other than normal active children. The best reviews or compilations of such studies appear in the work by Godfrey (1974) on the asthmatic child and the child with heart or lung disease. Other studies on these topics have also appeared in the summary edited by Borms and Hebbelinck (1974). These reports include studies on rheumatic children (Kasch 1974), children with complete heart block (Thoren et al. 1974), and diabetic children (Hebbelinck 1974) as well as the role of exercise in children as it might influence coronary heart disease (Boyer and Wilmore 1977).

Investigations into the physical working capacity of children are limited and appear to be particularly deficient in longitudinal studies and at early ages, especially before eight years of age. Reports are exceptionally scarce on the influence of habitual activity on the growth and development of children and how these influences might affect adult performance. Studies on the normal levels of physical activity of young children, such as the publication by Paterson et al. (1977), are also infrequent. Further work on the daily activity patterns of children would do much to describe the contribution of habitual activity to the physical working capacity of children and youth.

REFERENCES

Albinson, J. G. and G. M. Andrew. 1976. *Child in Sport and Physical Activity,* Baltimore: University Park Press.

Anderson, K. L., V. Seliger, J. Rutenfranz, and I. Berudt. 1974. Physical performance capacity of children in Norway. Part II. Heart rate and oxygen pulse in submaximal and maximal exercises—Population parameters in a rural community. *Europ J Appl Physiol,* 33, 197-206.

Astrand, I. 1960. Aerobic work capacity in men and women with special reference to age. *Acta Physiol Scand,* 49(Suppl. 169), 45-60.

Astrand, P.-O. 1952. *Experimental Studies of Physical Working Capacity in Relation to Sex and Age.* Copenhagen: Munksgaard.

Astrand, P.-O. and I. Rhyming. 1954. A nomogram for calculating of aerobic capacity from pulse rate during submaximal work. *J Appl Physiol,* 7, 216-221.

Bailey, D. A. 1973. Exercise, fitness and physical education for the growing child: A concern. *Can J Publ Hlth,* 64, 421-430.

Bailey, D. A., W. D. Ross, C. Weese, R. L. Mirwald, 1974. Maximal oxygen uptake and dimensional relationships in boys studied longitudinally from age 8 to 15. A paper presented at VI International Symposium on Pediatric Work Physiology. Prague, Czechoslovakia.

Bar-Or, O. 1972. Pediatric work physiology. *Proceedings of the Fourth International Symposium.* Tel-Aviv: Technodaf.

Bar-Or, O. 1976. Age-related changes in exercise perception. In *Physical Work and Effort,* G. Borg (ed.). New York: Pergamon Press.

Bar-Or, O., R. Dotan, and O. Inbar. 1977. A 30-sec all-out ergometer test: Its reliability and validity for anaerobic capacity. *Israel J Med Sci,* 13, 326.

Borms, J. and M. Hebbelinck. 1974. *Children and Exercise*. Proceedings of the Vth International Symposium held at the Zeepreventorium. Deltaan, Belgium. *Acta Paediatrica Belgia,* 23(Suppl), 296.

Boyer, J. L. and J. H. Wilmore. 1977. Physical Fitness Programs for Children. In *Exercise in Cardiovascular Health and Disease,* E. A. Amsterdam, J. H. Wilmore, and A. N. DeMaria (eds.). New York: Yorke Medical Books.

Cumming, G. R. 1971. Correlation of physical performance with laboratory measures of fitness. In *Frontiers of Fitness,* R. J. Shephard (ed.). Springfield, Ill.: C. C. Thomas.

Cumming, G. R. and W. Friesen. 1967. Bicycle ergometer measurement of maximal oxygen uptake in children. *Can J Physiol Pharmacol,* 45, 937-946.

Cumming, G. R., D. Goulding, and G. Baggley. 1969. Failure of school physical education to improve cardiovascular fitness. *Can Med Assoc J,* 101, 69-73.

Cumming, G. R. and R. Keynes. 1967. A fitness performance test for school children and its correlation with physical working capacity and maximal oxygen uptake. *Can Med Assoc J,* 96, 1262-1269.

Cunningham, D. A. 1970. Leisure activity and aging. *Can Assoc Hlth Phys Ed Rec,* 36, 11-13.

Cunningham, D. A. and R. B. Eynon. 1973. The working capacity of young competitive swimmers, 10-16 years of age. *Med Sci Spts,* 5, 227-231.

Cunningham, D. A., P. B. Goode, and J. B. Critz. 1975. Cardiorespiratory response to exercise on a rowing and bicycle ergometer. *Med Sci Spts,* 7, 37-43.

Cunningham, D. A. and J. A. Faulkner. 1969. The effect of training on aerobic and anaerobic metabolism during a short exhaustive run. *Med Sci Spts,* 1, 65-69.

Cunningham, D. A., P. Telford, and G. T. Swart. 1976. The cardiopulmonary capacities of young hockey players, age 10. *Med Sci Spts,* 8, 23-25.

Cunningham, D. A., B. M. Van Waterschoot, D. H. Paterson, M. Lefcoe, and S. P. Sangal. 1977. Reliability and reproducibility of maximal oxygen uptake measurements in children. *Med Sci Spts,* 9, 104-108.

Daniels, J. and N. Oldridge. 1971. Changes in oxygen consumption of young boys during growth and running training. *Med Sci Spts,* 3, 161-165.

Davies, D. T. M. 1968. Limitations to the prediction of maximum oxygen intake from cardiac frequency measurements. *J Appl Physiol,* 24, 700-706.

Davies, C. T. M., C. Barnes, and S. Godfrey. 1972. Body composition and maximal exercise performance in children. *Human Biol,* 44, 195-214.

Davies, J. A. and J. Dobbing. 1974. *Scientific Foundations of Paediatrics.* London: Heinemanns Medical Books.

Ekblom, B. 1969. Effect of physical training in adolescent boys. *J Appl Physiol,* 27, 350-355.

Eriksson, B. O., J. Karlson, and B. Saltin. 1971. Muscle metabolites during exercise in pubertal boys. *Acta Paediat Scand,* Suppl 217, 154-157.

Eriksson, B. O. and G. Koch. 1973. Effect of physical training on hemodynamic response during submaximal and maximal exercise in 11-13 year old boys. *Acta Physiol Scand,* 87, 27-39.

Godfrey, S. 1974. *Exercise Testing in Children*. Philadelphia: W. B. Saunders.

Goode, R. C., A. Virgin, T. T. Romet, P. Crawford, I. Duffin, T. Pallandi, and Z. Woch. 1976. Effects of a short period of physical activity in adolescent boys and girls. *Can J Appl Spt Sci*, 1, 241-250.

Hebbelinck, M., H. Iobb, and H. Meersseman. 1974. Physical development and performance capacity in a group of diabetic children and adolescents. In *Children and Exercise*, Proceedings of the Vth International Symposium, J. Borms and M. Hebbelinck (eds.). *Acta Pediatrica Belgica*, 28 (Suppl), 151-161.

Hermiston, R. T. and J. A. Faulkner. 1971. Prediction of maximal oxygen uptake by a stepwise regression technique. *J Appl Physiol*, 30, 833-837.

Howell, M. L. and R. B. J. MacNab. 1968. *The Physical Working Capacity of Canadian Children*. Ottawa: Canadian Association for Health, Physical Education and Recreation.

Hunsicker, P. A. and G. G. Reiff. 1965. A Survey and Comparison of Youth *Fitness, 1958-1965*, U.S. Office of Education, Report of Cooperative Research Project No. 2418. Ann Arbor, Michigan. University of Michigan.

Ikai, M. and K. Kitaqawa. 1972. Maximal oxygen uptake of Japanese related to age and sex. *Med Sci Spts*, 4, 127-131.

Kasch, F. W. 1974. Heart rate response of rheumatic children. In *Children and Exercise*. Proceedings of the Vth International Symposium. J. Borms and M. Hebbelinck (eds.). *Acta Pediatrica Belgica*, 28 (Suppl), 129-131.

Klissouras, V. 1971. Heritability of adaptive variation. *J Appl Physiol*, 31, 338-344.

Klissouras, V. 1973. Prediction of potential performance with special reference to heredity. *J Spts Med*, 13, 100-107.

Klissouras, V., F. Pirnay, and J. M. Petit. 1973. Adaptation to maximal effort: Genetics and age. *J Appl Physiol*, 35, 288-293.

Kobayashi, K., K. Kitamura, M. Miura, H. Sodeyama, Y. Murase, M. Miyashita, and H. Matsiu. 1978. Aerobic power as related to body growth and training in Japanese boys: A longitudinal study. *J Appl Physiol*, 44, 666-672.

Lariviere, G., H. Lavallee, and J. Shephard. 1974. Correlations between field tests of performance and laboratory measurements of fitness. *Acta Paed Bel*, 28 (Suppl), 19-28.

Macek, A., J. Vavra, and B. Mrzena. 1971. Intermittent exercise of supramaximal intensity in children. *Acta Paediat Scand* (Suppl), 217, 29-31.

Magel, J. R. and J. A. Faulkner. 1967. Maximal O_2 uptakes of college swimmers. *J Appl Physiol*, 22, 929-933.

Matsui, H., M. Miyashita, M. Miura, K. Kobayashi, T. Hoshikawa, and S. Hamei. 1972. Maximum oxygen uptake and its relation to body weight of Japanese adolescents. *Med Sci Spts*, 4, 27-32.

Mitchell, J. H., B. J. Sproule, and C. B. Chapman. 1958. The physiological meaning of the maximal oxygen intake test. *J Clin Invest*, 37, 538-547.

Morse, M., F. W. Schultz, and D. E. Cassels. 1949. Relation of age to physiologic response of the older boy (10-17 years) to exercise. *J Appl Physiol*, 1, 683-692.

Nagle, F. J., J. Hagberg, and S. Kamei. 1977. Maximal O_2 uptake of boys and girls — Ages 14-17. *Europ J Appl Physiol*, 36, 78-80.

Olree, H. and T. Nelson. 1965. Evaluation of the AAHPER youth fitness test. *J Spts Med*, 5, 67-71.

Paterson, D. H., D. A. Cunningham, D. S. Penny, M. Lefcoe, and S. Sangal. 1977. Heart rate telemetry and estimated energy metabolism in minor league ice hockey. *Can J Appl Sp Sci*, 2, 71-75.

Petäjokl, M. L., M. Arstila, and L. Välimälci. 1974. Pulse-conducted exercise test in children. *Acta Paediatrica Bel*, 28 (Suppl), 40-53.

Remigis, R. E., D. A. Cunningham, and D. H. Paterson. 1978. Anaerobic capacity of young male athletes. Unpublished manuscript.

Robinson, S. 1938. Experimental studies of physical fitness in relation to age. *Int Z angew Physiol einschl Arbeitphysiol*, 10, 251-323.

Saunders, R. L., H. J. Montoye, D. A. Cunningham, and A. J. Kozar. 1969. Physical fitness of high school students and participation in physical education classes. *Res Quart*, 40, 552-560.

Shephard, R. J. 1971. The working capacity of school children. In *Frontiers of Fitness*, R. J. Shephard (ed.). Springfield, Ill.: C. C. Thomas.

Shephard, R. J., C. Allen, O. Bar-Or, C. T. M. Davies, S. Degre, R. Hedman, K. Ishii, M. Kaneko, J. R. LaCorer, P. E. di Prampero, and V. Seliger. 1969. The working capacity of Toronto school children (Part I). *Can Med Assoc J*, 100, 560-566.

Silverman, M. and S. Anderson. 1972. Metabolic cost of treadmill exercise in children. *J Appl Physiol*, 33, 696-698.

Taylor, H. L., E. R. Buskirk, and A. Henschell. 1955. Maximal O_2 uptake as an objective measure of cardiorespiratory performance. *J Appl Physiol*, 8, 73-80.

Thorén, C. 1971. Pediatric Work Physiology. *Acta Paediatrica Scandinavia*, Suppl 217, 157.

Thorén, C., P. Herin, and J. Vavra. 1974. Studies of submaximal exercise in congenital complete heart block. In *Children and Exercise*. Proceedings of the Vth International Symposium. J. Borms and M. Hebbelinck (eds.). *Acta Pediatrica Belgica*, 28 (Suppl), 132-143.

Weber, G., W. Kartodihardso, and B. Klissouras. 1976. Growth and physical training with reference to heredity. *J Appl Physiol*, 40, 211-215.

Yamajii, K. and M. Miyashita. 1977. Oxygen transport system during exhaustive exercise in Japanese boys. *Europ J Appl Physiol*, 36, 93-99.

46

Coronary Heart Disease Risk in Children

Thomas B. Gilliam and Victor L. Katch

In the 1960s and 1970s there was a concerted effort by the allied medical professions to identify individuals who are susceptible to premature development of coronary heart disease (CHD). This had led to the establishment and use of *CHD Risk Factors* such as hypertension, elevated blood lipids (serum cholesterol and triglycerides), cigarette smoking, obesity, electrocardiographic abnormalities during rest and exercise, family history of heart disease, diabetes, and inadequate physical activity.

While identification of the preceding variables has been heavily stressed for the adult population, results of several research reports have substantiated the prevalence of coronary heart disease risk factors in children (Blumenthal et al. 1975; Court and Dunlap 1975; Fredrichs et al. 1976; Gilliam et al. 1977; Lauer et al. 1975; Wilmore and McNamara 1974). More importantly, the data support evidence of multiple risk factor development at an early age.

In a study conducted by Wilmore and McNamara (1974) on CHD risk in 95 boys, 8 to 12 years of age, 20 percent demonstrated elevated serum cholesterol (> 200 mg percent) and 8 percent had abnormally high triglycerides (> 100 mg percent). About 13 percent of the boys were considered obese (> 25 percent body fat). Of the total group, 64 percent had at least one risk factor and 14 percent had two or more. A similar study by Gilliam et al. (1977) showed that 62 percent of 47 boys and girls ages 7 to 12 had at least one coronary heart disease risk factor, and 21 percent had three or more risk factors. About 11 percent of the children were obese (> 25 percent body fat), and 18 and 11 percent had elevated triglycerides (> 100 Mg percent) and cholesterol (> 200 mg percent), respectively. Also, 18 percent of the children were classified as having Type IV hyperlipoproteinemia. Another 11 percent of the children had low physical work capacity, as measured by maximal aerobic power (30 ml•kg^{-1} min^{-1}).

The two most common blood lipids associated with CHD risk are elevated cholesterol and triglyceride (hyperlipidemias). Because of the variability in standards and methods employed to determine hyperlipidemias, it is difficult to establish norm-referenced standards for children. Drash (1972) suggests 200 mg percent as the upper limit for serum cholesterol values, while Levy and

Fredrickson (1968) suggest 230 mg percent and 140 mg percent as the upper limits for cholesterol and triglycerides, respectively. Others have used the 95th percentile or greater as an indicator of elevated lipids (Fredrichs et al. 1976; Hennekens et al. 1976).

Cholesterol and triglycerides do not circulate freely in the plasma but are transported as lipoproteins. The composition of each serum lipoprotein is differentiated by its lipid to protein ratio. The chylomicrons are the largest of the lipoproteins composed of triglycerides (80 to 95 percent) with lesser amounts of cholesterol (2 to 7 percent), phospholipid (3 to 6 percent), and protein (.5 to 1 percent). The very-low-density lipoproteins (VLDL, pre-beta) are also composed predominately of triglycerides (60 to 80 percent), with the remaining composition being cholesterol (5 to 13 percent), phospholid (5 to 18 percent), and protein (5 to 15 percent). The low-density lipoproteins (LDL, beta) contain about 25 percent protein and 45 percent cholesterol. LDL normally carry from one half to two thirds of the total plasma cholesterol. The fourth and smallest of the lipoprotein species, high-density lipoprotein (HDL, alpha), contain 45 to 50 percent protein, 30 percent phospholipid, and 20 percent cholesterol.

The etiologies of hyperlipidemias are generally considered to be complex and heterogeneous in nature (Jackson, Morrisett, and Gotts 1976; Levy and Rifkind 1973). Furthermore, hyperlipidemias manifest different forms of hyperlipoproteinemias (HLP), which also appear to be complex and heterogenic in nature in young children (Jackson et al. 1976; Lauer et al. 1975). These HLP have been classified (Types I, II, III, IV, V) electrophoretically according to the absence and/or presence of the four lipoproteins.

Type II HLP is the most common in young children, whereas Type IV is not generally identified until after age ten. Types III and V are generally not manifested in children, while Type I appears rarely. Type II HLP is characterized by increased levels of LDL and/or VLDL (Levy and Rifkind 1973) and is occasionally found to be secondary to other disorders that may occur in children, such as nephrosis, hypothyroidism, glycogen storage disease, or acute porphyria (Levi and Fredrickson 1968; Levy and Rifkind 1973). Sometimes it is secondary to very high dietary intakes of cholesterol and saturated fats (Levi and Fredrickson 1968; Levy and Rifkind 1973).

Type IV HLP is characterized by increased levels of very low density lipoproteins resulting in high triglycerides and occasionally high cholesterol levels (Levi and Fredrickson 1968; Levi and Rifkin 1973). In some cases it also appears secondary to other disorders in children such as diabetes mellitus, nephrosis, glycogen storage disease, malnutrition, hyperthyroidism, and idiopathic hypercalcemia (Levi and Rifkind 1973). Furthermore, its manifestation tends to be potentiated by the presence of overweightness (Levi and Rifkind 1973), which may be considered to be a secondary consequence of insulin resistance in peripheral tissues (Glueck et al. 1977).

The prevalence of familial hyperlipoproteinemia and hypercholesterolemia has been documented. Type II familial HLP is usually caused by an autosomal

496

dominant inheritance pattern (Levi and Rifkind 1973), whereas Type IV appe
to be heterogeneous with only some cases displaying an autosomal domina
mode of inheritance (Levi and Rifkind 1973). In a study involving 700 children
and their parents, Drash (1972) concluded that about two percent of the sample
had familial Type II hyperlipoproteinemia. Blumenthal et al. (1972) studied
familial aggregation of risk factors in two groups of families. In the "case"
group the fathers had experienced a myocardial infarction at least six months
prior to admission to the study. The control group consisted of fathers who had
no history of heart disease. The results showed that the chance of identifying a
child with hyperlipoproteinemia was three times greater if the father had
premature coronary artery disease (Hennekens et al. 1976).

Management of hyperlipoproteinemia in children is a relatively new venture.
Increased levels of dietary cholesterol and saturated fat intake have both been
implicated with elevated cholesterol levels (Holloszy et al. 1967; Levy and
Rifkind 1973). In addition, high intakes of refined sugars have also been related
to high triglyceride levels (Glueck, Fallat, and Tsang 1975). Glueck and his
coworkers (1977) reported that with mean weight loss of 1.8 kg and adherence
to a diet with 20 percent calories as protein, and 40 percent each as fat and
carbohydrate, the polyunsaturate to saturate ratios of 2.5 to 2.0 mean triglyceride
values were reduced from 238 to 140 mg percent in 11 of 16 obese children with
familial hypertriglyceridemia. Similarly cholesterol and triglyceride levels were
reduced with appropriate dietary modification (Blumenthal 1975; Fredrickson
1976; Levy and Rifkind 1973).

Levels of physical activity. These levels are thought to be negatively correlated
with elevated cholesterol and triglyceride levels in adults, as well as with
increased fatness in both children and adults (Friedman 1972; Keys 1972; Leon
et al. 1977; Mayer 1975; Oscai 1973; Pollock 1973). It appears that it is possible
to normalize triglyceride and, in some instances, cholesterol levels via habitual
physical activity (Bonanno and Lies 1974; Holloszy et al. 1964; Oscai 1973). It
should be noted, however, that triglyceride changes appear to be transistory,
returning to pre-exercise baseline levels within a few days following the cessation of exercise (Bonanno and Lies 1974; Holloszy et al. 1964). While cholesterol is synthesized in most tissues of the body including the arterial wall, it can
only be catabolized and excreted by the liver (Gordon et al. 1977). Therefore,
cholesterol is transported from these tissues to the liver during cholesterol
turn-over via high density lipoprotein-cholesterol (HDL-C). However, only the
unesterified cholesterol form can exchange readily between plasma lipoproteins
and tissues (Gordon et al. 1977; Miller and Miller 1975). Besides being involved
in tissue cholesterol clearance and transporting cholesterol to the liver for
breakdown, it has been suggested that decreased levels of HDL-C upset the
influx-efflux cholesterol balance from the arterial intima, thus promoting
atherosclerosis. It appears that increased levels of physical activity will increase
HDL-C levels (Bonanno and Lies 1974; Enger et al. 1977; Leon et al. 1977;

Lopez et al. 1974) in adults and may have the same effect in children (Burke and Gilliam 1977). As a result, less cholesterol will bind in the arterial intima, thus reducing atherosclerotic risk (Gordon et al. 1977; Miller and Miller 1975).

It is important to note that even though most training studies show no significant reduction in total serum cholesterol, significant changes involving the HDL-C to cholesterol ratio do occur. Therefore, it is probably more meaningful to assess the HDL-C to cholesterol ratio for assessing CHD risk than just cholesterol levels.

Obesity. One of the most predominant coronary heart disease risk factors in children is obesity (Gilliam et al. 1977; Wilmore and McNamara 1974). With the assessment of morphological characteristics of adipose tissue, recognition of distinct patterns of development of obesity have been noted. Hyperplasic obesity is defined as an excessive number of adipocytes, whereas hypertrophic obesity refers to enlarged fat cells. In obese adults hyperplasic and hypertrophic forms of adipose tissue morphology have been observed along with the recognition that the former tends to be characteristic of obesity development during childhood, while the latter characterizes accumulations of adipose mass after maturity (Bjorntorp and Sjostrom 1971; Knittle 1975).

In adults, obesity can be defined as the accumulation of body fat greater than 20 and 30 percent of total body weight for men and women, respectively. It is hypothesized that at these percentages individual fat cells are maximally filled with lipid material. While no such standards have been established for children, it is reasonable to use the adult standards. In addition, relative weight (percentage above or below the medium weight for subjects of the same mean weight and height) standards may be useful.

Caloric restriction appears to be the most common method of treating obesity (Keys 1972; Knittle 1975). Knittle (1975) states that "in childhood onset obesity one should institute dietary regimen prior to age six if lifelong history of obesity is to be avoided." Physical activity may also be useful in reducing fat in children (Mayer 1975; Parizkova 1961). Mayer found that extra weight gain in obese children takes place in the fall and winter when children are most sedentary. During the summer when children are most active there is less weight gain. He also noted that obese girls actually consume 300 to 400 calories less per day than thin girls. Consequently, the difference in body composition between the obese and thin girls was related to their level of physical activity. In another study with obese children who were able to increase their daily physical activity to one hour per day, five days a week, Mayer (1975) noted that after several years 60 percent of the children demonstrated significant fat weight loss. Parizkova (1961) has also shown that active children possess less fat (i.e., are leaner) when compared to age-paired, less-active children.

Probably the most significant aspect of obesity as a CHD risk factor is its apparent association with other risk factors. In children, much as with adults, association between body fatness and serum lipid levels tends to be more evident when subjects are stratified in relation to fatness. Moderate associations between body fatness and triglyceride levels are commonly evident when considering only obese children (Court, Dunlap, and Leonard 1974; Gilliam et al. 1977), and the degree of such associations have been further strengthened when the origin of obesity is shown to occur at ages one year and above (Court et al. 1974). Glueck, Fallat, and Tsang (1975) reported that a primary cause of hypertriglyceridemia in children (assuming the children were free from diseases that cause secondary hypertriglyceridemia) is excess fat weight. Glueck and his associates (1977) also suggested that obesity tends to facilitate the expression of the Type IV phenotype in children and indicated that weight reduction in such children may be effective in reducing elevated triglyceride levels. Court and Dunlap (1975), studying lipid levels in boys ranging in age from 11 to 19, reported a low correlation ($r = .23$) between skinfold thickness and triglyceride values. When computed for only obese children the correlation increased to $r - .40$. However, it has also been pointed out that a critical point occurs when very high triglyceride values are no longer correlated with body fat (Court and Dunlap 1975; Court et al. 1974). Recently, Glueck et al. (1977) reported correlations of $r - .25$ and $r = .11$ for fat mass versus hypertriglyceridemia levels (famililial type) and triglyceride levels, respectively. Additionally, Gilliam and his colleagues (1977) reported significant correlations of $r = .51$ and $r = .49$ between fat weight in fat children versus cholesterol and triglyceride levels, respectively, in comparison to correlations of $r = .31$ and $r = .16$ for nonfat children.

Physical inactivity. This is also recognized as a CHD risk factor. An inverse relationship between physical activity and coronary mortality has been reported in adults (Kannel 1970). It is believed that physical activity opens coronary arteries, decreases triglycerides, increases HDL-C levels, increases cardiac efficiency, helps to lower blood pressure, and maintains desirable body weight (Friedman 1973).

The relationship between physical activity in children to the reduction of CHD risk factors is not known. In a pilot study by Burke and Gilliam (1977) a strenuous six-week physical activity program involving 14 eight- to ten-year-old girls was shown to significantly increase HDL-C levels and lean body weight. Triglyceride levels in two of the three girls with confirmed hypertriglyceridemia were also lower following physical training. Probably the most significant finding in recent years concerning physical activity and CHD risk is its role in increasing HDL-C levels, which is known to reduce atherosclerotic development in adults (Carlson and Mossfeldt 1964; Enger et al. 1977; Leon et al. 1977; Lopez et al. 1974; Miller and Miller 1975). More research is needed in this area to delineate the interaction of such factors as age, exercise dosage, sex, and CHD prevention during adulthood. Although sufficient longitudinal data are not available, it seems probable that regular activity during childhood may serve a two-fold purpose in children: (1) as an aid in reducing or minimizing the development of coronary risk during adulthood, and (2) to set a pattern for a physically active way of life in adulthood.

Hypertension. During the 1970s hypertension in children received considerable attention (National Heart, Lung, and Blood Institutes Task Force 1977). Children whose systolic and diastolic blood pressures exceed the 95th percentile with respect to "normal" age-specific ranges are generally labelled as high-normals rather than hypertensive without more detailed tests. The mechanisms and causes of primary hypertension in children are not clearly understood. A higher incidence of primary hypertension (no identifiable cause) has been found associated with race (DeCastro et al. 1976; National Lung and Blood Institutes Task Force 1977) in that blacks tend to have a higher prevalence and more severe cases of hypertension.

Excessive salt intake and obesity are also associated with primary hypertension (National Heart, Lung, and Blood Institutes Task Force 1977). Therefore, salt intake should be reduced by individuals with hypertension or those with high CHD risk (Lopez et al. 1974; National Heart, Lung, and Blood Institutes Task Force 1977).

Blood pressure, age, overweightness, heart rate, plasma glucose, serum uric acid, and familial risk can be used to predict hypertension in children (National Heart, Lung, and Blood Institutes Task Force 1977). Familial tendency towards hypertension has been confirmed by several population studies (National Heart, Lung, and Blood Institutes Task Force 1977).

In summary, it appears that certain CHD risk factors are prevalent in children and that a few of these risk factors can be reduced by dietary management and/or weight reduction. Physical activity intervention programs have been successful in reducing obesity and hypertriglyceride levels and in raising HDL-C levels—the latter being inversely related to CHD risk (Fig. 46.1).

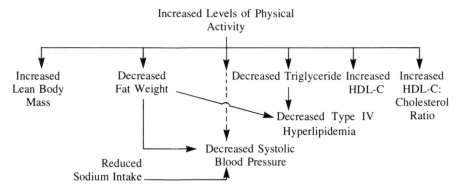

Fig. 46.1 Schematic representation of the effects of increased levels of strenuous physical activity on several coronary heart disease factors. The solid line represents a direct effect and the dashed line depicts an indirect effect.

REFERENCES

Bjorntorp, P. and L. Sjostrom. 1971. Number and size of adipose tissue fat cells in relation to metabolism in human obesity. *Metab,* 20, 703-713.

Blumenthal, S., M. Jesse, C. Hennekens, B. Klein, P. Rerror, and J. Gourley. 1975. Risk factors for coronary artery disease in children of affected families. *J Pediatr,* 87, 1187-1192.

Bonanno, J. and J. E. Lies. 1974. Effects of physical training on coronary risk factors. *Amer J Cardiol,* 33, 760-764.

Burke, M. B. and T. B. Gilliam. 1977. Effects of exercise on serum lipids and lipoproteins in girls, ages 8-10 years. Unpublished study, University of Michigan.

Carlson, L. A. and F. Mossfeldt. 1964. Acute effects of prolonged, heavy exercise on the concentration of plasma lipids and lipoproteins in man. *Acta Physio Scand,* 62, 51-59.

Court, J. M. and M. Dunlop. 1975. Plasma lipid values and lipoprotein patterns during adolescence in boys. *J Pediatr,* 86, 453-458.

Court, J. M., M. Dunlop, and R. Leonard. 1974. Plasma lipid values in childhood obesity, *Aust Pediatr J,* 10, 10-14.

deCastro, P. J., R. Biersbroech, C. Erickson, P. Farrell, W. Leong, D. Murphy, and R. Green. 1976. Hypertension in adolescents. *Clin Pediatr,* 15, 24-26.

Drash, A. 1972. Atherosclerosis, cholesterol, and the pediatrician. *J Pediatr,* 80, 693-696.

Enger, S. C., K. Herjormsem, J. Erikssen, and A. Fretland. 1977. High density lipoproteins (HDL) and physical activity: The influence of physical exercise age and smoking on HDL-cholesterol and the HDL-1 total cholesterol ratio. *Scand J Clin Lab Invest,* 37, 251-255.

Fredrichs, R., S. R. Srinivasan, L. S. Webber, and G. Berenson. 1976. Serum cholesterol and triglyceride levels in 3,466 children from a biracial community. The Bogalusa Heart Study. *Circulation,* 54, 302-309.

Friedman, G. 1972. A pediatrician looks at risk factors in atherosclerotic heart disease. *Clin Res,* 20, 250-252.

Gilliam, T. B., V. L. Katch, W. G. Thorland, and A. L. Weltman. 1977. Prevalance of coronary heart disease risk factors in active children, 7 to 12 years of age. *Med Sci Spts,* 9, 21-25.

Gilliam, T. B., W. G. Thorland, S. Sady, and A. L. Weltman. 1978. Blood lipids and fatness in children, ages 7-13. *Canad J Appl Spts Sci,* In Press.

Glueck, C. J., R. W. Fallat, and R. Tsang. 1975. A pediatric approach to atherosclerosis prevention. In *Childhood Obesity,* M. Winick (ed.). New York: John Wiley.

Glueck, C. J., M. J. Mellies, L. Srivastava, P. H. C. Knowles, R. W. Fallat, R. C. Tsang, S. Wacholder, and R. Buncher. 1977. Insulin, obesity and triglyceride interrelationships in sixteen children with familial hypertriglyceridemia. *Pediatr Res,* 11, 13-18.

Gordon, T., W. P. Castelli, N. C. Hjortland, W. B. Kannel, and T. R. Dawber. 1977. HDL factor against coronary heart disease: The Framingham Study. *Amer J Med,* 62, 707-714.

Hennekens, A., J. J. Jesse, B. E. Klein, J. E. Gourley, and S. Blumenthal. 1976. Cholesterol among children of men with myocardial infarction. *Pediatr,* 58, 211-217.

Holloszy, J. O., J. S. Skinner, G. Toro, and T. K. Cureton. 1964. Effects of six-month program of endurance exercise on the serum lipids of middle-aged men. *Amer J Cardiol,* 14, 753-760.

Jackson, R. L., J. D. Morrisett, and A. M. Gotts. 1976. Lipoprotein structure and metabolism. *Physiol Rev,* 56, 259-316.

Kannel, W. B. 1970. Physical exercise and lethal atherosclerotic disease. *N Eng J Med,* 282, 1153-1154.

Keys, A. 1972. Coronary heart disease: Overweight and obesity as risk factors. *Ann Intern Med,* 77, 15-27.

Knittle, J. L. 1975. Basic concepts in the control of childhood obesity, In *Childhood Obesity,* M. Winick (ed.). New York: John Wiley.

Lauer, R. M., W. Conner, P. Leaverton, M. Reiter, and W. Clarke. 1975. Coronary heart disease factors in school children: The Muscatine study. *J Pediatr,* 86, 697-706.

Leon, A. S., J. Conrad, D. Hunninghake, D. Jacobs, and R. Serfass. 1977. Exercise effects on body composition, work capacity and carbohydrate and lipid metabolism of young obese men. *Med Sci Spts,* 9, 60.

Levy, R. I. and D. S. Fredrickson. 1968. Diagnosis and management of hyperlipoproteinemia. *Am J Cardiol,* 22, 576-583.

Levy, R. I. and B. M. Rifkind. 1973. Diagnosis and management of hyperlipidproteinemia in children. *American Journal of Cardiology,* 31, 547-556.

Lopez, S. A., R. Vial, L. Balart, and G. Arroyave. 1974. Effects of exercise and physical fitness on serum lipids and lipoproteins. *Atherosclerosis,* 20, 1-9.

Mayer, J. 1975. Obesity during childhood. In *Childhood Obesity,* M. Winick (ed.). New York: John Wiley.

Miller, G. J. and N. E. Miller. 1975. Plasma high density lipoprotein concentration and development of ischaemic heart disease. *Lancet,* 1, 16-19.

Montoye, H. J., W. D. Bloc, H. L. Metzner, and J. B. Keller. 1976. Habitual physical activity and serum lipids: Males, ages 16-64 in a total community. *J Chron Dis,* 29, 697-709.

National Heart, Lung and Blood Institutes Task Force on Blood Pressure Control in Children. 1977. Report of the Task Force on blood pressure control in children. *Pediatr,* 59, Suppl.

Oscai, L. B. 1973. The role of exercise in weight control. In *Exercise and Sport Sciences Reviews.* J. H. Wilmore (ed.). Vol. 1. New York: Academic Press.

Parizkova, J. 1963. Impact of age, diet, and exercise on man's body composition. *Ann NY Acad Sci,* 110, 661-674.

Pollock, M. L. 1973. The quantification of endurance training programs. In *Exercise and Sport Science Reviews,* J. H. Wilmore (ed.). Vol. 1. New York: Academic Press.

Wilmore, J. H. and J. J. McNamara. 1974. Prevalence of coronary heart disease risk factors in boys, 8 to 12 years of age. *J Pediatr,* 84, 527-533.

47

Fitness Programs for the Overweight Child: A Suggested Approach

Robert P. Pangrazi

Physical educators have often placed their time and interest into helping the gifted and telented youngster while seemingly avoiding those children who are less fortunate. Those who are less able often include the obese child who not only experiences considerable psychological stress as a result of being over-weight, but seldom experiences success in any aspect of the typical physical education program. Programs have been developed for those youngsters who are subpar in strength, however, and have been quite successful in enhancing strength levels (Clarke 1976). Even though Rarick and Dobbins (1975) have identified strength as an important factor in learning motor skills, they qualify it in terms of body size. In other words, the obese child may be quite strong as compared to the normal weight youngster, but would not show a high strength to body weight ratio.

The purpose of this paper is to offer a brief review of past programs dealing with overweight or obesity in youngsters, followed by a step-by-step approach to treating individual cases. Inasmuch as a significant number of the problems affecting youngsters in physical education are caused by excessive body weight or related problems, it is important to deal with this area in a systematic fashion. This author believes that programs for the overweight child have been avoided because of the low success ratio and because it is an extremely complex problem. In a society that rewards physical attractiveness so heavily, it seems almost unpardonable not to make an effort for those students in need.

It has been well documented that America is an overweight society. Studies show that anywhere from 10 to 20 percent of our citizenry are overweight or obese depending on the criteria used (Corbin 1969). For example, Mayer (1966) reported that 16 percent of the American population under 30 years old was obese. Along with this widespread belief has grown a myth that children will grow out of the baby fat stage, most likely during adolescence.

There is good evidence that youngsters who are obese will become even more obese during adulthood.There is a high percentage of obese youngsters, and the number appears to have increased since the 1950s. A similar belief has been held that youngsters become more lean as they grow older and mature. However, Johnson, Burke, and Mayer (1956) found that for both boys and girls obesity prevalence rates were highest at the periods of greatest growth and immediately thereafter. This finding tends to indicate that rather than "grow out of" obesity, one tends to "grow into" obesity to a greater degree. Corbin (1969) also reported that the percentage of body fat in youngsters increases with age, and girls usually possess more fat than boys at all ages.

Approaches for helping low-fit and obese children have taken many directions. The majority of early efforts were directed at diet primarily in the form of restrictions and reduced intakes. As stated by Prugh (1961, p. 538), "After much initial enthusiasm, dietary methods seem to be of much less help today than had been hoped by many clinicians." Dealing with diet is an extremely complex problem and involves changing the eating habits of not only the obese youngster, but parents of the child. Nutritional approaches are usually out of the realm of the physical educator as the majority have only a minimal, if any, training in the area.

Another reason for not relying on the area of nutrition and diet control lies in the fact that in the majority of cases, the obese child neither eats more nor consumes a substantially different diet from that of normal-weight youngsters. As was pointed out by Gilliam and Katch in preceding chapter, Mayer (1961) has found that obese children's diets are similar in composition to normal weight youngsters and less in total caloric intake in many instances. Therefore, it would appear that the primary factor in controlling body weight is not in changing and/or restricting the diet of the obese child.

Counseling and dealing with the child's self-concept have also been used as approaches in dealing with childhood obesity. It is quite obvious, however, that counseling without any changes in the child's life-style would be ineffective. Bruch's (Prugh 1961) longitudinal studies indicate that diet control along with recommended exercise offers little promise in the treatment of the developmentally obese child who has associated serious emotional disturbances. In fact, Prugh (1961) concluded that the goal of the counseling approach may be only to produce a more happily adjusted and independently functioning obese child.

Seltzer and Mayer (1970) developed an effective weight control program in a public school system using dietary education, psychological support, and increased physical exercise. Rather than using a great deal of counseling, an area in which many physical educators lack expertise, the researchers offered psychological support based on encouragement and motivation from a wide variety of sources (members of the school staff, etc.). This sort of approach again appears to be possible in the school setting and identifies with the capabilities of the school personnel.

Of the three major variables—diet, counseling, and activity—increasing the activity level of the obese individual appears to be the most effective in aiding the control of obesity. Rather than caloric restriction, various studies revealed that inactivity among obese youngsters may be the factor that determines how effective a person will be in weight control efforts. Johnson, Burke, and Mayer (1956) noted a tendency for youngsters to gain excess weight, in proportion to height, during the autumn and winter as compared with spring and summer. This observation was used to support the theory that activity levels are decreased in the winter months, thereby contributing to an increase in body weight.

Bullen, Reed, and Mayer (1961) filmed adolescent girls participating in camp activities consisting of swimming, tennis, and volleyball. One group of girls was normal weight and a second group, obese. The motion pictures were later analyzed to measure the amount of activity each group demonstrated. Activity was classified as other than lying, standing, or sitting. When the two groups were compared, the obese group was two and a half times less active in swimming and tennis, and one and a half times less active in volleyball as compared to the nonobese group. The researchers concluded that inactivity is a significant factor in perpetuating obesity.

Corbin and Pletcher (1968) conducted a similar study in which they analyzed diet and activity patterns of obese and nonobese elementary school boys and girls. They found similar patterns of inactivity, as did Bullen and her associates (1964), and concluded "that inactivity may be as important or more important than excessive caloric intake in the development and maintenance of childhood obesity" (Corbin and Pletcher 1968, p. 922). The authors also found similar diets among all children regardless of body fat proportions.

Mayer (1961) hypothesized that exercise has been avoided for some time as a deterrent to obesity due to two misconceptions. One fallacy is that exercise consumes but a small amount of energy and thus is a waste of time. He wrote:

> This is obviously absurd. We all know you can triple the energy expenditure of human beings by exercising them vigorously enough. Just to give some examples of energy expenditure: an hour of walking is worth 300 to 400 calories in an adult. Swimming vigorously or playing tennis is worth about 700 calories per hour (Mayer 1961, p, 535).

The second misconception advanced to justify neglecting exercise is the idea that "if you exercise more, you eat more, and therefore the whole process is self-defeating." Mayer has found this is not true at low levels of energy expenditure. In fact, at vary minimal levels of activity, there may actually be a slight decrease in caloric intake as one goes from an extremely sedentary to a more active state. No appreciable increase in caloric intake is observed until one reaches a "normal" range of activity—about one hour per day.

Sharkey (1978) also concluded that exercise is effective in weight control. He reported that 30 minutes of vigorous and demanding activity will not only burn more calories during exercise, but will double caloric expenditure for six hours following the exercise period. This phenomenon is commonly referred to as the "metabolic after-effects" of exercise.

Based upon the preceding findings, a sound physical education program for the obese child should be focused on increasing the obese child's activity level. Such a program should be of high quality for a few individuals and administered and taught by the physical education specialist. In most cases, the amount of time that the specialist can realistically devote to low fitness instruction is limited and thus another reason for the limited number of participants. Another aspect to the program differing from other approaches is that youngsters will be selected on the basis of their opportunity for success. In too many cases, teachers select those youngsters who are the most obese, have the least interest in activity, and have parents who do not want to involve themselves in working to control the child's obesity. In such situations, it seems apparent that there is little chance for success, and parents, teachers, and students will all be disappointed by the continued failure. The approach here is to gather as much data as possible about the obese youngster and then assess the child's chance of success for losing weight.

Those students who appear to have a lesser chance for success should not be ignored, but referred to other more qualified personnel. As mentioned earlier, the physical education specialist has limited time and training in the area of nutrition and counseling of obese youngsters and will likely be more effective in dealing with less serious cases.

The following is a step-by-step approach to developing a program to aid the obese individual within the school system:

INITIAL SCREENING OF LOW-FIT INDIVIDUALS

1. *Informative letter of classroom teachers.* A letter should be sent to all classroom teachers explaining the approach that will be used for the operation of the low-fit program. Along with the letter, there should be a referral form so that the teacher can make a written referral of those students judged to be in need of treatment. The letter should inform the teachers of the following points:
   a. Some class time will be utilized for treatment of the obese youngster. The time will be kept to a minimum but will be necessary so that there is additional time given to physical education.
   b. Teachers will refer students that appear to need aid in treating obesity. Teachers should be encouraged to refer borderline cases as well as the obviously obese youngsters.
   c. Teachers should be made aware of the criteria that will be used in selecting students for treatment. Simply stated, students will be selected according to their apparent chance for success. This is important as many teachers and administrators will want to know why one youngster was selected over another or why a more obese student was not selected.

2. *Visual inspection.* Usually, it is quite obvious which students are obese. The classroom teacher can be of aid in identifying and listing those youngsters and then referring them to the physical education specialist. In most cases, if a youngster looks obese, he or she is.

3. *Communication with classroom teachers.* The physical education specialist should then sit down and talk with the classroom teachers the youngsters identified in steps one and two. Factors to discuss should include: (a) the student's awareness of his or her level of obesity; (b) the student's level of confidence; (c) the teacher's feeling about releasing the youngster from certain classroom activities; (d) the probability of the student's parents helping in the program; (e) the student's maturity level and ability to achieve personal goals; and (f) the student's feelings about physical education and the physical education specialist.

4. *Communication with low-fit candidates.* Following the discussions with the classroom teachers, the youngsters identified as potential candidates for the program should be contacted for a conference with the specialist. During the conference, the major point of understanding should be whether the student really wants to be part of the low-fit program. If the youngster feels that body fat is not a problem, the specialist should eliminate him or her from further consideration. The youngster should not be coerced into participating in the program.

   During the conferences with the student and classroom teacher, the specialist should make an anecdotal record of each case. Various points to consider might be some of the following (a) Is the student involved in other significant programs at school? It might not be feasible to take this youngster out of the classroom because other important demands are being made on his or her time. (b) Is the student genuinely interested in losing body weight or is this primarily an opportunity to escape from the classroom or receive special attention from another teacher? (c) Has the individual dealt with overweight problems prior to this referral? If the student has been involved in other weight control programs, it might be wise to inquire into the type of program, the approach used, and the duration of the effort. (d) Are the personalities of the specialist and the youngster compatible? In some cases, teachers have a difficult time feeling empathetic toward a youngster due to personality conflicts. If so, the youngster might receive more negative than positive feedback from participating in the program. The specialist has to genuinely want to help the youngster achieve success. (e) Does the specialist feel capable of helping the candidate reach desired goals? One must have an optimistic outlook before starting the program rather than waiting to see if progress is made and then offering affection and concern.

5. *Selection of youngsters for tentative inclusion in the program.* At this point, the anecdotal records developed and the comments received from other

teachers should be used to identify six to eight youngsters capable of finding success in the low-fit program. The students selected will be further tested and screened before they are enrolled in the program. A great deal of weight is often gained during preadolescence; thus it appears that the fourth through sixth grade years may be the most feasible time to deal with the problem of obesity. The longer one waits to deal with the problem, the more difficult it becomes to change life-styles. Conversely, if one elects to work with primary age children (five to eight years of age), there is usually not a great deal of personal motivation on the youngster's part to deal with the problem. Therefore, it is suggested that the pre-adolescent child be selected for the program.

The small number of recommended candidates reflects the philosophy of the program. It is a difficult and time-consuming task to work with the low-fit student, and it is usually prudent not to select too many students until one has definite knowledge concerning the extent of work and effort the program will demand.

EVALUATION AND SELECTION OF LOW-FITNESS CANDIDATES

Certain data should be collected to aid in making a meaningful appraisal of the candidate to see if the specialist can be of value to the youngster in reducing the amount of body fat.

1. The following areas should be evaluated and data gathered for developing a "success profile" on each candidate.
    a. *Height and weight.* The child should be accurately weighed and measured and the data recorded. Height and weight charts can be used to find the percentile ranking of the student in terms of physical growth. These data will also serve as a baseline for later comparison.
    b. *Skinfold measurements.* Two skinfold measurements should be taken, one on the back of the arm halfway between the acromion and olecranon (triceps) and the second on the back underneath the angle of the scapula (subscapular). Both measurements should be made on the right side of the body for consistency (Seltzer and Mayer 1965). The measurements should then be located on the percent body. fat chart (see Table 47.1) to find an estimation of the percent of body fat the child possesses. A cutoff point should then be decided upon as a determination of obesity—such as in excess of 20 percent (Seltzer and Mayer 1965).
    c. *Attitude toward physical activity.* The CATPA Attitude Inventory (Simon and Smoll 1974) should be administered to diagnose whether the student has a positive feeling about physical activity. A low score in comparison to other low-fit students may indicate that the youngster will be more difficult to treat due to low interest in physical activity.

Table 47.1A Percent Body Fat for Male Elementary School Children

SUBSCAPULAR SKINFOLD (MM)

	3	4	5	6	7	8	9	10	11	12	13	14	15	16	17	18
3	0.9	10.7	12.1	13.2	14.2	15.0	15.7	16.4	17.0	17.6	18.1	18.5	19.0	19.4	19.8	20.2
4	10.1	11.9	13.3	14.4	15.4	16.3	17.0	17.7	18.3	18.8	19.4	19.8	20.3	20.7	21.1	21.5
5	11.1	12.9	14.3	15.4	16.4	17.2	18.0	18.7	19.3	19.8	20.4	20.8	21.3	21.7	22.1	22.5
6	11.9	13.7	15.1	16.2	17.2	18.1	18.8	19.5	20.1	20.7	21.2	21.7	22.1	22.5	22.9	23.3
7	12.5	14.3	15.7	16.9	17.9	18.7	19.5	20.2	20.8	21.4	21.9	22.4	22.8	23.2	23.6	24.0
8	13.1	14.9	16.3	17.5	18.5	19.3	20.1	20.8	21.4	22.0	22.5	23.0	23.4	23.9	24.3	24.6
9	13.6	15.4	16.9	18.0	19.0	19.9	20.6	21.3	21.9	22.5	23.0	23.5	24.0	24.4	24.8	25.2
10	14.1	15.9	17.3	18.5	19.5	20.3	21.1	21.8	22.4	23.0	23.5	24.0	24.4	24.9	25.3	25.7
11	14.5	16.3	17.7	18.9	19.9	20.8	21.5	22.2	22.8	23.4	23.9	24.4	24.9	25.3	25.7	26.1
12	14.9	16.7	18.1	19.3	20.3	21.2	21.9	22.6	23.2	23.8	24.3	24.6	25.3	25.7	26.1	26.5
13	15.2	17.1	18.5	19.7	20.7	21.5	22.3	23.0	23.6	24.2	24.7	25.2	25.7	26.1	26.5	26.9
14	15.6	17.4	18.8	30.0	32.0	21.9	22.6	23.3	23.9	24.5	25.1	25.5	26.0	26.4	26.8	27.2
15	15.9	17.7	19.1	20.3	21.3	22.2	22.9	23.6	24.3	24.8	25.4	25.9	26.3	26.8	27.2	27.5
16	16.2	18.0	19.4	20.6	21.6	22.5	23.2	23.9	24.6	25.1	25.7	26.2	26.6	27.1	27.5	27.8
17	16.4	18.3	19.7	20.4	21.9	22.7	23.5	24.2	24.8	25.4	25.9	26.4	26.9	27.3	27.7	28.1
18	16.7	18.5	19.9	21.1	22.1	23.0	23.8	24.5	25.1	25.7	26.2	26.7	27.2	27.6	28.0	28.4
19	16.9	18.8	20.2	21.4	22.4	23.3	24.0	24.7	25.4	25.9	26.5	27.0	27.4	27.9	28.3	28.6
20	17.1	19.0	20.4	21.6	22.6	23.5	24.3	25.0	25.6	26.2	26.7	27.2	27.7	28.1	28.5	28.9
21	17.4	19.2	20.6	21.8	22.8	23.7	24.5	25.2	25.8	26.4	26.9	27.4	27.9	28.3	28.7	29.1
22	17.6	19.4	20.9	22.0	23.0	23.9	24.7	25.4	26.0	26.6	27.1	27.6	28.1	28.5	28.9	29.3
23	17.8	19.6	21.1	22.2	23.2	24.1	24.9	25.6	26.2	26.8	27.4	27.8	28.3	28.7	29.2	29.5
24	18.0	19.8	21.2	22.4	23.4	24.3	25.1	25.8	26.4	27.0	27.6	28.0	28.5	28.9	29.4	29.7
25	18.1	20.0	21.4	22.6	23.6	24.5	25.3	26.0	26.6	27.2	27.7	28.2	28.7	29.1	29.6	29.9
26	18.3	20.2	21.6	22.8	23.8	24.7	25.5	26.2	26.8	27.4	27.9	28.4	28.9	29.3	29.7	30.1
27	18.5	20.3	21.8	23.0	24.0	24.9	25.6	26.3	27.0	27.6	28.1	28.6	29.1	29.5	29.9	30.3
28	18.6	20.5	21.9	23.1	24.1	25.0	25.8	26.5	27.2	27.7	28.3	28.8	29.2	29.7	30.1	30.5
29	18.8	20.6	22.1	23.3	24.3	25.2	26.0	26.7	27.3	27.9	28.4	28.9	29.4	29.8	30.3	30.6
30	18.9	20.8	22.3	23.4	24.5	25.3	26.1	26.8	27.5	28.1	28.6	29.1	29.6	30.0	30.4	30.8

TRICEP SKINFOLD (MM)

SUBSCAPULAR SKINFOLD (MM) - CONTINUED

	19	20	21	22	23	24	25	26	27	28	29	30	31	32	33	34
3	20.5	20.8	21.2	21.5	21.8	22.0	22.3	22.6	22.8	23.0	23.3	23.5	23.7	23.9	24.1	24.3
4	21.8	22.2	22.5	22.8	23.1	23.3	23.6	23.9	24.1	24.4	24.6	24.8	25.0	25.2	25.4	25.6
5	22.8	23.2	23.5	23.8	24.1	24.4	24.6	24.9	25.1	25.4	25.6	25.8	26.1	26.3	26.5	26.7
6	23.7	24.0	24.3	24.6	24.9	25.2	25.5	25.7	26.0	26.2	26.5	26.7	26.9	27.1	27.3	27.5
7	24.4	24.7	25.0	25.3	25.6	25.9	26.2	26.5	26.7	26.9	27.2	27.4	27.6	27.8	28.0	28.2
8	25.0	25.3	25.6	26.0	26.3	26.5	26.8	27.1	27.3	27.6	27.8	28.0	28.3	28.5	28.7	28.9
9	25.5	25.9	26.2	26.5	26.8	27.1	27.4	27.6	27.9	28.1	28.4	28.6	28.8	29.0	2.92	29.4
10	26.0	26.4	26.7	27.0	27.3	27.6	27.9	28.1	28.4	28.6	28.9	29.1	29.3	29.5	29.7	29.9
11	26.5	26.8	27.1	27.4	27.7	28.0	28.3	28.6	28.6	29.1	29.3	29.5	29.7	30.0	30.2	30.4
12	26.9	27.2	27.5	27.8	28.1	28.4	28.7	29.0	29.2	29.5	29.7	29.9	30.2	30.4	30.6	30.8
13	27.2	27.6	27.9	28.2	28.5	28.8	29.1	29.3	29.6	29.8	30.1	30.3	30.5	30.8	31.0	31.2
14	27.6	27.9	28.3	28.6	28.9	29.2	29.4	29.7	30.0	30.2	30.4	30.7	30.9	31.1	31.3	31.5
15	27.9	28.2	28.6	28.9	29.2	29.5	29.8	30.0	30.3	30.5	30.6	31.0	31.2	31.4	31.6	31.8
16	28.2	28.6	28.9	29.2	29.5	29.8	30.1	30.3	30.6	30.8	31.1	31.3	31.5	31.7	32.0	32.2

TRICEP SKINFOLD (MM)

Table 47.1A (cont.)

SUBSCAPULAR SKINFOLD (MM) - CONTINUED

TRICEP SKINFOLD (MM)

	19	20	21	22	23	24	25	26	27	28	29	30	31	32	33	34
17	28.5	28.8	29.2	29.5	29.8	30.1	30.3	30.6	30.9	31.1	31.4	31.6	31.8	32.0	32.2	32.4
18	28.8	29.1	29.4	29.7	30.0	30.3	30.6	30.9	31.1	31.4	31.6	31.9	32.1	32.3	32.5	32.7
19	29.0	29.4	29.7	30.0	30.3	30.6	30.9	31.3	31.4	31.6	31.9	32.1	32.3	32.6	32.8	33.0
20	29.3	29.6	29.9	30.2	30.5	30.8	31.1	31.4	31.6	31.9	32.1	32.4	32.6	32.8	33.0	33.2
21	29.5	29.8	30.2	30.5	30.8	31.1	31.3	31.6	31.9	32.1	32.4	32.6	32.8	33.0	33.3	33.5
22	29.7	30.0	30.4	30.7	31.0	31.3	31.6	31.8	32.1	32.3	32.6	32.8	33.0	33.3	33.5	33.7
23	29.9	30.3	30.6	30.9	31.2	31.5	31.8	32.0	32.3	32.6	32.8	33.0	33.3	33.5	33.7	33.9
24	30.1	30.5	30.8	31.1	31.4	31.7	32.0	32.3	32.5	32.8	33.0	33.2	33.5	33.7	33.9	34.1
25	30.3	30.7	31.0	31.3	31.6	31.9	32.2	32.4	32.7	33.0	33.2	33.4	33.7	33.9	34.1	34.3
26	30.5	30.8	31.2	31.5	31.8	32.1	32.4	32.6	32.9	33.1	33.4	33.6	33.8	34.1	34.3	34.5
27	30.7	31.0	31.4	31.7	32.0	32.3	32.5	32.8	33.1	33.3	33.6	33.8	34.0	34.2	34.5	34.7
28	30.8	31.2	31.5	31.8	32.4	32.7	33.0	33.2	33.4	33.7	34.0	34.2	34.4	34.6	34.8	
29	31.0	31.4	31.7	32.0	32.3	32.6	32.9	33.2	33.4	33.7	33.9	34.1	34.4	34.6	34.8	35.0
30	31.2	31.5	31.9	32.2	32.5	32.8	33.0	33.3	33.6	33.8	34.1	34.3	34.5	34.8	35.0	35.2

SUBSCAPULAR SKINFOLD (MM) - CONTINUED

TRICEP SKINFOLD (MM)

	35	36	37	38	39	40	41	42	43	44	45	46	47	48	49	50
3	24.5	24.7	24.9	25.1	25.2	25.4	25.6	25.7	25.9	26.0	26.2	26.3	26.5	26.6	26.7	26.9
4	25.8	26.0	26.2	62.4	26.6	26.7	26.9	27.1	27.2	27.4	27.5	27.7	27.8	27.9	28.1	28.2
5	26.9	27.1	27.2	27.4	27.6	27.8	27.9	28.1	28.3	28.4	28.6	28.7	28.9	29.0	29.1	29.3
6	27.7	27.9	28.1	28.3	28.5	28.6	28.8	29.0	29.1	29.3	29.4	29.6	29.7	29.9	30.0	30.1
7	28.4	28.6	28.8	29.0	29.2	29.3	29.5	29.7	29.8	30.0	30.1	30.3	30.4	30.6	30.7	30.9
8	29.1	29.3	29.4	29.6	29.8	30.0	30.1	30.3	30.5	30.6	30.8	30.9	31.1	31.2	31.4	31.5
9	29.6	29.8	30.0	30.2	30.4	30.5	30.7	30.8	31.0	31.2	31.3	31.5	31.6	31.8	31.9	32.1
10	30.1	30.3	30.5	30.7	30.9	31.0	31.2	31.4	31.5	31.7	31.8	32.0	32.1	32.3	32.4	32.6
11	30.6	30.8	31.0	31.1	31.3	31.5	31.7	31.8	32.0	32.1	32.3	32.4	32.6	32.7	32.9	33.0
12	31.0	31.2	31.4	31.5	31.7	31.9	32.1	32.2	32.4	32.6	32.7	32.9	33.0	33.2	33.3	33.4
13	31.4	31.6	31.7	31.9	32.1	32.3	32.4	32.6	32.8	32.9	33.1	33.2	33.4	33.5	33.7	33.8
14	31.7	31.9	32.1	32.3	32.5	32.6	32.8	33.0	33.1	33.3	33.4	33.6	33.7	33.9	34.0	34.2
15	32.0	32.2	32.4	32.6	32.8	33.0	33.1	33.3	33.5	33.6	33.8	33.9	34.1	34.2	34.4	34.5
16	32.4	32.5	32.7	32.9	33.1	33.3	33.4	33.6	33.8	33.9	34.1	34.2	34.4	34.5	34.7	34.8
17	32.6	32.8	33.0	33.2	33.4	33.6	33.7	33.9	34.1	34.2	34.4	34.5	34.7	34.8	35.0	35.1
18	32.9	33.1	33.3	33.5	33.7	33.8	34.0	34.2	34.3	34.5	34.7	34.8	35.0	35.1	35.2	35.4
19	33.2	33.4	33.6	33.7	33.9	34.1	34.3	34.4	34.6	34.8	34.9	35.1	35.2	35.4	35.5	35.7
20	33.4	33.6	33.8	34.0	34.2	34.3	34.5	34.7	34.8	35.0	35.2	35.3	35.5	35.6	35.8	35.9
21	33.7	33.9	34.0	34.2	34.4	34.6	34.8	34.9	35.1	35.2	35.4	35.6	35.7	35.9	36.0	36.1
22	33.9	34.1	34.3	34.5	34.6	34.8	35.0	35.1	35.3	35.5	35.6	35.8	35.9	36.1	36.2	36.4
23	34.1	34.3	34.5	34.7	34.8	35.0	35.2	35.4	35.5	35.7	35.8	36.0	36.1	36.3	36.4	36.6
24	34.3	34.5	34.7	34.9	35.1	35.2	35.4	35.6	35.7	35.9	36.0	36.2	36.4	36.5	36.6	36.8
25	34.5	34.7	34.9	35.1	35.3	35.4	35.6	35.8	35.9	36.1	36.2	36.4	36.6	36.7	36.8	37.0
26	34.7	34.9	35.1	35.3	35.4	35.6	35.8	36.0	36.1	36.3	36.4	36.6	36.7	36.9	37.0	37.2
27	34.9	35.1	35.3	35.4	35.6	35.8	36.0	36.1	36.3	36.5	36.6	36.8	36.9	37.1	37.2	37.4
28	35.0	35.2	35.4	35.6	35.8	36.0	36.1	36.3	36.5	36.6	36.8	37.0	37.1	37.3	37.4	37.5
29	35.2	35.4	35.6	35.8	36.0	36.1	36.3	36.5	36.7	36.8	37.0	37.1	37.3	37.4	37.6	37.7
30	35.4	35.6	35.8	36.0	36.1	36.3	36.5	36.7	36.8	37.0	37.1	37.3	37.4	37.6	37.7	37.9

Table 47.1B Percent Body Fat for Female Elementary School Children

SUBSCAPULAR SKINFOLD (MM)

TRICEP SKINFOLD (MM)

	3	4	5	6	7	8	9	10	11	12	13	14	15	16	17	18
3	13.5	15.2	16.5	17.5	18.5	19.2	20.0	20.6	21.2	21.7	22.2	22.6	23.0	23.4	23.8	24.2
4	14.1	15.8	17.1	18.2	19.1	19.9	20.6	21.3	21.8	22.4	22.8	23.3	23.7	24.1	24.5	24.8
5	14.6	16.3	17.6	18.7	19.6	20.4	21.1	21.8	22.4	22.9	23.4	23.8	24.3	24.6	25.0	25.4
6	15.0	16.7	18.1	19.1	20.1	20.9	21.6	22.2	22.8	23.3	23.8	24.3	24.7	25.1	25.5	25.8
7	15.4	17.1	18.4	19.5	20.4	21.2	21.9	22.6	23.2	23.7	24.2	24.6	25.1	25.5	25.8	26.2
8	15.7	17.4	18.7	19.8	20.7	21.5	22.3	22.9	23.5	24.0	24.5	24.9	25.4	25.8	26.1	26.5
9	16.0	17.7	19.0	20.1	21.0	21.8	22.5	23.2	23.8	24.3	24.8	25.2	25.7	26.1	26.4	26.8
10	16.2	17.9	19.2	20.3	21.3	22.1	22.8	23.4	24.0	24.5	25.0	25.5	25.9	26.3	26.7	27.0
11	16.4	18.1	19.5	20.6	21.5	22.3	23.0	23.6	24.2	24.8	25.3	25.7	26.1	26.5	26.9	27.3
12	16.6	18.3	19.7	20.8	21.7	22.5	23.2	23.9	24.4	25.0	25.5	25.9	26.3	26.7	27.1	27.5
13	16.8	18.5	19.8	20.9	21.9	22.7	23.4	24.0	24.6	25.2	25.7	26.1	26.5	26.9	27.3	27.7
14	17.0	18.7	20.0	21.1	22.0	22.9	23.6	24.2	24.8	25.3	25.8	26.3	26.7	27.1	27.5	27.8
15	17.1	18.8	20.2	21.3	22.2	23.0	23.7	24.4	25.0	25.5	26.0	26.5	26.9	27.3	27.7	28.0
16	17.3	19.0	20.3	21.3	22.3	23.2	23.9	24.5	25.1	25.7	26.2	26.6	27.0	27.4	27.8	28.2
17	17.4	19.1	20.5	21.6	22.5	23.3	24.0	24.7	25.3	25.8	26.3	26.8	27.2	27.6	28.0	28.3
18	17.6	19.3	10.6	21.7	22.6	23.5	24.2	24.8	25.4	25.9	26.4	26.9	27.2	27.7	28.1	28.5
19	17.7	19.4	20.7	21.8	22.8	23.6	24.3	24.9	25.5	26.1	26.6	27.0	27.4	27.9	28.2	28.6
20	17.8	19.5	20.9	22.0	22.9	23.7	24.4	25.1	25.7	26.2	26.7	27.1	27.6	28.0	28.4	28.7
21	17.9	19.6	21.0	22.1	23.0	23.8	24.5	25.2	25.8	26.3	26.8	27.2	27.7	28.1	28.5	28.8
22	18.0	19.7	21.1	22.2	23.1	23.9	24.7	25.3	25.9	26.4	26.9	27.4	27.8	28.2	28.6	28.9
23	18.1	19.8	21.2	22.3	23.2	24.0	24.8	25.4	26.0	26.5	27.0	27.5	27.9	28.3	28.7	29.1
24	18.2	19.9	21.3	22.3	23.3	24.1	24.9	25.5	26.1	26.6	27.1	27.6	28.0	28.4	28.8	29.2
25	18.3	20.0	21.4	22.5	23.4	24.2	25.0	25.6	26.2	26.7	27.2	27.7	28.1	28.5	28.9	29.3
26	18.4	20.1	21.5	22.6	23.5	24.3	25.1	25.7	26.3	26.8	27.3	27.8	28.2	28.6	29.0	29.4
27	18.5	20.2	21.6	22.7	23.6	24.4	25.1	25.8	26.4	26.9	27.4	27.9	28.3	28.7	29.1	29.4
28	18.6	20.3	21.6	22.7	23.7	24.5	25.2	25.9	26.5	27.0	27.5	28.0	28.4	28.8	29.2	29.5
29	18.7	20.4	21.7	22.8	23.8	24.6	25.3	26.0	26.5	27.1	27.6	28.0	28.5	28.9	29.3	29.6
30	18.7	20.5	21.8	22.9	23.9	24.7	25.4	26.0	26.6	27.2	27.7	28.1	28.6	29.0	29.3	29.7

SUBSCAPULAR SKINFOLD (MM) - CONTINUED

TRICEP SKINFOLD (MM)

	19	20	21	22	23	24	25	26	27	28	29	30	31	32	33	34
3	24.5	24.8	25.1	25.4	25.7	25.9	26.2	26.4	26.6	26.9	27.1	27.3	27.5	27.7	27.9	28.1
4	25.2	25.5	25.8	26.1	26.3	26.6	26.9	27.1	27.3	27.6	27.8	28.0	28.2	28.4	28.6	28.8
5	25.7	26.0	26.3	26.6	26.9	27.1	27.4	27.6	27.9	28.1	28.3	28.5	28.7	28.9	29.1	29.3
6	26.1	26.5	26.8	27.0	27.3	27.6	27.8	28.1	28.3	28.6	28.8	29.0	29.2	29.4	29.6	29.8
7	26.5	26.8	27.1	27.4	27.7	28.0	28.2	28.5	28.7	28.9	29.1	29.4	29.6	29.8	30.0	30.1
8	26.8	27.2	27.5	27.7	28.0	28.3	28.5	28.8	29.0	29.3	29.5	29.7	29.9	30.1	30.3	30.5
9	27.1	27.4	27.7	28.0	28.3	28.6	28.8	29.1	29.3	29.5	29.8	30.0	30.2	30.4	30.6	30.8
10	27.4	27.7	28.0	28.3	28.6	28.8	29.1	29.3	29.6	29.8	30.0	30.2	30.4	20.6	20.8	31.0
11	27.6	27.9	28.2	28.5	28.8	29.1	29.3	29.6	29.8	30.0	30.3	30.5	30.7	30.9	31.1	31.3
12	27.8	28.1	28.4	28.7	29.0	29.3	29.5	29.8	30.0	30.2	30.5	30.7	30.9	31.1	31.3	31.5
13	28.0	28.3	28.6	28.9	29.2	29.5	29.7	30.0	30.2	30.4	30.7	30.9	31.1	31.3	13.5	31.7
14	28.2	28.5	28.8	29.1	29.4	29.6	29.9	30.2	30.4	30.6	30.8	31.1	31.3	31.5	31.7	31.9
15	28.4	28.7	29.0	29.3	29.6	29.8	30.1	30.3	30.6	30.8	31.0	31.2	31.4	31.6	31.8	32.0
16	28.5	28.8	29.1	29.4	29.7	30.0	30.2	30.5	30.7	30.9	31.2	31.4	31.6	31.8	32.0	32.2

Table 47.1B (cont.)

SUBSCAPULAR SKINFOLD (MM) - CONTINUED

TRICEP SKINFOLD (MM)

	19	20	21	22	23	24	25	26	27	28	29	30	31	32	33	34
17	28.7	29.0	29.3	29.6	29.9	30.1	30.4	30.6	30.9	31.1	31.3	31.5	31.7	31.9	32.1	32.3
18	28.8	29.1	29.4	29.7	30.0	30.3	30.5	30.8	31.0	31.2	31.5	31.7	31.9	32.1	32.3	32.5
19	28.9	29.3	29.6	29.8	30.1	30.4	30.7	30.9	31.1	31.4	31.6	31.8	32.0	32.2	32.4	32.6
20	29.1	29.4	29.7	30.0	30.3	30.3	30.8	31.0	31.3	31.5	31.7	31.9	32.1	32.3	32.5	32.7
21	29.2	29.5	29.8	30.1	30.4	30.6	30.9	31.1	31.4	31.6	31.8	32.1	32.3	32.5	32.7	32.9
22	29.3	29.6	29.9	30.2	30.5	30.8	31.0	31.3	31.5	31.7	32.0	32.2	32.4	32.6	32.8	33.0
23	29.4	29.7	30.0	30.3	30.6	30.9	31.1	31.4	31.6	31.8	32.1	32.3	32.5	32.7	32.9	33.1
24	29.5	29.8	30.1	30.4	30.7	31.0	31.2	31.5	31.7	31.9	32.2	32.4	32.6	32.8	33.0	33.2
25	29.6	29.9	30.2	30.5	30.8	31.1	31.3	31.6	31.8	32.0	32.3	32.5	32.7	32.9	33.1	33.3
26	29.7	30.0	30.3	30.6	30.9	31.2	31.4	31.7	31.9	32.1	32.4	32.6	32.8	33.0	33.2	33.4
27	29.8	30.1	30.4	30.7	31.0	31.3	13.5	31.8	32.0	32.2	32.5	32.7	32.9	33.1	33.3	33.5
28	29.9	30.2	30.5	30.8	31.1	31.4	31.6	31.9	32.1	32.3	32.6	32.8	33.0	33.2	33.4	33.6
29	30.0	30.3	30.6	30.9	31.2	31.4	31.7	31.9	32.2	32.4	32.6	32.9	33.1	33.3	33.5	33.7
30	30.0	30.4	30.7	31.0	31.3	31.5	31.8	32.0	32.3	32.5	32.7	32.9	33.2	33.4	33.6	33.7

SUBSCAPULAR SKINFOLD (MM) - CONTINUED

TRICEP SKINFOLD (MM)

	35	36	37	38	39	40	41	42	43	44	45	46	47	48	49	50
3	28.3	28.4	28.6	28.8	28.9	29.1	29.3	29.4	29.5	29.7	29.8	30.0	30.1	30.2	30.4	30.5
4	29.0	29.1	29.3	29.5	29.6	29.8	30.0	30.1	30.3	30.4	30.5	30.7	30.8	30.9	31.1	31.2
5	29.5	29.7	29.9	30.0	30.2	30.3	30.5	30.7	30.8	30.9	31.1	31.2	31.4	31.5	31.6	31.8
6	30.0	30.1	30.3	30.5	30.6	30.8	30.9	31.1	31.2	31.4	31.5	31.7	31.8	31.9	32.1	32.2
7	30.3	30.5	30.7	30.8	31.0	31.2	31.3	31.5	31.6	31.8	31.9	32.1	32.2	32.3	32.5	32.6
8	30.7	30.8	31.0	31.2	31.3	31.5	31.7	31.8	32.0	32.1	32.2	32.4	42.5	32.7	32.8	32.9
9	30.9	31.1	31.3	31.5	31.6	31.8	31.9	32.1	32.3	32.4	32.5	32.7	32.8	33.0	33.1	33.2
10	31.2	31.4	31.6	31.7	31.9	32.1	32.2	32.4	32.5	32.7	32.8	32.9	33.1	33.2	33.3	33.5
11	31.4	31.6	31.8	32.0	32.1	32.3	32.4	32.6	32.7	32.9	33.0	33.2	33.3	33.5	33.6	33.7
12	31.7	31.8	32.0	32.2	32.3	32.5	32.7	32.8	33.0	33.1	33.3	33.4	33.5	33.7	33.8	33.9
13	31.9	32.0	32.2	32.4	32.5	32.7	32.9	33.0	33.2	33.3	33.5	33.6	33.7	33.9	34.0	34.1
14	32.0	32.2	32.4	32.6	32.7	32.9	33.0	33.2	33.3	33.5	33.6	33.8	33.9	34.1	34.2	34.3
15	32.2	32.4	32.6	32.7	32.9	33.1	33.2	33.4	33.5	33.7	33.8	34.0	34.1	34.2	34.4	34.5
16	32.4	32.5	32.7	32.9	33.1	33.2	33.4	33.5	33.7	33.8	34.0	34.1	34.3	34.4	34.5	34.6
17	32.5	32.7	32.9	33.0	33.2	33.4	33.5	33.7	33.8	34.0	34.1	34.3	34.4	34.5	34.7	34.8
18	32.7	32.8	33.0	33.2	33.3	33.5	33.7	33.8	34.0	34.1	34.3	34.4	34.5	34.7	34.8	34.9
19	32.8	33.0	33.1	33.3	33.5	33.6	33.8	34.0	34.1	34.3	34.4	34.5	34.7	34.8	34.9	35.1
20	32.9	33.1	33.3	33.4	33.6	33.8	33.9	34.1	34.2	34.4	34.5	34.7	34.8	34.9	35.1	35.2
21	33.0	33.2	33.4	33.6	33.7	33.9	34.1	34.2	34.4	34.5	34.7	34.8	34.9	35.1	35.2	35.3
22	33.2	33.3	33.5	33.7	33.8	34.0	34.2	34.3	34.5	34.6	34.8	34.9	35.0	35.2	35.3	35.4
23	33.3	33.4	33.6	33.8	34.0	34.1	34.3	34.4	34.6	34.7	34.9	35.0	35.2	35.3	35.4	35.6
24	33.4	33.6	33.7	33.9	34.1	34.2	34.4	34.5	34.7	34.8	35.0	35.1	35.3	35.4	35.5	35.7
25	33.5	33.7	33.8	34.0	34.2	34.3	34.5	34.6	34.8	34.9	35.1	35.2	35.4	35.5	35.6	35.8
26	33.6	33.8	33.9	34.1	34.3	34.4	34.6	34.7	34.9	35.0	35.2	35.3	35.5	35.6	35.7	35.9
27	33.7	33.8	34.0	34.2	34.4	34.5	34.7	34.8	34.9	35.1	35.3	35.4	35.5	35.6	35.7	36.0
28	33.8	33.9	34.1	34.3	34.5	34.6	34.8	34.9	35.1	35.2	35.4	35.5	35.7	35.8	35.9	36.1
29	33.8	34.0	34.2	34.4	34.5	34.7	34.9	35.0	35.2	35.3	35.5	35.6	35.7	35.9	36.0	36.1
30	33.9	34.1	34.3	34.5	34.6	34.8	34.9	35.1	35.3	35.4	35.5	35.7	35.8	36.0	36.1	36.2

d. *Self-concept measurement*. The instrument employed by Pangrazi (1973), using Osgood's Sematic Differential Technique (1957), can be used to evaluate the student's physical self-concept. Self-concept measurement and the attitude toward physical activity measurement should be used later to evaluate whether the program is having any effect on the affective domain of the child.

e. *Physical fitness evaluation*. A test of physical fitness should be administered to each candidate. Bruno (1966) has recommended the following items: (1) bench push-ups, (2) curl-ups, and (3) squat jumps. Other test items can be substituted, however, if they include the major body parts and are sensitive to the small amount of improvement the obese child is likely to make. Due to the low-fitness level of the child, the 600-yard run-walk, rather than a longer distance, should be used to evaluate cardiovascular efficiency. These data will also serve as a baseline for comparisons later in the program.

2. When all data have been collected on the low-fit candidates, selection should be made based on the following criteria:

a. The student is obese—more than 20 to 25 percent body fat.

b. Specialist's feeling about the student—one must genuinely want to help this student. Hopefully, there will be a very limited number of students toward whom a negative feeling exists.

c. The classroom teacher's assessment of the student's chance for success.

d. Any assessments from other school and/or health related personnel such as the nurse, doctor, counselor, and principal.

e. Scores on the fitness survey, the attitude inventory, and self-concept scale. This judgment will be relative, and all low-fit students will be evaluated fairly. Students who have scored highest on the three test instruments should be treated as they will probably have the best chance for success.

3. Those students selected will now be considered probable candidates for the program. They will not be a part of the low-fit program until a conference with the parents has been carried out and found to be a beneficial and symbiotic relationship for student and teacher alike.

CONFERENCE WITH PARENTS AND/OR GUARDIAN

1. Parents should be notified by telephone that their child is a probable candidate for special help in the low-fitness program. This should be done after the above evaluation so that the gathered data can be shared with parents. If possible, it is best to contact all parents for a single conference and discuss the program in a question and answer format. When parents meet in a small group environment, they are usually more at ease in

observing that other parents have children with similar problems. Also, a wide range of questions may be asked in a small group setting.

The essence of the meeting with the parents is to clarify and finalize the following points:

a. the objectives of the program

b. the operation and organization of the program

c. the data gathered—each parent should be given an individual profile of his or her youngster

d. the responsibilities of the low-fit student

e. the responsibilities of the parents

f. the need for and scheduling of follow-up conferences with parents.

2. A handout should be distributed to the parents so that the discussion leaves them not only with a good understanding of the program, but also with a reference for later use. A sample low-fit notebook that includes copies of assignment sheets that youngsters will bring home also should be shared with parents.

3. Prior to the end of the conference, parents should be asked if they want their children in the program and whether they will support the implementation of the low-fit program approach. The parents should be advised that the purpose of the conference is to notify them of the possibility of offering help for their youngster but not a commitment on the school's part to include their son or daughter (this decision will be made later after the specialist has considered all the data and insights gathered from the varous conferences). Secondly, the parents should be told about the process of termination. If the youngster and/or parents fail to live up to their obligations, the child will be eliminated from the program. As a general rule, when either the parent or child has failed to meet his or her responsibilities for three weeks (intermittently or consecutively), the child should be terminated from the program. The duration of the program for those students who carry out all phases of the program, but appear to make little or no progress, should be 12 weeks. This should be a sufficient amount of time to make some progress and may indicate that there is little opportunity for success. Parents should leave the conference with a form they must sign and return if they desire their youngster enrolled in the program.

4. To reemphasize, low-fitness programs are very difficult situations for both the physical education specialist and student. Therefore, specialists should identify and accept for treatment only those youngsters who offer the best opportunity for success. These students will probably reveal higher (better) scores in most areas. Also, inasmuch as there are many youngsters who need help, there is little point in spending time with youngsters who do not carry out their responsibilities. Others need help and might be more cooperative.

THE CONFERENCES AND NOTEBOOK

After the youngsters have been selected for the program, periodic conferences with each youngster should be held. The time of the conference should be scheduled on a regular basis so youngsters realize that once a week they are required to meet with the physical education specialist. If possible, this meeting should not be arranged during recess, lunchtime, before or after school, as it almost makes it a punishment to be in the low-fit program. Free time is a commodity that students value highly, and it should not be taken from them. The following are some guidelines that should be considered in the conference time.

1. The conference should last 15 to 30 minutes. During this time the student should not feel rushed, but rather as though the specialist has time and concern for him or her. Items that should be discussed include personal problems, problems with the activity, reasons for not following the program, etc.

2. During the conference, the physical educator should check the child's notebook in order to determine if the student and parents have been fulfilling their responsibilities. If time permits, it would be beneficial to have the student perform the assignment for the coming week in order to get a feeling about the nature and extent of the work load. This will also give the youngster an opportunity to inform the specialist if he or she has been exercising regularly and has made good improvement.

3. The conferences can be conducted with two or three students if they are compatible. This should be done only if it enhances the experience for the student; not primarily as a convenience for the teacher. The program deals with only a small number of students, and there should be time for each individual. In some cases, working with another student will increase the enjoyment of the conference and activity for both students. Students should not compete with each other in the conference to the extent that one youngster dominates and causes the others to feel insecure.

4. Testing of the child's fitness level should be done every third week so that all involved personnel can evaluate the progress being made. This will also give the specialist a good indication of whether the work load is appropriate.

5. The notebook should be the property of the student, who should take it home each week and return it for the conference. In the notebook should be recorded the following:
   a. Description of the activities to be performed. They should be written so that they can be easily comprehended by both parents and students.
   b. Physical fitness record sheet.
   c. Daily checksheet.
   d. Weekly activity assignment form.
   e. Progress report to parents.

6. Before the child leaves the conference, the new exercise assignment should be clarified. This might mean demonstration, question and answer, or sending home a piece of equipment for the exercise sessions.

7. The physical education specialist should make it a point to visit with each low-fit student sometime during the week other than the conference period. This need not be a lengthy session, but perhaps only a short question or two to convey to the student a genuine interest in progress. It might also serve to remind the youngster of an obligation to carry out all tasks. Successful experiences can be increased by asking other school personnel to visit regularly with the low-fit student and offer support and interest.

ACTIVITY FOR THE LOW-FIT STUDENT

In assigning activities for low-fit youngsters, the following guidelines might be considered:

1. As mentioned earlier, in most efforts at weight control three variables have been manipulated: diet, self-concept, and activity level. Diet is difficult to control, and many researchers have found that it is not the crucial variable. Self-concept is important and serves to remind the teacher that successful experiences with the assigned activities should be encouraged. The variable that can be manipulated successfully in an environment such as the school is level of activity. Thus, most of the assigned activity should be aerobic in nature and result in greater caloric expenditure for a prescribed duration of time. Strength is an important variable in learning motor skills, but its development is brought about by short bursts of intense activity that usually does not demand a high expenditure of calories and, in turn, does little for the problem of obesity.

2. Exercise prescription should be based on the individual's tolerance for activity. For the most part, this will have to be a professional judgment based on the specialist's knowledge and experience. It is usually better to start at a level below the student's capability in order to assure that the first experiences with the program are successful. Extreme breathlessness or discomfort, excessive fatigue, and slow recuperation are usually indicators that an excessive amount of activity has been assigned. Start at a low level and gradually increase the work load to assure that the student's morale remains high.

3. Overload the child by gradually increasing the amount of activity he or she is asked to perform. This means that careful and accurate records of the demands being placed on the youngsters must be maintained. These records will be a source of pride for youngsters as they build up their tolerance to exercise and see the extent of their improvement.

4. The manner in which the specialist assigns activities to the child will have a great deal to do with how that youngster feels about performing them. The child must be able to see that some adults love activity and are willing to exercise with him or her at times. The student must be treated in a positive and enthusiastic manner so that the expectation for improvement increases with each counseling session. The student should be told why various activities are being assigned and why it is important to do certain things that will be of benefit in the future. It is crucial to discuss the necessity of exercising past the initial point of discomfort because in too many cases these youngsters have quit when they approached fatigue and thus have never felt the joy of doing things that seemed difficult or impossible. Conversely, however, this approach has to be gentle and sensitive or the youngster will become discouraged.

5. It would be wise to identify those aerobic activities that the youngster enjoys. For example, the youngster should not be started immediately on a jogging program if prior to the program he or she had never run for any distance. It would be better to start a walking or bike riding program before moving on to the more strenuous activities. On the other hand, if the youngster's present level of activity involves walking or biking, a more difficult activity should be assigned so that the organism is stressed by the activity assigned.

6. In assigning actual activities for the youngster, the following criteria may be helpful:

   a. The activity assigned should not be in lieu of activity already performed by the student. It is important to have some idea of the amount and type of activity in which the student is currently engaging and then assign activities that will surpass the present level.

   b. The weekly activity assignment should contain two or three alternatives so that the participant can have some choice in the activity requirement. For example, the student might be assigned 20 minutes of activity per day and could fulfill this by biking, hiking, or playing basketball.

   c. Activity assignments should be made in terms of minutes per day. A suggested starting point is 10 minutes per day, each week increasing the daily workout by 2 minutes per day until it has reached 30 to 40 minutes. The important point to remember is that the specialist is attempting to change the life-style of the youngster from one of a sedentary nature to that of increased activity.

   d. The following are some activities that can be used to increase the student's activity level. They appear in an approximate order of difficulty, and the teacher should select from the top of the list and proceed toward more difficult activities as the youngster's fitness level increases.

1) Walking
2) Skateboarding
3) Roller or ice skating
4) Bike riding
5) Moto cross biking
6) Hiking
7) Sport activities—unorganized
8) Running in place
9) Orienteering
10) Jogging
11) Swimming
12) Rope jumping

FOLLOW-UP ACTIVITIES

1. The parents should receive some type of communication at least every third week. This might be a note sent to the parents or perhaps a phone call or visit with the parents. This should be a progress report and discussion of the strengths and weaknesses in the program. The physical educator should not expect the parents to stay interested if communication does not occur on a regular basis.

2. Every other week the specialist should consult with the classroom teacher of the low-fit youngster. This conference should be for the purpose of apprising the teacher of the type of activity in which the student is participating, the extent of progress, and the assistance required of the classroom teacher. Inasmuch as the classroom teachers spend more time with the youngsters than anyone else in the school, they can be of great help!

SUMMARY

The approach offered here advocates changing the activity level of the obese youngster rather than altering diet, and providing counseling sessions to change self-concept. Because the physical educator is qualified to offer and monitor activity programs, those youngsters who show a propensity for success should be treated in the low-fit program. The selection process is based on both the objective data collected and professional judgment made by the physical educator. The approach offers a quality program for a few youngsters rather than treating a large number superficially. Hopefully, through positive experiences with the specialist and an increased activity level, the youngster will alleviate the problem of excess fat for a lifetime.

REFERENCES

Bruno, L. 1966. *Physical Fitness Test Manual for Elementary Schools*. Olympia, Wash.: State Department of Public Instruction.

Bullen, B., R. Reed, and J. Mayer. 1964. Physical activity of obese and nonobese adolescent girls appraised by motion picture sampling. *Am J Clin Nutrit,* 14, 211-223.

Clarke, H. H. (ed.). Oct. 1976. *Physical Fitness Research Digest*. Washington, D.C.: President's Council on Physical Fitness and Sports, 6, 13-16.

Corbin, C. 1969. Standards of subcutaneous fat applied to percentile norms for elementary school children. *Am J. Clin Nutrit,* 22, 836-841.

Corbin, C. and P. Pletcher. 1968. Diet and physical activity patterns of obese and nonobese elementary school children. *Res Quart,* 39, 922-928.

Johnson, M., B. Burke, and J. Mayer. 1956. The prevalence and incidence of obesity in a cross-section of elementary and secondary school children. *Am J Clin Nutrit,* 4, 231-238.

Mayer, J. 1961. Obesity: Physiologic considerations. *Am J Clin Nutrit,* 9, 530-537.

Mayer, J. 1966. Some aspects of the problem of regulation of food intake and obesity. *N Engl J Med,* 274, 610-616.

Osgood, C., G. Suci, and P. Tannenbaum. 1957. *The Measurement of Meaning*. Urbana, Ill.: University of Illinois Press.

Pangrazi, R. 1973. The long range effect of an innovative elementary physical education program. Doctoral dissertation, Washington State University.

Parizkova, J. 1961. Total body fat and skinfold thickness in children. *Metabolism,* 10, 794-807.

Prugh, S. E. 1961. Some psychologic considerations concerned with the problem of overnutrition. *J Clin Nutrit,* 9, 538-547.

Rarick, G. L. and D. A. Dobbins. 1975. Basic components in the motor performance of children six to nine years of age. *Med Sci Spts,* 7, 105-110.

Seltzer, C. C. and J. Mayer. 1965. A simple criterion of obesity. *Post Grad Med,* 38, A101.

Seltzer, C. C. and J. Mayer. 1970. An effective weight control program in a public school system. *Am J Pub Hlth,* 60, 679-689.

Sharkey, B. 1978. *Physiological Fitness and Weight Control*. Missoula, Mont.: Mountain Press.

Simon, J. and F. Smoll. 1974. An instrument for assessing children's attitudes toward physical activity. *Res Quart,* 45, 407-415.

Winick, M. (ed.) 1975. *Childhood Obesity*. New York: John Wiley.

ADULT FITNESS

Introduction

In recent years there has been a considerable escalation in interest in adult fitness. Americans have become more cognizant of the potential negative aspects of normally sedentary life-styles and, therefore, large numbers have considered and/or actually started participating in various forms of adult fitness programs. Unfortunately, many individuals lack an adequate understanding of the potential benefits, essential parameters, or types of programs available for development of adult fitness. This lack of understanding often leads to a hesitancy to participate or the initiation of inappropriate activity that soon produces problems and is discontinued. This section attempts to provide some of the necessary background to alleviate these problems.

In the first paper of the section Lundegren reviews those factors that motivate people to participate in fitness programs. The discussion reveals there may be numerous motives for involvement and a similar number of techniques for encouraging participation.

In the second paper, Everett takes a very nontraditional tack by applying economic theory to assess the value of adult fitness programs. The results are enlightening.

In the next four entries, Cureton, Adams, Kasch, and Sinning and Myers review the basic principles of sound adult fitness programs, present an overview of positive adaptations that can be expected as a result of training, and suggest a few alternatives available to the adult preparing to begin a training program. These reviews are not comprehensive, and the reader should consult Section I for specific training information as well as seek out available programs in his or her locale.

The potential association between the maintenance of an adequate level of physical fitness and the reduced incidence of coronary heart disease is reviewed by Blair in the seventh paper in the section. In the final paper, Serfass presents a very comprehensive review of the various aspects of exercise and the elderly — the subtopics presented range from potential benefits to organizational guidelines.

JTK

Section Editor

Dr. Jay T. Kearney is an associate professor of physical education and director of the Research Laboratories in Health, Physical Education, and Recreation at the University of Kentucky. He received his baccalaureate degree from the State University of New York at Brockport and the M.A. and Ph.D. degrees from the University of Maryland. Dr. Kearney has previously taught and coached at Appalachian State University in Boone, North Carolina.

Dr. Kearney is a life member of AAHPERD and Phi Epsilon Kappa and also holds membership in the Kentucky AHPER and the National Association for Physical Education in Higher Education. A Fellow in the American College of Sports Medicine, Dr. Kearney has authored more than 15 articles published in a wide range of professional journals. He also contributed a chapter to a textbook and presented more than a dozen scientific papers at various professional meetings.

48

Motivation for Participation in Adult Fitness Programs

Herberta M. Lundegren

"Probably the most important single psychological determinant in motor performance is motivation. . . . a general level of arousal to positive action" (Howell and Alderman 1967, p. 723). Motivation seems to be situation specific, varies with age, and is influenced by personality and ability. It reflects social, emotional, and physiological factors, and these factors can cause denial of ability or, conversely, achievement beyond all expectations. It is an internal element in humans and its existence, form, and quality are inferred from behavior. Motivation has been variously defined in terms of reflexes, fear, anger, aggression, curiosity, exploration, play, and achievement. One is said to be motivated to action by goals, needs, desire to test one's capabilities and to master the environment, self-actualization, work, health, and beauty. Any or all of these reasons have been found to impinge on motivation for both initiating and continuing participation in exercise programs for adults. It has been stated that: "a man's adherence to an exercise program depends almost entirely on his motivation" (Stoedefalke 1974 p. 788). When exercise and exertion are the issue, Astrand (1967) is quick to point out that the human being is naturally lazy and motivation to act is extremely important.

The question of motivation for fitness can be examined from several perspectives: (1) factors that motivate adults to want to be physically fit; (2) psychological types whose characteristics seem to cause them to join fitness programs, whatever their present fitness levels; or (3) factors that cause people to avoid fitness programs. Although there are some data on the latter two approaches, the first is the overriding concern of exercise specialists and the focus of this essay.

Concern for fitness in the adult population is a relatively recent phenomenon gaining in impetus through the late 1960s and into the 1970s, and has largely been focused on the male population in connection with cardiovascular health. In the mid-seventies increasing interest in fitness of adult women has been notable. Research in this field is largely directed to the physiological, psychological, and social parameters of fitness programs. Articles representative of the literature available on motivation in regard to this topic are reviewed here.

In October 1966 the Ontario Heart Foundation, the Ontario Medical Association, and the Canadian Medical Association jointly sponsored an international symposium devoted to physical activity and cardiovascular health. Among the papers presented at that meeting was one dealing directly with motivation for sports participation in the community (Stiles 1967). While sports and fitness programs are not synonymous, the observations and findings of the author are pertinent to both groups of participants. A group of physically active adults (skiers) ranging from the late 30s to age 70 were interviewed regarding the initial and continuing motivation for participation in sports. There was one woman in the group. Most of the subjects listed several factors that attracted them to participate rather than just one overriding reason. These factors generally clustered around reasons of health, reassurance that one can still do active things, and need to be with others. In addition, they tended to be competitive and had a family sports background. All subjects were asked why they continued in activity once they had started participating. Feelings of well-being, enjoyment of sports, desire for buoyant health, and increased self-image as new challenges were met were stressed. Stiles recommended that children be encouraged to participate and that the critical period for motivation to a continuing life-style that includes regular sports participation is during the late 20s and 30s when concerns over career and money are often so pressing that time seems limited and actual participation frivolous.

Brunner (1969) studied two groups of adult males, one group participants in vigorous activity and the other group, nonparticipants. Subjects were tested regarding their personality (Adjective Check List) and factors motivating their participation (revision of a questionnaire devised by Willert in 1948, to gain biographical data and information related to physical recreation participation patterns and personal beliefs regarding benefits of physical exercise). Participants stated that the primary reason for regular participation was a desire to keep physically fit with the associated feeling of well-being. The nonparticipants gave as their primary reason for not participating the fact that they were too busy to do so. When asked what benefits they perceived they would derive from exercise should they engage in it, the participants listed as their salient reasons: (1) keep physically fit, (2) feel better physically and mentally, and (3) provide fun and enjoyment from participation. The nonparticipants listed: (1) relax the mind from the day's vocations, (2) feel better physically and mentally, and (3) provide fun and enjoyment from participation and benefit from being out-of-doors. Brunner suggested that the educational process regarding the need for physical fitness had failed when supposedly educated adults do not consider fitness important enough to take the time to pursue it.

As part of a collaborative research project among several universities supported by the Public Health Service, Harris (1970) investigated a group of middle-aged men who were clinically healthy but possessed two or more coronary heart disease risk factors. The subjects were divided into three groups—sedentary nonexercise, sedentary exercise, and volitionally active. All subjects were given a Physical Activity Questionnaire and a Physical Activity Attitude Inventory. Although attitudes toward no motivation for exercise were analyzed, the attitude statements reflected motivation, and thus are applicable here. Results indicated a difference between sedentary and active men in the attitude held, with sedentary men who exercised becoming more like the volitionally active group in their answers. Examples of statements in which the active and exercise groups differed from the nonexercise were: (1) I play because it will improve my stamina; (2) When I feel sluggish, exercise tends to pep me up; and (3) I like the feeling one has after a good physical workout. There was also interest in knowing how their performances compared to other men their ages. Harris stated that positive feedback from participation and a sense of satisfaction were motivating aspects of continued regular physical activity, with positive attitude toward activity a motivation toward learning new sports and games. Without exception, Harris's subjects who exercise regularly said that they did so because they felt better as a result. This finding bears out those of other researchers.

Heinzelmann and Bagley (1970) also collaborated in Public Health Service interuniversity pilot studies on cardiovascular risk in terms of patterns of health behavior and associated changes in response to participation in an 18-month physical activity program. Subjects (N = 239) were men from a metropolitan area and two university settings. Each volunteer was asked to rank order at the beginning and again at the end his reasons for participation in the program. Those factors ranked highest in terms of reasons influencing the initiation of the program were: (1) desire to feel better and healthier, (2) concern about reducing the chance of a heart attack, and (3) to help the cause of medical research. At the end of the program, the factors that subjects said most influenced them to continue in the program were identified as: (1) social aspects of the activity group, (2) a chance to compare their fitness level with those of others, and (3) enjoyment of the activity. It was interesting to note that, although the initial decision to participate was not greatly influenced by wives, a wife's attitude during the study strongly influenced continuation in the program. When the wives' attitudes were positive, 80 percent of the subjects showed good to excellent adherence to the program. In contrast, when the wives' attitudes were neutral or negative, only 40 percent of the husbands showed good to excellent adherence.

In an assessment of the physiological and psychological effects of a 28-week training for sedentary middle-aged men, Massie and Shephard (1971) administered the Shephard Motivation Test, Kenyon's Attitude Toward Physical Activity Scales, Maudsley Personality Inventory, Taylor Manifest Anxiety Scale, and the McPherson Mood Test. Results related to motivation for continued activity indicated that feedback about their achievement in making progress toward greater fitness is a desirable feature for subjects, as is making the experience and participating in a group rather than alone. This suggestion is consistent with the findings of Heinzelmann and Bagley (1970) who concluded that the social aspects of an activity group inspire continued participation in its members. The authors cautioned that emphasis on the "stern call of cardiovascular duty" was *not* the most motivating approach.

In 1974 Lundegren administered to 151 young adult women a 75-item Q-sort of statements on motives for participation in physical activity. Data were treated by means of an inverse factor analysis in order to establish factor types representing groups of people with similar motives for participation. Five significant activity types were established for those women who were in majors other than physical education. These types were named according to the semantic content of the statements chosen to represent the category and were: (1) Appearance Conscious, (2) Skill Developers, (3) Fitness Fadists, (4) Healthy Long Livers, and (5) Groupies. The physical education majors shared with the nonmajors social reasons for participation but also participated for a sound mind and body and to share their skills with others. Results of this study made it clear that the women questioned were keenly interested in physical fitness and all its ramifications regarding health and appearance and that they were well aware of the role of regular activity in the maintenance of fitness. The young women studied were unlike their mothers in that only ten percent had mothers who modeled positive physical activity participation behavior.

In a national adult physical fitness survey conducted by the President's Council on Physical Fitness and Sports (1973) 3875 men and women were interviewed regarding their exercise background and current exercise habits. Among those who exercised, the most salient reasons given for doing so were: (1) for good health, (2) good for you in general (makes me feel better), (3) to lose weight, and (4) enjoyment.

Stoedefalke (1974) addressed the question of motivation in an article on physical fitness programs for adults. He stated that adults exercise for a variety of reasons including: (1) health, recreation, relaxation; (2) opportunities for social contact; and (3) personal image and self-esteem. No matter what the motivation, once engaged in the program, benefits accrue to the participants, so it behooves the exercise program leader to ascertain the most effective motivation for each individual and utilize it.

Perceived motivation to exercise was included in a study of the elderly (12 men and 20 women) and their attitudes toward physical activity (Sidney and Shephard 1976). Subjects were asked to list up to three reasons for joining the exercise program. The most important reasons for both men and women were health (especially improved fitness) and availability of programs and facilities (with special emphasis on instruction). Both sexes were also interested in a good body image, while the women were interested in participation for social benefits. Implications from this study are that communities should make fitness programs and facilities readily accessible to the elderly. Data collected from the administration of the Kenyon Attitude Inventory showed that the elderly subjects valued exercise as an aesthetic experience and as a means for gaining health and fitness.

A factor worthy of note on the negative side of participation is a reason often found to deter people from participation, especially as age increases, and that is fear of injury or strain of body parts and of suffering a heart attack. This observation speaks to the concern for proper education regarding fitness supported by Brunner (1969).

In summary, adults appear to be motivated to continue to participate in physical activity primarily for reasons of: (1) fitness and health, (2) social contacts with others who exercise, (3) achievement of a feeling of well-being, (4) improvement of self-image, (5) fun and enjoyment, and (6) feedback on achievement.

REFERENCES

Astrand, P. O. 1967. Concluding remarks. In Proceedings of the international symposium of physical activity and cardiovascular health. *Canadian Med Assoc J,* 96, 907-911.

Brunner, B. C. 1969. Personality and motivating factors influencing adult participation in vigorous physical activity. *Res Quart,* 40, 464-469.

Fisher, A. C. 1976. *Psychology of Sport.* Palo Alto: Mayfield.

Hammet, V. B. O. 1967. Psychological changes with physical training. In Proceedings of the international symposium on physical activity and cardiovascular health. *Canadian Med Assoc J,* 96, 764-767.

Harris, D. V. 1970. Physical activity history and attitudes of middle-aged men. *Med Sci Spts,* 2, 203-208.

Heinzelmann, F. and R. W. Bagley. 1970. Response to physical activity programs and their effects on health behavior. *Pub Hlth Rept,* 85, 905-911.

Howell, M. L. and R. B. Alderman. 1967. Psychological determinants of fitness. In Proceedings of the international symposium on physical activity and cardiovascular health. *Canadian Med Assoc J,* 96, 721-726.

Lundegren, H. M. 1974. Motives of college women for participating in physical activities. Paper read at AAHPER Convention, Anaheim.

Massie, J. F. and R. J. Shephard. 1971. Physiological and psychological effects of training. *Med Sci Spts,* 3, 110-117.

Morgan, W. P., J. A. Roberts, and A. D. Feinerman. 1971. Psychologic effect of acute physical activity. *Arch Phys Med Rehab,* 52, 422-425.

National Adult Physical Fitness Survey. May, 1973. *Newsletter.* President's Council on Physical Fitness and Sports.

Naughton, J., J. B. Gruhn, and M. T. Lategola. 1968. Effects of physical training on physiologic and behavioral characteristics of cardiac patients. *Arch Phys Med Rehab,* 49, 131-137.

Sidney, K. H. and R. J. Shephard. 1976. Attitudes towards health and physical activity in the elderly. Effects of a physical training program. *Med Sci Spts,* 8, 246-252.

Stiles, M. H. 1967. Motivation for sports participation in the community. In Proceedings of the international symposium on physical activity and cardiovascular health. *Canadian Med Assoc J,* 96, 889-892.

Stoedefalke, K. G. 1974. Physical fitness programs for adults. *Am J Cardiol,* 33, 787-790.

Vernon, M. D. 1969. *Human Motivation.* Cambridge, England: The University Press.

Willert, R. F. 1948. Motivation in relationship to conditioning exercise in adult life. Master's thesis, State University of Iowa.

49

The Economics of Exercise for Physical Fitness and Health

Michael D. Everett

The increasing prevalence of chronic degenerative diseases among middle-aged Americans along with soaring medical treatment costs have generated interest in individual health practices as important medical inputs (Milio 1976). One group of analysts believes that changes in health habits can produce substantially greater health benefits for the average American than increased medical treatment and technology (Fuchs 1974). For example, cardiovascular disease (CVD), the leading cause of death in the United States, killed over 165,000 males under age 65 per year, imposing economic costs of over $10 billion in direct treatment and almost $30 billion in lost income during 1972 (Rice and Cooper, in press). One school of thought holds that consistent physical exercise for adults could substantially reduce this loss (American Heart Association Committee on Exercise 1972; also see "Physical Activity and Coronary Heart Disease" by Steven Blair, Chapter 54, for a further discussion of this topic).

Strategies to increase adult exercise range from education and exhortation through formal exercise and sports programs, to economically efficient labor-intensive technologies such as bicycle-pedestrian systems in congested urban and recreation areas. Limited resources will force decision makers to choose between numerous attractive strategies, but imperfect information makes rational choice difficult. For example, the medical literature has not conclusively demonstrated that even vigorous exercise reduces CVD; planners do not know which strategy will most effectively increase adult participation in exercise programs; and no rigorous benefit-cost analyses of exercise programs exist. However, recent developments in managerial economics can provide important insights for physical fitness planning. The approach involves utilizing a few simple economic and statistical concepts to extract ranges of values from imperfect data and to predict direction of human behavior over large numbers of observations. This chapter demonstrates the economic approach by exploring: (1) the relation between exercise and CV health, (2) the barriers to adult exercise, and (3) the economic efficiency of various strategies to increase adult exercise.

EXERCISE AND CARDIOVASCULAR DISEASE

Substantial uncertainty surrounds the relationship between exercise and protection against cardiovascular disease. This has led to controversies between pro-exercise groups and those who contend that present data do not support massive physical fitness programs (National Heart and Lung Institute Task Force 1971) or those who fear vigorous exercise among deconditioned adults may actually precipitate cardiac problems (Friedman and Roseman 1974). Concepts in managerial economics can help physical fitness planners extract useful information from these imperfect data and make more rational decisions.

The first step involves defining "exercise." Well-controlled clinical studies have consistently shown that three or four vigorous 30-minute exercise sessions—reaching about 75 percent of safe, age-health adjusted pulse rates—per week can improve a number of cardiovascular functions (Cureton 1969; Hellerstein et al. 1973; National Heart and Lung Institute Task Force 1971). Most epidemiological studies, on the other hand, have failed to specify the levels of physical activity, which may account for some of their conflicting findings. Some investigators now believe that a threshold effect holds where only vigorous or extensive exercise will provide protection (Cassel 1971). Their studies have found that an energy expenditure of about 5 to 7 kcal (which include basal metabolism) or more per minute (a brisk walking rate) for several hours a day comprises a threshold for adult males (Morris et al. 1973; Paffenbarger and Hale 1975).

The concept of a trade-off curve can combine these two definitions of exercise into a continuum of exercise prescriptions rather than an either-or proposition. Fixing duration as one 30-minute session, exercise reduces to two basic characteristics—intensity and frequency (the number of 30-minute sessions per day or week). Plotting intensity on the vertical axis and duration on the horizontal axis, the curve in Fig. 49.1 represents a continuous trade-off between the clinical exercise prescriptions and those suggested by the epidemiological studies.

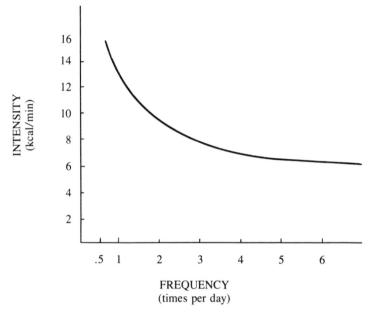

Fig. 49.1 Intensity-frequency trade-offs for threshold exercise. This curve is designed for well conditioned adult males and may require adjustment for individual conditioning, body weight, and metabolic reaction to various activities. Note that experts recommend that most adults not exceed 75 percent of their safe, age-health adjusted pulse rates (1, 14).

For example, a well-conditioned adult male could engage in one vigorous 30-minute session such as running six- to eight-minute miles (12 to 18 kcal per minute at about 75 percent of maximum safe puls rate) just three or four times a week. Or at the other extreme, he could play social tennis, consuming about 6 kcal per minute for roughly two hours or more daily. The clinical and epidemiological data cited above tend to support these two approaches. The curve in Fig. 49.1 also assumes he could utilize various combinations of tennis and running or other activities between these two extremes to reach threshold exercise levels.

Although the curve in Fig. 49.1 basically applied to well-conditioned males, similar curves could be drawn for females, deconditioned males, and persons with known CVD by adjusting the maximum kcal on the vertical axis of Fig. 49.1 to 75 percent of safe, age-health adjusted levels (Hellerstein et al. 1973). Even moderate (3.5 mph) walking programs entailing 5 or 6 kcal per minute can represent an intense effort for a person with existing CVD. Thus, threshold exercise uncertainty surrounds exercise's impact on CVD. Consistent and conclusive evidence does not currently exist to demonstrate clearly that threshold exercise prevents arteriosclerosis (thickening and hardening of the arteries), which comprises the major form of CVD. Moreover, persons with tendencies toward CVD may have selected themselves out of physically demanding activities leading to a positive relationshp between high levels of physical activity and reduced CVD in most epidemiological studies. This and other factors such as heredity, smoking, diet, stress, and medical treatment could explain the higher CVD rates among the less active groups. Given this uncertainty, most literature reviews simply conclude that studies have not proven that exercise reduces CVD and, at most, list lack of exercise as one of the risk factors (Keys 1975; National Heart and Lung Institute Task Force 1971).

Basic techniques in managerial decision making with uncertainty can extract considerably more information from the available studies (Hertz 1964). For example, Fox (1973) listed various epidemiological studies in terms of CV disease and mortality for physically active groups as a proportion of CVD for inactive groups. These studies plus the more recent threshold studies (Cassel 1971; Morris 1973; Paffenbarger and Hale 1975) have found that life-long exercise produced between a zero and 80 percent reduction in CVD rates. However, most of these studies show the reduction in CVD rates ranged from 40 to 60 percent with the remainder of the studies falling more or less evenly on either side.

Analysts can use such frequency distributions, other data, theory, and personal judgment to construct subjective (probability) distributions (e.g., Spector 1956) of the ranges through which threshold exercise may reduce the risk of CVD. For instance, expanding the distribution to range from a negative 10 percent to a positive 90 percent reduction in CVD rates would encompass the two major opposing positions on exercise. The distribution would represent some probability that vigorous exercise might both precipitate CV problems in deconditioned adults and through well supervised programs might provide greater benefits than epidemiological studies indicate.

By developing such distributions and their assumptions clearly, the analyst can provide the individual and public decision maker with more information for choosing appropriate risks, trade-offs, and programs. For analytical purposes in the following section, the author will assume that a threshold effect does operate. Further, the assumption will be made that threshold exercise over an adult's life will produce a zero to 80 percent reduction in the risk of incurring CVD.

ECONOMIC DETERMINANTS OF EXERCISE PARTICIPATION

Data from the National Physical Fitness Survey (President's Council on Physical Fitness and Sports 1973) indicate that most adult Americans realize the possible relation between exercise and health and desire more exercise than they presently receive. However, while over 50 percent of the adult respondents in the survey indicated they received some type of exercise, less than 10 percent exercised consistently (three times or more a week). Probably less than half of those received anywhere near threshold levels of exercise.

Economists have successfully utilized theoretical models to predict general tendencies for human behavior over large numbers of observations (Becker 1976). Applied to health, these models would assume that individuals are rational utility (welfare) maximizers seeking a cost minimization combination of health inputs such as reductions in smoking, diet changes, and drugs as well as exercise. Moreover, individuals will seek improvements in health only so long as the expected benefits exceed expected costs (at the margin). Such models can provide important insights for understanding the barriers to consistent adult exercise.

For example, the process of industrialization has reduced drastically the opportunities for exercise as a by-product to production, transportation, and recreation. Today, exercise during leisure time for long-run possible health benefits generally lacks immediate reinforcement and requires conscious effort to initiate. Industrialization also has increased the opportunity cost of time and made time-intensive activities such as exercise more expensive and less attractive (Burenstam 1970). Recall that threshold exercise as defined in Fig. 49.1 comprises a very demanding activity requiring considerable effort for short sessions or more moderate effort for up to several hours per day.

Even if life-long threshold exercise does reduce the risk of incurring CVD substantially, other less time-consuming inputs such as dieting and drugs are available. Moreover, for males 20, 30, and perhaps even for 40 years old, the risk exists well in the future and does not comprise an immediately pressing problem such as family or career obligations. For example, the President's Council's (1973) physical fitness survey found "lack of time" constituted the major barrier to adult exercise. In addition, sociological studies have found that mass media education or small group approaches have had limited success in altering individual health practices including exercise (Maccoby 1975; and Steele and McBroom 1972).

Table 49.1 uses available economic data to illustrate the low net economic returns to threshold exercise for various age groups of white American males. First, the economic benefits for the average individual avoiding CVD range up to about $10,000 in expected increased income and reduced medical expenditures. Since it has been assumed that life-long threshold exercise can produce a zero to 80 percent reduction in the risk of developing CVD, the expected returns to exercise are even lower, ranging from zero to about $8000 to some age groups (see column 2).

Secondly, individuals must engage in thousands of exercise sessions to receive these expected benefits (see column 3). This means that the high expected benefits may amount to only about $2 or less per session (see column 4). Netting out time costs of zero to $2 per session yields generally negative expected returns and only slightly positive high returns (see column 5). Widely different assumptions about number of exercise sessions and value of time still yield small expected returns to exercise. For example, reducing the high number

Table 49.1

Subjective Ranges of Health Benefits and Time Costs of Threshold Exercise[1]

(Dollars)

Age Groups White Males (1)	Present Value[2] of Health Benefits (2)		Exercise Sessions Needed to Generate Health Benefits (3)		Present Value of Exercise Per Session (4)			Benefits Net of Time Costs[3] per Session (5)		
	Low	High	Low	High	Low	Expected	High	Low	Expected	High
25-34	0	6,147	7,000	70,000	0	.44	.88	-2.00	-.56	.88
35-44	0	8,360	5,250	52,500	0	.80	1.60	-2.00	-.20	1.60
45-54	0	8,016	3,500	35,000	0	1.15	2.30	-2.00	.15	2.30
55-64	0	2,862	1,750	17,500	0	.82	1.64	-2.00	-.18	1.64

[1]Calculations based on Figure 49.1 and (Holtmann, 1973, pp. 354-61; Rice, 1966; and Rice and Cooper, in press)—adjusted for inflation. All extreme values were found by cross dividing. For example, low number of exercise sessions (3) divided into high health benefits (2) yielded high values per exercise session (4).

[2]Present value means the future benefits have been reduced (discounted) by some interest rate to reflect the notion that present income is worth more than future income.

[3]Zero to two dollars per session.

of exercise sessions to 10,000 for the 25 to 34 age group and to fewer for the others gives expected net benefits ranging from negative to $1.29 per session.

Therefore, if threshold exercise involves considerable effort and initial discomfort, adults may exhibit economic rationality in eschewing this long-run health input. The dollar savings represent relatively small intangible future benefits while the pain, effort, and time costs occur immediately. Certainly such reasoning will not maximize long-run health, but economic analysis indicates that individuals attempt to balance a number of desirable goals including family, income, and career as well as health. For example, studies on the effect of air pollution on residential housing indicate that many individuals value avoiding future possible disease crudely in terms of the present discounted cost of the disease (Ridker 1967).

PUBLIC POLICY

While avoiding exercise as a long-run health input may comprise a rational position for most individuals, modern societies may not be rational in developing institutions and constraints that tend to restrict physical activity. Much of the economic cost of cardiovascular disease (CVD) falls on society in general through public and private insurance programs. Moreover, deconditioned adults probably require more energy and other resources for heating, air-conditioning, and transportation than physically fit adults. Nevertheless, sweeping institutional changes or massive exercise programs would cost more than the measurable health benefits they could generate. Hence, decision makers must constantly choose among evolving alternatives.

Given the uncertainties surrounding exercise strategies and health, no rigorous benefit-cost studies exist. Nevertheless, the managerial-economic approach can help extract useful information from existing data to aid decision making. For example, the low economic returns to exercise suggest that well supervised formalistic programs designed purely to produce fitness for long-run health might generate low benefits relative to costs. Such programs for middle-aged adults with known CVD could constitute an exception since clinical studies have established a stronger link between exercise and improved CV function, and the economic values of exercise would be higher for this group than for the average middle-aged person (Table 49.1).

For the general adult population exercise programs that generate a bundle of socially desirable outputs such as recreation and transportation would stand the greatest chance of success. By providing individuals with immediate reinforcement, such strategies could increase adult participation. Including the nonhealth outputs also would elevate the benefits. For example, walking and cycling, largely for utilitarian purposes, account for 75 percent of consistent adult exercise (three to seven times a week) and 70 percent of the exercise sessions exceeding 20 minutes in duration (President's Council on Physical Fitness and

Sports 1973). Bicycle pedestrian systems also may reduce congestion, roadside air pollution, and transportation costs. Studies of university campus systems have yielded very high benefit-cost ratios suggesting that these modes may be more efficient than motor vehicles in some congested urban and recreational areas (Everett 1977).

On the other hand, many of these exercise programs may not generate consistent threshold exercise or may entail offsetting health hazards. For example, golf probably does not involve high enough sustained intensity to satisfy criteria for a few short-intense sessions per week; moreover, few individuals play enough golf to fit the lower intensity, longer duration criteria (see Fig. 49.1). Utilitarian bicycle and pedestrian transportation tends to provide much more consistent daily exercise hovering around minimal threshold levels for multiple weekly sessions (Everett 1976). However, without adequate facilities they may expose their participants to traffic accidents and roadside air pollution hazards that could offset the CV benefits (Everett 1974).

This suggests the value of increasing information flows to individuals and policy makers not just on the possible value of exercise but on specific criteria for threshold exercise and overall safety in exercise programs. Moreover, increased information on the possible efficiency of labor-intensive technology that can increase exercise and other socially desirable outputs could result in substantial economic savings. For example, transportation officials often develop inappropriate capital-intensive strategies for congested areas partly because they and their clientele have very little information on the possible benefits of labor-intensive approaches.

CONCLUSION

The economic approach suggests that substantial increases of adult participation in threshold exercise will require combining exercise with more immediately desired outputs. This will help overcome the time, effort, and psychological costs that form the major barriers to consistent vigorous adult exercise. Such strategies will involve a total systems approach integrating efficient labor-intensive technologies into daily life as well as continuation of more traditional sports and formalistic exercise programs. Basic managerial economic approaches can both provide insights into the efficiency of specific programs and also can help increase the flows of useful information essential to more rational individual and public decision making.

REFERENCES

American Heart Association Committee on Exercise. 1972. *Exercise Testing and Training Apparently Healthy Individuals: A Handbook for Physicians*. New York: American Medical Association.

Bandura, A. and R. H. Walters. 1963. *Social Learning and Personality Development.* New York: Holt, Rinehart and Winston.

Becker, G. S. 1976. *The Economic Approach to Human Behavior.* Chicago: University of Chicago Press.

Burenstam, L. S. 1970. *The Harried Leisure Class.* New York: Columbia University Press.

Cassel, J. C. (ed.). 1971. Evans County cardiovascular and cerebrovascular epidemiological study. *Arch Int Med,* 128, all pages.

Cureton, T. K., Jr. 1969. *The Physiological Effects of Exercise Programs on Adults.* Springfield, Ill.: Charles C. Thomas.

Everett, M. D. 1977. Benefit-cost analysis of labor-intensive transportation systems. *Transportation,* 6, 57-60.

Everett, M. D. 1976. Measuring the economic value exercise in labor-intensive urban transportation systems. Paper presented at the Fifty-fifth Annual Meeting of the Transportation Research Board, Washington, D.C.

Everett, M. D. 1974. Roadside air pollution hazards in recreational land use planning. *J Am Instit Planners,* 40, 83-90.

Fox, S. M., III 1973. Relationship of Activity Habits to Coronary Heart Disease. In *Exercise Testing and Exercise Training in Coronary Heart Disease,* H. K. Hellerstein and J. P. Naughton (ed.). New York: Academic Press.

Freidman, M. and R. Roseman. 1974. *Type A Behavior and Your Heart.* New York: Knopf.

Fuchs, V. R. 1974. *Who Shall Live: Health, Economics, and Social Choice.* New York: Basic Books.

Heart Information Center. 1969. *National Heart Institute.* Washington, D.C., U.S. Government Printing Office.

Hellerstein, H., et al. 1973. Principles of Exercise Prescription. In *Exercise Testing and Exercise Training in Coronary Heart Disease,* H. K. Hellerstein and J. P. Naughton (ed.). New York: Academic Press.

Hertz, D. B. 1964. Risk analysis in capital investment. *Harvard Business Rev,* 42, 95-106.

Holtmann, A. G. 1973. The size and distribution of benefits from U.S. medical research: The case of eliminating cancer and heart disease. *Pub Finance,* 28, 254-361.

Keys, A. 1975. Coronary heart disease—The global picture. *Atherosclerosis,* 22, 149-192.

Maccoby, N. May 7-8, 1975. Achieving behavior change via mass media and interpersonal communication. Washington, D.C. U.S. Senate Hearings on National Health Promotion and Education, Subcommittee on Health.

Milio, N. 1976. A framework for prevention: Changing health-damaging to health-generating life patterns. *Am J Pub Hlth,* 66, 435-439.

Morris, J. N., et al. 1973. Vigorous exercise in leisure-time and the incidence of coronary heart-disease. *Lancet,* 1, 333-339.

538

National Heart and Lung Institute Task Force. 1971. *Arteriosclerosis*. Washington, D.C.: National Institutes of Health.

Paffenbarger, R. S., Jr. and W. E. Hale. 1975. Work activity and coronary heart mortality. *New Eng J Med,* 292, 545-550.

President's Council on Physical Fitness and Sports. May, 1973. National Adult Physical Fitness Survey. *Newsletter*. Special Edition.

Rice, D. P. 1966. *Estimating the Cost of Illness*. Washington, D.C.: U.S. Dept. of Health, Education and Welfare, U.S.G.P.O.

Rice, D. P. and B. S. Cooper. In press. *The Economic Cost of Illness Revisited*. Washington, D.C.: Office of Research and Statistics, Social Security Administration.

Ridker, R. G. 1967. *Economic Costs of Air Pollution*. New York: Praeger.

Spector, W. S. (ed.). 1956. *Handbook of Biological Data*. Philadelphia: W. B. Saunders.

Steele, J. and W. H. McBroom. 1972. Conceptual and empirical dimensions of health behavior. *J Hlth Soc Behav,* 13, 382-392.

U.S. Public Health Service. 1974. *Vital Statistics of the United States 1970 Vol. II Mortality Part A*. Washington, D.C.: U.S. Government Printing Office.

50

Basic Principles to Guide Physical Fitness Work

Thomas K. Cureton, Jr.

This chapter discusses basic principles that should be used as guidelines by adults exercising in beginning classes or individually. There are individual exceptions and variations for particular individuals that can be pointed out by an experienced teacher of adult fitness work. Many discover these principles for themselves, but the inexperienced will have less trouble if they follow an experienced teacher (or leader) in a low-gear exercise approach for health. Thirteen of these guidelines are included in the chapter.

WARM-UP

Warm-up implies a gradual, progressive approach, such as: walking before running; light preliminary calisthenics, which may be done with walking, called walking calisthenics; then progression may be made to jogging alternated with walking; and alternating a 400-meter or 440-yard jog with walking an equal distance. It is not necessary to work at high-intensity exercise until one has been thoroughly prepared with preliminary exercises. Indoor work can alternate easy jogging in place with walking around a room with deep breathing, one to two minutes of each; and followed after a time with floor exercises. About 15 to 20 minutes should be sufficient for a start assuming little previous exercise. The purpose is to gradually increase the body temperature and the circulation of blood to the muscles. One will feel better if the stomach is relatively empty. Clothing should be light but adapted to temperature conditions, which should be cool to moderate, rather than hot. Violent movements should be avoided for the first 15 to 20 minutes of exercise. The progression is from slow to moderate speeds, with avoidance of sudden, violent movements, Older people may do moderate stretching but should avoid extreme or ballistic stretching because muscles and musculo-tendinous junctions are more easily injured.

REGULATION OF EXERCISE

The regulation of dosage is a matter of judgment and feel, both during and after the workout. If there is considerable soreness, then the exercise was too vigorous. A little soreness should be tolerated from day to day, and stretching both before and after the exercise period may help reduce residual muscle soreness. For most people the dosage may be increased gradually by alternating a good walk in substitution for the exercises, or by extending the time of the daily workouts, or by exercising four to five days per week. The goal should be to work in the light activity category until exercise can be tolerated for 30 minutes more or less continously. Within three to six months the normal individual will be ready to introduce more intense exercises after the usual warm-up and extend the time to 40 to 45 minutes.

Certain individuals, especially older people or those who start in very poor condition, may need to exercise initially only every other day. Their progression toward a moderate activity program would be much more gradual.

OVERLOAD PROGRESSION

The normal progression should be from light to moderate (low gear and middle gear, see Chapter 11), with workouts totalling 35 to 45 minutes and with harder exercises incorporated after the warm-up period. The principle is *more and more work,* regardless of how it may be done. Speed work, however, is not too important, as the better benefits will come by exercising to the extent of more and more endurance. While the basic elements of motor fitness (balance, flexibility, agility, strength, power, and endurance) are important, the most valuable benefits for adults seem to be in doing endurance work. It must be approached with the concept that month after month there will be a moderate increase in the endurance work done—plus some of the other basic motor fitness exercises.

The first three to six months might well be spent in light exercise; then gradually move into moderate activity with longer and a few harder exercises; then if all goes well, and the background of sports and exercise is good (and there may be many individual differences), a few intense (all-out) exercises may be tried, one or more, depending on how one feels. The approach should be a cautious one as few people can tolerate intense exercises for the entire period, even with rest periods in between the exertions. A large proportion of people over 60 cannot take highly intense work (high gear, see Chapter 11) except an occasional exercise now and then, even after creeping up on these. It is better to be cautious rather than sorry. Experience has shown that overwork is a very common cause of excessive fatigue and lethargy, pulled muscles and injured musculo-tendinous junctions, and aches and pains of a chronic nature. While therapy may help, the best remedy is to work hard only occasionally, such as one day per week, one week per month, or three months per year—all depending on one's background and experience. High intensity exercise is necessary for successful competition but not for most of the fitness and health benefits that may accrue. Rest may be the best cure for overwork.

RECUPERATION

Recuperative procedures must be understood and applied to prevent trouble. In a single day's work, rest periods may be taken after an exercise that feels unusually hard. After finishing a hard bout or series, it is better to walk about than to sit down, as the circulation will be better in walking than sitting. Many believe that stretching helps after a hard-tensive exercise, such as push-ups, chin-ups, hops, squat-jumps, etc. After a workout, a warm shower helps, or a soak in a tub of warm water (if sore) but a swim is also relaxing and very recuperative for those who are moderately experienced. The muscles relax in swimming and this is also a good way to stretch. The purpose of any activity at the end of a workout should be to slowly cool the body back to normal temperature and to avoid pooling of blood in the veins of the legs.

GENERALITY OF EXERCISE

Exercise programs should be designed to incorporate all major body segments in exercise. This is one of the major reasons why a well-directed gym program is better for most "starters" than a sport, as the all-around exercise program is usually aimed at all parts of the body, one after the other, until all are worked enough. Feet and legs may usually get most of the work (along with the circulatory-respiratory system) as in walking, jogging, or running. If warm-up calisthenics are performed and other exercises are inserted between the locomotive bouts, better all-around results will accrue.

CARDIOVASCULAR PROTECTION

Protection of the cardiovascular system from undue stress is secured, as far as is reasonably possible, by adhering to the guidelines previously described. No exercise for middle-aged adults is fully "aerobic," as adults who are out of condition will develop some "oxygen debt" (or deficiency) very easily. The human is so constituted that both aerobic and anaerobic processes are working. Overexertion has been known to harm a vulnerable heart and may precipitate a temporary embarrassment to the heart because it needs oxygen for its work, and interference with its blood supply will cause such embarrassment—as for instance, by held-tensive exercises with inadequate breathing. The best protection is in doing nearly all of the work at first with rhythmic-exercises, even with some rest (by walking) when distress begins to mount. The oxygen debt mechanism is so well developed in an experienced exerciser that energy may be gradually obtained for several minutes through anaerobic channels in the body; and economical-efficiency reduces the felt stress. Unless well conditioned, the novice should not try to see how much stress he or she can stand. It is better to do reasonably moderate work with good breathing, and even over-breathing while exercising and after easing off in recovery. The felt stress soon disappears. With good circulation the heart is less embarrassed; and exercise may be resumed after recuperation is felt sufficiently. Some like to count the pulse rate, and such a system has some value but is seldom perfected by good understanding of the many variations that may occur.

The coronary circulation may be poor and unadaptable in some deteriorated adults, and is not the same as the central (aortic) circulation nor the peripheral circulation to body parts. A sudden dizziness, a part of the body going numb or becoming uncontrollable, exceedingly poor vision, heavy—feeling like a weight on the chest, or inability to get the breath or recuperate reasonably well—are all danger signs that should be heeded by reducing all exercise and resting a day to two. If a medical check-up has been made preceding the exercise, that may be helpful, but it may or may not account for what is observed in apparently normal people in beginning fitness classes. Many of such signs of embarrassed circulation or heart action are only temporary, and may go away with a moderate approach to the exercise program—but a report should be made to the instructor and one's personal physician.

Heart embarrassment may occur more frequently in very hot weather, accompanied by high humidity. It may be brought about by heavy clothing that obstructs the ventilation to the skin. It may be brought about also by long, hot showers following a workout.

It is a good rule after a hard run not to suddenly sit-down, as it is better to walk; and in a very hot environment a cool shower will bring quick relief, as will a plunge into a pool.

Instructors are now usually trained in cardiopulmonary resuscitation (CPR), as well as members of an exercise class, or individually. With sudden collapse (an apparent cardiac arrest or fibrillation) CPR should be started as soon as possible. It is a mistake to assume that an unfavorable report on a stress-test will preclude exercise or that a normal report guarantees safety. A moderate rather than "heroic" approach is indicated, and good supervision and medical attention promptly when needed, is important.

REDUCTION OF BODY FAT

Body fat is easily measured by the "pinch-up" caliper method, which is commonly done in fitness work. The reduction of fat varies with the amount of work done and the way it is done, but there are constitutional differences in the adult population that cause variable results. It is known that a very well-conditioned ectomorph or ecto-medial will lose very little fat; but the fat-mesomorph may lose a lot of fat with long, continued work; and the endomorph may not lose much at all, partly because he will not be able to do the work. A lean-mesomorph may lose very little.

Usually, a beginning program will not cause much fat loss, but as the program advances to more and more work, the loss of fat comes. With normal, middle-aged people a two-year program may average a 2 to 3 kg (5 to 10 pounds) loss as an average. Middle-aged people who go into training very seriously, doing six to eight miles of walking-jogging per day, may lose 20 to 30 pounds, if they are fat to begin with and are the type to lose that much.

The fuel for exercise is predominantly carbohydrate and fat, with more carbohydrate being used at the start of exercise, and after 20 to 40 minutes of warm-up and relatively easy-rhythmical exercise, more fat begins to be used, and longer work begins to use it from the body. The fat cells are not destroyed but the adipose tissue will then begin to secrete free fatty acid molecules into the blood stream. It may also be restored. A balance of income in calories of food and outgo in calories of work is established, but this fluctuates from day to day and week to week. Short-duration work of relatively high intensity is less effective in using fat than the longer, slower-paced work. After 30 minutes of preliminary warm-up work, and another hour of work, the loss may be on the scales as much as three to five pounds, most of which is water loss. However, as such long-duration work is continued, there will be a reduction of the measured fat and an increase in specific gravity. Carbohydrate is "readily used" but fat is used more slowly, but nevertheless it can be markedly reduced.

Not much protein is used up in exercise but amounts needed to replace deteriorated or injured tissues are used up; and excess protein may be converted to carbohydrate in the body and then into fat if not needed. Short-duration static or tensive exercises, although they may feel hard, do not use up much fat. It is the long, slow work that reaches high calorie levels that uses up fat.

A novice, not in very good condition, may use up as much as 150 to 300 kcal in the light exercise program of 30 minutes per day, but even this takes several weeks to adjust to—and the work may not be done every day at first. If the light-type program is extended to an hour per day, this may be doubled without doing violent exercise. A well-adapted person up to one to two hours of moderate but continuous walk-jog work per day may use up 600 to 1000 kcal per day in such exercise. With moderate eating, such a program may cause the loss of considerable fat in a person who has excess fat for his constitutional body build.

POSTURE

Posture and fitness may be related, as posture may influence breathing, circulation, and metabolism. Posture is also a reflection of the mental state and bodily well-being. Poor posture is frequently seen in people with poor nutrition, or in those who have had severe loss of sleep, or great misfortune. Good posture is associated also with not being "too tense" but well poised and efficiently balanced. Long held, unnatural tensions hurt the circulation; this has been shown in connection with a pronounced droop of the head and chest in leaning over desk work, especially when working in dim light. In the lying posture the muscles are more relaxed, and the circulation is better; but in long standing posture with little movement, there is frequently poor circulation. Posture also influences many types of sport performances, as the right posture for a given play may mean efficient rather than inefficient application of force (as in tennis or golf). Postural muscles may fatigue easily, as in poorly conditioned posterior neck muscles, abdominal muscles, or back muscles. Muscles keep the shoulders reasonably well retracted, the head up, the chest in position for full rather than shallow excursion, the viscera in place, and the pelvis in good balance. The foot muscles govern the alighment of the foot in supination or pronation, as well as toed-in or toed-out. Muscles hold the knees in balance and ready for action. Muscles also control the symmetry, right versus left side, of the body postures. Habit, more than anything else, fixes posture. It may be improved, and after enough practice, becomes automatic, rather than consciously forced.

FLEXIBILITY

Everyone needs some daily flexibility work, as the range of motion in unused joints tends to decrease. Muscles relax, connective tissues elongate, and joints maintain functionality when systematically stretched. Joint ligaments or the muscular attachments may be more susceptible to strain or even rupture when the attached muscles have shortened too much as a result of disuse.

The fact that flexibility usually diminishes with age may be realized but such a tendency can be minimized with flexibility exercises, persistently and systematically performed every day. Flexibility exercises may also involve work of a moderate amount due to the stretching of the antagonistic musculature— connective tissue system.

TENSION

Neuromuscular and emotional tensions may be reduced by exercise programs that are noncompetitive in nature. It is well known that nervous tensions may develop when exercise is very competitive. Competitions are sometimes used in fitness work, but generally, competition is discouraged when individuals are expected to compete out of their class group or age group, trying to do the impossible. Properly done exercise may reduce neuromuscular and emotional tensions, provided time is taken to adapt properly, and in a gradual manner. Otherwise many frustrations and excessive tensions may develop.

High blood pressures may be reduced through carefully managed exercise programs, but it is more commonly seen that pulse rates will reduce even more than blood pressures. Such comparisons between blood pressures and pulse rates can only be made with and reasonable exactness by means of standard score tables. Many such tables exist now (Cureton 1972).

Mental states may cause high tensions often reflected in the blood pressures. Exercise is usually too strenuous if an individual's blood pressures exceed the upper limits of normal responses. This is true also for pulse rates. In carefully controlled or supervised work frequent checks may be made on pulse rates and blood pressures in relation to performances on standardized exercises. It is known that violent emotions may jeopardize an individual's safety. If an individual is so prone to become upset, then the person should avoid situations that bring it about. In this regard, psychologists and psychiatrists report that it is not wise to abuse or frustrate such people, and that they are not easily changed.

STRENGTH

Strength may usually be developed to a considerable extent in any unfit person (see Chapter 2), but is may be developed most in natural mesomorphs who are temporarily out of condition. To develop strength, high resistance is usually used, but for adults over 40 years old it is best to seek only moderate development of strength unless it is greatly needed. Hard strength work may bring a marked rise in blood pressures for people who do not respond naturally to strength efforts. In physical fitness work there is extensive use of bar bells, dumb bells, and also lifting loads, carrying a partner, or heavy-muscular endurance exercises such as chin-ups, push-ups, side leg-raisings, leg raising while lying on the back, squat-jumps, extended press-ups, and many such exercises.

It is probable that for most adults, who are not aiming for competition, that the dynamic (moving) types of muscular resistance exercises are better for health benefits, without upset of the blood pressures, and neuromuscular or emotional tensions. Examples of such activities include: flutter kicks lying prone on the floor, pulley-weights with moderate loading, imitation movements of swimming, tennis strokes, baseball batting, throwing, heaving and catching weighted medicine balls, or loaded bars (or two bats), etc. There are many methods.

CIRCULATORY FITNESS

Circulatory fitness is the result of the blood being pumped from the heart through the arterial, capillary, and venous return systems. There is great concern also about the coronary circulation. In modern society with its automation, use of automobiles, and general disregard for long and hard physical labor, "Let's get a machine that will do it" is a common attitude. There are fundamental requirements of enough blood (volume), good development of the capillaries (which are multiplied in long endurance work), a normal red blood cell count, and good veins.

Most rhythmic endurance exercise is best for improving the circulation, provided nutrition is adequate, and the nervous system is normal. There are many abberations, inadequacies, and pathologies. It is not our purpose here to go into the many diseases of the circulatory system. Circulation may be helped greatly by physical training methods. Just being physically active is helpful. Swimming regularly and for endurance is beneficial, as are cycling, rowing, skating, walking, jogging, and regular rhythmic exercises done for endurance-fitness.

The highly skillful refinements are not especially related to developing circulatory fitness. Improvements have been measured by means of pulse rates, blood pressures, pulse waves—or by more sophisticated laboratory methods. Combinations of the previously mentioned measurements (tests) may be used to approximate the gross circulation through heart and large blood vessels—but distal parts to the heart must be tested by sphygmographic or peripheral circulatory methods (plethysmograph); the electrocardiogram does not measure circulation. Tables and normal standards are easily available.

Circulatory fitness is frequently found to be poor in fitness work. Many experiments have been conducted in physical education, health and fitness work to determine the individual status, improvements and relative value of the various physical activities and sports (Cureton, 1962).

GLANDULAR FITNESS

Glandular fitness is dependent on the function of the glands, especially the adrenal glands, which secrete from the medulla the adrenalin (epinephrine) that may act to increase circulation, respiration, and physical ability. The adrenal glands respond to long, continued exercise training and become larger and more functional. It has long been considered that some of the differences between female and male adult fitness responses are due to differences in the adrenal gland function. The cortex of the gland also furnishes various corticoids that help man or woman bear stress. Such stress resistance is "conditionable" but also depends upon the basic inherited characteristics of the individual.

The glandular functions are tied together in a "central glandular" functional system and usually respond together and cooperatively (synergistically). The nervous system (sympathetic) is also involved in stimulating or depressing (parasympathetic) the adrenal functions. Exercise of high effort acts to stimulate the sympathetic nervous system, and by such means may stimulate the adrenal glands to stronger function. Thus, easy exercise (low effort) has less stimulation to the adrenals, and long, continued training brings about an adaptation so that it takes more and more effort to bring about the adrenal response. Long-trained people may even react parasympathetically, with slower pulse rate, lower basal metabolic rate, and lower level of conscious and subconscious excitement. In general, physical training is helpful and increased ability depends upon the adrenal response, which is better through training, provided the training is long and hard enough in intensity.

Long, continued training at a moderate pace may usually develop a parasympathetic dominance (slow pulse rate, and more economy of metabolism, heat release, and stronger digestive functions); whereas sympathetic excitement is accompanied by faster pulse rate, stronger (taller) R and T-waves of the electrocardiogram, greater systolic amplitude of the heartograph (sphygmograph) and ballistocardiogram (BCG), and higher metabolic rate. Variations may be interpreted by an expert in light of physical fitness meanings. One of the principal interpretations is that, as the strength of the sympathetic-adrenal system (combination) wanes with age and lack of sympathetic stimulation, the pulse rate, metabolic rate, and physical ability may steadily decline—especially in speed and power performances. This decline is frequently associated with physiological aging.

REFERENCES

Affleck, G. B. 1941. Physical Fitness. *Res Quart* (Suppl), 12, 298-493.

Cureton, T. K., Jr. 1962. *The Physiological Effects of Exercise Programs on Adults.* Springfield, Ill.: C. C. Thomas.

Cureton, T. K., Jr. 1972. *Physical Fitness Workbook for Adults.* Springfield, Ill.: C. C. Thomas.

Cureton, T. K., Jr. 1973. *Physical Fitness and Dynamic Health.* New York: Dial Press.

Franks, B. D. (ed.). 1969. *Exercise and Fitness—1969.* Chicago: Athletic Institute.

McCurdy, J. H. and L. A. Larson. May 1935. Measurements of Organic Efficiency for the Prediction of Physical Condition. *Res Quart* (Suppl), 6, 11-41.

Staley, S. C., T. K. Cureton, Jr., L. Heulster, and A. Barry. 1960. *Exercise and Fitness.* Chicago: Athletic Institute.

51

Improvements in Circulatory Fitness in Response to Training

Gary E. Adams

The use of exercise as a training, therapeutic, and rehabilitative method to improve the overall physical fitness levels of adults is common. As many as eight million adults engage in exercise on a regular basis for cardiovascular fitness (Froelicher and Oberman 1973). It is difficult to review all of the literature documenting beneficial hemodynamic, cardiovascular, and cardiorespiratory changes resulting from many different forms of training techniques since it is a popular topic both in lay journalism and scientific literature. Many conclusions have been formulated from experiments conducted in animal and human populations as well as the large amount of epidemiological evidence relating life style and vocation to cardiovascular disease. Although this chapter deals primarily with humans, a recent review by Scheuer and Tipton (1977) has thoroughly documented the chronic effects of training in animal populations.

LIFE STYLE AND VOCATIONAL PHYSICAL ACTIVITY ON CIRCULATORY DYNAMICS

Atherosclerosis is responsible for more morbidity and mortality than any other pathological process in the United States and Western Europe (Apstein 1975). Early evidence from a great number of epidemiological studies conducted during the past quarter century demonstrate that as occupational activity levels increase, there is an inverse prevalence of symptomatic coronary heart disease and a reduction in the rate of mortality from heart attack. While much of the epidemiological evidence supports the notion that habitual physical activity can favorably alter both the incidence of morbidity and mortality from coronary vessel disease among industrialized populations, no single report provides proof of an actual protective effect. The role of physical activity in reducing or preventing atherosclerosis, whether occupational or recreational, remains unclear.

Froelicher and Oberman (1973) have reviewed the status of inactivity as a risk factor in coronary artery disease. By examining epidemiological evidence and after reviewing 32 studies involving a total of 3,631,215 individuals in sample populations ranging from 1 (autopsy study) to 2,000,000 (retrospective study), the authors concluded that the evidence concerning the protective influence of physical activity on coronary artery lesions is inconclusive.

Experimental studies that have examined the direct effect of physical activity on atherosclerosis have been contradictory. Froelicher and Oberman's review (1973) of a number of studies suggests, however, that regular exercise may prevent the onset of coronary artery disease by: (1) improving myocardial perfusion due to increased cardiac capillary-fiber ratio; (2) opening the coronary collaterals; (3) enlarging the coronary arteries; (4) improving the metabolic capacity and changing the morphologic characteristics of peripheral and cardiac muscle; (5) increasing myocardial hypertrophy and contractility; (6) decreasing the effect of the neurohumoral adrenergic system on cardiovascular dynamics; and (7) developing electrophysiological changes in the myocardium that protect against fatal arrhythmias.

The above findings make an impressive case for the beneficial effects of exercise on the physiological state of the cardiovascular system. They support the rationale for continuing to apply physical activity as a preventive or rehabilitative procedure. Although the findings of nationally funded programs designed to answer these important questions are not yet available, the evidence offered by many programs that use exercise to improve cardiovascular fitness and rehabilitate those with cardiovascular disease is encouraging.

CIRCULATORY PHYSIOLOGY AND PHYSICAL TRAINING

This chapter summarizes the known effects of training upon some of the important physiological parameters and the beneficial changes in the dynamics of the blood tissues (hemodynamics), the heart, and the artery-vein relationship (cardiorespiratory dynamics). It is important to note that while the physiological systems are often taxonomized as if to imply they are unique and independent, they are, in fact, each part of a highly integrated system that serves to maintain a constant internal working environment.

Physical training is an interruption of the resting physiological state that results in adaptations that permit the individual to perform more work with greater efficiency and less effort. Trained individuals can also work for longer periods of time at higher intensities than their untrained counterparts before the symptoms of fatigue or possibly dangerous cardiac abnormalities result in a reduction or termination of the work output.

Physical training produces an alteration of the normal resting physiological state due to acute changes in the systems of the body that often appear similar to certain signs and symptoms of a pathological state (Scheuer and Tipton 1977). Physical training is, therefore, a powerful stimulus that is capable of being quantified and is shown to improve the quality of selected systems in response to long-term application.

Physical training involves the habitual use of specific forms of exercise to produce specific desired outcomes (strength, speed, improved work capacity, fat reduction, etc.). The desired outcome is influenced by the type of activity used that, in turn, dictates the type of muscular contraction producing the movement. While some programs have used isometric contraction techniques as a form of training, it is the rhythmical movement of large muscles through wide ranges of motion (isotonic contractions) at a prescribed intensity, duration, and frequency that result in the desired alterations that improve physical work capacity (aerobic capacity). This section reviews only the effects of training in adult fitness programs that have employed aerobic training methods and have reported the effects of such programs on hemodynamic, cardiovascular, and cardiorespiratory dynamics.

Table 51.1 is a summary of the effects of training upon the circulatory dynamics of human subjects. The table was constructed from the reviews of Adams et al. (1977), Astrand and Rodahl (1977), Cureton (1969), Pollock (1973), and Wilmore (1977).

The status of the cardiovascular system can be assessed through a variety of measurements. The most commonly reported measurements have been heart rate, blood pressure, cardiac output, stroke volume, and oxygen uptake. In addition, some investigators have documented the effects of training on heart weight, heart volume, peripheral vascular resistance, peripheral blood flow, peripheral capillary density in active muscle tissue, and changes in collateral vessel opening or development within the myocardium (Astrand and Rodahl 1977; Pollock 1973).

Heart Rate

The most noticeable effect of habitual physical training on the cardiovascular system is the reduced heart rate (bradycardia) at rest, during submaximal exercise, and sometimes at maximal exercise (Pollock 1973). Pollock reports that heart rate is reduced with training, independent of whether the experimental subjects participates in a highly controlled study or in a less supervised adult fitness program. While the reduction in heart rate that can be anticipated is dependent upon the initial level of fitness, an individual can expect to reduce his resting heart rate to at least 65 beats per minute with training (Pollock 1973). While endurance athletes do have lower resting heart rates than moderately trained adults, it is not presently known whether they are more efficient because of inherited superior function, superior training, or perhaps a combination of the two.

Blood Pressure

Middleton (1915) and Scott (1924) were two of the first investigators to make the observation that the blood pressures of active individuals are lower than less active adults. In the past 80 years, several studies have demonstrated slight reductions in resting blood pressures after controlled training. However, the literature does not conclusively support the notion that training produces significant reductions in blood pressure. It is of interest to observe, however, the effect of physical activity on blood pressure. It appears that when a person starts a training program with normal blood pressures, training has little measurable effect. In middle-aged, older, and hypertensive adults, desirable changes in blood pressure have been documented. For example, deVries (1970) has demonstrated significant reduction of both systolic and diastolic blood pressures in older adults. Boyer and Kasch (1970) reported that their hypertensive adults (mean age = 29 years) experienced significant reductions in systolic blood pressure from 156 mm Hg to 145 mm Hg and in diastolic blood pressure from 105 mm Hg to 93 mm Hg. Thus, it appears that exercise cannot only help maintain blood pressures with increasing age, but it can also reduce elevated blood pressures in groups over 40 years of age and in others who are hypertensive.

Oxygen Uptake and the Cardiac Output

The laboratory procedure most often employed to measure the effects of an exercise load is oxygen uptake. The ultimate receptor of oxygen in the body is the cells of the tissues doing work. Physical work above the resting state is accomplished by skeletal muscle tissue that depends upon an adequate blood supply of oxygenated blood. As oxygenated blood passes through the tissues, the extraction rate of oxygen by the muscle cells has been shown to increase, thus improving the efficiency of the tissues to accomplish the work. As the tissues become more efficient in their ability to utilize the oxygen being delivered, the demands upon the heart to replenish the tissues at less than maximal work is decreased. During maximal work, a level of work that few people can sustain for extended periods, the circulatory dynamics after training are characterized by a reduction in heart rate and increases in cardiac output, oxygen uptake, and arteriovenous oxygen difference. At work levels below maximal, the trained individual accomplishes work with a lower heart rate, cardiac output, and oxygen uptake accompanied by increased stroke volume and arteriovenous oxygen difference. Presently, theories helping to explain how physical training

Table 51.1

Summary of the Effects of Training on Circulatory Dynamics in Adult Males and Females of Different Age Groups during Rest, Submaximal and Maximal Work

	Rest						Submaximal						Maximal					
	Men			Women			Men			Women			Men			Women		
	Y	MA	O	Y	MA	O	Y	MA	O	Y	MA	O	Y	MA	O	Y	MA	O
Cardiovascular																		
Heart Rate	→	→	→	→	→	→	→	→	→	→	→	→	NC	NC	NC	NC	NC	NC
Systolic Blood Pressure	?	→	?	?	→	?	→	?	→	→	?	→	?	?	→	?	?	→
Diastolic Blood Pressure	?	?	?	?	?	?	→	?	→	→	?	→	?	?	→	?	?	→
Rate - Pressure Product	→	→	→	→	→	→	→	→	→	→	→	→	→	→	→	→	→	→
Heart Weight	←	?	?	?	←	?	?											
Heart Volume	←	?	?	←	←	?	?											
Peripheral Capillary Density	←	←	?	←	←	?	?											
Myocardial Collateral Circulation	?	?	?	?	?	?												

NOTE: When chronic changes have been documented within a system that are not dependent upon acute exercise conditions, the changes are noted under the resting columns only.

	Rest Men			Rest Women			Submaximal Men			Submaximal Women			Maximal Men			Maximal Women		
	Y	MA	O	Y	MA	O	Y	MA	O	Y	MA	O	Y	MA	O	Y	MA	O
Cardiorespiratory																		
Oxygen Uptake (Peripheral Respiratory Exchange)	NC	NC	NC	NC	NC	NC	↓	↓	↓	↓	↓	↓	↑	↑	↑	↑	↑	↑
Arteriovenous Oxygen Difference	NC	NC	NC	NC	NC	NC	↑	NC	NC	↑	NC	NC	↑	NC	?	↑	NC	?
Myocardial Respiratory Exchange Myocardial Oxygen Uptake	↓	↓	↓	↓	↓	↓	↓	↓	↓	↓	↓	↓	↓	↓	↓	↓	↓	↓
Hemodynamic																		
Cardiac Output	NC	NC	NC	NC	NC	NC	↓	↓	↓	↓	↓	?	↑	↑	NC	↑	↑	NC
Blood Volume	↑	↑	?	↑	↑	?												
Total Hemoglobin	?	?	↑	?	?													
Hematocrit	NC	NC	NC	NC	NC	NC												

Y = Young   MA = Middle Age   O = Old Age
↑ = Increased   ↓ = Decreased   ? = Questionable
NC = No Change

Constructed from the review of Adams (1977, pp. 322-343), Astrand and Rodahl (1977, p. 681), Cureton (1969, pp. 33-89), Pollock (1973, pp. 155-188) and Wilmore (1977, p. 67).

effects the efficiency of the circulatory dynamics at submaximal work levels have been offered by Clausen (1969), Rochelle et al. (1971), and Rowell (1969). Clausen has proposed that the reduction in cardiac output is due to an increased arteriovenous oxygen difference in the blood that circulates through the working tissues, thereby reducing the need for greater blood flow in the working tissues. Rowell and Rochelle et al. have proposed that the heart rate and cardiac output are reduced due to a greater percentage of the total cardiac output being diverted to the working muscle tissue. Thus, the increased arteriovenous oxygen difference is a result of increased blood flow to the muscle tissues which enhances the oxygen extraction rate. The difference, therefore, between the two proposals is where physical conditioning is having its greatest effect. Clausen emphasizes peripheral cellular respiratory adaptation as being most affected, while Rowell and Rochelle point to the augmented distribution of the blood flow, thus placing the primary effect of physical conditioning upon the enhanced tissue perfusion. Whatever the mechanism is, at rest and during submaximal work levels, trained people accomplish the work with a reduction in cardiac output, oxygen uptake, and heart rate accompanied by increased stroke volume and increased oxygen extraction per unit of blood circulating through working tissues.

CIRCULATORY COMPARISONS BETWEEN MEN AND WOMEN AFTER TRAINING

The amount of literature available form which to formulate conclusions about the physiological response of women to physical training is small when compared to the investigations devoted to the study of men. A comprehensive discussion on the topic has been written by Drinkwater (1973). A few studies have thoroughly documented the physiological effects of training in women of young, middle, and old age (Kilbom and Astrand 1971; Van Handel et al. 1976).

Hemodynamic, cardiovascular, and cardiorespiratory data for women are presented in Table 51.1. The evidence shows that through training women can significantly reduce their heart rates, regardless of age, at rest and for any submaximal work level (Drinkwater 1973). In addition, maximal oxygen uptake and maximal cardiac output have been shown to improve regardless of age (Kilbom and Astrand 1971). Reduction of heart rate is accompanied by an increase in stroke volume and arteriovenous oxygen difference in young and middle-aged women at submaximal working conditions (Kilbom and Astrand 1971; Van Handel et al. 1976). The cardiovascular data for older women are not complete enough to formulate conclusions regarding stroke volume and arteriovenous oxygen difference. In addition, reductions in blood pressure regardless of age have been demonstrated (Kilbom and Astrand 1971). Structural and volume differences between age-matched men and women of the same height and weight show that men can achieve greater absolute values for oxygen uptake and cardiac output.

SUMMARY

The chronic use of physical training can elicit desirable changes in the dynamics of the cardiovascular, cardiorespiratory, and blood tissue systems. In general, through vigorous training an individual can expect to increase his or her maximal physical work capacity (oxygen uptake). In addition, training causes a reduction in heart rate, blood pressure, and the work of the heart at rest and during submaximal exercise. Training also increases maximum cardiac output, stroke volume, and the arteriovenous oxygen difference. Although the specific mechanism by which blood is distributed to working muscles is still not fully understood, physical work is enhanced by increased blood flow to active tissue and improved extraction of oxygen at the working muscle level. While men achieve higher absolute values, both men and women seem to profit in a similar manner as a result of training.

REFERENCES

Adams, W. C., et al. 1977. Long-term physiologic adaptations to exercise with special reference to performance and cardiorespiratory function in health and disease. In *Exercise In Cardiovascular Health and Disease*. New York: Yorke Medical Books.

Amsterdam, E. A., et al. 1977. Exercise testing in the indirect assessment of myocardial oxygen consumption: Application for evaluation of mechanisms and therapy of angina pectoris. In *Exercise in Cardiovascular Health and Disease*. New York: Yorke Medical Books.

Apstein, C. S. 1975. Current methods of reducing the serum cholesterol concentration: Rationale and an approach to therapy. In *Coronary Artery Medicine and Surgery Concepts and Controversies*. New York: Appleton-Century Crofts.

Astrand, P. -O. and K. Rodahl. 1977. *Textbook of Work Physiology*. 2nd ed. New York: McGraw-Hill.

Boyer, J. and F. Kasch. 1970. Exercise therapy in hypertensive men. *JAMA* 211, 1668-1671.

Carlsten, A. and G. Grimby. 1976. *The Circulatory Response to Musculature Exercise in Man*. Springfield, Il. Charles C. Thomas.

Clausen, J. P. 1969. Effects of physical conditioning. *Scand J Clin Lab Invest*, 24, 305-313.

Cureton, T. K., Jr. 1969. *The Physiological Effects of Exercise Programs on Adults*. Springfield, IL. Charles C. Thomas.

deVries, H. A. 1970. Physiological effects of an exercise training regimen upon men aged 52-88. *J Gerontol*, 25, 325-326.

Drinkwater, B. L. 1973. Physiological responses of women to exercise. In *Exercise and Sports Sciences Reviews*, J. H. Wilmore (ed.). Vol 1. New York: Academic Press.

Froelicher, V. F. and A. Oberman. 1973. Analysis of epidemiologic studies of physical inactivity as risk factor for coronary artery disease. *Prog in CV Dis*, 15, 41-65.

Hamilton, M., et al. 1954. The etiology of essential hypertension. I. The arterial pressure in the general population. *Clin Sci,* 13, 11-35.

Kilbom, A. and I. Astrand. 1971. Physical training with submaximal intensities in women. *Scand J Clin Lab Invest,* 28, 163-175.

Kitamura, K., et al. 1971. Hemodynamic correlates of myocardial oxygen consumption during upright exercise. *J Appl Physiol,* 32, 516-522.

Middleton, W. S. 1915. The influence of athletic training on blood pressure. *Am J Med Sci* (Series 2), 150, 426-431.

Pollock, M. L. 1973. The quantification of endurance training programs. In *Exercise and Sports Sciences Reviews,* J. H. Wilmore (ed.). Vol 1. New York: Academic Press.

Rochelle, R. H., et al. 1971. Peripheral blood flow response to exercise consequent to physical training. *Med Sci Spts,* 3, 122-129.

Rowell, L. B. 1969. Circulation. *Med Sci Spts,* 1, 15-22.

Scheuer, J. and C. M. Tipton. 1977. Cardiovascular adaptation to physical training. *Ann Rev Physiol,* 39, 221-251.

Scott, V. T. 1924. A study of the effects of daily exercise on the pulse and arterial pressure. *Military Surgeon,* 55, 334-336.

Van Handel, P. J., et al. 1976. Central circulatory adaptations to physical training. *Res Quart,* 47, 815-823.

Wilmore, J. H. 1977. Acute and chronic physiological responses to exercise. In *Exercise in Cardiovascular Health and Disease.* New York: Yorke Medical Books.

52

The San Diego State University Program: A Systematic Approach to Adult Physical Fitness Programs

Fred W. Kasch

Vigorous exercise programs may be classified as preventive or rehabilitative. The former is of primary importance in forestalling disease and improving general health. The latter type is a necessity for diseased people (for example, with coronary heart disease) who must be returned to productivity. Each program is monetarily valuable to the recipient and family as well as to the employer and society.

THE SAN DIEGO STATE UNIVERSITY PROGRAM

Since 1958 a vigorous fitness program for adults has been in continuous operation at San Diego State University. It operates 12 months of the year, meeting three times per week. About 175 people are involved in nine different exercise groups, with about 40 having serious heart disease. Nearly all of the so-called normal subjects have at least one or more of the coronary risk factors, more than 60 percent were originally overweight, and over 25 percent were hypertensive.

The annual fee for the program helps to bear the costs of operation, including leadership, laboratory assessments, and program administration. Subjects are admitted under rather rigid criteria: age 25 to 70 years, a promise of strict adherence to the program, a medical history suggesting a need for participation in such a program, and a medical examination by the person's own physician.

The approach at San Diego includes:

1. Medical examination—(a) a general physical examination, (b) resting electrocardiogram (ECG), (c) serum cholesterol, (d) urinalysis, (e) hematocrit, and (f) hemoglobin.

2. Laboratory exercise evaluation—(a) resting and exercise ECG, (b) blood pressure, (c) maximum oxygen uptake and associated measurements, (d) nutritional counseling plus body composition by hydrostatic weighing and skinfolds, and (e) 23 blood chemistries.

3. Motor fitness—(a) gross body flexibility, (b) minimal muscular strength, and (c) body mechanics.

4. Personal counseling and evaluation.

4. Exercise prescription and assignment to a group leader.

6. Periodic re-evaluation.

THE EXERCISE REGIMEN AND MONITORING

All groups are under competent leadership, which is the key to a successful program. The exercise aims include: (1) improved range of joint motion or flexibility, (2) development of an understanding of principles of body movement and mechanics, (3) release of tension, and (4) increased cardiovascular efficiency.

Muscular strength is minimized. Two main forms of cardiovascular exercise are used: interval running and swimming. Each person's capacity is determined from the laboratory-exercise test (bicycle ergometer). The intensity of exercise is determined by use of Karvonen's formula, and a target heart rate is set for each subject. The leader permits each subject to elevate his or her heart rate only to the prescribed level by periodically checking it for ten seconds and recording the same. Thus, each subject is monitored to prevent overstress and yet each obtains enough dosage to improve his or her cardiovascular system. Dosage initially is 40 to 70 percent of maximum HR, and later 70 to 90 percent. Each subject progresses at his or her own rate yet is a part of a larger gruop of 30 to 40 persons. Records are kept of frequency, mileage, or duration; rate in meters per minute; and exercise and two-minute recovery heart rates. The latter is expected to return to 110 to 120 beats per minute within a two-minute period.

Balke (1960) has provided a means for determining the amount of energy expenditure and, thus, the level of work capacity during running. By knowing the time and distance, one can calculate the rate and estimate the oxygen consumed or intensity of work performed. It is thus possible to prescribe the exact amount of work for each subject. During swimming, heart rate is also monitored and recorded as well as the distance and rate. Running requires mainly a field, a competent leader, and a clock. The main drawback is musculoskeletal injury. To minimize muscle and joint problems, 20 minutes of careful stretching-flexibility-relaxation exercises are given prior to interval running. Only mild resistance work aimed at strength development is included. Valsalva and breath-holding are avoided at all times by exhalation on each repetition of each exercise. Many of the calisthenic-type rhythmic exercises are performed on the floor to release tension by minimizing the effect of gravity.

Games are not used and competition is avoided. No land exercise is performed by the swimmers. The caloric cost per session is about 600 calories. Annually this would amount to about 25 pounds of fat or weight loss.

RESULTS

Anthropometric and Physiological Effects

An analysis of the results of past participants reveals that valuable changes have occurred in most normal subjects within one year. Some subjects did not show positive results as rapidly. However, the mean body weight after one year was reduced about 3.2 kg, while body fat declined 14 to 15 percent (Carter and Phillips 1969). This change in body composition was reflected in the max VO_2 by an increase of 24 percent, 32 to 40 ml $\cdot$ kg^{-1} $\cdot$ min^{-1}. Gross O_2 uptake (true change) climbed 17 percent, from 2.60 to 3.05 liters per minute (Kasch and Boyer 1968; Kasch et al. 1973). The latter two measures are indicative of improvement in the heart and circulation. Pulmonary ventilation (V_E) improved some 13 percent within one year, while O_2 pulse, which is indicative of stroke volume, showed an increase of 17 percent from 14.4 to 17.4 ml per beat. Maximum heart rate (HR) was reduced 5 to 6 beats, from about 180 to 174 beats per minute. The production of lactic acid during maximal work remained relatively stable, 99 to 91 mg percent.

Swim training gave almost identical results as running, with improvements in max VO_2 from 31 to 38 ml $\cdot$ kg^{-1} $\cdot$ min^{-1} (23 percent). Men with coronary heart disease (CHD) improved 23 percent in max VO_2 after 12 months of physical training, 1.91 to 2.44 l $\cdot$ min^{-1} (Kasch and Boyer 1969). Table 52.1 summarizes the findings during maximal work over a two-year period in normal high-risk men and matched controls.

Table 52.1

Physiological Responses of High-Risk Men Resulting from
Twenty-four Months of Training

Group	Time	$\dot{V}O_2$ max 1/min	$\dot{V}O_2$ max ml/kg $\cdot$ min^{-1}	V-TBPS 1/min	O_2 Pulse ml/beat	HR max bpm	Lactate mg%
Experimental	0 mos.	2.59	32.6	115.1	14.4	180	99
	24 mos.	3.04	39.9	123.0	17.4	174	91
Percentage Change		+17.4	+22.4	+6.9	+20.8	−3.3	−8.1
Control	0 mos.	2.43	34.0	115.3	14.0	174	103
	24 mos.	2.38	32.7	105.9	13.8	173	94
Percentage Change		−2.1	−3.8	−8.1	−1.4	−0.1	−8.7

Training and Adherence to Program

Attendance averaged 71 percent over a 12-month period for the running program. The dropout rate at one year was about 10 to 12 percent, at two years about 30 percent. After six years retention has been 42 percent; seven years, 20 percent; eight years, 18 percent; and nine years, 11 percent.

The average mileage run per participant per year is about 370, or 3.7 miles per session. In one typical group of men, attendance was in excess of 84 percent of the possible sessions, 117 out of 140 days. These men averaged 464 miles per year, or 4.0 miles per session, and 9.9 miles per week. Each man averaged 2.3 miles of continuous nonstop running per session in 21 minutes at a rate of 177 meters per minute. This is equivalent to an oxygen uptake of 39 ml $\cdot$ kg^{-1} $\cdot$ min^{-1} $\pm$ 10 percent (Balke 1960).

The exercise heart rate (HR) during running averaged 159 beats per minute and after two minutes of recovery it dropped to 116 per minute. From the exercise HR of 159, it is estimated that the work level was about 85 percent of capacity.

The swimmers had a poorer attendance than the runners, being only 53 percent compared to 71 percent. The men swam an average of 48 miles per year. Those participants with musculoskeletal problems benefited greatly from use of the pool. Some people preferred training in water in contrast to land, and some cannot exercise on land due to permanent joint or similar problems.

Unquestionably, max VO$_2$ can be increased in previously sedentary middle-aged people. The 17 percent decrease in mean max VO$_2$ with increasing age can be offset with adequate physical training. Whether this increase will have an effect on the incidence of coronary heart disease (CHD) is still unknown. However, it is reasonable to assume that there has been an improvement in cardiovascular function and, clinically, this improvement is valuable to the life and health of the subject.

ADVANTAGES AND DISADVANTAGES OF THE SYSTEMATIC APPROACH

It is our opinion that presently a sports-oriented program will not produce adequate or lasting fitness. The degree of intensity of the exercise in sports varies greatly and is uncontrolled. At times it may be too much for the participants' capacity and at other times too little. Sports usually lack a continuous stimulus above 70 percent of capacity in order to create an aerobic response. The American sport culture has been in vogue for 50 years, yet the public is unfit today. The cost would be prohibitive to produce enough sport facilities for the masses. That is not to say that we should avoid sports. On the contrary, they should be in addition to the fitness program. Get fit first, then play sports, but do not depend upon sports for fitness. We need new sports for mass participation with limited space, equipment, and skill. We do not have these last three requirements as yet. Therefore, we recommend a systematic method of mass exercise for today's world. The factors necessary to advance the systematic approach to fitness are:

1. The required space is easily accessible and workout time is short.
2. Exercise prescription is safe and reliable.
3. Sure, reliable results of fitness can be obtained.
4. Minimum or no equipment is required.
5. The demonstration of measurable results, not dependent upon skill or win-loss records, will improve motivation.
6. No age and few physical limitations need be imposed.

Factors that tend to inhibit use of systematic fitness programs include:

1. A lack of adequate motivation to participate exists in many people.
2. Experienced laboratory personnel are not available.
3. Trained leaders and appropriate programs are not readily accessible.
4. The general public prefers sport or game type activities.

The advantages of health gained after 20 years of systematic fitness appear to far outweigh the disadvantages of such a program.

REFERENCES

Balke, B. 1960. Biodynamics. In *Medical Physics*. Chicago: Yearbook Publishers.

Carter, J. E. L. and W. H. Phillips. 1969. Structural changes in exercising middle-aged males during a 2-year period. *J Appl Physiol,* 27, 787-794.

Kasch, F. W. and J. L. Boyer. 1968. *Adult Fitness*. Palo Alto: National Press Books.

Kasch, F. W. and J. L. Boyer. 1969. Changes in maximum work capacity resulting from six month training in patients with ischemic heart disease. *Med Sci Spts,* 1, 156-159.

Kasch, F. W., W. H. Phillips, J. E. L. Carter, and J. L. Boyer. 1973. Cardiovascular changes in middle-aged men during two years of training. *J Appl Physiol,* 34, 53-57.

53

Physical Fitness in the Young Men's Christian Association (YMCA)

Wayne E. Sinning and Clayton R. Myers

HISTORY OF FITNESS IN THE YMCA

The YMCA was first organized in London, England in 1844 by George Williams, a young draper's assistant, to provide for the improvement of the spiritual and mental condition of young men employed in the commerce of that time. It spread rapidly among employees of business firms in London. Since then, the YMCA has become an international organization. Vigorous programs in physical fitness and sports education can be found in YMCAs throughout the world. The review in this chapter is limited, however, primarily to its involvement in physical fitness in the United States.

The YMCA was established in the United States in 1851 in Boston, Massachusetts by Thomas V. Sullivan, a retired sea captain. As in England, the movement spread rapidly—by 1860 there were 205 YMCAs with 25,000 members in cities throughout the United States. Sectarianism was abandoned early, and programs were opened to all who accepted the general purpose of the YMCA.

The YMCA in the United States recognized the value of physical activity for the well-being of mankind almost from its beginning. In 1855 the first swimming pool was constructed in a Brooklyn, New York, YMCA. In 1858 the same YMCA installed bowling alleys in recognition of the need for physical recreation by people employed in jobs requiring "brain work." By 1856 groups within the YMCA began advocating the inclusion of "properly conducted" gymnasiums and baths in Y facilities. The 1860 National Convention of the YMCA adopted a resolution favoring the establishment of gymnasiums "as a safeguard against the allurements of objectionable places of resort, which have proved the ruin of thousands of the youth of our country." The symbol of the YMCA, which is a down pointed equilateral triangle representing the three sides

The authors express their appreciation to Mr. Donald S. McCuaig, Director, Physical Education, National Council of YMCAs of Canada, for providing information about YMCAs in Canada and reviewing this article.

of a balanced personality, recognizes the development of the body as well as that of the mind and spirit as an essential feature of the "whole man."

The first true YMCA gymnasium was constructed in 1869 as part of the new 23rd Street YMCA in New York City. It was planned by pioneer enthusiast Robert R. McBurney and has since been named after him. The YMCA experienced a building boom in the early 1900s and thereby became the nation's largest operator of gymnasiums, health clubs, and swimming pools. It still holds that distinction. A recent survey of 1842 YMCAs throughout the United States identified 3700 gymnasiums, swimming pools, running tracks, and other facilities suitable for physical fitness programs. YMCAs also run programs in other local facilities such as schools and recreation centers.

Prior to 1950 YMCAs provided many exercise programs for adults, primarily in the form of calisthenics. Jogging has also been a regular program in YMCAs since the late 1800s. The modern fitness thrust, however, came in the 1950s due to the increased interest in physical fitness under the impetus of the Kraus-Weber report. Bonnie Prudden and Dr. Hans Kraus conducted a series of clinics certifying testers to use the Kraus-Weber test. Millions of school-age youngsters were tested, and "fitness" as a YMCA program feature was firmly established.

YMCAs were well prepared for the fitness era. Association colleges (George Williams College in Downer's Grove, Illinois and Springfield College in Springfield, Massachusetts) had long emphasized physiology of exercise in the training of young YMCA professionals. Early and significant contributions were made by Dr. Arthur Steinhaus of George Williams and Dr. Peter V. Karpovich of Springfield.

The most profound influence on YMCA fitness was made by Dr. Thomas K. Cureton of the University of Illinois. Dr. Cureton, already an established fitness authority, researcher, and teacher, offered a series of graduate summer courses to better prepare physical educators for scientific fitness programming in the 1950s. This preparation, followed by hundreds of one-, two-, or three-day clinics in local Ys, fully established the YMCAs as centers of adult fitness in this country. This emphasis on fitness was profound enough to make the inclusion of physical fitness testing rooms and running tracks common in new construction, as well as to inspire such modifications to existing structures.

The 1950s and 1960s saw new physical fitness programs develop and flourish across the United States. In the 1960s the YMCA underwent an extensive reorganization in its physical education leadership. At that time Dr. Lloyd Arnold was chosen to direct the physical education policy in the YMCA, while Dr. Clayton Myers was made responsible for the physical fitness program.

As a result of a survey of YMCA facilities, programs, and personnel, it became apparent that the Y had a need to identify and develop its own physical fitness program. Steps were thereafter taken to develop a program that was national in scope and representative of the general consensus of YMCA leaders throughout the country. Research and writing teams covering several areas of interest were formed and some 70 experts in medicine, physiology, and physical education became involved. In October 1971 the teams met in Philadelphia to share and refine manuscripts. In addition, a National YMCA Consultation on Physical Fitness was held in conjunction with these meetings to inform the public about physical fitness and to serve as a vehicle to announce the new National YMCA Physical Fitness Programs (Special Report, National YMCA Physical Fitness Consultation 1972).

Subsequent to the Philadelphia meeting, manuscripts were further edited and organized for publication. The final product was the book, *The Y's Way to Physical Fitness,* which was published in 1973 and has become the YMCA's guide to organizing and leading physical fitness programs. (See References for list of fitness materials published by the YMCA.) The guide contains information on organizing and administering programs, pertinent questions related to exercise physiology, physical fitness testing, a basic exercise program, special exercise programs, leadership training, and physical fitness resources.

The publication of *The Y's Way to Physical Fitness* was followed by extensive training programs for physical fitness leaders. Workshops ranging in length from one day to one week were conducted by colleges and universities as well as in YMCAs to introduce professional and lay personnel to the concepts and procedures set down in the official guide.

Leadership for the conduct of YMCA programs is provided through national and regional offices. Each of the six regions that comprise the national YMCA employs a physical education consultant and designates a Regional Fitness Commissioner whose duty it is to provide leadership and oversee physical fitness programming in the region. For the most part, the Consultant is a coordinator of, and advisor to, YMCAs in his region.

The YMCA has continued to conceive new approaches to developing physical fitness since the advent of *The Y's Way to Physical Fitness.* There are now eight major segments included in the overall nationwide program. They are designed for youths as well as adults and are discussed in some detail in the following sections.

The YMCArdiac therapy protocol was introduced at a second National Consultation on Cardiovascular Health held in Chicago in November 1975. This conference was highlighted by presentations by recognized experts in the field of physical fitness and cardiovascular health (Special Report, National Consultation on Cardiovascular Health 1976).

A characteristic of YMCA physical fitness programs has been the utilization of local, regional, and national leadership and resources. Most programs rely on local medical, business, and professional people for advice and guidance. Nonprofessional or lay people frequently lead programs or administer tests under the supervision of trained professionals. On the national level, people such as Dr. Thomas K. Cureton, Dr. Gary Fry, Dr. Hans Kraus, and Dr. Lawrence Golding have provided long-term leadership for the YMCA's national effort.

PHYSICAL FITNESS PROGRAMS OFFERED BY THE YMCA

YMCA-Feelin' Good Program

This program, developed by Dr. Charles Kuntzleman, is designed for youth. Modern health concepts, especially those related to physical fitness, are taught through physical activity experiences. Participants complete both textbook and reading assignments. Both classroom and home activities are incorporated in this program.

YMCA-Activetics Program

Activetics, also designed by Dr. Kuntzleman, is focused on the need for more physical activity as an aid in controlling weight. It emphasizes the relationship between becoming fit and feeling better and is directed toward teenagers and adults (Kuntzleman 1975).

Y's Way to Physical Fitness

This is the fitness program most frequently used by YMCAs today and is described in the YMCA publication of that name. Following medical clearance, participants take a test of physical fitness including measures of strength, physical work capacity, flexibility, and body composition. The exercise sessions are planned to provide warm-up; vigorous calisthenics to develop strength, muscular endurance, and flexibility; jogging to develop cardiovascular-respiratory fitness; and a cool-down period. These programs are usually community-oriented and conducted by certified professional personnel with the assistance of lay people from the program. Policy and procedures are established with the assistance of a physical fitness council or committee made up of interested and professionally qualified people (Myers, Golding, and Sinning 1973).

Cardiovascular Health

This program is an expansion of the previous program, the primary distinction being an emphasis on risk factor screening for cardiovascular disease. Exercise electrocardiograms are required as part of the medical clearance procedure, and exercise prescription is emphasized. Medical advisory committees help plan local adaptations and supervise medical aspects of the program.

YMCArdiac Therapy

Medically prescribed and supervised exercise is provided for postcoronary and postsurgical patients as well as for those at high coronary risk through YMCArdiac Therapy. The protocols for testing, exercise, and supervision were written and evaluated by cardiologists, physiologists, and physical educators experienced in working with cardiac rehabilitation programs. All cardiovascular disease risk factors are dealt with through participant practice and education. These programs are often planned with the cooperation of American Heart Association affiliates and are conducted under the direct supervision of local physicians serving on Medical Advisory Committees.

The national YMCA cardiovascular health program is conducted in YMCA Cardiovascular Health Centers, Physical Fitness Centers, and Activity Centers throughout the United States. The functions and program offerings of these centers are dependent on the leadership and physical resources available locally and the specific needs of the community.

Risk Factor Education Program

Risk factor evaluation and education is a new dimension of the physical fitness programs developed in the YMCA. Strictly educational in nature, these programs amplify the role of smoking, weight control, and stress management in the prevention of coronary heart disease and strive to modify behavior accordingly. Program models have been developed for YMCA use by Dr. Joyce Nash of the Stanford Heart Disease Prevention Clinic.

Y's Way to a Healthy Back

Chronic low back problems are dealt with in this program developed under the leadership of Dr. Hans Kraus and Alexander Melleby. The special exercises making up the program are designed to produce relaxation and relieve mild back pain for sufferers who have no pathology.

Y's Way to Slim Living

The Y's Way to Slim Living emphasizes behavior modification to help people with chronic weight problems. It was designed primarily for the obese under the direction of JoAnn Ploeger. Although not an exercise program in itself, it is part of the YMCA's national effort to improve the nation's health.

Special Programs

YMCAs frequently offer special programs that are not national in scope. These include fitness activities for preschoolers, special conditioning for sports such as skiing or hiking prior to the season, and individualized exercise routines when group programs are not available.

Another outreach of YMCA fitness in recent years has been an extension into business and industry. Many YMCAs are now organizing and conducting physical fitness programs for major companies, many times in facilities owned and operated by them.

PROFESSIONAL TRAINING

An important YMCA resource is its pool of professionally trained personnel developed through in-service training experience. Each of the programs offered has a certification procedure by which people become qualified to conduct the programs previously described. Many of these are one- or two-day workshops with standardized curricula and instructors' materials.

The most specialized workshops are those for the *Y's Way to Physical Fitness* (Goldberg 1976) and *YMCArdiac Therapy* (Fry 1976). These are usually offered in colleges and universities with exercise physiology laboratories and other resources necessary for advanced instruction in fitness testing and programming. Currently, there are two levels of certification provided by the YMCA, the Physical Fitness Specialist and the Advanced Physical Fitness Specialist. Over 1200 of the former and 500 of the latter have been certified. YMCArdiac Therapy training utilizes the team approach involving the cardiologist, fitness director, nurse, and business director of the program.

CANADIAN PROGRAMS

The physical fitness movement in the YMCAs of Canada developed much like it did in the United States. Its primary thrust emerged in the early 1960s when the National Council, under the direction of J. Wesley McVicar, conducted a pilot project in physical fitness funded by the Directorate of Fitness and Amateur Sports of the Federal Government. The project included fitness clinics and testing seminars as well as television and radio presentations. Since that time, the Canadian YMCA fitness programs have developed much like those in the United States through the involvement of interested and committed lay personnel as well as trained, professional physical educators. The movement there has been enhanced by greater commitment and financial support by the federal government than in the United States.

The Canadian YMCA also has professional development programs leading to certification as assistant instructor, instructor (specialist), certified instructor, certified supervisor, and director, the last being full-time Y personnel with professional training culminating in a university degree in physical education, medicine, public health, or a related field. Specific programs sponsored by the Canadian YMCA are YMCA L.I.F.E., Lower Back Problems, Postcoronary Assessment and Rehabilitation, Nutrition Education, Prenatal and Postnatal, Geriatrics and Fitness, Yoga, "Heart Alert," Conditioning for Specific Sports, and Rhythmics. They also train personnel (assistant instructors) to administer specific physical fitness tests.

PROMOTIONAL PROGRAMS

YMCAs in both the United States and Canada have characteristically been able to involve large numbers of people in physical fitness projects. Especially significant have been jogging promotions to encourage physical fitness involvement. For example, in one event celebrating the YMCA's 125th anniversary in the United States, 28,000 runners logged an estimated 3,500,000 miles. In 1967, Canadian YMCAs sponsored "Expo-'67," a 100-mile fitness run, to celebrate Canada's centennial year—1100 Centennial Spoons were awarded to runners completing the task. Similar projects have been done with swimming. Using such techniques and its nationwide resources, the YMCA has been able to generate widespread interest in physical fitness.

RESOURCE INFORMATION

The YMCA continually re-evaluates existing programs and develops new ones. Current information can be obtained from the following addresses: In the United States—National Council of YMCAs of the USA, 291 Broadway, New York, NY 10007; in Canada—The National Council of YMCAs of Canada, 2160 Yonge Street, Toronto, Ontario M4S 2A9.

REFERENCES

Canadian YMCA Physical Fitness Program. 1977. Toronto: National Council of YMCAs of Canada.

Fitness Appraisal Programs and Practices in the YMCA. 1977. Toronto: National Council of YMCAs of Canada.

Fry, G. A. 1976. YMCArdiac therapy: A distinctive community service. *J Phys Ed,* 144-146.

Golding, L. A. 1976. The Y's Way to Physical Fitness. *J Phys Ed.*

Kuntzleman, C. T. 1975. *Activetics.* New York: Peter H. Wyden.

Leadership Training and Development. 1977. Toronto: National Council of YMCAs of Canada.

Myers, C. R. 1976. The nationwide YMCA cardiovascular health program. *J Phys Ed,* 141-143.

Myers, C. R. 1975. *The Official YMCA Physical Fitness Handbook.* New York: Popular Library.

Myers, C. R. 1973. Physical fitness needs to become major focus of YMCA program. *J Phys Ed,* 11-14.

Myers, C. R., L. A. Golding, and W. E. Sinning (eds.). 1973. *The Y's Way to Physical Fitness.* New York: The National Council YMCA, U.S.A.

Special Report, National YMCA Consultation on Cardiovascular Health, 1976. *J Phys Ed.*

Special Report, National YMCA Physical Fitness Consultation, 1972. *J Phys Ed,* 98-174.

54

Physical Activity and Coronary Heart Disease

Steven N. Blair

Cardiovascular disease is one of the major health problems facing the United States today. More than 25 million Americans may have some form of cardiovascular disease. In 1973 heart and vascular diseases accounted for 53.8 percent of all deaths reported in the United States. These one million deaths are three times the number attributed to the second leading cause, cancer. The economic impact of cardiovascular disease is estimated at over $40 billion per year.

Although several separate causes of cardiovascular mortality can be identified, more than 80 percent of all heart and vascular disease deaths are caused by a single problem, atherosclerosis, and most of this is in the form of coronary heart disease (CHD). This disease is characterized by the development of atheromatous plaque inside the arterial wall. This plaque is composed of smooth muscle cells, lipid, and scar tissue. As this deposit grows it may impede or stop the flow of blood through the artery. The culmination of the atherosclerotic process is a complete blockage of an artery accompanied by injury to the distal tissues that it supplies. Arteries delivering blood to the heart and brain appear to be especially susceptible to this disease, with the end result being heart attack or stroke.

The basic etiology of atherosclerosis is not completely understood; however, at the present time there are two main theories as to how the development of the atherosclerotic plaque is initiated. Many investigators believe that plaques form in response to injury to the arterial wall. Numerous animal experiments have shown that repeated injury to the wall seems to set the disease process in motion. It is hypothesized that the injury can be caused by mechanical irritation, high lipid concentrations in the blood, carbon monoxide in the blood, or perhaps numerous other conditions. The process seems to begin as a fatty streak on the arterial wall to which platelets adhere, into which smooth muscle cells proliferate, and fibrous connective tissue accumulates. Some investigators believe that development of the fatty streak into an atheromatous plaque is dependent upon an elevated concentration of low-density lipoprotein (LDL). (See Chapter 46.)

A competing hypothesis on how plaques develop states that plaques are benign tumors. Investigators favoring this view report that the cells in a given plaque appear to be progeny of a single cell. It has been suggested that cigarette smoking, for example, may cause these tumors to develop because of the mutagenic characteristics of cigarette smoke. It is also possible that plasma lipoproteins might carry fat-soluble mutagens to the arteries.

Regardless of the basic mechanism of the development of atherosclerosis, much evidence supports the generalized risk factor hypothesis. Epidemiological research of the last two or three decades has consistently demonstrated that CHD prevalence and incidence are associated with characteristics that have come to be known as risk factors. That is, individuals possessing those factors have a higher risk of developing CHD than individuals who do not possess such characteristics. Currently identified risk factors include age, sex, hypercholesterolemia, hypertension, cigarette smoking, sedentary living habits, obesity, and stress. Those risk factors appear to be independent but accumulative. Modest elevations of several risk factors increase risk of CHD as much as very large elevations of a single risk factor. Most available evidence is correlational, and causality cannot be established at the present time. Most experts believe, however, that it is extremely prudent to act on the basis of currently available data. Several large scale experimental clinical trials (Multiple Risk Factor Intervention Trial or MRFIT, Hypertension Detection and Follow-up Program or HDFP, and Lipid Research Clinics or LRC) under the aegis of the National Heart, Lung, and Blood Institute are currently under way and should provide extremely useful data on the risk factor hypothesis.

PREVENTION OR TREATMENT?

The large number of deaths per year, the number of sudden deaths, deaths without warning in apparently well individuals, and the lack of treatment procedures for advanced disease, support the concept of prevention of CHD. As many as 70 percent of CHD deaths occur before the victim reaches a hospital and medical care; therefore, a major reduction in mortality must come from preventive rather than therapeutic measures.

Two contrasting professional views of atherosclerosis have been elucidated by Blackburn (1975). The academic view of atherosclerosis holds that CHD is largely a metabolic abnormality due primarily to genetic defects. The solution to the problem then is to conduct more basic research into the mechanism of lipid abnormalities and develop specific therapy using medical and surgical techniques.

Conversely, the pragmatic view states that CHD is largely a "life-style" disease due to living habits that elevate known risk factors. The expression of elevated risk factors is due to environmental and cultural determinants and not to one or more inherited characteristics. This position holds that the known risk factors are probably causal in nature and that the modifiable risk factors should be lowered by prudent living habits.

The practical approach to managing CHD requires changes in eating, drinking, smoking, and exercise habits to reduce the known risk factors and to prevent the disease. No "scientific breakthrough" is likely to occur, as required by the academic view, which will allow obese, sedentary, hypercholesterolemic, cigarette-smoking, hypertensive Americans to avoid the manifestations of CHD.

There is widespread agreement in the scientific community that the three major risk factors of hypertension, hypercholesterolemia, and cigarette smoking should be treated. Less than unanimous opinion exists when other less well documented risk factors are considered.

Regular physical exercise is widely held by the public to exert a protective effect on the development of CHD. It is mentioned by many respected scientific writers and prestigious groups as one of the healthful living habits that should be employed in the preventive effort for CHD. Unfortunately, as is the case with so many scientific issues, the role of exercise in CHD prevention is not as obvious as it may appear on the surface. Therefore, a review of the evidence regarding CHD and regular physical activity is necessary.

EXERCISE AND CHD RISK FACTORS

The effect of regular physical activity on blood pressure is still uncertain. Several experimental studies have shown a decrease in blood pressure with physical training. Other studies have shown no effect. Interpretation of these studies is made difficult by the different populations studied, different types of training programs employed, and variation in the length of time the participants were observed. Epidemiologic data from several population studies are also inconclusive, although in general more active individuals appear to have lower blood pressures. One large, communitywide investigation found lower blood pressures in active subjects even when the confounding factor of relative weight was statistically controlled.

The effects of physical activity on serum lipids is controversial. Interrelationships among serum lipids, dietary factors, overweight, and physical activity make it difficult to determine causality. In many studies in which the effect of exercise on serum lipids have been recorded, the effects of body composition and age were not considered. Any relationship between physical activity and serum lipids becomes less confusing when the initial lipid levels and the intensity, duration, and type of physical activity are considered. Some studies suggest that if individuals with initially high serum cholesterol levels are given vigorous and dynamic exercise, researchers are more likely to find an exercise effect, but definitive work on the question remains to be done. There is general agreement, however, that regular physical activity results in lower serum triglycerides.

The effect of regular exercise on serum cholesterol has recently been complicated by a consideration of the cholesterol fractions. The available epidemiologic evidence suggests that an elevated low-density lipoprotein (LDL) cholesterol is associated with an increased risk of CHD, but high-density lipoprotein (HDL) cholesterol is inversely related to CHD. Preliminary data from cross-sectional studies indicate that physically active individuals may have increased HDL levels. Middle-aged runners have been found to have higher HDL cholesterol levels than controls. The lipid profiles of these runners were similar to the profiles of young women who have a low risk of CHD. Similar differences between women runners and control women have also been observed. Other studies have reported positive relationships between occupational physical activity and HDL cholesterol. As of this writing, controlled experimental studies on this question have not been published, although several are known to be under way.

Although little specific work has been done on the question, there appears to be no strong relationship between habitual physical activity and cigarette smoking. Results of the few available studies are conflicting with some reports showing slightly less smoking among active individuals and other studies reporting no association. In contrast to data on some of the other risk factors, there appear to be no reports on experimental studies between cigarette smoking and physical activity.

The role of obesity in the development of CHD has been equivocal. Although some studies have shown no independent effect of obesity, there is general agreement that obesity is related to other CHD risk factors such as hypertension, hyperlipidemia, and abnormalities in carbohydrate metabolism. Recent long-term follow-up studies support the concept of obesity as an independent risk factor. It appears that obese young men followed for extended period of time have an increased incidence of CHD even when researchers have been able to account for the other associated risk factors.

The relationship of physical activity to weight control has been the subject of much investigation. It is clear that increasing exercise habits can have a beneficial effect on the energy balance of an obese individual by causing an increased caloric expenditure. Although exercise cannot be listed as a cure for obesity, data from experimental studies generally show a reduction in body fat with increased physical activity. Epidemiologic data support the concept that physically active individuals tend to be less obese.

A few studies can be found supporting the notion that individuals who participate in regular physical exercise have fewer electrocardiographic abnormalities. Tentative conclusions from experiments on the therapeutic effect of exercise in individuals with ECG abnormalities suggest a beneficial effect of training.

EXERCISE AND CHD MORBIDITY AND MORTALITY

Several dozen retrospective, cross-sectional, and prospective epidemiological investigations have examined the issue of sedentary living habits and the development of CHD. These studies involved both occupational and leisure time physical activity. A clear majority, perhaps as many as 80 percent of these studies, suggest a cardio-protective effect for more active groups. This over-simplified generalization applies to: (1) farmers versus nonfarmers or farmers with little heavy work; (2) railroad switchmen versus clerks; (3) Kibbutzin residents active versus sedentary; (4) men enrolled in an insurance plan, active versus inactive; (5) strenuous versus sedentary physical activity at work; (6) longshoremen, heavy versus light or moderate job activity; and (7) vigorous versus sedentary leisure-time activities. While the above listing is not exhaustive, it may serve to illustrate the scope of populations that have been studied. Although the evidence seems generally favorable, several methodological problems are inherent in these studies. For example, it is difficult to quantify levels of habitual physical activity in population studies. Classification of individuals into active or inactive groups has been accomplished by using job titles or questionnaires. Both of these methods lack rigid precision. Results of the studies on sedentary living and CHD may well be confounded by differential effects of other risk factors (such as smoking and diet), and by demographic variables such as socioeconomic status. Individuals who lead sedentary life-styles may have selected that life-style (occupational and/or recreational) because of poor health status. This bias could clearly produce more CHD endpoints in the inactive group. Several of these apparent weaknesses have been addressed in the more recent studies.

SUMMARY

Direct experimental evidence on the sedentary living-CHD hypothesis is not available. The magnitude and expense of such an experimental clinical trial are such that it is doubtful that this evidence will ever be forthcoming. Limitations in the currently available studies notwithstanding, sufficient information does exist to suggest a plan of action. Numerous investigators have observed the presence of fewer CHD risk factors in physically active individuals. These results are found in cross-sectional as well as experimental studies. In addition to the risk factor studies, the effect of physical activity on the atherosclerotic process has been studied more directly by making observations on the incidence and prevalence of CHD. Virtually all the epidemiological studies support the hypothesis that more physically active groups are less likely to have clinical CHD. Although the cardio-protective effects of regular physical activity have not been conclusively established, one cannot find support for the alternative hypothesis that regular physical activity actually enhances CHD. Since regular physical activity may have a beneficial effect by retarding the athersoclerotic process, it seems prudent for sedentary individuals to change to a more physically active life-style.

Lending additional support to the prevention of CHD by exercise is the fact that the dose or amount of exercise that has been discovered to be necessary to produce a training effect appears to be approximately the same dose that researchers in CHD risk factors have independently determined to be beneficial. The active groups in the epidemiological studies on CHD appear to be getting about the same exercise dose. It must be remembered that all studies do not give adequate information, but the similarity in exercise dose from different kinds of research is interesting to note. Thus, it appears that the three major approaches to medical investigation—clinical, experimental, and epidemiological—provide congruent findings relative to habitual exercise and CHD. The results of studies from these divergent areas generally support the hypothesis that exercise may help prevent CHD.

Data from a large comprehensive epidemiological investigation on the effects of health status on morbidity and mortality have recently been published by Breslow (1977). In general, these results confirm the wisdom of common sense health practices of good nutritional habits, adequate rest and relaxation, moderation in alcohol consumption, and regular physical exercise. A reasonable conclusion is that regular physical activity is a sound health practice. There are many good reasons for selecting a life-style that includes physical activity, not the least of which may be its favorable effect on CHD.

REFERENCES

Blackburn, H. 1975. Contrasting professional views on atherosclerosis and coronary disease. *New Eng J Med,* 292, 105-107.

Breslow, L. 1977. A policy assessment of preventive health practice. *Prevent Med,* 6, 242-251.

Cooper, K. H., et al. 1976. Physical fitness levels vs selected coronary risk factors. *JAMA,* 236, 166-169.

Fox, S. M. 1977. Physical activity in the community. In *Prevention of Heart Attack: A Challenge to the Professions,* G. A. Helmuth (ed.). Ann Arbor: University Microfilms International.

Froelicher, V. F. and A. Oberman. 1972. Analysis of epidemiologic studies of physical inactivity as risk factor for coronary artery disease. *Prog in Cardiovasc Dis,* 15, 41-65.

Kolata, G. B. and J. L. Marx. 1976. Epidemiology of heart disease: Searches for causes. *Science,* 194, 509-512.

Montoye, H. J. 1975. *Physical Activity and Health: An Epidemiologic Study of an Entire Community.* Englewood Cliffs, N.J.: Prentice-Hall.

Morris, J. N., et al. 1973. Vigorous exercise in leisure-time and the incidence of coronary heart-disease. *Lancet,* 1, 333-339.

Natio, H. K. 1976. Effects of physical activity on serum cholesterol metabolism. *Cleveland Clin Quart,* 43, 21-49.

National Heart and Lung Institute. 1971. *Arteriosclerosis.* Washington: National Institutes of Health.

Paffenbarger, R. S., Jr., et al. 1977. Work-energy level, personal characteristics and fatal heart attack: A birth-cohort effect. *Am J Epidemiol,* 105, 200-213.

Rabkin, S. W., F. A. L. Mathewson, P. H. Hsu. 1977. Relation of body weight to development of ischemic heart disease in a cohort of young North American men after a 26-year observatorial period: The Manitoba study. *Am J Cardiol,* 39, 452-458.

Stamler, J. 1973. Epidemiology of coronary heart disease. *Med Clin North Am,* 57, 5-46.

55

Physical Exercise and the Elderly

Robert C. Serfass

It is somewhat ironical that when an elderly person is ill, measures are taken to restore or rehabilitate his or her functions. Surgical procedures are undertaken, physiotherapy and rehabilitation after a stroke, etc. There is faith in the potential of the organism to respond, and it very frequently does respond. This faith and this approach need to be extended to the fit—but aging—organism. The attitude that "one is not getting any younger" produces resignation and discourages rational ways of preventing disabilities. This our society can ill-afford, since the numbers of elderly people are rising and every effort should be made to keep them as fit and as independent as possible—even if the span of life cannot be significantly extended (Gore 1972).

The preceding statement effectively portrays the impending challenge to allied health-oriented professionals relative to the activity needs of the steadily increasing number of elderly citizens. People over 65 years already represent ten percent of the population of the United States (20 million) and are now the fastest growing segment of the population (Butler 1975). The number of people over age 75 is expected to increase at more than twice the rate of the total population and, by the year 2000, the number of elderly people in this country will have surpassed 28 million (Havighurst 1969).

A National Adult Physical Fitness Survey conducted for the President's Council on Physical Fitness and Sports (1973) indicated that 45 percent (49 million) of American adults do not engage in purposeful, nonjob related physical activity. Furthermore, these nonexercisers tend to be older Americans who have not had optimal educational or practical experience with physical education and/or sport. About 71 percent of the people over 60 years of age who were interviewed indicated that they thought they received enough exercise.

Conrad (1976) has described the elderly as individuals who are generally satisfied with their low level of physical activity and who underestimate their ability to exercise. Support for this characterization has recently come from McAvoy (1976), who conducted a recreational survey of 540 randomly selected Minnesota residents of age 65 and older. The predominant barrier to participation in the preferred recreational activity of McAvoy's interviewees was their perceived lack of physical ability. The elderly Minnesotans wanted to involve themselves in more active recreational activities but felt that they did not possess the physical capability to pursue them.

Sidney and Shephard (1977) have confirmed the paradox of perceived adequate activity level in the presence of average or below average fitness levels in their study of elderly Canadian city-dwellers. Most subjects felt that they were more active than the general population for their age; however, cardiorespiratory fitness tests revealed that they were similar to other Canadian city-dwellers of the same age. Tape-recorded heart rates indicated that their daily activity seldom approached the intensity necessary for a cardiorespiratory training effect and that 80 percent of their waking hours were spent at heart rates less than ten beats per minute higher than those attained during sleep. Stamford (1972) has demonstrated that an exercise program as simple as graded treadmill walking, using the preferred walking speed of institutionalized geriatric patients, can be used to improve their cardiorespiratory fitness. Twelve weeks of tri-weekly, 20-minute bouts of walking at treadmill grades sufficient to elicit 70 percent of their age-adjusted maximal heart rate, significantly decreased heart rate and systolic blood pressure responses of such subjects to constant work loads. Although evidence suggests that it may take somewhat longer for the elderly to attain significant improvement in cardiorespiratory fitness, it appears that they can obtain relative changes in fitness similar to those found in young and middle-aged subjects (American College of Sports Medicine 1978).

Clearly there seems to be a need for providing the elderly with effective educational and practical experiences related to increased physical activity or exercise. Although research efforts relative to exercise and aging have increased substantially within the past ten years, several important questions remain to be answered before optimal programs can be implemented. Undoubtedly many factors relate to the inevitable process of physiological aging that will eventually slow the human organism and necessitate decreased activity levels. Several excellent reviews of physiological alterations resulting from the aging process are available (Masoro 1972; Moss 1970; Rockstein 1974; Shock 1962; Simonson 1971). Several others deal effectively with aging as related specifically to physical activity and fitness (Brunner and Jokl 1970; Clarke 1977; Hodgsen and

Buskirk 1977; Shock 1974; Taylor and Montoye 1972). A key issue for physical educators and researchers is to determine the extent to which the loss of functional capacity with aging represents a true physiological response and the extent to which the decrement is a result of a gradual change in living habits that expose the elderly to less demand for high functional effort. It is likely that much of the physical decrement is due to culturally imposed inactivity (Sidney and Shephard 1977) and that we may have to give serious reconsideration to the question of "normal" values for the elderly (Gore 1972).

PHYSICAL EXERCISE AND LONGEVITY

The extent to which physical activity plays a role in the prevention of premature death is very difficult to ascertain at the present time. Some experimental studies subjecting young animals to regular bouts of physical activity throughout their lifetime have produced significant increases in longevity over nonexercised controls. Young rats subjected to daily ten-minute bouts of exercise lived 25 percent longer than their nonexercised littermates (Retzlaff 1966). Conversely, a study of survival rates of rats that were older ($\rangle$ 400 days) at the onset of forced exercise compared with those that were younger ($\langle$400 days) revealed that the older rats had a lower percentage of survival than their controls (Edington, Cosmas, and McCafferty 1972). Goodrick (1980) has reported that rats that were allowed voluntary wheel exercise throughout their lifetimes lived longer than control animals deprived of such exercise. He also suggests that the effect exercise, or the lack of it, has indirectly on growth duration and/or growth rate may be an important factor related to extension of the life span. It appears, however, that a considerable amount of additional evidence must be uncovered before the role of exercise relative to longevity in animals is fully understood.

Several studies of former athletes have been undertaken to investigate the relationship of athletic involvement to longevity. Typical of the studies showing positive results are those by Karvonen et al. (1956), who reported the Finnish championship skiers had a life expectancy three years longer than the general population, and by Prout (1972), who reported that college rowers lived 6.3 years longer than randomly selected classmates. Studies of this nature are fraught with problems of self-selection and limited sample size, and careful review of the athletic studies reveals that, while athletes are likely to be more active and more fit in later life, their life expectancy compared with their college classmates is very similar (Montoye 1974).

Physical activity level is very likely only one of many probable factors that may be related to the incidence of premature death, and the modification of several life-style conditions may be necessary in order to significantly increase life expectancy. Moderate exercise was one of several health habits found to affect early mortality in Californians. Other important positive health habits were abstinence from smoking, not snacking between meals, maintenance of normal body weight, moderate drinking, eating breakfast, and receiving adequate sleep. The average added life expectancy for those who followed six or seven of these habits was 11 years for men and 7 years for women (Belloc 1973). Individuals who remain active in heavy off-job related activities from the third through the fourth decades of life are reported to live 7.1 years longer than those who drop from heavy off-job activities in their 20s to light activities in their 40s. Other health related factors, however, were better predictors of longevity than physical activity, including incidence of illness, degree of smoking, and amount of worry (Rose and Cohen 1977).

The fact that coronary heart disease is the primary cause of premature death in the United States and other industrialized nations (Leon and Blackburn 1977) warrants some attention in a discussion of exercise in the elderly relative to longevity. Leon (1973) and Fox (1973) have effectively outlined the possible role physical activity may play in the modification of the course of coronary disease. Improvement of myocardial efficiency and myocardial vascularization may provide protection against fatal arrhythmia. Even more important may be the effect that an active life-style—including physical exercise—has on the attenuation of other coronary risk factors (Cooper et al. 1976; Hickey et al. 1975; Mann et al. 1969). Excellent reviews of the relationships of physical activity and coronary heart disease are available (Fletcher and Cantwell 1974; Fox and Naughton 1972; Froelicher and Oberman 1977; Leon and Blackburn 1977). While hard epidemiological evidence will not permit a definitive conclusion that habitual exercise is beneficial in reducing morbidity or mortality related to coronary heart disease, it seems realistic to propose that a prudent course of action would be for sedentary individuals to increase their activity levels (Fox 1973; Leon and Blackburn 1977). Evidence is available to demonstrate that individuals who survive myocardial infarction can increase functional capacity and return more quickly to a life of normal activity through the use of carefully supervised exercise programs (Leon and Blackburn 1974; Kellerman 1977).

Indirect evidence for the importance of physical activity to longevity can be obtained by examining those cultures in the world that produce larger than usual numbers of surviving centenarians. A common characteristic of the Georgians (Russia), Hunzakuts (Pakistan), and the Vilcabambians (Ecuador) is a high daily physical activity level. Although factors of genetics, diet, and isolation from the stress of industrialized society may also contribute to the long lives of these people; it does seem that a vigorous life-style is possible well into the eighth and ninth decades of life (Leaf 1973). Until more systematic data are gathered on such populations, reports relative to the possible reasons for their longevity must remain in the realm of unsubstantiated anecdotal evidence (Schenfeld 1973).

Although the modification of behavior for the purpose of producing longer life is certainly a laudable goal, adding years to life may be secondary to adding life to years. It may be more useful and productive for researchers to attend to finding reasons for and ways of preventing the "loss of vigor which is characteristic of aging'' (Lefroy 1970). When considering such a preventive approach, it is useful to contemplate the advice of Blackburn (1975): "Don't equate the potential for preventing premature death and disability with the vain and fanatical search for immortality.'' It seems that a realistic goal for physical educators and physicians would be to encourage the sedentary elderly to become more active in an attempt to improve their functional ability and to maintain that ability at an optimal degree throughout their lifetime. Increased activity levels will probably attenuate other health practices in a positive direction and, if an increase life span is a concomitant result of attempts to lead healthier lives, we can consider ourselves doubly fortunate. Increasing activity in previously sedentary elderly citizens is not without attendant risks, but the fundamental question is whether the risks of carefully prescribed exercise are greater than the risk of extended inactivity.

ACTIVITY PATTERNS AND STRESS OF INACTIVITY

The tendency for individuals to become more sedentary as they age is common. Nonexercising Americans tend to be older (PCPFS 1973), and elderly Canadian city-dwellers have been described as "taking insufficient physical activity to sustain fitness" (Sidney and Shephard 1977). Physical activity in the elderly can be inhibited by several factors including disease and disability, lack of supervision, lack of companionship in exercise, lack of knowledge of appropriate conditioning principles, and lack of appropriate facilities (Heikkinen and Käyhty 1977).

Studies of activity patterns relative to aging have demonstrated significant decreases in both occupationl and leisure activity with increasing age. In a major epidemiological study of residents in Tecumseh, Michigan (Montoye 1975), a small but significant decrease in hours worked per week and in strenuousness of work was reported. Reasons proposed for the small drop in occupational energy expenditure with aging were that (1) many occupations were already sedentary, making it hard to decrease expenditure as one became older, and (2) it was somewhat difficult to change occupation after years of same-job employment. There was a decrease with age in all leisure activities studied with the exception of walking and gardening, and the decrease was greatest in the most strenuous activities. Reduction in physical activity may not occur until age is well advanced, but small differences in energy expenditures from age 25 to 60 may be due to the general lack of physical activity in all age groups rather than a decrement of physiological change with age (Durnin and Passmore 1967). Little evidence is available on the daily energy expenditures of the institutionalized elderly, but it can be assumed that their expenditure is significantly less than that of their self-sufficient, noninstitutionalized counterparts. There is little activity left for individuals to perform if most of the major household chores like grocery shopping, cooking, bed making, and house cleaning are done for them. The average daily energy expenditures of elderly men and women in their eighth decade of life who were living in local authority homes in England were 2116 and 1566 kilocalories, respectively (Salvosa, Payne, and Wheller 1971). This is 90 percent of the value for noninstitutionalized elderly retired men and 80 percent of the value for elderly housewives reported by Durnin and Passmore (1967). Female custodial care nursing home patients with a mean age of 84 years who were ambulatory and who could care for themselves have been reported to have maximal voluntary work capacities of merely two and a half times their resting metabolic rates (Smith 1978). Of 80 such subjects, only 30 could walk for two minutes on a level treadmill at 1.4 miles per hour using hand support.

Ever since the popularization of the term "hypokinetic disease" by Kraus and Raab (1961), researchers have been devoting greater attention to the detrimental effects of insufficient activity levels. Wear (1977) reviewed the major problems associated with hypokinetic disease as increased incidence of cardiovascular disease, hypertension, low back pain, decline of muscular strength and endurance, and stiffening of the joints. The weakening of antigravity muscles important to good posture produces a hump-back appearance in the elderly, with restricted respiratory movements leading to reduced physical activity. In addition, conditions of arthritis and cerebral atherosclerosis affect coordinated locomotion, which further restricts activity levels (Harris 1977).

Studies on deconditioning as a result of bed rest can provide insight into the decrements in functional capacity of individuals who spend large amounts of time in a recumbent position (Taylor et al. 1949; Saltin et al. 1968; Stremel et al. 1976). Bed rest produces decreased lean body mass, decreased aerobic capacity, and decreases in cardiac output and stroke volume in response to upright exercise (Saltin 1968). Bed rest also increases the probability of phlebothrombosis, pulmonary embolism, constipation (Clarke 1975), and decreased adaptability to changes in posture (Wenger 1973). While chronic bed rest may be somewhat limited to institutionalized geriatric patients, similar results have been demonstrated in studies on extended chair rest. Ten days of chair rest have been shown to decrease total blood volume and red cell volume to lower levels than 11 days of bed rest, and chair rest produced progressive diminished exercise tolerance as measured by heart rate response to standardized work loads (Lamb, Johnson, and Stevens 1965). Five of six healthy airmen exhibited significant disturbances in circulatory dynamics and manifestation of orthostatic intolerance when subjected to chair rest. Symptoms included dizziness, fainting, circulatory collapse, nausea, and vomiting (Lamb, Johnson, and Stevens 1964).

Complete immobilization of normal limbs can produce muscular strength losses ranging from 1.3 to 5.5 percent per day depending on the muscle groups involved (Müller and Hettinger 1953), and previously trained muscles can lose as much as 5.0 percent of attained strength per week if training is discontinued (Smith 1973). A 1.0 to 1.5 percent decrement of initial strength per day produced by two weeks of bed rest has been suggested as the expected loss of strength during voluntary inactivity (Müller 1970), and the minimal stimulus required to prevent a progressive loss of strength is estimated as at least one daily contraction of 20 percent of the maximal voluntary strength (Hettinger 1961).

Inactivity has been proposed as a major factor in obesity (Mayer and Bullen 1974), and the secondary consequences of obesity have been thoroughly reviewed by Buskirk (1974). Higher incidence of premature and sudden death, adult onset diabetes, vascular disease, hypertension, respiratory abnormalities, and psychological disorders are all problems of obesity with which the sedentary elderly must cope.

Immobilization of joints weaken ligament strength and produce loss of full range of motion due to joint infiltration with fatty and fibrous tissue (Edington and Edgerton 1976), and dense connective tissue can replace areolar connective tissue with as little as one week of inactivity (Kottke 1966).

Any decreases in fitness levels in the elderly involving cardiorespiratory function, muscular strength, body composition, or flexibility can become a catalyst for further inactivity, thereby producing a vicious cycle from which it is difficult to escape. Additional evidence for the debilitatory effects of inactivity on the elderly can be found in the relationships of activity levels to health practices and attitudes. Elderly individuals who report low participation in locomotor activities are 2.5 times more likely to spend more than two weeks in the hospital and 4.0 times more likely to rate their health as poor when compared with those who are more active (Palmore 1970). Also, as activity levels fall off with age, individuals seem to become less satisfied with life (Maddox 1963).

It is far from inevitable that the elderly will lead inactive lives. A substantial amount of variation in daily activity within all age groups including the elderly (Sidney and Shephard 1977) and extremely active, nonathletic elderly persons can be found (Durnin and Passmore 1967; Leaf 1973). Further, factors other than age may be more important in the determination of activity patterns of the elderly including personality (Havighurst 1961) and activity patterns in youth (Montoye 1975; Zbarowski 1962). Former athletes who remain active well into their advanced years maintain fitness levels well above the nonactive segment of the population (Pollock 1974; Robinson et al. 1976; Shephard and Kavanagh 1978). Evidence has also been presented to suggest that elderly individuals who have been sedentary for most of their lives, and who are subjected to carefully planned exercise programs, can make relative gains in fitness similar to those found in younger age groups (deVries 1976). Participation by the elderly in formal exercise programs may also stimulate them to become more active in other daily pursuits (Clark et al. 1975; Sidney and Shephard 1977).

EFFECTS OF EXERCISE PROGRAMS ON FITNESS COMPONENTS
IN THE ELDERLY

Although there may be a difference in the relative importance of various fitness components for the elderly compared with younger groups, it seems that optimal levels of cardiorespiratory fitness, muscular strength and endurance, body weight and composition, and flexibility are all important to the maintenance of high levels of functional capacity with advancing age (Conrad 1977; deVries 1974; Harris 1975). Learning proper techniques of relaxation has also been identified as a major fitness consideration for the elderly (deVries 1974; Friedrich 1977; Harris 1975) but will not be treated in this review.

Cardiorespiratory Fitness

Excellent reviews of the decline of aerobic capacity as measured by max VO_2 with age have been compiled by Hodgson and Buskirk (1977) and Taylor and Montoye (1972). Pooled data of cross-sectional studies of men aged 18 to 60 yield a yearly decline of 0.45 ml $\cdot$ kg^{-1} $\cdot$ yr^{-1} $\cdot$ (Hodgson and Buskirk 1977), and a lower rate of decline of 0.30 ml $\cdot$ kg^{-1} $\cdot$ yr^{-1} has been demonstrated in sedentary women (Drinkwater, Horvath, and Wells 1975). Athletes who remain active in later life seem to maintain a higher aerobic capacity than their sedentary counterparts but decrease at relatively the same rate with age. Longitudinal studies on the same sedentary individuals over several years indicate that the true decline of aerobic capacity may be double that represented by the cross-sectional studies, and that sedentary individuals decline at a faster rate than their active counterparts (Dehn and Bruce 1972). Sixty-year-old men at the tenth percentile of the distribution of max VO_2 (23.8 ml $\cdot$ kg^{-1} $\cdot$ min^{-1}) could find many routine daily activities extremely fatiguing as they would have to work at high percentages of their aerobic capacity to perform them. On the other hand, if training in the elderly can be expected to produce similar cardiorespiratory effects to those obtained in younger subjects, sedentary individuals in the lower portion of the distribution of max VO_2 can attain fitness levels that will allow them to pursue relatively active recreational pursuits such as golf, social dancing, or heavy gardening (Taylor and Montoye 1972). A survey of the conditioning literature suggests that 60-year-old men can increase their aerobic capacity 11.5 percent compared to a value of 16.7 percent improvement in 30 year olds (Hodgson 1971).

Few training studies of subjects beyond 60 years of age have used directly measured max VO_2 in the assessment of improvement. Benestad (1965) was unable to show changes in max VO_2 by training 70- to 81-year-old subjects three times per week for six weeks. Exercise was provided by treadmill walking for as long as 34 minutes and at intensity levels as high as 50 percent or more of aerobic capacity for ten of the 34-minute training bouts. Kasch and Wallace (1976) demonstrated that it is possible to maintain max VO_2 at the same level over a ten-year span from age 45 to 55 years by tri-weekly, one-hour bouts of running and/or swimming, but it is unknown whether this effect can be maintained past the seventh decade.

Several studies have used measurements of physiological responses to standardized submaximal work or the indirect assessment of max VO_2 from submaximal data to indicate the training effects of exercise programs in elderly males (Barry et al. 1966a; deVries 1970; Stamford 1972; Sidney, Shephard, and Harrison 1977; Tzankoff et al. 1972). Training modes in these studies include bicycle ergometer work, walk-jog programs, preferred walking speed on a treadmill, recreational sports, and warm-up calisthenics. The value of such training regimens for the improvement of functional capacity has been clearly demonstrated through significant post-training decreases of heart rate, systolic blood pressure, blood lactate, ventilation, and oxygen consumption in response to standardized work. Similar results have also been obtained in elderly female subjects (Adams and deVries 1973; Sidney et al. 1977; Suominen et al. 1977).

Muscular Strength and Endurance

Compared to other physical fitness components, adequate levels of muscular strength seem to be retained for a longer period of time with aging, and large decreases do not appear until the seventh or eighth decade of life. Based on a compilation of data through 1960, Hettinger (1961) suggests that there is a 20 percent decrease in strength in men from age 30 to age 65 and that the strength of women at age 30 is two-thirds that of men and decreases at the same rate. No differences in grip strength or grip endurance at 40 percent of maximal contraction could be demonstrated from the third through the sixth decades in male machinists who were occupationally active with their hands (Petrofsky and Lind 1975). However, a significant and linear decrease in grip strength was demonstrated in women aged 19 to 65 who were more heterogenous with respect to occupational activity (Petrofsky, Burse, and Lind 1975). The women also increased in grip endurance at 40 percent maximal contraction even though their strength decreased with age. Burke et al. (1953) suggest that there is a gradual decrease in both grip strength and grip endurance after age 25, and that strength and endurance at ages 75 to 79 are similar to that found at ages 12 to 15. In another study, composite strength of muscles in the arms and shoulders decreased 28 percent from age 30 to 80 (Shock and Norris 1970). Ten percent of the loss was attributed to body weight loss and the greatest decrease occurred in the eighth and ninth decades. Further, maximal work rate, as measured by arm cranking, fell to 45 percent of the 30-year value in the 80-year-old subjects and was attributed to lack of coordination. Most strength studies dealing with aging are cross-sectional and may underestimate the true decrease with age. Subjects tested at 5-, 10-, and 15-year intervals have shown a 60 percent loss from age 30 to age 80, and the lower strength losses in the cross-sectional estimates may be the result of fewer weak individuals in the older samples (Clement 1975). Strength loss in males may be associated with lower levels of testosterone secretions with age as the administration of testosterone in older men engaged in training had produced significant increases in both muscular strength and endurance compared to training conditions without the hormone (Simonson, Kearns, and Enzer 1944; Hettinger 1961).

Several studies have demonstrated favorable strength changes due to training in elderly subjects. Hettinger (1961) reviewed a series of studies on men and women from age 6 to age 65 and suggest that by the sixth decade the strength trainability of men and women is similar and amounts to approximately 30 to 40 percent of the maximal trainability of males at 20 to 30 years of age. Significant increases of leg power, as measured by vertical jump, and muscular endurance, as measured by a V-sit, have been reported in older men and women in response to a three-month calisthenic and stationary bicycle program (Barry et al. 1966b). Elbow flexion strength has been shown to increase as a result of a walk-job program that included calisthenics and swimming. Gains in strength were measured at 6.4 percent after six weeks and at 11.9 percent after 42 weeks of conditioning (deVries 1970). A comparison of the effects of a progressive resistance isotonic weight training program on the index finger strength of old and young men indicates that the older men not only increase significantly in strength but that their strength increase is of the same magnitude as that of the younger subjects (Chapman, deVries, and Swezey 1972). Both maximal and submaximal isometric programs have been found effective in producing strength increases in older subjects (Daykin 1967; Perkins and Kaiser 1961); however, since static work is more stressful to the cardiovascular system (Bruce 1973) it is probably wise to relegate its use in older individuals to closely supervised clinical programs.

Body Composition

The aging process has been associated with several detrimental changes in body composition including the loss of lean body mass and bone mineral along with the increases in body weight and body fat (Sidney, Shephard, and Harrison 1977). Inactivity with aging may be a primary factor in these changes as physical activity levels have been suggested as one of the most important factors affecting body composition from childhood through old age (Parizkova 1963). For example, a comparison by Brozek and Keys (1973) of active and inactive subjects in the sixth decade revealed that the active group had lower percentages of body fat and higher levels of lean body mass.

In 1952 Brozek reported that body fat in men increased from a low value of 25.01 percent at age 55, and fat-free weight decreased from 60.6 kg to 57.6 kg during the same time span. Although no increase in body fat with age was reported in a study of men from the third to the eighth decade (Norris, Lundy, and Shock 1963), the highest incidence of moderately and severely overweight subjects appeared in the sixth decade. By the eighth decade no subjects were severely overweight; however, 20 percent were underweight as measured by relative ideal weight. Study of the loss of lean body mass with age, as measured by 24-hour creatinine excretion, suggests that men in the eighth decade have 9.0 kg less muscle mass and 3.4 kg more connective tissue and fat than men in the fifth decade, and that muscle mass loss with age may not be a totally irreversible factor (Tzankoff and Norris 1977). Increases in body weight and body fat with age have also been shown in female subjects (Wessel 1963). Decreases in body density of women after age 40 have been observed, and increases in percent body fat from 28.69 at age 20 to 44.56 at age 60 have been reported (Young et al. 1963).

Favorable changes in lean body mass, body fat, and bone mineral levels as a result of exercise have been demonstrated in young and middle age subjects (Oscai 1973; Clarke 1975), but few body composition studies have dealt with the elderly. A small but significant decrease in body fat of elderly men was reported after six weeks of an exercise program that included calisthenics, walk-jogging, stretching, and aquatics. Extension of the exercise program to 42 weeks produced no significant difference in body fat compared to controls even though the trend of fat loss was similar to the first six-week period; however, only eight subjects remained in the program for the entire 42-week training period (DeVries 1970). Endurance training by walking and jogging in elderly men and women in their seventh decade produced a significant reduction in the sum of eight skinfolds at 7, 14, and 52 weeks of conditioning. The loss of body fat in the presence of a stable body weight suggested an increase of lean body mass with training (Sidney, Shephard, and Harrison 1977).

One of the most potentially debilitating factors associated with aging is the development of osteoporosis. An excellent review of the relationship of osteoporosis to physical activity and aging has been compiled by Smith (1977). A reduction in cortical bone mass coupled with a decrease in bone strength makes the elderly who suffer from this condition extremely susceptible to broken bones and the associated hypokinetic stress involved with hospitalization and immobilization. Bone mineral, as measured by photon absorption, increased 2.29 percent in 12 subjects 69 to 95 years of age in response to a light to moderate physical activity program performed three times per week for three years. Control subjects who remained inactive lost an average of 3.28 percent bone mineral (Smith 1973). Body calcium, as measured by neutron activation, was shown to remain stable for over one year in elderly men and women who engaged in an endurance training program, and a small group of subjects who exercised at relatively low levels of intensity and frequency showed a nine percent calcium loss (Sidney, Shephard, and Harrison 1977). Cortical bone area, as measured by hand and wrist x-ray, has been shown to decrease significantly from ages 45 to 54 to ages 55 to 64; however, there were no differences in loss between the most active and the least active groups of elderly men in the study. It has been suggested that only a minimal amount of activity may be necessary to maintain a "normal" amount of cortical bone (Montoye 1975).

Flexibility

There is a steady decrease of flexibility from childhood through old age (Wright and Johns 1960b), and most of the mobility of joint is related to the condition of the surrounding muscles and the joint capsules with their associated ligaments (Johns and Wright 1962). LaBella and Paul (1965) have shown significantly greater cross linkage of collagen with age using samples of Achilles tendon obtained at autopsy. Akeson (1968) has reviewed the possible connective tissue mechanisms for decreased flexibility as a result of his studies involving the immobilization of the legs of dogs and has suggested that inactivity may play a substantial part in decreased mobility with age.

Excellent reviews are available on the anatomical and physiological factors determining range of motion (Holland 1968) and on the effects of training and disease on connective tissue (Booth and Gould 1975). An enlighted perspective of the effects of aging on flexibility is virtually impossible, however, because of the scarcity of studies in this area. Wright and Johns (1960a) have indicated that subjects in the sixth decade are ten times stiffer than those in the first decade. The sum of the range of motion in five joints of university community women decreased from about 820 degrees at ages 30 to 34, to 730 degrees at ages 65 to 69; however, the lowest values for flexibility were found at ages 50 to 54 years (Wessel et al. 1963). It has also been demonstrated that 30 percent greater torque is required to passively oscillate the index finger of older men through a fixed range of motion than is required for younger men (Chapman, deVries, and Swezey 1972).

Exercise programs are effective in the improvement of flexibility in elderly subjects. Ankle, hamstring, and lower back flexibility were significantly improved in female subjects aged 71 to 90 years after seven months of bi-weekly, 30-minute sessions in an exercise program that emphasized flexibility, muscle tone, and balance (Frekany and Leslie 1975). A program of 10 minutes of warm up exercises and 25 to 50 minutes of walk-jogging twice weekly for 14 weeks produced an increase in trunk flexibility in men between the ages of 60 and 79 years (Buccola and Stone 1975). Flexibility of the index finger of older men improved significantly in response to a progressive resistance weight training program, and the training response of the older subjects was the same as the improvement of flexibility in a much younger comparison group (Chapman, deVries, and Swezey 1972).

It is obvious that elderly individuals can respond favorably to programs designed to improve the primary fitness components. It must be remembered, however, that results presented in the research experiments above were obtained under exacting conditions of subject screening and program supervision. It is imperative, given the great variability in fitness levels in the aged, that sound principles of exercise prescription are followed in order to conduct safe as well as effective programs.

EXERCISE PROGRAMS FOR THE ELDERLY

Much work remains to be done in the area of exercise program development for older individuals. There are, however, several valuable resources that presently deal with the principles of exercise prescription for the elderly, and several exercise programs specifically for elderly exercisers are available.

Program Principles

The American College of Sports Medicine (1975) and the American Heart Association (1972) have both developed excellent handbooks on the guidelines for exercise testing and training in adults. Several texts dealing with cardiovascular rehabilitation present valuable information on the principles of conducting exercise programs (Amsterdam, Wilmore, and DeMaria 1977; Naughton and Hellerstein 1973; Wilson 1975) and have particular relevance since many healthy but sedentary elderly are not too dissimilar from patients with low functional capacity resulting from cardiovascular disease. The general principles of exercise prescription for the elderly are the same as those for other apparently healthy adult grups and include: (1) medical clearance or screening; (2) determination of functional capacity; (3) exercise prescription considering mode, intensity, frequency, and duration of exercise; (4) a slow and gradual progression both within the daily exercise period and throughout the early stages of the exercise program; (5) consideration of personal safety; (6) attention to motivation and enjoyment; and (7) regular reevaluation of functional capacity and exercise prescription.

DeVries (1976) revealed the necessity for adequate screening and regular reevaluation of prescription in programs for the elderly by pointing out that of 29 older men who had been cleared by their physician to participate in an exercise program, 15 developed cardiovascular abnormalities with stress testing and 7 had to discontinue before reaching volitional fatigue. Further, several men demonstrated a lowering of functional capacity after the first six weeks of conditioning, apparently as a result of overtraining. One must realize that the elderly will probably exhibit higher incidence of heart disease, atherosclerosis, hypertension, cerebral atrophy, osteoarthritis, and diabetes than younger individuals, and that by the age of 90, nine out of ten people will have some type of chronic illness (Hendricks and Hendricks 1977). This will undoubtedly have an effect on the development of programs for this population. Intensity of exercise necessary for producing a training effect is lower for elderly individuals than for their younger counterparts (deVries 1977), and modes of exercise should be selected that emphasize dynamic, rhythmic movements conducive to the improvement of endurance and flexibility. Evenly spaced exercise sessions at a frequency of three times per week will assure reasonable functional improvement or maintenance. Warming up and cooling down with calisthenics and stretching exercises allow for attention to specific strength needs and to the prevention of muscular soreness. Further information on the principles of exercise and prescription are available in the works of Clarke (1977) and Pollock (1973).

Available Programs

Several excellent examples of programs developed specifically for the elderly are available for the benefit of those who are beginning in the area of geriatric exercise. The National Association of Human Development (1976) has a variety of training manuals and booklets on exercise and fitness programs for older persons. Leslie and McLure (1975) of the University of Iowa have developed an exercise program emphasizing flexibility, muscle tone, and balance, and Smith and Stoedefalke (1978) of the University of Wisconsin have developed an excellent low intensity exercise program with accurately assigned energy and heart rate levels. A vigorous walk-jog program (de Vries 1974a) has been utilized in many geriatric settings, and a program of aqua-therapy has been described by Kacavas, Morrison, and Hurley (1977). Two of the most complete references on all aspects of exercise relative to exercise and the elderly are texts by Harris and Frankel (1977) and by Frankel and Richards (1978). The American Alliance for Health, Physical Education, Recreation, and Dance has formed a Committee on Aging and has compiled a directory of community and college/university exercise programs developed primarily for the elderly participant. The directory and other resource information on geriatric exercise programs, projects, and/or research are available from their national office: AAHPERD/Aging, 1201 Sixteenth St., N.W., Washington, D.C. 20036.

REFERENCES

Adams, G. M. and H. A. deVries. 1973. Physiological effects of an exercise training regimen upon women aged 52 to 79. *J Gerontol*, 28, 50-55.

Akeson, W. H. 1968. Connective tissue response to immobility: An accelerated aging response. *Exp Gerontol*, 3, 289-301.

American College of Sports Medicine. 1975. *Guidelines for Graded Exercise Testing and Exercise Prescription*. Philadelphia: Lea and Febiger.

American College of Sports Medicine. 1978. Position statement on the recommended quantity and quality of exercise for developing and maintaining fitness in healthy adults. *Med Sci Spts*, 10, vii-viii.

American Heart Association. 1972. *Exercise Testing and Training of Apparently Healthy Individuals: A Handbook for Physicians*. New York.

Amsterdam, E. A., J. H. Wilmore, and A. N. DeMaria. 1977. *Exercise in Cardiovascular Health and Disease*. New York: Yorke Medical Books.

Barry, A. J., J. W. Daly, E. D. R. Pruett, J. R. Steinmetz, H. F. Page, N. C. Birkhead, and K. Rodahl. 1966a. The effects of physical conditioning on older individuals. I. Work capacity, circulatory-respiratory function, and work electrocardiogram. *J Gerontol*, 21, 182-191.

Barry, A. J., J. R. Steinmetz, H. F. Page, and K. Rodahl. 1966b. The effects of physical conditioning on older individuals. II. Motor performance and cognitive function. *J Gerontol*, 21, 192-199.

Belloc, N. B. 1973. Relationship of health practices and mortality. *Prev Med*, 2, 67-81.

Benestad, A. M. 1965. Trainability of old men. *Acta Med Scan*, 178, 321-327.

Blackburn, H. 1975. Prevention: A challenge and a promise. *Med Opin,* 4, 14-19.

Booth, F. W. and E. W. Gould. 1975. Effects of training and disease on connective tissue. In *Exercise and Sports Science Review,* J. H. Wilmore (ed.). Vol 3. New York: Academic Press.

Brozek, J. 1952. Changes of body composition in man during maturity and their nutritional implications. *Fed Proc,* 11, 784-793.

Bruce, R. A. 1973. Prevention and control of cardiovascular complications. In *Exercise Testing and Exercise Training in Coronary Heart Disease,* J. P. Naughton and H. K. Hellerstein (eds.). New York: Academic Press.

Brunner, D. and E. Jokl (eds.). 1970. *Physical Activity and Aging.* New York: S. Karger.

Buccola, V. A. and W. J. Stone. 1975. Effects of jogging and cycling programs on physiological and personality variables in aged men. *Res Quart,* 46, 134-139.

Burke, W. E., W. W. Tuttle, C. W. Thompson, C. D. Janney, and R. S. Weber. 1953. The relation of grip strength and grip strength endurance to age. *J Appl Physiol,* 5, 628-630.

Buskirk, E. R. 1974. Obesity: A brief overview with emphasis on exercise. *Fed Proc,* 38, 1948-1951.

Butler, R. N. 1975. *Why Survive? Being Old in America.* New York: Harper & Row.

Chapman, E. A., H. A. deVries, and R. Swezey. 1972. Joint stiffness: Effects of exercise on young and old men. *J Gerontol,* 27, 218-221.

Clark, B. A., M. G. Wade, B. H. Massey, and R. VanDyke. 1975. Response of institutionalized geriatric mental patients to a twelve-week program of regular physical activity. *J Gerontol,* 30, 565-573.

Clarke, D. H. 1975. *Exercise Physiology.* Englewood Cliffs: Prentice-Hall.

Clarke, H. H. (ed.). 1975. Exercise and fat reduction. *Phys Fit Res Dig,* Series 5, No. 2. April.

Clarke, H. H. (ed.). 1977. Exercise and aging. *Phys Fit Res Dig,* Series 7, No. 2. April.

Clement, F. J. 1974. Longitudinal and cross-sectional assessments of age changes in physical strength as related to sex, social class and mental ability. *J Gerontol,* 29, 423-429.

Conrad, C. C. 1976. When you're young at heart. *Aging,* Administration on Aging. U.S. Department of Health Education and Welfare. April, 11.

Conrad, C. 1977. Physical fitness for older Americans—A national responsibility and opportunity. In *Guide to Fitness After Fifty,* R. Harris and L. J. Frankel (eds.). New York: Plenum Press.

Cooper, K. H., M. L. Pollock, R. P. Martin, S. R. White, A. C. Linnerud, and A. Jackson. 1976. Physical fitness levels vs. selected coronary risk factors. A cross sectional study. *JAMA,* 236, 116-169.

Daykin, H. P. 1967. The application of isometrics in geriatric treatment. *Am Corr Ther J,* 21, 203-205.

Dehn, M. M. and R. A. Bruce. 1972. Longitudinal variations in maximal oxygen intake with age and activity. *J Appl Physiol,* 33, 805-807.

deVries, H. A. 1970. Physiological effects of an exercise training regimen upon men aged 52 to 88. *J Gerontol,* 25, 325-336.

deVries, H. A. 1974a. *Vigor Regained.* Englewood Cliffs, N.J.: Prentice-Hall.

deVries, H. A. 1974b. *Physiology of Exercise for Physical Education and Athletics.* 2nd ed. Dubuque: Wm. C. Brown.

deVries, H. A. 1976. Fitness after fifty. *JOPER,* 47, 47-49.

deVries, H. A. 1977. Physiology of physical conditioning for the elderly In *Guide to Fitness After Fifty,* R. Harris and L. J. Frankel (eds.). New York: Plenum Press.

Drinkwater, B. L., S. M. Horvath, and C. L. Wells. 1975. Aerobic power of females ages 10 to 68. *J Gerontol,* 30, 385-394.

Durnin, J. V. G. A. and R. Passmore. 1967. *Energy Work and Leisure.* London: Heinemann.

Edington, D. W., A. C. Cosmas, and W. B. McCafferty. 1972. Exercise and longevity: Evidence for a threshold age. *J Gerontol,* 27, 341-343.

Edington, D. W. and V. R. Edgerton. 1976. *The Biology of Physical Activity.* Boston: Houghton Mifflin.

Fletcher, G. F. and J. D. Cantwell. 1974. *Exercise and Coronary Heart Disease.* Springfield: Charles C. Thomas.

Fox, S. M. III. 1973. Relationship of activity habits to coronary heart disease. In *Exercise Testing and Exercise Training in Coronary Disease,* J. P. Naughton and H. K. Hellerstein (eds.). New York: Academic Press.

Fox, S. M. III and J. P. Naughton. 1972. Physical activity and the prevention of coronary heart disease. *Prev Med,* 1, 92-120.

Frankel, L. J. and B. B. Richard. 1978. *Be Alive as Long as You Live.* Charleston: Preventicare Publications.

Frekany, G. A. and D. K. Leslie. 1975. Effects of an exercise program on selected flexibility measurements of senior citizens. *Gerontol,* 15, 182-183.

Friedrich, J. A. 1977. Tension control techniques to combat stress. In *Guide to Fitness After Fifty,* R. Harris and L. J. Frankel (eds.). New York: Plenum Press.

Froehlicher, V. F. and A. Oberman. 1977. Analysis of epidemiological studies of physical inactivity as risk factor for coronary artery disease. In *Exercise and Heart Disease,* E.. H. Sonnenblick and M. Lesch (eds.). New York: Grune and Stratton.

Goodrick, C. L. 1980. Effects of long term wheel exercise on male and female wistar rate: I. Longevity, body weight, and metabolic rate. *Geront,* 26, 22-33.

Gore, I. Y. 1972. Physical activity and aging —A survey of Soviet literature. III. The character of physical activity, training and longitudinal results. *Gerontol Clin,* 14, 78-85.

Harris, R. 1975. Physical activity and mental health in the aged. In *Physical Exercise and Activity for the Aging.* Uriel Simri (ed.). Wingate Institute for Physical Education and Sport.

Harris, R. 1977. Fitness and the aging process. In *Guide to Fitness After Fifty,* R. Harris and L. V. Frankel (eds.). New York: Plenum Press.

Harris, R. and L. J. Frankel. 1977. *Guide to Fitness After Fifty,* New York: Plenum Press.

Havighurst, R. J. 1961. The nature and values of meaningful free-time activity. In *Aging and Leisure,* R. W. Kleemier (ed.). New York: Oxford University Press.

Havighurst, R. J. 1969. Status of research in applied social gerontology. *Gerontol,* 9, 5-9.

Heikkinen, E. and B. Kayty. 1977. Gerontological aspects of physical activity— Motivation of older people in physical training. In *Guide to Fitness After Fifty,* R. Harris and L. J. Frankel (eds.). New York: Plenum Press.

Hendricks, J. and C. D. Hendricks. 1977. *Aging in Mass Society.* Cambridge: Winthrop Publishers.

Hettinger, T. 1961. *Physiology of Strength.* Springfield: Charles C. Thomas.

Hickey, N., R. Mulcahy, G. J. Bourke, I. Graham, and K. Wilson-Davis. 1975. Study of coronary risk factors related to physical activity in 15,171 men. *Brit Med J,* ii, 507-509.

Hodgson, J. L. 1971. Age and Aerobic Capacity of Urban Midwestern Males. Doctoral dissertation, University of Minnesota.

Hodgson, J. L. and E. R. Buskirk. 1977. Physical fitness and age with emphasis on cardiovascular function in the elderly. *J Am Geriat Soc,* 25, 385-392.

Holland, G. J. 1968. The physiology of flexibility: A review of the literature. In *Kinesiology Review.* Washington: AAHPER.

Johns, R. J. and V. Wright. 1961. Relative importance of various tissues in joint stiffness. *J Appl Physiol,* 17, 824-828.

Kacavas, J. J., D. Morrison, and M. Hurley. 1977. The use of aquatherapy with geriatric patients. *Amer Corr Ther J,* 31, 52-59.

Karvonen, M., J. Kihlberg, J. Maata, and J. Virkajarvi, 1956. Longevity of champion skiers. *Duodecim,* 72, 893-903.

Kasch, F. W. and J. P. Wallace. 1976. Physiological variables during 10 years of endurance exercise. *Med Sci Spts,* 8, 5-8.

Kellerman, J. J. 1977. Rehabilitation of patients with coronary heart disease. In *Exercise and Heart Disease,* E. H. Sonnenblick and M. Lesch (eds.). New York: Grune and Shatton.

Kottke, F. J. 1966. The effects of limitation of activity upon the human body. *JAMA,* 196, 825-830.

Kraus, H. and W. Raab. 1961. *Hypokinetic Disease.* Springfield: Charles C. Thomas.

LaBella, F. S. and G. Paul. 1965. Structure of collagen from human tendon as influenced by age and sex. *J Gerontol,* 20, 54-59.

Lamb, L. E., R. L. Johnson, and P. M. Stevens. 1964. Cardiovascular conditioning during chair rest. *Aerosp Med,* 35, 646-649.

Lamb, L E., P. M. Stevens, and R. L. Johnson. 1965. Hypokinesia secondary to chair rest from 4 - 10 days. *Aerosp Med,* 36, 755-763.

Leaf, A. 1973. Observations of a peripatetic gerontologist. *Nutr Today,* 8, 4-12.

Lefroy, R. B. 1970. Expectations in old age. *Med J Austral,* 1, 1275-1281.

Leon, A. S. 1973. Comparative cardiovascular adaptations to exercise in animals and man and its relevance to coronary heart disease. In *Comparative Pathophysiology,* C. M. Bloor (ed.). New York: Plenum Press.

Leon, A. S. and H. Blackburn. 1974. Exercise and coronary heart disease *Minn Med,* 57, 106-107.

Leon, A. S. and H. Blackburn. 1977. The relationship of physical activity to coronary heart disease and life expectancy. *Ann N Y Acad Sci,* 301, 561-578.

Leslie, D. K. and J. W. McLure. 1975. *Exercise for the Elderly.* Des Moines: Iowa Commission on Aging.

Maddox, G. L. 1963. Activity and morale: A longitudinal study of selected elderly subjects. *Soc For,* 42, 195-204.

Mann, G. V., H. L. Garrett, A. Farki, H. Murray, and F. T. Billings. 1969. Exercise to prevent coronary heart disease: An experimental study of the effect of training on risk factors for coronary disease in man. *Am J Med,* 46, 12-27.

Masoro, E. 1972. Other physiological changes with age. In *Epidemiology of Aging,* A. M. Ostfeld and D. C. Gibson (eds.). U.S. Department of Health, Education, and Welfare. DHEW Pub. No. (NIH) 75-711.

Mayer, J. and B. A. Bullen. 1974. Nutrition, weight control and exercise. In *Science and Medicine of Exercise and Sport,* W. R. Johnson and E. R. Buskirk (eds.). 2nd ed. New York: Harper and Row.

McAvoy, L. H. 1976. Recreation Preferences of the Elderly Persons in Minnesota. Doctoral dissertation, University of Minnesota.

Montoye, H. 1974. Health and longevity of former athletes. In *Science and Medicine of Exercise and Sport,* W. R. Johnson and E. R. Buskirk (eds.). 2nd ed. New York: Harper and Row.

Montoye, H. J. 1975. *Physical Activity and Health: An Epidemiologic Study of an Entire Community.* Englewood Cliffs, N.J.: Prentice-Hall.

Moss, B. B. 1970. Normal aging. *Nurs Homes,* 19, 33-35.

Müller, E. A. 1970. Influence of training and of inactivity on muscle strength. *Arch Phys Med,* 51, 449-462.

Müller E. A. and T. Hettinger. 1953. Unterschiede der trainings—geschwindigkeit atrophierten und normaler muskeln. *Arbeitsphysiol,* 15, 223-230.

National Association for Human Development. 1976. *Join the Active People Over 60.* Washington: Administration on Aging.

Naughton, J. P. and H. K. Hellerstein. 1973. *Exercise Stress Testing and Exercise Training in Coronary Heart Disease.* New York: Academic Press.

Norris, A. H., T. Lundy, and N. W. Shock. 1963. Trends in selected indices of body composition in men between the ages 30 and 80 years. *Ann N Y Acad Sci,* 110, 623-639.

Oscai, L. B. 1973. The role of exercise in weight control. In *Exercise and Sports Science Reviews,* J. H. Wilmore (ed.). Vol 1. New York: Academic Press.

Palmore, E. 1970. Health practices and illness among the aged. *Gerontol,* 10, 313-316.

Pařizková, J. 1963. Impact of age, diet and exercise on man's body composition. *Ann N Y Acad Sci,* 110, 661-673.

Perkins, L. C. and H. L. Kaiser. 1961. Results of short-term isotonic and isometric exercise programs in persons over sixty. *Phys Ther Rev,* 41, 633-635.

Petrofsky, J. S., R. L. Burse, and A. R. Lind. 1975. Comparison of physiological responses of women and men to isometric exercise. *J Appl Physiol,* 38, 863-868.

Petrofsky, J. S. and A. R. Lind. 1975. Aging isometric strength and endurance and cardiovascular response to static effort. *J Appl Physiol,* 38, 91-95.

Pollock, M. L. 1973. The quantification of training programs. In *Exercise and Sports Sciences Reviews,* J. H. Wilmore (ed.). Vol 1. New York: Academic Press.

Pollock, M. L. 1974. Physiological characteristics of older champion track athletes. *Res Quart,* 45, 363-373.

President's Council on Physical Fitness and Sports. 1973. National adult physical fitness survey. *Newsletter,* Special Edition, Washington, D.C.

Prout, C. 1972. Life expectancy of college oarsmen. *JAMA,* 220, 1709-1711.

Retzlaff, E., J. Fontaine, and W. Furuta. 1966. Effect of daily exercise on life-span of albino rats. *Geriat,* 21, 171-177.

Robinson, S., D. B. Dill, R. D. Robinson, S. P. Tzankoff, and J. A. Wagner. 1976. Physiological aging of champion runners. *J Appl Physiol,* 41, 46-51.

Rockstein, M. (ed.) 1974. *Theoretical Aspects of Aging.* New York: Academic Press.

Rose, C. L. and M. L. Cohen. 1977. Relative importance of physical activity for longevity. *Ann N Y Acad Sci,* 301, 671-697.

Saltin, B., G. Blomquist, J. H. Mitchell, R. L. Johnson, Jr., K. Wildenthal, and C. B. Chapman. 1968. Response to exercise after bed rest and after training. *Circul Suppl,* 7, 1-78.

Salvosa, C. B., P. R. Payne, and E. F. Wheeler. 1971. Energy expenditure of elderly people living alone or in local authority homes. *Am J Clin Nutr,* 24, 1467-1470.

Schenfeld, A. 1973. Longevity. *JAMA.* 225,526.

Shock, N. W. 1962. The physiology of aging. *Sci Amer,* 206, 100-110.

Shock, N. W. 1974. Exercise in the adult years. In *Science and Medicine of Exercise and Sport,* W. R. Johnson and E. R. Buskirk (eds.). 2nd ed. New York: Harper and Row.

Shock, N. W. and A. H. Norris. 1970. Neuromuscular coordination as a factor in age changes in muscular exercise. In *Physical Activity and Aging,* D. Brunner and E. Jokl (eds.). Baltimore: University Park Press.

Shephard, R. J. and T. Kavanagh. 1978. The effects of training on the aging process. *Phys Spts Med,* 6, 32-40.

Sidney, K. H. and R. J. Shephard. 1977. Activity patterns of elderly men and women. *J Gerontol,* 32, 25-32.

Sidney, K. H., R. J. Shephard, and J. E. Harrison. 1977. Endurance training and body composition of the elderly. *Am J Clin Nutr,* 30, 326-333.

Simonson, E. 1971. Effect of age on work capacity and fatigue. In *Physiology of Work Capacity and Fatigue,* E. Simonsen (ed.). Springfield: Charles C. Thomas.

Simonson, E., W. M. Kearns, and N. Enzer. 1944. Effect of methyltestosterone treatment on muscular performance and the central nervous system of older men. *J Clin Endocrin,* 4, 528-534.

Smith, B. E. 1973. Effect of Various Detraining Intervals on the Retension of Newly Acquired Levels of Strength. Master's thesis, University of Maryland.

Smith, E. L. 1973. Effects of physical activity on bone on the aged. In *International Conference on Bone Mineral Measurement,* R. B. Mazess (ed.). U.S. Department of Health, Education and Welfare. DHEW Pub No. (NIH) 75-683.

Smith, E. L. 1977. Physical activity and bone accretion. Paper presented at conference on Exercise in the Elderly—Its Role in Prevention of Physical Decline and in Rehabilitation. Bethesda: National Institute on Aging and PCPFS.

Smith, E. L. 1978. Personal Communication.

Smith, E. and K. Stoedefalke. 1978. *Aging and Exercise.* Madison: University of Wisconsin. Copyright by authors.

Stamford, B. A. 1972. Physiological effects of training upon institutionalized geriatric men. *J Gerontol,* 4, 451-455.

Stremel, R. W., V. A. Convertino, E. M. Bernauer, and J. E. Greenleaf. 1976. Cardiorespiratory deconditioning with static and dynamic leg exercise during bed rest. *J Appl Physiol,* 41, 905-909.

Suominen, H., PhLic, E. Heibbinen, and T. Parkatti. 1977. Effect of eight weeks' physical training on muscle and connective tissue of the m. vastus lateralis in 69-year-old men and women. *J Gerontol,* 32, 33-37.

Taylor, H. L., A. Henschel, J. Brozek, and A. Keys. 1949. Effects of bed rest on cardiovascular function and work performance. *J Appl Physiol,* 2, 223-239.

Taylor, H. L. and H. J. Montoye. 1972. Physical fitness, cardiovascular function and age. In *Epidemiology of Aging,* A. M. Ostfeld and D. C. Gibson (eds.). U.S. Department of Health, Education and Welfare. DHEW Pub No. (NIH) 75-711.

Tzankoff, S. P. and A. H. Norris. 1977. Effect of muscle mass decrease on age-related BMR changes. *J Appl Physiol,* 43, 1001-1006.

Tzankoff, S. P., S. Robinson, F. S. Pyke, and C. A. Brawn. 1972. Physiological adjustments to work in older men as affected by physical training. *J Appl Physiol,* 33, 346-350.

Wear, R. E. 1977. Conditioning exercise programs for normal older persons. In *Guide to Fitness After Fifty,* R. Harris and L. J. Frankel (eds.). New York: Plenum Press.

Wenger, N. K. 1973. The early ambulation of patients after myocardial infarction. *Cardiol,* 58, 1-6.

Wessel, J. A., A. Ufer, W. D. VanHuss, and D. Cederquist. 1963. Age components of body composition and functional characteristics in women aged 20-69 years. *Ann N Y Acad Sci,* 110, 608-622.

Wilson P. K. 1975. *Adult Fitness and Cardiac Rehabilitation.* Baltimore: University Park Press.

Wright, V. and R. J. Johns. 1960a. Observations on the measurement of joint stiffness. *Arth Rheum,* 3, 328-340.

Wright, V. and R. J. Johns. 1960b. Physical factors concerned with the stiffness of normal and diseased joints. *Bull Johns Hop Hosp,* 105, 215-231.

Young, C. M., J. Blondin, R. Tensuan, and J. Fryer. 1963. Body composition studies of "older" women, thirty to seventy years of age. *Ann N Y Acad Sci,* 110, 589-607.

Zbarowski, M. 1962. Aging and recreation. *J Gerontol,* 17, 302-309.

Biographical Appendix

Gary E. Adams received his B.A. (1968) and M.A. (1970) in physical education from California State University at Long Beach. He attended Southern Illinois University and received the Ph.D. degree in exercise physiology in 1974. In 1975 Dr. Adams became coordinator of cardiac rehabilitation at Wake Forest University and is presently assistant professor in physical education and clinical associate in the Department of Medicine at Bowman Gray School of Medicine. His professional memberships include AAHPERD, NCAHPER, American College of Sports Medicine, and the American Health Association.

Steven N. Blair is professor and director of the Human Performance Laboratory at the University of South Carolina. He is a coprincipal investigator in the Multiple Risk Factor Intervention Trial, a collaborative national study on heart disease prevention conducted under the auspices of the National Heart, Lung, and Blood Institute. Dr. Blair received his B.A. from Kansas Wesleyan University and his M.S. and P.E.D. from Indiana University.

William J. Bowerman has retired after 40 years as a track coach and professor of physical education. During his 27 years at the University of Oregon, his track teams won four NCAA championships, and 14 of his milers were clocked in less than four minutes. In 1972 he was the United States Olympic Track Coach. He has published three books, numerous articles, received many awards including those from the NHSCA, the NCAA, and the President's Council on Fitness.

Elsworth R. Buskirk is a professor of applied physiology and director of the Laboratory of Human Performance Research at the Pennsylvania State University. Previously he was physiologist in charge of the Metabolic Chamber Facility, National Institutes of Arthritis and Metabolic Diseases, National Institutes of Health, Bethesda, Md. Dr. Buskirk also worked with the Environmental Research Center, Natick, Mass., and the Laboratory of Physiological Hygiene at the University of Minnesota. He has held many federal advisory appointments and has published numerous papers and articles.

David H. Clarke received his B.S. and M.S. degrees from Springfield College and the Ph.D. degree from the University of Oregon. He taught at the University of California at Berkeley, 1958-64, and joined the faculty of the University of Maryland where he is currently professor and director of graduate studies in the Department of Physical Education. Included among his many professional affiliations are AAHPERD, American Academy of Physical Education, and American College of Sports Medicine. He has published more than two dozen articles in research journals and has authored or coauthored four textbooks.

David A. Cunningham was born in Toronto in 1937. He completed his baccalaureate degree at the University of Western Ontario in 1960 and his doctorate at the University of Michigan in 1966, when he joined the Department of Epidemiology. In 1969 he returned to the University of Western Ontario. His main research interests are related to the role of physical activity in heart disease and the influence of regular physical activity upon the growth and development of children.

Kirk J. Cureton is an assistant professor of physical education and director of the Human Performance Laboratory at the University of Georgia. He received his master's degree from the University of Illinois in 1972 and taught for two years at Ball State University before returning to Illinois to complete requirements for his Ph.D. degree. Dr. Cureton has published research relating to the body composition and biological determinants of physical performance capabilities in children. His professional memberships include the American College of Sports Medicine, AAHPERD, and NAPEHE.

Thomas K. Cureton, Jr. See Series Editor, page v.

David Essig earned his undergraduate degree at Bowling Green State University in biology and chemistry and his master's degree in human bioenergetics at Ball State University. While at Ball State he concentrated in the area of carbohydrate and lipid metabolism and coauthored several articles during the course of study. Recent investigations with caffeine and exercise prompted interest in the mechanisms whereby caffeine may mediate its effects. Presently, Mr. Essig is enrolled as a doctoral student at the University of Michigan in the area of exercise biochemistry.

John Evans is an outdoor instructor in the University of Calgary's Outdoor Pursuits Program. Highly skilled as a smallcraft instructor, he has canoed

Alberta, Ontario, and Quebec and instructed at the Canadian Recreational Canoe Association Instructors' School since 1971. In addition to teaching orienteering, navigating, and backpacking, he also possesses an interest in physical fitness and the functioning of the body in environmentally stressful situations.

Michael D. Everett received a Ph.D. in economics from Washington University (1967) and held academic positions in Mexico and at Florida State University before coming to the East Tennessee State University as an associate professor of economics. His work in environmental economics and urban transportation led him into the economics of exercise for health as a byproduct to efficient labor-intensive technology. He has published professional articles on these subjects in the *Journal of the American Institute of Planners,* the *Journal of Economic Issues, Traffic Quarterly,* and *Transportation.*

Edward L. Fox is professor and director of the Laboratory of Work Physiology in the School of Health, Physical Education and Recreation at the Ohio State University. He also holds an appointment as associate professor of preventive medicine. Dr. Fox has authored or coauthored three books and over 70 articles in the area of exercise physiology. He is a fellow and on the board of trustees of the American College of Sports Medicine. Other professional memberships include AAHPERD, American Physiological Society, New York Academy of Science, and AAAS.

Larry R. Gettman is director of exercise physiology at the Institute for Aerobics Research, Dallas, Texas. He graduated with the Ph.D. degree from Kent State University (Ohio) in 1971 and taught three years at the University of Denver before moving to Dallas. He is active in various committees of the American College of Sports Medicine and AAHPERD organizations. Dr. Gettman has authored numerous articles on physical fitness and sports.

Thomas B. Gilliam completed his Ph.D. at Michigan State University and spent one year at Syracuse University before joining the University of Michigan faculty in 1974. Dr. Gilliam has been involved in the study of physical fitness and coronary heart disease risk in children and youth. He participated in the 1975 National Youth Fitness Study, which updated the national norms on physical fitness items used by the President's Council on Physical Fitness and Sports. Dr. Gilliam is currently engaged in research on the screening of coronary heart disease risk in children and the study of youth sports competition.

Emily M. Haymes is an associate professor of physical education at Florida State University in Tallahassee. She formerly taught at the University of Colorado at Boulder, Valparaiso University, Valparaiso, Indiana, and Mary Washington College, Fredericksburg, Virginia, and was a postdoctoral research fellow at the Pennsylvania State University. Dr. Haymes is a fellow of the

American College of Sports Medicine and a member of the research consortium of AAHPERD. She has authored a dozen papers on the effects of nutrition and environmental stress upon performance.

William G. Herbert is director of the Human Performance Laboratory and an associate professor of physical education at Virginia Tech. Before earning the Ph.D. in exercise physiology at Kent State University, he coached wrestling at both high school and university levels. He holds certification from the American College of Sports Medicine as a director of Preventive and Rehabilitative Exercise Programs and directs cardiac rehabilitation and adult fitness programs at Virginia Tech. He has published or presented 20 research papers, largely concerned with body fluid balance problems in sports.

Edward T. Howley received his B.S. degree in physical education from Manhattan College. He studied at the University of Wisconsin for his Ph.D. and spent one year as a postdoctoral fellow at the Pennsylvania State University. He is now an associate professor of physical education at the University of Tennessee, Knoxville. Dr. Howley teaches courses in human physiology, physiology of exercise, and human growth and motor development. He is currently involved in research on the energy requirements of physical activities and on the hormonal responses to exercise.

Eric Hultman MD, is currently professor of clinical chemistry and head of the Department of Clinical Chemistry at Serfimerlasarettet in Stockholm, connected to the Karolinian Institute. In addition, he has established a research program on energy and carbohydrate metabolism in muscle and liver at the Metabolic Research Laboratory of St. Eriks Hospital, Stockholm.

Frederick W. Kasch a fellow in the American College of Sports Medicine, has been teaching at universities for over 40 years. His early research and publications were in collaboration with Dr. T. K. Cureton. Dr. Kasch's doctoral dissertation was done on the exercise tolerance of rheumatic and normal boys. Since 1958 he has concentrated on preventive and rehabilitative cardiology through a program he founded at San Diego State, resulting in a number of publications on the long-term effects of exercise on ischemic heart disease and aging.

Frank I. Katch is chairman of the Department of Exercise Science, University of Massachusetts, Amherst. He is author or coauthor of 50 research articles in scientific journals and has authored two books. He is a research fellow, American College of Sports Medicine, and a member of the advisory board of the *Research Quarterly*, Research Consortium of AAHPERD, advisory board of the Health and Tennis Corporation of America, Sigma Xi, New York Academy of Sciences, Human Biology Council, and consultant on physical fitness to professional sports teams.

Victor Katch, a graduate of the University of California at Berkeley in physical education, is currently an associate professor of physical education at the University of Michigan. His research area includes exercise and body composition and energy metabolism. Dr. Katch is the author of over 35 articles in refereed journals, a consultant for several professional football teams, and teaches on the undergraduate as well as the graduate level in the area of exercise physiology and research methods.

Jay T. Kearney. See Section Editor, Adult Fitness, page 524.

George R. Kinnear received his M.A. and Ph.D. degrees in physical education at the University of Maryland and instructed outdoor education and exercise physiology at Western Kentucky University in 1973. He is currently involved in teaching and research at the University of Calgary, where his special interest is physical fitness and its relationship to environmental stress. In addition he teaches climbing, backpacking, and cycling in the faculty's outdoor pursuits program. He is the chairman of the Calgary Section of the Alpine Club of Canada and during 1976 organized a successful ascent of Mt. McKinley.

Gary S. Krahenbuhl. See Section Editors, Youth Fitness, page 406.

Herberta M. Lundegren, a graduate of Tufts, earned her master's degree at the University of North Carolina at Greensboro and the Ph.D. from the State University of Iowa. She has taught at Miss Porter's School, Wellesley, and the Pennsylvania State University. Interests include self-concept, obesity, fitness, motor development, and performance of exceptional populations. Publications include articles in *Journal of Applied Physiology, Annals of Human Biology, Research Quarterly,* and *JOPER.* Dr. Lundegren is a member of AAHPERD, ACA, ACSM, NRPA, NAPEHE, NASPSPA, and CEC.

Robert M. Malina is professor of anthropology and of physical and health education at the University of Texas, Austin. His teaching and research endeavors deal with physical growth and development, and human adaptability. In addition to work with children in the United States, Professor Malina has conducted field research in Guatemala, Mexico, and Canada. Professor Malina completed his baccalaureate degree in physical education at Manhattan College, his master's and doctoral degrees in physical education at University of Wisconsin, and a doctorate in anthropology at the University of Pennsylvania.

Robert E. McAdam, presently serving as director of Research Services and Grants for Illinois State University, has been a professor of physical education at Northern Illinois University and the University of Minnesota and a department chairman at Illinois State University. His background in fitness testing is extensive. He has authored many articles for professional journals and has written an eight-book sports series for elementary children, entitled *Play the Game*. He has also served as associate editor for the *Research Quarterly*.

William D. McArdle is professor of physical education at Queens College, New York. He is director of the Laboratory of Applied Physiology and is involved in research in the metabolic and cardiorespiratory adjustments to exercise in different environments and the effects of training. Dr. McArdle has authored three books and 42 articles. He is a fellow in the American College of Sports Medicine, a fellow in the Research Consortium of AAHPERD, and a reviewer for several scientific journals.

Patricia J. Campobello McSwegin received a B.A. from Illinois State University in 1965, an M.S. from Northern Illinois University in 1972, and a Ph.D. from Kent State University in 1976. An exercise physiologist particularly interested in physical fitness, she helped direct the Exercise Clinic at Iowa State University in 1976-1977. Presently on the faculty at Kansas State University, she is director of the Physical Fitness Evaluation Laboratory, supervising the physiological assessment of all freshmen. She also serves on the NAGWS Research Committee.

Clayton R. Myers has been a physical education instructor, planner, and developer for the YMCA since 1950. After serving as physical director of several local YMCAs, he joined the Ohio-West Virginia Area staff, then the Great Lakes Region staff, and more recently the National Council of YMCAs as director of the Nationwide YMCA Cardiovascular Health Program. He has received three scholarship grants for advanced study, the Roberts-Gulick award for outstanding service, and the Dr. Paul Dudley White Award for leadership in physical fitness.

William A. R. Orban received his B.S. degree from McGill University in 1949 and the M.S. and Ph.D. degrees from the University of Illinois in 1954 and 1957. He has served as director of the School of Physical Education and director of athletics at Loyola College in Montreal, director of the School of Physical Education at the University of Saskatchewan, and dean of the School of Human Kinetics and Leisure Studies. He is currently a professor of kinanthropology at the University of Ottawa.

Lawrence B. Oscai received his B.S. degree from La Sierra College, Riverside, California, the M.S. degree from the University of Colorado, and the Ph.D. from the University of Illinois. In addition, he was a USPHS postdoctoral fellow at Washington University School of Medicine in St. Louis. He is currently a professor of physical education at the University of Illinois at Chicago Circle and is a member of the American College of Sports Medicine, the American Institute of Nutrition, and the American Physiological Society.

John Patrick O'Shea, a graduate of Michigan State University, earned his doctorate at the University of Utah. He is a professor of physical education at Oregon State University. His teaching interests are highly diversified—from exercise physiology to mountaineering. He has authored a textbook on strength fitness, conducted biochemical research in the use of anabolic steroids, and has published some 40 research and technical papers dealing with a wide variety of topics. His pursuit of mountaineering has taken him and his wife from the lofty Cascades of the Pacific Northwest to the high reaches of Alaska's Mount McKinley.

Robert P. Pangrazi. See Section Editors, Youth Fitness, page 406.

Robert W. Patton is currently an associate professor of physical education at North Texas State University and an adjunct associate professor of physiology at the Texas College of Osteopathic Medicine. Dr. Patton is the coordinator of graduate studies in physical education and divides time equally between administration, teaching, and research. His research interests are broadly conceived in the area of exercise physiology and he has authored 15 research papers and 23 articles. His professional memberships include ACSM, AAHPERD, and NCPEAM.

Sharon Ann Plowman. See Section Editor, Training and Conditioning for Physical Fitness and Sport, page 4.

John T. Powell received his D.P.E. from the University of Liverpool and his M.S. and Ph.D. from the University of Illinois. He has taught at Cambridge University in England, Rhodes University in South Africa, and the University of Illinois. In 1956 he originated the School of Physical Education and for ten years served as chairman of the Department of Human Kinetics at the University of Guelph, Ontario, Canada. He is currently a member of that faculty. Many of his track and field athletes have won gold, silver, and bronze medals in the Olympic, European, Commonwealth, and Maccabiah Games.

Peter B. Raven, born in Essex, England, graduated with a doctoral degree from the University of Oregon in 1969. Presently he holds positions of assistant director of research at the Institute for Aerobics Research and associate professor of physiology at North Texas State University. He has formerly served as supervisor of the Human Experimentation Laboratory of the Institute of Environmental Stress in Santa Barbara (1970-75) and has published 40 major articles on various aspects of the environment and its influence on human performance. His professional memberships include the American Physiological Society, fellow of the American College of Sports Medicine, and the New York Academy of Sciences.

Paul M. Ribisl is an associate professor of physical education at Wake Forest University, where he is director of the Human Performance Laboratory. He teaches in the undergraduate and graduate departments and is involved in research dealing with exercise and fitness. Dr. Ribisl also has an appointment as associate in medicine at Bowman Gray School of Medicine and is currently the director of the Cardiac Rehabilitation program at Wake Forest. He is a fellow of the American College of Sports Medicine and is serving on the ACSM Preventive and Rehabilitation Programs Committee.

Robert C. Serfass received his B.S. from East Stroudsburg State College and his M.S. and Ph.D. from the University of Minnesota. He is currently an associate professor of physical education and director of the Human Performance Laboratory in the School of Physical Education, Recreation, and School Health Education. He has teaching responsibilities in anatomy and exercise physiology. His professional affiliations include AAHPERD, MAHPER, American College of Sports Medicine, Phi Epsilon Kappa, and Kappa Delta Phi.

Roy J. Shephard is a professor of applied physiology at the University of Toronto and is also consultant to the Toronto Rehabilitation Centre, the Gage Research Institute, and the Department of Health Sciences, University of Quebec at Trois Rivieres. Former appointments include cardiac research fellow at Guy's Hospital, medical officer at the RAF Institute of Aviation Medicine, assistant professor of preventive medicine at the University of Cincinnati, and principal scientific officer of the U.K. Chemical Defense Experimental Establishment. He is the author of several books on exercise physiology and more than 300 scientific papers. He is also a past president of the American College of Sports Medicine and the Canadian Association of Sports Sciences.

Wayne E. Sinning is presently professor of physical education and director of the Applied Physiology Research Laboratory at Kent State University, Ohio. Previously he was the Buxton Professor of Physical Education and director of the Physiological Research Laboratory at Springfield College, Springfield, Mass. In addition to teaching and research in exercise physiology at both institutions, he has conducted workshops for YMCA physical fitness leaders.

Edward B. Souter is professor of physical education at California State University, Long Beach, which is the West Coast Affiliate of the President's Council on Physical Fitness. He coordinates university fitness efforts and serves as chairperson for the Long Beach Mayor's Council on Physical Fitness. Dr. Souter has been featured on nationally syndicated MEDIX television programs, one of which was entitled "The Pre-Game Stretch" and demonstrated static stretching. Dr. Souter has served CAHPER and has organized numerous fitness clinics.

Peter J. Van Handel is an associate professor of physical education at Ball State University. In addition to serving as coordinator of the science component of the physical education curriculum, he has research responsibilities in the Human Performance Laboratory. He is a professional member of the AAHPERD, American College of Sports Medicine, and the American Diabetes Association.

Wayne D. Van Huss received his B.Ed. from Illinois State University and his M.S. and Ph.D. from the University of Illinois. Dr. Van Huss has taught at Michigan State University since 1953. His research emphasis is in energy metabolism, longevity and morbidity of athletes, and muscle physiology. He has published six books or monographs and approximately 100 research journal articles. He is a member of American College of Sports Medicine, American Association of Anatomy, New York Academy of Science, American Academy of Physical Education, and AAHPERD.

Christine L. Wells. See Section Editor, Environmental Aspects of Physical Performance, page 122.

Melvin H. Williams. See Section Editor, Nutritional Aspects of Physical Performance, page 220.

Harold E. Wingard, an assistant professor of health education, is the health coordinator at Old Dominion University. He is involved with research and teaching in the graduate and undergraduate programs. Dr. Wingard formerly taught health and physical education in the public schools of Indiana, Pennsylvania, where he also coaches gymnastics. His professional memberships include the AAHPERD, American School Health Association, and AAUP.

Edward J. Zambraski received his Ph.D. from the University of Iowa and while at Iowa conducted studies on kidney function in wrestlers. Current research interests involve basic research on kidney function with regard to neural control of sodium reabsorption and the renin and prostaglandin hormonal systems. He is presently teaching and doing research in the Department of Physiology at Rutgers University.

Index